WALTER W. WILCOX
Senior Specialist in Agriculture
Legislative Reference Service
Library of Congress

WILLARD W. COCHRANE
Professor of Agricultural Economics
The University of Minnesota

ECONOMICS of AMERICAN AGRICULTURE

SECOND EDITION

PRENTICE-HALL, Inc.   *Englewood Cliffs, N. J.*   **1960**

Library of Congress Catalog Card No.: 60-10780

To our wives, Pauline and Mary,

  who helped in many, many ways in the writing of this book

Preface

THIS EDITION is, for all practical purposes, a new book. Besides the usual updating of statistical series and informational materials, this edition has been completely reorganized. The organization of major subject areas and chapters is new. Several new chapters have been added, several old ones have been dropped, and many of the chapters included from the first edition have been completely rewritten. However, the level of analysis, the coverage, and the point of view of this edition are similar to the first edition.

In this edition, as in the first, the authors have tried to treat the agricultural sector of the economy in a comprehensive manner. Production activities, marketing activities, the behavior of consumers, the influences of nonfarm agencies and institutions, and the role of government are described and meshed into a total analysis of the operating farm economy. In this analysis, particular attention is given to the force of modern technology: its development, its adoption, and its implications for farm and nonfarm people. In sum, this volume seeks to describe and to analyze the operating farm economy in the context of a modern, advanced, rapidly changing over-all economy.

The plan of writing has been, first, to describe each segment or problem area in American agriculture, giving the latest available information, and second, to introduce modern economic analysis as a means of helping the readers understand the forces at work in these areas. Thus, we have sought to strike a balance between factual description on the one hand, and the use of analytical methods and economic analyses on the other. Those who wish to emphasize economic analysis may wish to supplement this volume with readings from intermediate economic theory books. For those who are more interested in descriptive materials, supplementary reading may be done in the current publications of the state agricultural experiment stations and in the publications of the United States Department of Agriculture.

The authors fully recognize and wish to acknowledge the research work of the many, many professional workers that has contributed to the writing of this book; a listing of the men involved would include much of the profession of agricultural economics. Much has been added to the attractiveness and clarity of the volume by the large number of excellent illustrations obtained from the Agricultural Marketing and Research Services; and of course, the statistical materials of these Services were indispensable to the entire project. Substantial improvements in over-all organization and in the treatment of materials in several chapters were suggested by George E. Brandow of the Pennsylvania State University.

WALTER W. WILCOX
WILLARD W. COCHRANE

Table of Contents

Part One—The Production of Farm Products

1. FARM PEOPLE AND THE FARMS THEY OPERATE 3
2. DETERMINING WHAT TO PRODUCE 16
3. AREA SPECIALIZATION IN PRODUCTION 29
4. RESOURCE USE TO MAXIMIZE RETURNS 39
5. COSTS, RETURNS, AND SIZE OF FARM 57
6. THE AGGREGATE SUPPLY RESPONSE IN AGRICULTURE ... 71

Part Two—Marketing Farm Products

7. THE FARM MARKETING SYSTEM—WHAT IS IT? 89
8. THE FARM MARKETING SYSTEM—AN ATLAS 113
9. THE CHANGING STRUCTURE OF FARM MARKETS 143
10. MARKETING SERVICES AND COSTS 158
11. CONSUMER NEEDS, WANTS, AND DEMANDS 174

Part Three—Toward an Understanding of Farm Prices

12. THE PRICE-INCOME STRUCTURE OF AGRICULTURE 199
13. HOW FARM PRICES ARE DETERMINED 222
14. THE ROLE FARM PRICES PLAY 242
15. TWO FARM PRICE PROBLEMS 262

Part Four—Farmers in the National and World Economies

16. BUSINESS FLUCTUATIONS AND AGRICULTURE 287
17. AGRICULTURE IN A DYNAMIC, DEVELOPED ECONOMY ... 314
18. FOREIGN MARKETS, SURPLUS DISPOSAL AND AGRICULTURE 338

Part Five—Human Resource and Land Policy Problems

19. THE POVERTY PROBLEM 361
    APPENDIX—INCOME IMPROVEMENT PROSPECTS IN
       LOW-INCOME AREAS 372
20. FARM TENANCY, FARM TRANSFERS, AND CREDIT 377
21. HIRED LABOR IN AGRICULTURE 401
22. ECONOMICS OF SOIL CONSERVATION 418
23. TAXATION AND SOCIAL CONTROL OF LAND USE 431
24. WESTERN LAND USE PROBLEMS 447

Part Six—Price-Income Policy Problems

25. THE GROWTH OF GOVERNMENT IN AGRICULTURE 461
26. POLICIES TO REDUCE RISK AND UNCERTAINTY 477
27. RECENT PRICE AND INCOME PROGRAMS IN AGRICULTURE 491
28. UNSOLVED POLICY ISSUES 507
    INDEX 525

PART ONE

The Production of
Farm Products

CHAPTER 1

Farm People
and the Farms They Operate

ALTHOUGH MOST of this book will be concerned with economic
analyses of farm problems, we begin with a consideration of farm
people and the farms they operate. How successful are farm families
in achieving their goal of farm ownership in the United States?
What constitutes a farm, as the term is used in our official statistics?
To what extent is farming organized into efficient-sized family farming units? How much capital is required in the operations of typical
farms of different types? These are questions that concern us in
this chapter.

Farm people fall into three groups. Farm people may be divided
into three broad groups, on the basis of their relation to the land.
First is the large group of farm families who own all or part of the
farms they operate. In 1954, some 3.6 million farms were operated
by owners, or were farms on which the operator owned a part of
the land and rented the balance. These were 76 per cent of all farms.
The second largest group of farmers are called renters or tenants:
farm families who lease the farms they operate from owners or landlords. The third group is made up of hired workers. Hired farm
managers directed the day-to-day operations on 21,000 farms in
1954. By far, most of the hired farm workers, however, work for
the owner-operators or the tenants on a cash wage basis, without
participating in the management or profits from the farm business.

The distinction between these three groups of farmers, the owners,
the tenants, and the hired workers, is important, although variations
within each group are equally important. Within the owner group
we have farmers who own large units, free of debt, who are not
limited in their farming operations except by their own managerial

3

abilities. But this group also includes owners of such small units that they cannot obtain a satisfactory income from their farm business; owners who are so heavily indebted on their property that the creditor dictates many of the key farm management policies; and owners who rent most of the land they operate.

Renters or tenants may be divided into cash tenants, share tenants, and sharecroppers. In general, cash tenants assume more responsibility and risk than share tenants and are more independent of the landlord in formulating their farming plans than are the share tenants. Even within the group of cash tenants, important differences exist. Some have leased their farm for a period of years and can plan their farming operations much as an owner-operator does. Others have only one-year leases. Many of the cash-rented farms, like many of the owner-operated farms, are too small to be satisfactory business units.

Share tenants fall largely into two groups: crop-share, those who rent their farms on the basis of sharing the crops produced, and livestock-share, those who share the livestock and livestock product sales with their landlord. A combination of the cash and share methods of renting is common. Farmers often lease farms by giving the landlord a share (usually one-third to one-half) of the crops that are readily salable, such as corn, wheat, cotton, and soybeans, and pay a cash rental for the hay land, pasture, and buildings.

An important group of share tenants differs from the majority in that they do not own the power and machinery used on their farms. Most tenants, either cash or share, own their power and machinery and plan their own farming operations. It has been customary for years, however, to have cotton, tobacco, and a few other crops grown on a share basis, the landlord furnishing the land, power, and machinery and the tenant, often called a sharecropper in this case, furnishing only the labor used in growing and harvesting the crop. The sharecropper also pays his pro-rata share of the cash costs of seed, fertilizer, and insecticides. In reality, these families perform the same economic role as hired workers, with their wage being a share of the crop, rather than a fixed rate per day. These sharecroppers have no responsibility other than to produce the crops on the land assigned to them by the landowner. The landowner decides when he will use his power machinery to prepare the land, the rate of fertilization, and even directs the sharecropper in his planting, tillage, and harvesting operations. The number of farms operated by owners, part owners, and tenants in the United States in 1940, 1950, and 1954 is given in Table 1-1.

TABLE 1-1

Number of Farms and Cropland Harvested, by Tenure of Operator,
United States, Selected Census Years

Tenure of Operator	Number of Farms (in thousands)			Cropland Harvested (millions of acres)		
	1940	1950	1954	1939	1949	1954
Reported numbers and acreages:						
Full owner	3,084	3,090	2,745	115.4	121.4	110.8
Part owner	615	825	868	71.0	113.6	124.2
Manager	36	24	21	6.4	7.1	6.1
Tenant	2,361	1,444	1,149	128.4	102.2	93.1
Sharecropper*	541	347	268	12.8	8.3	6.1
Total, all farms	6,096	5,383	4,783	321.2	344.3	334.2
Percentages of total:						
Full owner	50.6	57.5	57.4	35.9	35.2	33.2
Part owner	10.1	15.3	18.2	22.1	33.0	37.1
Manager	.6	.4	.4	2.0	2.1	1.8
Tenant	38.7	26.8	24.0	40.0	29.7	27.9
Sharecropper*	8.9	6.4	5.6	4.0	2.4	1.8
Total, all farms	100.0	100.0	100.0	100.0	100.0	100.0

* South only. Included in total for tenants.
Source: 1954 Census of Agriculture.

Farm people versus urban people. It is of social and economic significance that the rural farm population contains more than its prorata share of people too young to work, although people over 64 years of age are also more numerous in the farm than in the urban population (Table 1-2).

TABLE 1-2

Farm and Urban People Under 15 and Over 64 Years of Age
as a Percentage of Those of Working Age

	Farm People	Urban People
Under 15 years	58%	45%
Over 64 years	17%	14%

Source: Computed from the United States Census, 1954.

Urban people have more education than do farm people. In 1940, of the farm population, 25 to 29 years of age (those young enough to have dropped out of school in the 1920's), only 63 per cent had completed grammar school. This figure was lowest in the South, where only 45 per cent of the farm people had completed grammar school, in contrast to 72 per cent for the urban South. In the North and West, about 85 per cent of the farm population had completed grammar school, in contrast to 93 per cent of the urban population. Even greater differences exist in regard to high school and college educations. There were two to three times as many high school and college graduates per hundred in the urban population as in the farm population.[1]

The low level of education of the families on the low production farms in the United States is one of the greatest obstacles to the improvement of their situation. Farm operators in Class IV, V, and VI farms in the South had completed fewer than seven years of school in 1950 (Table 1-3).

TABLE 1-3

Median Years of School Completed by Farm Operators, 1950

Economic Class of Farm	United States	North and West	South
All farms	8.3	8.7	7.2
Commercial farms:*			
Classes I and II	10.2	10.2	10.5
Class III	8.7	8.8	8.5
Class IV	8.4	8.6	6.8
Class V	8.0	8.6	6.8
Class VI	6.9	8.3	6.1
Other farms:			
Part-time and abnormal ..	8.3	8.8	7.5
Residential	7.8	8.7	7.0

* See Table 1-4 for description of farm classes.
Source: 1950 Census of Agriculture.

A farm defined. We turn our attention now from farm people to farms. Farms in the United States, in terms of units counted in our official statistics, vary from small suburban acreages to units of over one million acres, in the cases of a few livestock ranches. According to the census,

A farm . . . is all the land on which some agricultral operations are performed by one person, either by his own labor alone or with the assistance of members of his household, or hired employees. . . . A farm may consist of a single tract of land or a number of separate tracts. . . . When a land owner has one or more tenants, renters, croppers, or managers, the land operated by each is considered a farm . . . dry lot or barn dairies, nurseries, greenhouses, hatcheries, fur farms, mushroom cellars, apiaries, cranberry bogs, etc. [are considered farms]. . . .[2]

---

[1] *Differences Between Rural and Urban Levels of Living,* Part II (Mimeo.) (Bureau of Agricultural Economics, June 1958).

[2] *Special Report,* 1945 Sample Census of Agriculture, United States Bureau of the Census, page 8 and 1950 Census of Agriculture, Vol. II, page xxix.

Essentially this same definition of a farm has been used by the Census Bureau since 1925. Beginning with the 1959 Census, property of 10 acres or more having a value of farm products sold of $50 or more and property of less than 10 acres having a value of farm products sold of $250 or more is called a farm. In earlier censuses a minimum of 3 acres or sales of farm products totaling $250 usually were required to qualify as a farm. The census definition of a farm permits a number of suburban homes with small acreages of land to be counted as farms, even though the family may spend most of its time in urban employment.

Farms vary fully as much in terms of volume of business as in acreage, although farms with the largest acreage do not always have the largest incomes. As already noted, the definition of a farm encompasses a wide variety of production processes as well as a wide range in scale of operations. The production of mink and fox furs in Wisconsin and the production of mohair in Texas is farming in the United States, as is citrus fruit production in Florida, Texas, and California. The usual conception of a farm, however, is the crop- and livestock-producing unit on which the operator and his family do most of the work and from which a few common farm products, such as cotton, corn, tobacco, wheat, hogs, cattle, milk, or eggs and poultry, are sold. Most farms fall into this category, although, at the extremes, we get some unusual units classed as farms.

Major economic classes of farms. One of the more useful classifications of farms is based on scale of operations, measured in terms of value of products sold. Table 1-4 shows the number of farms and related data in each of nine classes.

The limits of these economic classes were set after intensive study. They attempt to segregate groups of farms and farmers that are somewhat alike in scale of operations, so that an accurate description can be made of the farms in each group. The Class I farms had an average of 398 acres of crops harvested and employed 5.4 workers per farm in 1954. The Class II farms had an average of 201 acres of crops harvested and 1.8 workers per farm. But the most numerous farms, those in Class IV, had only 76 acres of crops and 1.3 workers per farm, in terms of man equivalents, including both family and hired workers. The contrast is even greater when one considers the Class V farms, 16 per cent of the total. These small farms had an average of 41 acres of crops harvested, 1.0 workers per farm, and produced an average total value of farm sales of $1,851 in 1954.

What forces cause farm families to operate farms that vary so widely in size? To what extent are differences in farm tenure associated with the size of the farm operated? Is there a distinct regional distribution of the farms in the different economic classes? The remainder of this chapter will be devoted to a consideration of these and related questions.

TABLE 1-4

Economic Classification of Farms, United States, 1954

Economic Class	Sales per Farm	Number of Farms (thousands)	Percentage of All Farms	Percentage of Value of Products Sold
"Commercial" farms:				
Class I ....$25,000 and over		134	2.8	31.4
Class II ....$10,000 to $24,999 ...		449	9.4	26.9
Class III ....$5,000 to $9,999		707	14.8	20.5
Class IV ....$2,500 to $4,999		812	17.0	12.1
Subtotal		2,102	44.0	90.9
Class V ....$1,200 to $2,499		763	16.0	5.7
Class VI ....$250 to $1,199*		462	9.6	1.4
Subtotal		1,225	25.6	7.1
All "commercial"		3,327	69.6	98.0
Part time ....$250 to $1,199*		575	12.0	1.4
Residential ....Under $250		877	18.3	.3
Abnormal†		3	.1	.3
Subtotal		1,455	30.4	2.0
All farms		4,782	100.0	100.0

* Farms with sales of from $250 to $1,199 were classified as part-time if the operator worked off the farm 100 days or more or if the family's nonfarm income exceeded the value of farm products sold.
† Public and private institutional farms, etc.
Source: 1954 Census of Agriculture.

Class I farms. These farms, only 2.8 per cent of the total in terms of numbers, produced 31 per cent of the farm products marketed in 1954. On further study we find the large-scale farms most frequently in the Great Plains and in the states further west. In the far West, these large-scale farms tend to be specialized vegetable, fruit, or nut farms, and in the Plains and Mountain states they are usually livestock ranches. In the Corn Belt, about two-thirds of the large-scale farms are livestock farms and about one-third are cash-crop and general farms.

On a national basis, over half of these Class I farms are specialized crop and fruit farms. Migrant labor is utilized on these farms to do the handwork in weeding the vegetable crops and in harvesting the vegetables and fruits. Two reasons largely account for the existence and the growth of these particular types of farms in competition with family farms. Most important during the years from 1900 to 1935 was the availability of low-cost migrant labor (often from Mexico), which could be hired to do the handwork at such low wages that they had a competitive advantage over family farms. More recently, the development of specialized machinery for use in producing and harvesting the truck crops, vegetables, and fruits and the development of direct marketing have continued the competitive advantage of large-scale units in these specialized lines of production.

Although the over-all trend in number of large-scale farming units (those with value of products in excess of $25,000 at 1954 price levels) has been upward in recent years, distinct differences exist by regions. In the Southeast, the number of large plantations has decreased sharply since 1910. In the Corn Belt, large-scale units, depending primarily on hired labor, have declined, while mechanization has permitted some of the more aggressive families to develop large-scale units with a minimum of hired labor. In the Pacific region, however, there has been a substantial upward trend in the number of large-scale units operated primarily by hired labor.

Class II and III farms. Farms having total sales in 1954 within a range of $5,000 to $25,000 are classified as Class II and III farms. These family farms accounted for 24.2 per cent of the farms and 47.4 per cent of the total value of products sold. Together with the Class I farms discussed earlier, they accounted for 78.7 per cent of the total value of products sold off farms. The wide differences in economic scale of commercial farms operated by families is evident from the data in Table 1-4 which indicate that 73 per cent of all farms and 61 per cent of all commercial farms have total sales of less than $5,000 per farm.

The large farms are most numerous in the Corn Belt and Great Plains states, and the small farms are most numerous in the South. On the Class II and III farms, family labor is supplemented with an average of 1.5 man equivalents of hired labor per farm. In addition, there is a high ratio of land and machinery per worker, since these farms usually do not specialize in hand-labor crops.

In contrast, the family labor on small farms is supplemented with only 0.2 man equivalents of hired labor per farm; the ratio of land and machinery per worker is much lower. Many of these small farms grow the high hand-labor crops, cotton, and tobacco. A commercial farm is indeed a flexible unit. It may be either a highly mechanized, highly efficient unit producing a large volume of products per worker, or it may be a small, unmechanized unit utilizing 1 horse, or 1 mule tools, and large amounts of hand labor. The net farm income available for family living is roughly in proportion to the economic scale

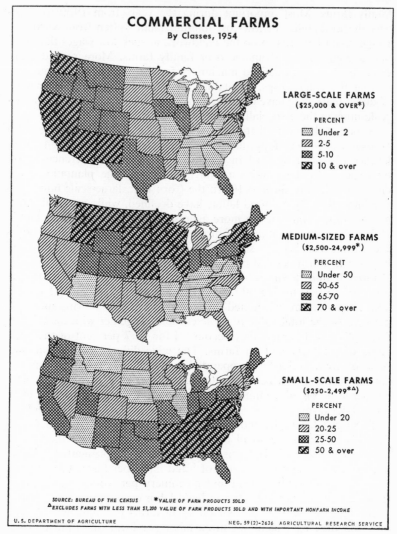

COMMERCIAL FARMS
By Classes, 1954

LARGE-SCALE FARMS
($25,000 & OVER*)

PERCENT
- Under 2
- 2-5
- 5-10
- 10 & over

MEDIUM-SIZED FARMS
($2,500-24,999*)

PERCENT
- Under 50
- 50-65
- 65-70
- 70 & over

SMALL-SCALE FARMS
($250-2,499*△)

PERCENT
- Under 20
- 20-25
- 25-50
- 50 & over

SOURCE: BUREAU OF THE CENSUS   *VALUE OF FARM PRODUCTS SOLD
△EXCLUDES FARMS WITH LESS THAN $1,200 VALUE OF FARM PRODUCTS SOLD AND WITH IMPORTANT NONFARM INCOME

U. S. DEPARTMENT OF AGRICULTURE   NEG. 59(2)-2636 AGRICULTURAL RESEARCH SERVICE

Fig. 1-1. Geographic distribution of large-, medium-, and small-scale farms.

of the farm operated. The percentage of all farms in economic classes I through IV by states in 1954 is shown in Figure 1-1.

Investment in typical farms. Special studies by the United States Agricultural Research Service make available detailed estimates on investment, income, expense, crop acreages, livestock numbers, and production for a number of different types of farms in each of the important farming regions of the United States. As might be expected, investment and net income vary widely on the typical farms of the different regions. Detailed data for four types of farms are set forth in Table 1-5, for illustrative purposes.

A farm family on a hog- and beef-fattening farm in the Corn Belt manages an investment five times that of the Mississippi Delta farm family and almost twice that of the dairy farmer in southern Wisconsin. There is a wide range in the size of each of these types of farms, yet the important fact to note is the sharp difference in size, investment, and income of average farms of the different types.

TABLE 1-5

Investment and Related Data for Four Types of Farms, 1957

	Dairy Southern Wisconsin	Hog-Beef Fattening Corn Belt	Cotton Mississippi Delta	Wheat Southern Plains
Investment:				
Real estate	$21,810	$40,990	$ 8,930	$63,890
Machinery	7,120	6,990	2,880	9,400
Crops and livestock	7,140	14,590	640	5,070
Total investment	36,070	62,570	12,450	78,360
Gross income	8,841	20,306	3,216	10,572
Operator's net farm income	3,806	8,116	1,205	2,853
Livestock numbers:				
Milk cows	20	6	1	3
All cattle	31	52	44	33
Hogs	28	143	6	4
Poultry	102	125	35	70
Crop acreages:				
Corn	17	72	6	—
Hays	27	30	3	10
Small grain	25	43	4	100
Cotton	—	—	11	—
Other crops	1	—	10	180

Source: "Farm Costs and Returns," *Commercial Family-Operated Farms by Type and Location, Agricultural Information Bulletin 176* (U.S.D.A., Agricultural Research Service, June 1958).

Reasons for continuing differences. Some of the reasons for this continuing wide range in scale of operations and income per family from farming will be discussed later. Now, we want to point out the interdependence of many influences that caused family farming to continue on a small, one-mule and hand-labor basis in some parts of the country, while it shifted to a highly mechanized motor-power basis in others.

Without question, the man-land ratio has been important. Large numbers of families in the South produce cotton and tobacco by hand-labor methods. Although the resulting family income is low, lack of education and finances prevent them from adopting desirable new farming methods and from increasing the size of farm as rapidly as competitors already located on the larger, more productive family farms.

Another interdependent factor has been the more rapid development of machinery used in the production and harvesting of crops other than cotton and tobacco. The slow rate of mechanization of cotton and tobacco production reflects, in part, the difficulty of developing machinery that will satisfactorily substitute for hand labor in growing these crops. The availability of large supplies of labor at low wage rates also has been a factor tending to discourage the development of labor-saving equipment.

But all small family farms are not located in the South. Small family farms are either the largest or the second largest economic class of farms in every region of the United States. The reasons for the large numbers of these farms vary from region to region. Undoubtedly, difficulties in capital accumulation and difficulties in obtaining the credit necessary to expand farming operations keep many farm families in this class throughout their entire lives.

Differences in managerial ability also reflect themselves in the size of farm operated. The more aggressive, resourceful, and competent managers on the smaller farms find ways and means of overcoming their capital and credit problems in order to push up into the medium- or large-family farm class. In many communities in which small family farms predominate, the topography of the land is too rough for the efficient use of modern labor-saving machinery. Either the families in these communities must continue operating relatively small farms, or they must migrate to other communities.

Class V and VI farms. As noted in Table 1-4, there were 1,225,000 farms enumerated in 1954 with a total sales of $250 to $2,499. These units were so small that the operator did not have employment throughout the year, yet he reported less than one hundred days of work done off the farm in the case of Class VI farms. They averaged only 34 acres of crops harvested and sales averaged $1,851 and $756, respectively, for the Class V and VI farms in 1954.

Perhaps one-fourth to one-third of the operators of these farms were over 65 years of age. These small-scale units, especially the Class VI farms, are at the heart of the poverty problem in agriculture. Many of these farms are found in the Appalachian, Southeast, and Delta states. These farms make up 20 to 30 per cent of all the farms enumerated by the census. Farm operating expenses must be paid out of the $756, the average sales derived from a typical Class VI farm, leaving little more than half this amount for family living. Children raised in families whose income is so low, often have poor diets, insufficient clothes for participation in community affairs, and an inadequate education. Communities in which these small units are numerous do not have a sufficient economic base to support good public schools and other community enterprises. This, in turn, prevents the young people from having the health, general education, and skills needed to be most productive and retards their migration to jobs outside their community. Lack of capital in the family to assist the child in getting established in a job away from home is another important factor.

Such suggestions as have been made for dealing with this problem of continued farming on units too small, either for efficient utilization of labor or for the production of an adequate family income, will be summarized in Chapter 19.

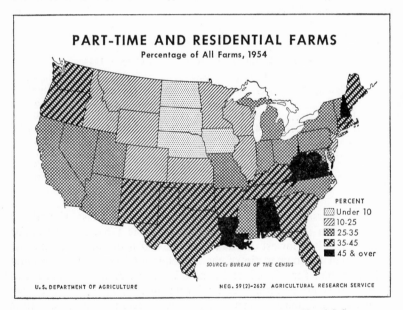

Fig. 1-2. Geographic distribution of part-time and residential farms.

Other farms. Out of 4,783,021 farms enumerated in 1954, 1,682,838, or 30 per cent, were classified as part-time, residential, or abnormal units. These farms are used primarily as a place to live or a place to earn a small supplemental income, while obtaining most of the living elsewhere. Farms from which the value of products sold was between $250 and $1,199 and the operators of which worked off the farm one hundred days or more in 1954 were classed as part-time units. Residential units include all census farms with less than $250 total value of products sold in 1954. The geographic distribution of these units is shown in Figure 1-2.

For most purposes, these part-time and residential units should not be considered as farms. Operators of such farms do not have the usual problems of organizing and operating an efficient farm business. Furthermore, the economic welfare of the family is not dependent on the scale and efficiency of the farm business. In many cases, the major interests of the family lie outside of agriculture and are distinctly different from the interests of farmers whose vocation is making a living from farming.

Farm tenure and economic class. We will close our discussion of farm sizes with a consideration of the tenure of the operators of the various classes of farms.

TABLE 1-6

Tenure of Operators by Economic Class of Farm, 1954

Class of Farm	Full Owners (per cent)	Part Owners (per cent)	Managers (per cent)	Tenants (per cent)
I...............	35.2	38.2	4.4	22.2
II...............	35.2	33.3	1.0	30.5
III..............	42.0	28.2	.5	29.4
IV...............	48.3	21.9	.2	29.6
V...............	53.2	16.5	.2	30.1
VI...............	63.6	11.5	.1	24.8
Other farms.....	79.1	7.7	.2	13.0

Source: Agricultural Information Bulletin 200 (U.S.D.A.), Table 37.

Full ownership is most common on the small Class V and VI farms and on the noncommercial farms (Table 1-6). And as might be expected, it is lowest on the larger units. It is of particular interest to note that full ownership of the inadequate Class VI farming units is higher than for the Class IV and V farms. Hence, we find that ownership is no assurance of achieving an adequate operating unit for a family. When the owners and part owners are combined, they account for 71 per cent of all the full-time farm operators, although only 35 per cent of the operators of the Class I and II farms and 42 per cent of the operators of Class III farms own all the land they operate. This inverse relationship between size and proportion of farms operated by full owners is what one might expect. It is much more difficult to accumulate sufficient savings to permit the purchase of a large farm than to organize and operate it on a rental or part-rental basis. This suggests some conflict between the two goals: organization of agriculture into farms that result in high output per worker, and the attainment of full ownership of the farms operated.

REFERENCES

Bachman, K. L., and R. W. Jones, "Size of Farms in the United States," *Technical Bulletin 1019*, U.S.D.A. (1950).
McElveen, J. U., "Family Farms in a Changing Economy," *Agricultural Information Bulletin 171*, U.S.D.A. (1957).

POINTS FOR DISCUSSION

1. Enumerate the major differences between farm people and urban people in the United States.
2. Formulate a working definition of a farm.
3. Why do farms vary so greatly in size within small communities?
4. To what extent is size of farm operated a function of managerial ability?
5. Which problem is more important: the crowding out of family farms by large farming corporations or the continued attempts of many farm families to make a living on inadequate units?

CHAPTER 2

Determining
What To Produce

FARMERS IN the United States produce a wide variety of products. This chapter is devoted to an analysis of the economic forces that cause farmers to specialize in the production of a few products, yet almost never to specialize in a single product.

American agriculture is several hundred years old. Farmers in most communities today think they produce what they do because of their fathers' experience and training. Custom is an important factor—too important from an economic point of view. However, it can be overcome by economic considerations. For example, farmers in the last generation produced draft horses in most sections of the United States until their production became unprofitable and was stopped because of the general adoption of the tractor. Similarly, thousands of farmers have shifted from the production of wheat and other cash crops to the production of more forage crops and livestock as their soil resources became depleted and the demand for livestock increased during the last forty years.

Two problems in determining what to produce. The problem of determining what to produce has two parts. They are: (1) what particular crops or livestock or combination of them should be produced on a particular farm or in a community, and (2) how much of each of several crops or livestock should be combined on a particular farm. The first part of this problem draws on the principle of comparative advantage. The second part of the problem requires the application of the principles of enterprise combination.

The basis of differentiation in production. Variations in soil and climate from one community to another and variations in soils within a community give rise to most of the specialization in farm production. On some of the western hills differences in altitude and air movements have led to plantings of oranges near the tops of the slopes, walnuts farther down the slope and alfalfa and other crops in the valleys.[1] Door County, Wisconsin, is a concentrated red sour cherry producing area largely because of its unique climate. It is a narrow strip of land with large bodies of water on three sides: Green Bay on the west, Lake Michigan on the east, and Lake Superior on the north. The moderating effect of these bodies of water produces a climate unusually well-suited for sour cherry production.

Although fruits are more sensitive to temperature and soil differences than most farm crops, the specialization in the production of other crops is closely correlated with critical climatic and soil resource factors. The large areas of spring and winter wheat in the Great Plains and in the Pacific Northwest, which are described in the following chapter, are areas of productive soils and scant rainfall. Enough rain falls to mature a wheat crop, but not enough to produce the usual Corn Belt feed and forage crops. We find that the dairy regions of the United States are areas where soils, rainfall and temperatures favor the production of forage crops—hay and pasture. The Corn Belt is limited on the south and east by rough, unproductive soils, and growing season temperatures and rainfall at the northern and western boundaries set the limits of intensive corn production.

Cost of transportation to consuming centers also influences the selection of crops and livestock on farms. Products with a high value per unit of weight tend to be produced in those areas farthest from consuming centers. Farms located adjacent to ocean transportation may be able to purchase certain supplies more cheaply than farms located in the interior. Availability of these cheaper supplies influences the kind and amount of farm products produced with any particular set of natural resources.

In addition to natural and economic factors, we find that biological factors, such as prevalence of disease and insects, influence the selection of crops and livestock grown on farms. Within communities, the likes and dislikes of the farm operator and his family have a great influence on the selection of crops they shall produce.

The principle of comparative advantage. The basic principle that explains the economic motivation for specialization in farming is the principle of comparative advantage. This principle states that an area tends to specialize in the products in which the ratio of advantage

---

[1] Black, Clawson, Sayre, and Wilcox, *Farm Management* (New York: The Macmillan Company, 1947), page 872.

is highest, or the ratio of disadvantage is lowest exchanging products for those from other areas which have an advantage over other products.

A good example of this basic principle is the localization of beef cattle and wheat production. Wheat can be grown successfully both in the Corn Belt and in the Great Plains. Farmers can expect to get 15 to 25 bushels an acre if they grow wheat in the Corn Belt. This same land will produce feed and forage crops for beef cattle. The better land in the Corn Belt will produce feed enough for a beef cow and calf on 1 to 2 acres, or produce from 350 to 450 pounds of beef an acre.

Where crops are produced in the Great Plains, wheat yields 10 to 20 bushels an acre. But if this land is used for feed and forage crop production, three to five acres are required to support a cow and calf for a year. Only 80 to 120 pounds of beef are produced per acre. Each of the areas can produce both beef cattle and wheat, but, if the Corn Belt averages 20 bushels of wheat or 400 pounds of beef per acre and the Great Plains averages 15 bushels of wheat or 100 pounds of beef per acre, the Corn Belt has a greater ratio of advantage in beef cattle than in wheat. If labor and power costs of wheat production were the same in the Corn Belt and in the Great Plains (an assumption somewhat at variance with the facts), wheat production costs in terms of land and labor required must be higher in the Great Plains than in the Corn Belt. The Great Plains, nevertheless, must specialize in wheat production as long as demand exists for both products for its ratio of disadvantage is less in wheat than in beef cattle production.

In a real sense, specialization in dairying in the Lake States and in the Northeast results from the fact that their ratio of disadvantage is least in this line of production, rather than that their ratio of advantage in dairying is greatest. In the Lake States of Minnesota, Wisconsin and Michigan, the feed and forage crops from three to four acres of land will support an average dairy cow producing around 7,000 pounds of milk a year. It will probably require fifty hours of man labor to harvest the crops and one hundred and fifty hours of man labor to care for the cow. Thus, it takes around 3 to 4 acres of land and 200 hours of man labor, in addition to power, machinery, and fertilizer requirements, to produce 7,000 pounds of milk in the Lake States. In the Corn Belt 2 to 3 acres of land will produce the necessary feed for the cow, reducing both the land and man-labor requirements for milk production.

But in the Corn Belt, the feed from 2 to 3 acres of land will produce 1,200 to 1,500 pounds of hogs. In the dairy area of the Lake

States, where small grains and forage crops produce more feed per acre than corn, the feed supply is not adapted for hog production. Probably not over 800 pounds of hogs could be produced from the feed on three to four acres of land and much of the forage would be wasted if only hogs were raised. In summary, an acre of land and the labor associated with it produces the following amounts of milk and hogs in the two areas:

Lake States Dairy Area	Corn Belt
330 pounds hogs	480 pounds hogs
2,000 pounds milk	2,800 pounds milk

Dairy products can be produced with the same amount of labor, fewer acres of land, and smaller quantities of purchased feeds and fertilizers in the heart of the Corn Belt than elsewhere. Yet the central Corn Belt does not specialize in dairy production. Its ratio of advantage is even greater in meat-animal production, in which it specializes.

Specialization in cotton production in the South is another example of the operation of the principle of comparative advantage. Farmers in the Corn Belt and in the dairy area could produce their own fibers for clothing if necessary. The season is too short to grow cotton, but they could produce their own wool by keeping sheep and they could produce linens by raising fiber flax in some areas. Instead, they specialize in feed and livestock production and buy cotton goods made from raw materials produced by farmers in the Cotton Belt. Here we find that, because of climatic limitations, only one part of the country can grow a particular product.

Substitute products can be produced in other areas, but they are more expensive and less satisfactory for many purposes. Both areas gain by specializing in the products for which they have a comparative advantage and by exchanging them with each other.

Regional specialization in production, following the principle of comparative advantage, occurs not only in the United States, but also in other parts of the world where freedom to trade with other areas exists. Thus, we import most of our coffee, bananas, and sugar, because the United States farmers cannot profitably produce these products in the quantities desired by American consumers. In contrast, producers in other countries find it profitable to specialize in the production of coffee, bananas, and sugar for export to the United States.

Farmers in one area do not sit down and work out their ratios of advantage or disadvantage as compared with farmers in other areas. Instead they take their direction from the price system. Farmers in the dairy region find that they can realize a higher income from specialization in dairying, rather than in hogs or sheep. Farmers in the Corn Belt find that they can realize a higher income by producing meat animals rather than anything else. Farmers in the Cotton Belt find it more profitable to raise cotton than any other crop.

The changing nature of the comparative advantage. One might think that when farmers in a particular area find which products give them the best returns, they have found a permanent solution to their problems of what to produce. Anyone who has studied the history of production in the different areas of the United States knows that this is not so. Comparative advantage is a changing phenomenon. The ratio of advantage or disadvantage in producing a particular product on a particular farm or in an area may change for any one of the following reasons:

1. changes in natural resources such as loss through soil erosion.
2. changes in biological factors such as increased infestations of crops by pests and disease.
3. changes in consumer demand.
4. increased mechanization which is better adapted to level land free of stones than to hilly and stony land.
5. cheaper and more efficient transportation which decreases the disadvantage of areas most distant from markets.

Changes under each of these five headings are constantly in process. One can see a pattern in these changes and their effects on regional specialization in production.

Trends in regional specialization. Specialization in production, both on individual farms and in particular areas, is increasing. Improved technology and the development of specialized mechanical equipment is the primary economic force leading to increased specialization. Potato production is an excellent example of this trend. As compared with twenty years ago potato producers today select a much higher quality seed and use much heavier applications of fertilizer. In areas where rainfall is ample or where irrigation is used, as much as 3,000 pounds of fertilizer per acre is now applied annually. Potatoes are sprayed several times during the growing season with different spray materials. The hand labor in picking up potatoes can now be replaced by machines, on level stone-free fields (putting those farms with hilly and stony fields at a disadvantage), under favorable conditions. In addition to the usual growing and harvesting practices of twenty years ago, potato producers today usually grade and sometimes package their potatoes before selling them.

The requirements for efficient, low-cost potato production can only be met by using the best adapted lands in combination with modern machinery and specialized sprays and fertilizers. It takes a higher degree of technical competence to organize and manage such a producing unit now than it did in the past when potatoes were produced by planting the potatoes in the spring, keeping the weeds out during the summer and digging them with horse power and hand labor in the fall. Potato yields have doubled in recent years on the best adapted lands under good management. Supplemental irrigation is being used to an increasing extent throughout the eastern states. With no increase in the demand for potatoes, farmers who cannot apply the new technology under high quality management are planting fewer acres of this crop.

This same tendency toward specialization in fruit production has been in process for years. The same general trend is in progress for all lines of farm production. In general, our better lands are being farmed more intensively with fewer crops and fewer kinds of livestock than they were twenty years ago. Our poorer lands are being used less intensively, or are being shifted to permanent pasture and forestry.

Importance of alternative opportunities. It is important to re-emphasize that it is relative, rather than total, costs that are important in the inter-regional competition of farm products. Farms and areas with limited opportunities for shifting to other lines of production will continue specializing in a particular product, even though prices fall below average production costs, while areas with greater opportunities for shifting will change to new lines of production. Thus, in the northern parts of Minnesota, Wisconsin, and Michigan, low productivity soils and the short growing season limit the crops that can be grown in addition to hay and pasturage. The cost of producing 100 pounds of milk is higher than in the southern parts of the same states and in the Corn Belt. Yet a drop in milk prices relative to other farm product prices would cause shifts out of dairying in the lower-cost areas farther south, which have the better alternative opportunities. Little change would occur in the production in the northern part of the states.

One of the undesirable social consequences of these economic forces is that farmers with inferior, less productive natural resources tend to sink to sub-standard levels of living (see Chapter 19). Technological improvements have increased the relative advantages to farmers with more productive natural resources causing the value of the land and invested capital in the areas of inferior resources to drop. Producers in these areas "lower costs" by writing down their capital .nvestments. If perfect mobility of human resources existed, undesirable social consequences would not follow. Families would leave the area if they could not earn incomes comparable to families elsewhere and the land would be retired from farming, or organized into larger farming units. This has happened on a considerable scale in the New England and eastern states where industrial employment opportunities exist nearby.

More often, families in the densely populated areas of inferior agricultural resources, especially those located some distance from industrial centers, do not find opportunities for leaving the area, or are unwilling to do so. They accept the lower standard of living forced on them by their inability to take advantage of technological changes. Their children, reared under conditions of inferior public education, nutrition, health and medical care, do not migrate as readily as children from the better areas. This is particularly true in some parts of the Southeast.

Principles of enterprise combination. We turn now from a consideration of the principles that govern inter-regional specialization to an analysis of the forces that govern the combination of enterprises on individual farms. On every farm the activities are directed toward the production of one or more major products and a limited number of related products. One of the simplest farm organizations is found on the specialized dairy farms of New York. Their major product is fluid milk for urban consumption. All the feed produced on the farm is fed to the dairy herd and to a small flock of chickens kept for household uses. But even on such a specialized farm as this, milk is not the only product sold. Sales of veal calves and cull cows usually average 5 to 15 per cent of the value of the milk sold. The veal calf is a joint product in the production of milk. Sale of cull cows is a salvage operation, the farmer recovering as much as possible from worn-out capital assets. Thus, on this very highly specialized fluid milk farm we find joint production of two commodities: milk and calves.

Joint products. Joint products are two or more products obtained, in relatively fixed proportions, from a single production process. Usually, however, even in the case of joint products, the farmer may vary the output of one product relative to the others. As soon as the calf is born the dairyman has the alternative of selling it for a nominal sum or feeding it until it reaches prime market condition. Some farmers, with Guernsey and Jersey cows producing milk for high-priced city markets, kill their calves at birth. The calves are too small to have a market value at birth and the milk is too valuable to feed them until they reach a marketable weight.

This illustrates the principle that, when two or more products are produced jointly, the joint products should be considered as one enterprise up to the point at which one or more products may be separated in the production process. At this point, productive resources should be divided between the two products in such a way that the last unit of resources used for each product will bring equal returns. The amount of weight to be put on veal calves will depend on the price of milk and labor, as well as on the price of veal calves. All things considered, calves should be raised until the point is reached at which the value of the last milk fed to them is equal to that of the milk sold for fluid use. When the condition is fulfilled, we say that the marginal returns from resources expended on each product are equal.[2]

Many joint products have few competitive relations, either during the joint-production process or after they are separated. Wheat and straw are classic examples of joint products wherein most of the economic value is associated with one product. A farmer seldom sacrifices a part of his potential yield of grain to obtain a higher yield or higher quality of straw. After the harvest, the decisions he will make concerning how he will dispose of the straw will not depend on the decisions he makes concerning how he will handle the wheat.

At the other extreme, take the case of the joint products mutton and wool. Animals bred to give the best yields of wool do not produce the best carcasses and vice versa. The sheep raiser must decide how to balance these competing demands in terms of marginal analysis, in which the reduction in prospective wool yield is balanced against the prospective increase in the carcass value of the sheep. *This solution may be generalized into the principle that, whenever the quantity or quality of two or more joint products relative to each other may be varied in the productive process, the farmer plans his production to maximize the total value of the joint products.*

Supplementary relations among enterprises. A farmer may raise more than one crop in order to take advantage of his resources throughout the year. A farmer who produces only cotton has no productive work to do on his farm during the winter months. He has worked long hours planting, cultivating, and harvesting during the growing season, and is idle or works away from the farm the rest of the year. Farm power units have similar periods of peak loads and idleness. An enterprise that utilizes the farmer's time when he is not busy with cotton, supplements the main cotton enterprise.

---

[2] "Marginal returns," a term which will be found many times in the following pages, refers to the returns (or economic value of the output) from the last unit of resources used.

Farmers, generally, find it profitable to supplement the main enterprise with one or more additional enterprises in order to utilize their labor and machinery more fully throughout the year. Thus, livestock enterprises supplement crop production in the use of labor. Small-grain production supplements corn production since the same power, seed bed, and harvesting machinery may be used for both crops. Many of the dairy farmers of the Northeast and North Central states grow a few acres of cash crops to supplement their feed and livestock enterprises. They find it possible and profitable to utilize a small part of their labor, machinery, and land for a high-value cash crop. Limits on the cash crops are set either by the amount of land that can be spared from the production of feed crops, or by the labor that is available during the peak planting and harvesting seasons.

American farmers supplement their major enterprise, when they find it possible, with other enterprises in order that they may use, more fully, such resources as lands, buildings, family labor, and equipment which are relatively fixed and are somewhat of an overhead cost to the business. Oftentimes an enterprise that is primarily supplementary competes with the main enterprise at particular points. *The careful farmer meets this situation by developing his supplementary enterprise until the returns from the two enterprises combined are at a maximum.*

Complementary relations among enterprises. Hogs running in the feed lots with fattening cattle pick up considerable grain that otherwise would be wasted. On farms where separated cream is sold, hogs and chickens utilize the waste skim milk. When two or more enterprises are interdependent, as illustrated above, they are said to have complementary relations. Livestock is *supplementary* to crops in permitting fuller employment of labor during the winter months. It is *complementary* to crops, however, in utilizing low-quality crops, unmarketable gleanings left in the field, and pasture grasses. Feeding the crops on the farm to well-bedded livestock produces manure, which helps maintain high crop yields.

The complementary relations among the crops, in the usual rotation, are important. The intertilled crops permit weed eradication, beneficial to the close-growing legumes in the rotation. Conversely, the organic matter and nitrogen added to the soil by legumes boosts the yields of intertilled crops.

American farmers keep in mind these technical and, thus, economic relations among enterprises. They start with a main enterprise, which has a comparative advantage in the area, and keep adding complementary and supplementary enterprises until the marginal returns from all resources used in farm production are equalized and the returns from all enterprises combined are maximized. Any further expansion in the output of one of the joint, supplementary, or complementary products would divert resources from another more profitable use. When this point has been reached in the allocation of resources on the farm, the only means of increasing income further is to increase the size of business or, if possible, lower production costs by introducing new, lower-cost production practices.

Comparative advantage of enterprise combinations. At this point, we should elaborate briefly on our discussion of the principle of comparative advantage. It was inferred earlier that the relative advantage of individual products could be determined directly for each area. Now we see that we must consider comparative advantage between regions in terms of groups of products having joint, supplementary, and complementary relations.

Thus, wheat continues to be grown in Indiana and Ohio, because of the place wheat fills in the eastern Corn Belt rotations. Rotations including wheat must be compared with rotations substituting some other crop for wheat, in the eastern Corn Belt, to determine the relative advantage to this area for growing wheat rather than some other crop. Similarly, the relative advantage of producing wheat in the small-grain regions can only be determined by a consideration of the related enterprises in which various proportions of wheat are raised, in combination with other small grains, and cattle.

The determination of the competitive position of an area for the production of a particular product turns out to be exceedingly complicated. Probably the simplest and most helpful rule to remember is that areas with resources adapted to the production of a number of different products make the shifts in production, which grow out of changing technology and changing demand conditions. Areas of few alternatives, already highly specialized in one product, tend to continue in their specialty, accepting reduced land values and standards of living, if necessary, as the price of their product falls.

Specialization vs. diversification. The practice of diversification in farm production, that is, developing several enterprises rather than specializing in one or two, has been advocated by farm management specialists for many years. We see the economic basis for this diversification in the joint, supplementary, and complementary relations found among farm enterprises. The land, family labor, and capital equipment on the farm is more fully utilized, and otherwise wasted products are converted into marketable form by the addition of livestock to most crop farms. The total production of the land in most sections of the country is increased when crops are rotated. In addition to promoting efficient use of the farm resources, diversified production reduces the risk in farming. Dangers of serious losses by disease or unfavorable weather are reduced when a number of products are produced. Economic risks associated with price changes also are lower with diversified farming.

The general problem of meeting risk and uncertainty in farming will be the subject of a later chapter. Here we want to supplement our discussion of trends in regional specialization with a consideration of the trends in progress affecting the advantages of diversification and specialization on individual farms. Improved technology for the most part favors increasing specialization on the individual farm as well as by regions. First, much improved technology requires large capital investments in specialized equipment, which, in turn, requires a large volume of output if costs per unit of output are to be kept low. Second, improved technology has reduced the hazards of disease losses in specialized production of many crops and livestock products. Weather hazards also are reduced by such developments as new frost-resistant seed stocks and mechanical equipment that removes the excess moisture from grains and hays. Third, the application of improved technology requires increased specialization on the part of management. A farmer finds it difficult to acquire all the necessary skills and to keep up to date in a number of different fields. Fourth, government price-support programs, marketing agreements, and similar price-stabilization measures have reduced the danger of serious price declines for most of the major farm products.

Marketing requirements are another factor making for specialization on a number of farms. To a certain extent, cooperative marketing associations permit small-scale diversified farmers to market their products efficiently in competition with the specialized larger-scale producers. An examination of the competitive advantage of many large-scale specialized producers, however, indicates that economies in marketing and in the furnishing of large quantities of uniformly high-quality products are even more important in the success of these farms than their economies in production.

The advantages of extensive diversification under these newer conditions are much less than they were several decades ago. The advantages of specialization are much greater. The trend is toward a greater specialization in a major product and one or two supplementary and complementary enterprises on the more progressive farms in the community. With farming carried on by several million different entrepreneurs, however, highly specialized farming will be a gradual development.

Livestock production in the South. A special case of changing comparative advantage and one of much popular interest in recent years is the competitive position of dairy- and beef-cattle production in the southern states relative to the Corn Belt and the dairy area. Observers point out that the ability to utilize pastures most of the year in the southern states and the mild winters that greatly reduce building requirements give the South important economic advantages in dairy and beef production. Northern livestock producers have expressed a fear that they may be driven out of livestock production by lower-cost southern producers.

As the current expectations of the southern enthusiasts are fulfilled and more livestock is produced in the South, rather than driving northern producers out of business, the competitive effect will be to increase land values in the South and to decrease land values in the North until costs are equalized. The roughest and least productive soils in both areas may be retired from farming, as the families living on them seek other employment.

Regional specialization and farm programs. Although a full consideration of farm programs must be deferred to the last part of the book, the relation between trends in specialization and farm programs should be noted. Price-support programs that require acreage allotments of the crops, for which prices are supported, tend to slow down adjustments in production in line with changing comparative advantage. Acreage allotments are set largely on the basis of past acreages of the crop grown on the farm. Every producer is required to reduce his acreage by the same percentage. Production changes are "put in a strait jacket." This is one of the most serious charges made against these programs. To the extent that acreage allotments are set at some uniform percentage of previous acreage on the farm, the charge is justified. Thus far, the programs appear to have slowed down the rate of change, but sufficient flexibility has been maintained to permit a continuation of trends which were in progress.

REFERENCES

Black, Clawson, Sayre, and Wilcox, *Farm Management,* Chapter 15. New York: The Macmillan Co., 1947.

Forster, G. W., and M. C. Leager, *Elements of Agricultural Economics,* Chapter 8. Englewood Cliffs, N.J.: Prentice-Hall, Inc., 1950.

Heady, E. O., and H. R. Jensen, *Farm Management Economics,* Chapter 5. Englewood Cliffs, N.J.: Prentice-Hall, Inc., 1954.

POINTS FOR DISCUSSION

1. What is the most important crop in your home community?
2. Why does it have a greater comparative advantage than other crops?
3. What other crops and livestock are combined with this key crop on most farms? Explain their joint, supplementary and complementary relations.
4. From United States Department of Agriculture statistics determine whether specialization has been increasing or decreasing in your home county.
5. How will a rise in the cost of farm labor affect the competitive position of the northern and southern states in producing livestock? Why?

CHAPTER 3

Area Specialization in Production

FARMERS, utilizing the principles of comparative advantage and enterprise combination outlined in Chapter 2, have developed distinct patterns of farming in the different sections of the United States. If one travels from New York City to San Francisco, he will find dairying the predominant pattern of farming until he gets west of Chicago. From western Illinois to eastern Nebraska, corn and hog production, or beef-cattle feeding, takes the place of the dairying farther east.

If the traveler goes southwest from Omaha, crossing central and southwest Kansas, he will find highly specialized wheat production covering hundreds of square miles in Kansas and eastern Colorado. This wheat-growing area also extends north into Nebraska. Specialized wheat production gives way to cattle ranching in Colorado. Farther west, in the intermountain valleys, one finds farmers growing irrigated crops, often in combination with livestock production. In many of these valleys, especially as one approaches the west coast, he finds the farmers specializing in vegetable, truck, and fruit crops.

In this chapter, we will systematically examine the major farming regions in the United States and isolate the critical factors that have influenced the development of the patterns of farming prevailing in each region. When this systematic examination has been completed, the possibilities of further expansion in our cropland will be appraised.

Farm-management specialists, after studying the patterns of farming carried on in all sections of the United States, have classified the country into nine major type-of-farming areas with a number of sub-type areas within each major area. The location and boundaries of these major type-of-farming areas are shown in Figure 3-1.

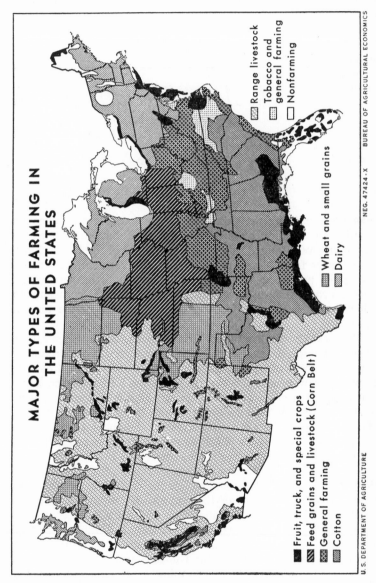

MAJOR TYPES OF FARMING IN THE UNITED STATES

Range livestock
Tobacco and general farming
Nonfarming
Wheat and small grains
Dairy
Fruit, truck, and special crops
Feed grains and livestock (Corn Belt)
General farming
Cotton

U. S. DEPARTMENT OF AGRICULTURE   NEG. 47424-X   BUREAU OF AGRICULTURAL ECONOMICS

Fig. 3-1.

Many factors influence the type of farming followed in a community. Biological conditions, such as the prevalence of insect pests, weeds, and plant and animal diseases, are important. Economic forces, such as the availability of relatively cheap labor in the South and Southwest, or the location of nearby market outlets for perishable products are the critical influences in certain areas. Institutionalized economic forces, such as tariffs, freight-rate zones, and local sanitary regulations, also influence local production. For example, city sanitary regulations, governing milk sold within the city limits, have directly influenced the location of dairies producing milk for fluid consumption.

But the differences in the physical factors, climate, topography, and soils dominate the boundaries of the major farming regions and most type-of-farming areas. This close correlation between variations in physical resources and variations in systems of farming will become more evident as each of the farming regions is examined in detail.

Feed grains and livestock region. This region is usually known as the Corn Belt. Corn is the key crop because it gives high yields on the deep, warm, fertile soils of the region. Oats, wheat, soybeans, hay, and pasture crops, grown in rotation with corn, permit the farmer to use his labor and equipment throughout the year and maintain the productivity of his soils. Meat producers base their enterprises on the utilization of the dominant crop, corn, and the small-grain and forage crops.

Differences in topography and soils within the central section of the Corn Belt lead to three different, characteristic types of farming: (1) Cash-grain production, featuring corn, oats, and soybeans, is found on the most level areas of the region. (2) Cattle feeding and hog production are found on the wind-blown, loessial soil areas bordering on the Missouri and Mississippi rivers, where the land is more rolling. (3) Hogs are the dominant livestock and soft winter wheat the main cash crop in the east central sections of the Corn Belt, where the soils are lighter and the farms smaller.

The southern part of the Corn Belt is rolling, has less-productive soils and hotter summers. Oats do not yield as well here as farther north and more of the land must be in pasture. Beef-cattle grazing, rather than the beef-fattening and hog production common to the central part, is found here. As rainfall drops off toward the western border of the Corn Belt, the acreage of wheat increases relative to corn and oats. Substantial quantities of wheat and feed grains are sold for cash in the western Corn Belt, partly because of the uncertainty of the rainfall. Farmers understock with livestock to avoid getting caught without feed in dry years.

The northern part of the Corn Belt in southwest Minnesota and southeast South Dakota is similar to the west central areas, its variable rainfall being one of the dominant factors in both the cropping and livestock system. The northern part of the Corn Belt, from northeastern Iowa on east, is covered with glacial drift soils, which are more leached and more acid and have less native productivity than the newer soils farther south. Corn and oats have less advantage over forage crops on these soils and more of the land is too rough for cropping. Hay and pasture make up a large part of the feed supply, and dairying is the dominant livestock enterprise on most farms.

The cotton region. Climate is the main factor that determines the location of cotton production. Cotton is grown up to, but seldom north of, the line of two hundred frost-free days. On the west, the 20-inch rainfall line limits the expansion further westward, except under irrigation. Heavy rainfall, during the fruiting and harvesting seasons, limits cotton production adjacent to the Atlantic Ocean and the Gulf of Mexico.

Cotton is produced on a wide variety of soils. But differences in soils and topography are largely responsible for differences in the intensity of cotton production in the various parts of the Cotton Belt. Thus, the Mississippi Delta, with its large areas of level land, is the most intensive cotton-producing area depending entirely on natural rainfall. The High Plains and Corpus Christi areas in Texas, characterized by large farms and productive soils with level topography, have expanded cotton production rapidly in the last twenty years. With the help of mechanization, they have become more intensive cotton areas than the old Cotton Belt of the Southeast.

Grain sorghums are competitive with cotton in the western Cotton Belt. In the eastern part of the Cotton Belt, peanuts, truck crops, and, in some areas, tobacco are grown in combination with cotton. In the Black Belt of Alabama and Mississippi and in the brown loam area of Tennessee, Mississippi, and Louisiana, forage and livestock production are replacing cotton. This is also true to a considerable extent throughout the entire eastern part of the Cotton Belt. On the poorer soils from east Texas to the Atlantic Coast, woodland and self-sufficing operations supplement the farmer's income from small acreages of cotton grown on many owner-operated farms.

Dairy regions. The dairy regions of the United States are characterized by soils and topography that are not as favorable to the production of feed grains as those in the Corn Belt. The cool climate and the ample, well-distributed rainfall in this region are favorable for hay and pasture. Farms are smaller than in the southern Corn Belt, and they are located nearer the urban consuming centers. For this and other reasons dairy, rather than beef cattle-raising is associated with the extensive hay and pasturage production.

In the southern and western sections of the dairy region, where the growing season and the soils permit substantial acreages of feed crops to be grown, hogs, poultry, and some beef cattle-feeding operations supplement the dairy enterprise. In the northern and eastern sections of this region, silage corn and small grains are the only crops grown in addition to hay and pasture. Dairy cattle are often the only livestock on the farm and a large part of the grain required for the dairy herd is shipped in from the cash-grain areas of the Corn Belt.

Wheat and small-grain regions. The major wheat-producing regions of the United States are characterized by productive soils with level to rolling topography, but with a rainfall too scant for most other crop production. Grain sorghums and cotton compete with wheat in the southern Great Plains, but in much of the specialized wheat producing area the only alternative to wheat is to return the land to permanent grazing.

The western boundary of the major wheat and small-grain area is set by limitations in both topography and rainfall, which require that the land be kept in permanent range. Much of the land between the winter-wheat area in the southwest and the spring-wheat area in the northwest is too rough for crop production. Where it is sufficiently level and rainfall is adequate, corn is often grown in combination with wheat and other small grains. It will be noted in Figure 3-1 that these sections are included as a part of the western Corn Belt. Other small grains and livestock production are more often combined with spring-wheat production than with winter-wheat production.

In the Pacific Northwest area, winter wheat is preferred, although spring wheat often is seeded if winter kills the fall sown wheat. Rainfall ranges from 10 to 20 inches in this area and the land is rolling. Summer fallowing is practiced in much of this area, as well as in the western parts of both the winter- and spring-wheat areas on the Great Plains. Dry edible peas are the principal alternative crop to wheat in this area. It is entirely surrounded by lands adapted only to grazing.

Range livestock region. Range land, which accounts for more than one-third of the total land area of the United States, is unsuited for cropping for one reason or another. Rainfall on most of the range land is low and uncertain. Some of the range lands are at altitudes that prevent their use for crops. Others are too steep and broken. Differences between cattle and sheep ranges are described as follows:

> Cattle do better than sheep in the rougher and sandy short-grass areas and where few browse plants and annual weeds are found. . . . Sheep are more likely to be on fine-textured soils or moderately rolling lands where there is a combination of grass, perennial browse and annual weeds. . . .
>
> Sheep are usually grazed on open range throughout the year; but they must be moved, often long distances from one seasonal range to another. In winter many sheep are kept in the desert areas which can be used only when snow is present to furnish stock water. . . .
>
> In general, cattle are grazed on the mountain summer ranges for 3 to 5 months, pastured on hay or crop land during spring and fall or run on spring-fall range, and fed during the winter.[1]

Fruit, truck crop, and mixed farming region. This region is made up of 17 widely scattered areas grouped into four subregions on the basis of similarity of crops produced. Even where fruit and truck farming dominate the community, other farming enterprises are found on the less adapted lands. Many fruit and truck crops are highly specialized in their physical requirements for optimum output of a high-quality product. Skilled producers select soils with proper water and air drainage and other characteristics for their high value fruit and truck crops. These specialized crops often crowd out the more general feed, forage, and cereal crops on the irrigated lands.

General farming regions. In the East, general farming areas are located between the Corn Belt and the dairy region on the north and the Cotton Belt on the south. These areas are characterized by rolling to rough lands of low productivity or, as in southern Illinois and Indiana, silt loams with heavy clay subsoils. They include the Ozark hills of southern Missouri and northern Arkansas and much other semimountainous country. General farming predominates in most of these areas because of a relatively dense rural population and the absence of a crop or land use that is definitely superior to others. Hay and pasturage are required in the rotations, hence livestock are an important source of income on most farms, although cash crops, ranging from wheat to fruit, are grown on many of the farms.

In the West, the general farming areas are small and often widely scattered. Most of them are irrigated and their location depends on availability of water for irrigation. Hay, dairying, livestock, potatoes, sugar beets, and dry beans are some of the more important products sold by farmers in these western general farming areas.

Tobacco and general farming region. There are four distinct sub-

---

[1] *Agricultural Information Bulletin 3* (U.S.D.A., 1950), pages 12-13.

regions, each of which grows a different type of tobacco. The flue-cured tobacco area includes a section of the Piedmont in Virginia and North Carolina and a section of the central Coastal Plains in North Carolina. Although tobacco is grown on only a small proportion of the crop land in these sections, its high hand labor requirements and high value per acre cause it to dominate the farming. Supplementary crops are corn, cotton, and hay. Tobacco cannot be grown in combination with legumes and much idle land is found on farms on which tobacco is an important crop in the Piedmont.

Livestock is raised in combination with burley tobacco production in north central Kentucky. Fertile soils derived from phosphatic limestone in this area are peculiarly well-adapted to the production of blue grass. One or two crops of high-quality burley tobacco every eight to ten years are grown in rotation with blue grass on much of this land.

The dark air-cured tobacco region of southwestern Kentucky and northwestern Tennessee is an area in which a third of the farm land is in crops, much land is idle, and livestock production is limited by the small production of feed crops and low quality of pastures. Heavy population pressure and the presence of reasonably favorable soils for tobacco production have kept the farming enterprise in this area organized around tobacco.

The southern Maryland tobacco area is made up of the five southern Maryland counties lying between the Chesapeake Bay and the Potomac River. It grows a distinct type of tobacco known as the Maryland leaf. Tobacco is grown on these farms as the major cash crop, with much of the cropland lying idle. Forage crops are not raised extensively and there is relatively little livestock in the area.

Special crops and general farming regions. Soils and climate are the dominant factors in the development of small areas of specialized crop production. Thus, we find the soils and climate of Aroostook County in Maine the dominant factors influencing specialized potato farming. Sugar-beet growing areas require special soils and climate, but their localized production is primarily the result of accessibility to sugar-beet factories. The growth of the sugar-beet industry in the United States has been limited by the availability of lower cost sources of sugar from Cuba and other offshore countries. Imports of sugar and sugar cane are limited by a system of quotas and domestic sugar-beet producers receive special government subsidies. The sugar-cane areas of Louisiana and Florida are largely limited by the extent of the flat, alluvial soils adapted to sugar-cane production.

Rice is grown intensively in three areas of the United States: southwestern Louisiana, eastern Arkansas, and parts of the Central

Valley in California, where dependable supplies of fresh water are available for irrigation and impervious subsoils reduce water losses from seepage.

Peanuts are grown intensively in three areas on sandy loam soils with friable subsoils. Substantial shifts have been taking place in peanut production, largely associated with acreage restrictions on cotton and attractive price programs on peanuts.

Non-farming areas. These areas are either desert, swamp, mountain, or forest areas, where little or no farming is done.

Trends in total cropland. One of the basic questions regarding American agriculture is its ability to maintain or expand its area of harvested crops as population continues to grow. At what rate will we add new cropland in the years ahead? At what rate will it be necessary to retire worn-out cropland? Aware of the continued erosion losses on our present cropland, many people are concerned about our ability to continue to feed our growing population.

Harvested crops area stabilized. From a land area standpoint, American agriculture has been stabilized for the past twenty-five years. Since 1920 the area of cropland has remained relatively constant and the small increase in land in farms has been in the form of pasture land. The area of farm land in various uses from 1910 to 1954 is shown in Table 3-1.

TABLE 3-1

Utilization of Land in Farms in the United States, 1910-1954

(millions of acres)

	1910	1920	1930	1940	1954
Cropland used for crops	324	374	379	363	380
Cropland idle or in cover crops	23	28	34	36	19
Grassland pasture	284	328	379	461	526
Forest and woodland:					
Pastured	98	77	85	100	121
Not pastured	93	91	65	57	76
Farmsteads, roads, and waste	57	58	45	44	36
Total land in farms	879	956	987	1,061	1,158

Source: Agricultural Statistics (U.S.D.A., 1956), Table 603.

New cropland added since 1920 by drainage, clearing, and irrigation has been offset by the withdrawal of an equal amount. Land is withdrawn from use as cropland primarily because of erosion losses and depletion of inherent fertility. Thus, although our total cropland area has been stabilized at around 370 to 380 million acres of crops and 400 million acres of total cropland, the new land added each year is probably more productive than the worn-out land retired from crop production. With the new, more efficient methods of land-clearing, irrigation, and drainage will it be possible to increase the total crop acreage in the years ahead?

Irrigated land area increasing. Some 320,000 farmers in the western states, where rainfall is inadequate for crop production, have farming programs based wholly or in part on irrigated crop production. The area under irrigation has increased from around 14 million acres of crops and pasture land in 1910 to 42 million acres in 1954. Although the area under irrigation increased threefold in the past 45 years and will continue to increase in the future, irrigated land amounted to only 10 per cent of the total cropland in 1954.

Additional cropland available. In addition to the upward trend in irrigated land noted above, recent government reports are reassuring regarding our ability to increase the total cropland if necessary. Although the better and the more easily drained lands have been developed, soil specialists estimate that as many as 50 million additional acres could be brought into crop production as needed. Around 30 million acres of partly improved land would be greatly improved for crop production by drainage. Another 20 million acres of unimproved lands, mostly along the Atlantic and Gulf coasts and along the Mississippi River, could be improved and put into crop production.[2] Production specialists point out that farm output has expanded faster than population growth since the cropland acreage was stabilized at its present level in 1920. They expect the same situation to continue indefinitely in the future.

REFERENCES

Kellogg, Charles E., *The Soils That Support Us*. New York: The Macmillan Company, 1941.

Timmons, J. F., and W. G. Murray, *Land Problems and Policies*. Ames, Iowa: Iowa State College Press, 1950.

"Generalized Types of Farming in the United States," *Agricultural Information Bulletin 3*, U.S.D.A. (1950).

"Inventory of Major Land Uses, United States," *Miscellaneous Publication 663*, U.S.D.A. (1949).

"Soil," *Yearbook of Agriculture* (1957).

"Land," *Yearbook of Agriculture* (1958).

[2] *Miscellaneous Publication 663* (U.S.D.A., 1949), pages 56-57.

1. From the detailed type-of-farming map in *Agricultural Information Bulletin 3*, listed above, identify the type-of-farming area in which you live.
2. What physical or other factors change at the boundaries of your type-of-farming area?
3. What important changes in types-of-farming are in process today?
4. What developments permitted farm output to increase more rapidly than population without increasing the acreage of crops harvested in the last twenty years?
5. How do you reconcile this with the current statements regarding soil depletion and soil erosion?

CHAPTER 4

Resource Use to
Maximize Returns

IN ANY PARTICULAR year, farmers in the United States report a wide range in yields per acre of crops or production per animal. Many factors are responsible for this situation. Some farmers are more skilled than others in using identical production techniques. There is a substantial variation in the inherent productive capacity of the land from one farm to another in most communities of the United States. The same holds true for the animals in the breeding herds. Variation in rates of production also result from variations in the weather and from the fact that farming operations are often based on custom. Crops are planted and livestock cared for on many farms just as they were twenty-five years ago. Farming is a way of life rather than a business occupation for a substantial number of farm families.

But each year an increasing number of farmers consider farming a business; in fact, the farmers who produce the bulk of the market supplies organize their farming operations on business principles. They are interested in maximum net income from their farming operations over a period of years. Given the technology, the machinery, supplies, and seed strains that are currently available, what combination of these and what amount of each will it be most profitable to combine with the land and buildings used for crop and livestock production? Important progress has been made in recent years in the technical experiments that provide needed information to answer such questions. This is well illustrated by recent studies of corn breeding and fertilization carried on in North Carolina. The foreword to a report on these studies has the following to say about corn growing there:

Progress does not always follow a steady course. . . .

Before the turn of the century, the average yield of corn in the state was around 11 to 14 bushels per acre year in and year out. Then came the 4-H corn clubs and an intensive educational program acquainting the farmers and farm youth with what was then known about corn production. In the short space of twelve years, the average yield increased to around 18 to 20 bushels per acre. There it remained almost three decades.

Now we are in the midst of another period of progress which promises to be much more far reaching than that experienced in the period of 1903 to 1915. This was set off by two research programs, jointly sponsored by the North Carolina Agricultural Experiment Station and the Bureau of Plant Industry, Soils and Agricultural Engineering, namely (1) a breeding program begun in 1938 to develop corn hybrids adapted to this area; and (2) an intensive program begun in 1933 on the cultural and fertilization requirements for corn production in this area. . . .

When [the] facts and . . . corrective measures were brought together in one corn production program, it [became] common for practical farmers from one end of the state to the other to get yields of 100 bushels per acre or more. . . .[1]

The production function: the fertilizer example. To deal in a rigorous way with the question—How should resources be employed on a farm to maximize returns?—we must first have at our command physical input-output data, which describe how output changes as different factor inputs are varied. Sets of input-output data which do this are called production functions. And such data are available from the North Carolina experiments with different applications of nitrogen to corn production. Figure 4-1 shows the yield of corn per acre in years of fair to good moisture and under dry weather conditions with applications of nitrogen varying from 0 to 120 pounds per acre. In years of adequate moisture, farmers were able to increase corn yields from 29 to 88 bushels an acre by the addition of 120 pounds of nitrogen; this is the production function for nitrogen fertilizer under good moisture conditions; it describes how output varies as nitrogen inputs vary, all other factors held constant. In dry years, similar applications increased corn yields from 27 to only 56 bushels. Although data on the response to heavier applications are not published, the report states, "In most of the experiments, nitrogen application above the 120-pound level gave little or no response even under conditions of fairly good moisture distribution."[2] On the basis of this statement, the line in Figure 4-1 has been projected for a

---

[1] "Fertilize Corn for Higher Yields," *Bulletin 366* (Raleigh: North Carolina Agricultural Experiment Station, 1949).

[2] *Ibid.,* page 10.

160-pound application of nitrogen under fair to good moisture conditions to 90 bushels per acre. It is highly probable that, in years of dry weather, corn yields actually dropped when more than 120 pounds of nitrogen were added. Accordingly, a yield of 50 bushels is estimated when applications of 160 pounds of nitrogen are made.

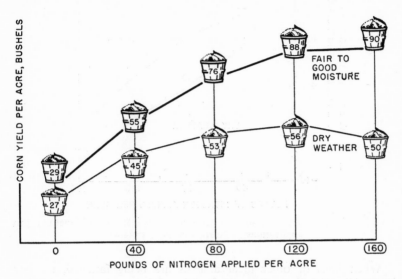

Fig. 4-1. Yield of corn per acre with varying applications of nitrogen, North Carolina, 1944-48. (Adapted from Fig. 3, North Carolina Agr. Exp. Sta. Bul. 366.)

The response of corn yield to additional applications of nitrogen fertilizer, as illustrated in Figure 4-1, is typical of the relations one finds in all processes of production as varying amounts of one factor are combined with relatively fixed amounts of another. As more of the variable factor (fertilizer) is associated with the fixed factor (land, seed, labor, and equipment, in this case), output fails to increase proportionately; the marginal product of corn declines as nitrogen inputs are added. It is the old principle of diminishing returns encountered in the general economics texts. The relationship becomes evident when one plots the additional corn output obtained from successive 40-pound applications of nitrogen (Figure 4-2).

If sufficient quantities of the variable factor are added, one reaches a point at which the last unit fails to increase the output or may actually decrease it. Increasing the nitrogen used from 120 to 160 pounds an acre actually decreases corn yields in dry weather (Figure

4-2). This principle of diminishing returns underlies all physical combinations of factors in farm production, as well as in other lines of production.

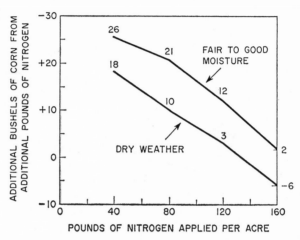

Fig. 4-2. Additional bushels of corn per acre resulting from additional nitrogen applications in North Carolina, 1944-48.

When hogs or other meat animals are being fattened, as they become heavier they use more feed for maintenance of weight they have already gained and less for additional weight. For this reason, the gains on hogs up to 225 pounds are more economical than they are at heavier weights. A 400-pound calf puts on more weight per 100 pounds of feed consumed than a 1,000-pound steer. The same principle also applies to fattening lambs and growing chickens and turkeys.

Most profitable combination of resources. The general application of this principle may be seen by observing that, in farming, many of the resources with which a farmer works each year are relatively fixed. Thus, he can grow only so many acres of corn in his rotation, his barn, for example, holds only 12 cows, or he may have saved only 60 pigs in any particular year. His general problem is that of adding variable factor inputs to these fixed ones: fertilizer to the corn land, feed to the 12 cows, and feed to the 60 pigs, until the most profitable combination of factors is reached.

Farmers, in general, are aware of this principle and make their production plans accordingly. When they know the physical production ratios (that is, the input-output ratios), they are able to calculate the most profitable rate of application of fertilizer. When corn is $1.20 per bushel (in the field before harvest) and nitrogen costs $.12 a pound, given the input-output ratios presented in Figure 4-2, it will pay to add nitrogen to the point where the last 40 pounds of nitrogen adds just 4 bushels to the corn yield. At that point marginal cost will equal marginal revenue ($4.80 spent for 40 pounds of fertilizer = $4.80, the value of 4 bushels of corn). In favorable moisture years this would call for around 140 pounds of nitrogen per acre, but in dry-weather years only 100 to 110 pounds of nitrogen would be profitable (Figure 4-2).

The additional cost (marginal cost) associated with producing the additional output (marginal output) can be easily calculated by dividing the cost of the additional input by the additional output obtained. Assuming the price of nitrogen to be $.12 a pound and using the "good moisture" input-output data from Figure 4-2, the marginal cost data for corn are as follows:

TABLE 4-1

Level of Nitrogen Fertilization (Pounds per Acre)	Total Yield of Corn (Bushels per Acre)	Cost of Additional Applications of Nitrogen (40 lbs. × $.12 = $4.80)		Marginal Product of Corn	Marginal Cost per Bushel of Corn
0	29	—	÷	—	—
40	55	$4.80	÷	26	$ .18
80	76	4.80	÷	21	.23
120	88	4.80	÷	12	.40
160	90	4.80	÷	2	2.40

The marginal cost curve constructed from these data is presented in Figure 4-3, as well as the cost curve for "dry weather conditions." (The marginal unit cost $.18 is plotted against a yield per acre of 55 in Figure 4-3, the total yield following the marginal increase of 26 bushels.) In this presentation of marginal costs, all costs other than nitrogen fertilizer are assumed to be fixed; nitrogen is the only variable input in this illustrative case. But fertilizer is one of the few factor inputs that is easily and readily varied in farming operations; hence the illustration is representative of the actual world situation.

In terms of Figure 4-3, it will pay farmers to apply nitrogen fertilizer to their corn enterprise until the cost of the fertilizer used in obtaining the last bushel of corn is just equal to the selling price of corn. At any lesser amount, marginal cost is less than marginal revenue ($1.20 per bushel of corn in this case); at any greater

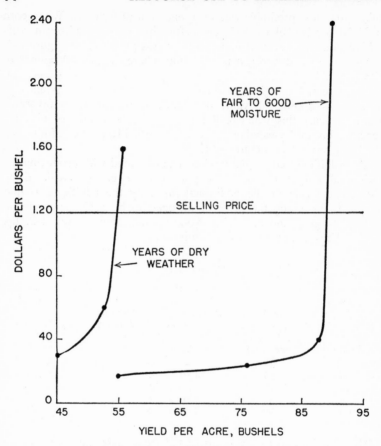

Fig. 4-3. The marginal cost of producing additional corn as the input of nitrogen is varied per acre.

amount, marginal cost exceeds marginal revenue. In dry years, this point is reached when the yield is pushed up to between 53 and 56 bushels per acre, but in the good moisture years farmers in North Carolina can profitably push their yields up to 88 bushels per acre. Disregarding for the moment the problem of determining in advance the years when the rainfall will be adequate, we reach the conclusion that, with technical rates of production, cost of the variable factor, and price of the product known, the farmer can determine his most profitable rate of nitrogen application. This in turn determines his most profitable level of corn production under the conditions described above. In point of fact, these physical input-output data are extremely difficult to obtain, and farmers rarely know them with the accuracy suggested here. But, given their imperfect knowledge, farmers must, if they are rational profit-seekers, pursue a decision process involving these principles. The actual world problem is— given their imperfect knowledge—how closely can farmers approach the most profitable output positions enterprise by enterprise?

Problems in achieving the most profitable combination of resources. The combination of production supplies or factors to produce crops or livestock is seldom easy. We have already noted that the amount of nitrogen applied on corn in North Carolina should be varied according to the moisture conditions. This is possible because a substantial part of the nitrogen is applied as side dressings to the corn when it is about 2 feet high. If dry weather is prevailing at that time, the cautious farmer will reduce his nitrogen applications as compared with years of more favorable rainfall conditions. But if the farmer is to obtain profitable returns from using heavy applications of nitrogen fertilizer in years of normal rainfall, he should make heavier applications of potash and phosphate fertilizer. Corn must be planted thicker than normal to produce more plants per acre if the full potential results of heavy fertilization are to be realized.

One of the more obvious examples of joint response is in the use of fertilizer in potato production. When potatoes are grown without irrigation in the humid sections of the United States, they are commonly fertilized at the rate of 300 to 700 pounds per acre. But supplemental irrigation is being used to an increasing extent in growing potatoes in the humid sections. Where the potatoes are irrigated, applications of from 2,000 to 2,500 pounds of fertilizer per acre are common. Irrigation without heavier applications of fertilizer would not be profitable. Conversely, without irrigation, heavy applications of fertilizer are positively harmful.

Although the marginal analysis is implicit in all decisions concerning how much to extend production, the farmer's problem is not so simple that he can vary one factor alone, leaving all others unchanged. Usually, he must change a number of factors. The potato grower in the humid regions, when deciding whether or not to undertake supplemental irrigation, does not balance merely the cost of the irrigation system against an increased yield, with all other factors held constant. He must use more labor to get the water on the land and more seed and fertilizer to take full advantage of the additional water. He must know the functional relationships between these different factors and balance the increased cost of the most economical combination against the value of the increased output. A further refinement is appropriate in the case of potato production. Supplemental irrigation and heavy rates of fertilization not only increase the total output of potatoes, but also increase the proportion of No. 1 potatoes. In many cases, the new production techniques involving additional production supplies improve the quality of the output in addition to increasing the quantity. This improved quality must be valued as a part of the increased output.

Budgeting changes in production practices. Because it is extremely difficult to obtain functional input-output data, and therefore equally as hard to develop empirical marginal data, most farm-management analyses are made in terms of comparative budgets. These analyses involve the preparation of several budgets: statements of physical supplies used in production, volume of output and expected expenses, and the variation in income which would result from the use of different resource combinations which are possible. Consider, as a simple example, how the use of an improved variety of oats benefits a Midwest farmer, who grows 30 acres of oats a year. Two and one-half bushels of home-grown seed per acre might cost him $1.50, or $.60 a bushel. Fertilizing and preparing his seedbed as usual, the farmer obtains 45 bushels of oats for a gross revenue of $27 per acre (45 bushels at $.60 per bushel). A new variety of oats that yields 50 bushels an acre costs $1.50 a bushel for seed. A little mental arithmetic indicates to the farmer that the new seed would cost him $3.75 an acre as against $1.50 for his own seed. At an extra cost of $2.25 he can produce $3.00 more oats per acre; the difference, $.75, multiplied by 30, the number of acres grown, indicates the advantage of using the new seed oats, $22.50. This example is simple because no other changes in farming operations are required to take advantage of the new variety of oats.

Most alternatives are not this simple. Supplemental irrigation, for example, involves a large number of changes in the farming operation. Before undertaking such changes, the business-minded farmer sets up a budget of his present operations and a budget of his operations utilizing supplemental irrigation. Because he has installed supplemental irrigation, the farmer may find it necessary to hire extra labor during the watering seasons; he may find it desirable to change his cropping plans to make more complete use of the new irrigation equipment. He prepares several alternative budgets and finally selects the operating plan which promises him the best returns. Even though all alternative plans are not worked out on paper, the farmer who is a good businessman goes through such a process when determining his production plans.

Achieving the most profitable combination of enterprises. Most farmers maintain a cropping sequence or rotation on their land and often have one or more livestock enterprises. The level of output of each crop and livestock enterprise is determined by achieving the most profitable combination of variable factors and fixed factors involved in each enterprise. The operator in his business-management function is thus faced with a series of situations similar to those illustrated in Figure 4-3. Given the state of the arts (that is, the pattern and level of technology) and the fixed production factors in each enterprise and on the total farm, the farmer varies those inputs that can be varied so as to equate marginal revenue and marginal cost in each enterprise. In terms of Figure 4-3, he pushes output in each enterprise to the point where marginal cost in each enterprise equals the price line (that is, marginal revenue). If the farmer takes each commodity price as given (which is common in agriculture and the reason the farmer is called a price-taker) and equates marginal revenue with marginal cost in each enterprise, he is maximizing the net return from the total farm operation. It, of course, follows that price is not the same in each commodity line: in one it is high, in another low, and so on. It is the task of the manager to adjust resources among the enterprises so that marginal costs and marginal revenue are equal in each.

Whether marginal costs are extremely inelastic as under "dry weather" conditions in Figure 4-3, or whether marginal costs change from inelastic to elastic as under "good moisture" conditions depends upon the physical input-output relationship involved. If several important inputs, for example, fertilizer or labor, are technically variable and can in the total farm operation be varied, then marginal costs will exhibit some significant degree of elasticity. But if inputs combine in fixed, or relatively fixed, proportions, then costs rise with no appreciable increase in output, and marginal costs are perfectly, or exceedingly, inelastic.[3] The configuration and elasticity of the marginal-cost relation in each enterprise is thus a question of empirical fact, and must in each case rest upon research results or judgment.

It can be deduced, however, that the elasticity of the marginal-cost relation will increase as the number of resource inputs in an enterprise can be and are varied; and the number that can be and are varied will increase as more time elapses. Given sufficient time, the farmer can convert a general-purpose barn to a dairy barn, or conversely; or given sufficient time, a potato-digger can be traded for a hay-baler. Thus, the marginal-cost curve for a particular farm enterprise becomes more elastic in the long run.

[3] The concept of elasticity is explained and illustrated in Chapter 13.

The supply curve of the enterprise. The marginal-cost curve of the enterprise is logically interpreted as the supply curve of the enterprise. This interpretation is evident from Figure 4-4. At price *OA,* the manager of this enterprise will produce, and thereby stands ready to supply, *OR* amount. At *OR* amount, marginal cost is equal to price, that is, marginal revenue. If the price increases to *OB,* the manager will re-allocate resources so as to move along the marginal-cost curve to P_2, or *OS* amount. At the new price, *OB,* the marginal cost and marginal revenue are equated at output *OS.* From this we see that the marginal-cost curve of the enterprise turns out to be the supply curve of the enterprise; it describes those quantities of the commodity in question that this enterprise will produce and offer for sale at varying prices.

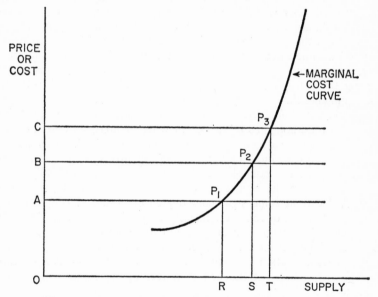

Fig. 4-4. The marginal cost supply-curve of the enterprise.

The supply curve of a commodity, say wheat, at the farm level is the summation of all enterprise-supply curves for wheat. Thus, the elasticity of the commodity-supply relation is dependent upon the elasticity of the enterprise marginal-cost curves. The elasticity of the enterprise marginal-cost curves in the world of practice are, in turn, dependent, first, upon the physical production coefficients (that is, the production functions), and, second, upon the ability and willingness of farmers to substitute one productive factor for another. In other words, the elasticity of the marginal-cost curve, in practice, depends upon the "know-how" of the farmer to substitute one factor for another, as well as on the physical production coefficients. It also depends on the absence of any strong influence by custom and inertia. Further, when the price, of wheat, for example, fluctuates relative to that of oats or barley, farmers are not limited in their operations to varying the application of such inputs as fertilizers and weed sprays; they can and do shift land and labor inputs among farm enterprises. Thus, land and labor, which tend to be fixed inputs for the farm as a whole, are varied among enterprises as the prices of the products vary and as the technical production requirements permit. For example, should the price of wheat rise in comparison to the price of oats or barley, farmers would surely shift some of their land out of oats and barley into wheat, but probably not all of it because of restrictions in the use of labor over the season and of harvesting equipment. In this example, land is the variable input, and labor and harvesting equipment the fixed factors.

Commodities with the more elastic supply curves will be those in which the important input factors can be and are varied *in* the commodity enterprise. And input factors can be varied *in* one farm enterprise: (1) by shifting inputs among enterprises on the same farm (for example, land), and (2) by varying inputs obtained from the nonfarm sector, for example, fertilizer. But our rather limited statistical studies of supply suggest that many short-run commodity supply relations at the farm level are relatively inelastic: wheat and corn have elasticities in the neighborhood of 0.1 to 0.2; cotton, 0.3; potatoes, 0.3 to 0.4; dairy products, 0.1 to 0.2; and hogs, 0.3 to 0.4.[4]

Changing technology in agriculture and on the farm. The discussion of resource use to maximize returns to this point has assumed no change in the state of the arts—has assumed a constant technology. This is the traditional theory of the firm. All factor inputs are assumed to be homogeneous, and all outside conditioning factors (for example, weather, technology) are assumed to be constant, and within this static context the theory of the firm describes how resources are allocated among enterprises as product prices vary to maximize returns for the total farm operation. But technology has not been constant in agriculture over the past fifty years; it has advanced rapidly as hundreds of millions of dollars have been spent

---

[4] As explained in Chapter 13, a supply elasticity of 0.3 means that the change in supply associated with a percentage change in price is only 0.3 as great as the change in price. In this case a 3 per cent change in supply would be associated with a 10 per cent change in price.

by private and governmental agencies to develop and disseminate new production techniques. New and improved production techniques have, in fact, become the key variable in American agriculture and the principle means for increasing the output of farm enterprises.

Technology and crop production. The higher yields which the American farmers have been obtaining in recent years, result, fundamentally, from the investment of increased quantities of capital in crop production. This has caused several changes, one of the most important being the substitution of motor power for horse power and hand labor. The tractor has made possible both more thorough and timely cultural operations. Farmers with tractors have adopted the practice of plowing their land deeper than they did with horses. They work the seed bed more and cultivate the intertilled crops with fewer delays than they did when horses were the primary source of power. This improvement is possible, both because the tractor is an untiring source of power and because it usually gives a higher ratio of power per man. The advantage of the tractor over horse power is most evident during the rainy seasons. Farmers who use tractors may change operators and keep their power units in continuous operation when soil conditions permit. Farmers who use horses must allow them to rest twelve to fourteen hours out of every twenty-four. Because of this, tractors permit more timely operations in periods when the farmer might otherwise be delayed by unfavorable weather.

Improved seed strains used in crop production today represent another form of increased capital in agriculture as compared with earlier years. Much of the capital investment required in developing these improved seed strains has been made by the Federal and state governments in the experimental work carried out at the state agricultural experiment stations. More recently, hybrid seed corn companies have invested large sums in breeding work and in equipment for producing and processing the hybrid seed. Almost all the farm seeds today have a productive capacity far superior to that of similar seeds used in earlier years. This increased productive capacity is the result of capital investments over a long period of years.

Farmers, today, are making increased investments in fertilizers. They are now using several times as much fertilizer as they did in prewar years and twice as much nitrogen and potash as in 1945 (Figure 4-5). The increase in yields of such crops as potatoes, vegetables, corn, cotton, and legume hays, which resulted from the heavier application of fertilizer, is another change brought about in crop production by the investment of increased quantities of capital. The widespread use of agricultural limestone to correct soil acidity has been especially important in increasing legume yields. Other capital investments have been made in drainage and irrigation which have produced similar results. Favorable prices for farm products during the war and postwar years stimulated a large amount of drainage both of land already cropped and of other land not previously used for crop production. Similarly, irrigation brought some new land into crop production and increased yields on existing cropland. Supplemental irrigation is being used to an increasing extent in the humid sections of the United States to increase the yields of such crops as potatoes and truck crops.

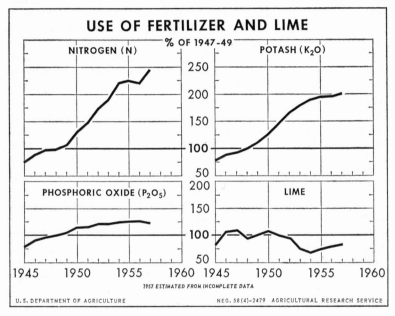

Fig. 4-5.

A final group of capital goods must be mentioned as playing an important part in increasing crop yields in recent years. This is the group of pesticides that are now used to control diseases and insect pests. Both their use and their potency have increased greatly in recent years.

Technology as a form of capital. When one reviews the capital inputs now combined with land and labor to produce crops, he notes that most of the capital goods are in a form not available a few decades ago. Without the technical discoveries of the internal combustion engine, the pneumatic tire, the vigor of crossed inbred seed strains, and the lethal qualities of new chemical compounds, there would be little economic basis for the representative farm increasing its capital investments relative to land and labor in crop production. But new discoveries usually do not just happen. They are the result of months or years of patient experimental work. Improved technology, which has been incorporated in all the production supplies and seedstocks used in farm production, is as much a form of increased capital as are the physical goods one sees in the farmer's buildings.

We can now state a generalization regarding the dynamics of capital use in farm production, which has contributed so much to our current high levels of efficiency in United States agriculture. Progress in technology, either in analyzing the components of the soil or in adapting the capital goods to perform their functions more efficiently, results in a progressively increasing ratio of capital to land and labor in farm production. A later chapter will be devoted to an analysis of the economic problems associated with the introduction of new technology. At this point it is sufficient to point out that most farmers fail to take prompt advantage of desirable new technological developments. The unusual profits of the superior farm managers result, to a large extent, from their ability to discover which are the profitable new techniques or new machines and to adopt them promptly.

Technology and livestock production. The upward trend noted in crop yields is even more pronounced in livestock-production rates. Livestock production per animal unit in 1958 was almost 50 per cent higher than it was thirty years earlier. In 1928, the average laying hen or pullet on hand January 1 produced 119 eggs a year. Egg production per layer has increased almost steadily since that time, until it is now over 200 eggs per layer. Milk production per cow has shown a similar increase. In 1928, average milk production per cow in the United States was 4,516 pounds; it is now slightly over 6,400 pounds per cow. Hog production per sow has increased in a similar manner in the past thirty years for several reasons: (1) sows now farrow and save more pigs per litter than in earlier years; (2) more sows now farrow two litters a year; and (3) better feeding and disease control result in more pork going to market per pig weaned. Similar, although less striking, improvements have been made in beef-cattle and sheep production.

Just as increasing yields per acre are a normal development in a progressive economy, we should expect continually increasing livestock production per breeding animal as a part of economic progress. Much of the upward trend is the result of capital investment. Capital investment in four broad areas has resulted in most of the increase noted to date: (1) improved housing, including brooding equipment

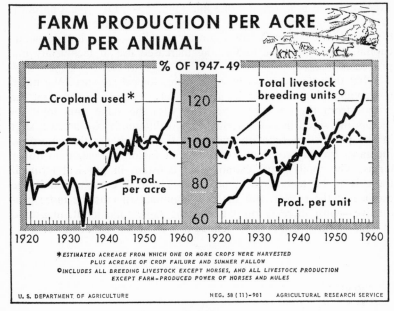

FARM PRODUCTION PER ACRE AND PER ANIMAL

% OF 1947-49

Cropland used*

Total livestock breeding units°

120

100

Prod. per acre

80

Prod. per unit

60

1920   1930   1940   1950   1960   1920   1930   1940   1950   1960

*ESTIMATED ACREAGE FROM WHICH ONE OR MORE CROPS WERE HARVESTED
PLUS ACREAGE OF CROP FAILURE AND SUMMER FALLOW
°INCLUDES ALL BREEDING LIVESTOCK EXCEPT HORSES, AND ALL LIVESTOCK PRODUCTION
EXCEPT FARM-PRODUCED POWER OF HORSES AND MULES

U. S. DEPARTMENT OF AGRICULTURE   NEG. 58 (11)-901   AGRICULTURAL RESEARCH SERVICE

Fig. 4-6.

for poultry and hogs, (2) improved disease control, (3) improved breeding and selection, and (4) improved nutrition.

As in the case of crop production, however, it is improvements in technology that have formed the basis of the increased use of capital. We have our central-hatching and artificial-brooding development in poultry, year-round farrowing equipment for hogs, and the ventilated-dairy-barn-with-automatic-drinking-cups for dairy cows. Innovations have been particularly important in disease control. Cross-breeding of hogs is a rather recent innovation. Studies of nutritional needs of animals and of the nutritive content of feeds have been the basis for improved rations. Increased production of high-protein-content legume hay and the expansion of soybean production are the key factors in the better balanced rations fed to livestock in recent years.

Farm technological advance defined. The foregoing discussion has indicated that capital investment in agriculture and the adoption of new technologies have gone hand in hand. Rarely these days do we get additional capital investment in a farm that does not involve new and improved techniques. And even more rare is the case of the introduction of a new production practice that does not involve the expenditure of more capital of some kind. Thus, the typical development in farm enterprises in recent years has been the additional use of capital, but not capital of a constant quality—not a homogeneous capital. What we have had is the increased use of technically improved capital.

What then do we mean by farm technological advance? We mean a recombination of factor inputs in a farm enterprise such that the output from the enterprise increases with the same total input of factors measured in dollar terms. Stated differently, we mean a shift in the production function such that the output for the enterprise increases for any constant total input of factors measured in dollar terms. The total inputs cannot hold constant in physical terms if there is to be technological advance. The new combination is the essence of the matter. But the new combination must be more productive—must increase output with the same total input, measured in dollar terms—if it is to be defined as a technological advance.

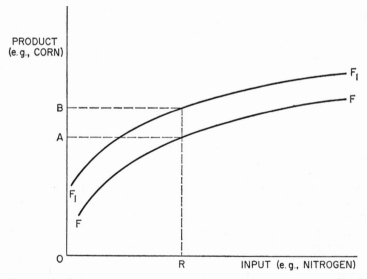

Fig. 4-7. A shift in the production function with technological advance.

The concept of farm technological advance is illustrated in Figure 4-7. Let us assume that a new type of nitrogen fertilizer is developed, which costs no more per pound and is more easily assimilated as a plant food than was the previous type. Hence, for any given input of nitrogen (OR), the output of corn increases. This increase in output is described by the shift in the production function from FF to F_1F_1 and at nitrogen input OR, the increase is equal to AB. This nitrogen example is highly oversimplified, but it illustrates the nature of a farm technological advance.

Farm technological advance shifts the supply curve. The adoption by farmers of a new and improved technology (for example, improved seeds, insecticides, antibiotics) shifts the production function for the enterprise involved as we have observed. This in turn has the effect of lowering the marginal cost of the enterprise (Figure 4-8). Marginal unit costs for any output (OR) are lower after the adoption of the new technique than before. The farmer has made a farm technological advance.

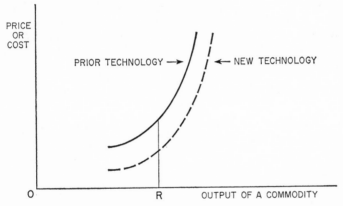

Fig. 4-8. Marginal cost curves before and after a farm technological advance.

Since the effect of a farm technological advance is to lower and shift to the right the marginal cost curve of the enterprise, and since, further, the marginal cost in its inclining phase is the supply curve of the enterprise, it then follows that a farm technological advance has the effect of shifting the commodity supply curve to the right. And this has been the over-riding consequence of the widespread adoption of new technologies on farms since the middle 1930's—the persistent expansion in supply, commodity by commodity.

Maximizing returns in a dynamic world. The task of maximizing total returns on a multiple-enterprise farm in the changing world of today is not easy. The farm operator in response to commodity price changes must do more than vary the inputs of the usual variable factors in the old production functions. He must and does initiate production practice changes that shift production functions and lower cost relations. This action then entails further shifts in resources among enterprises. Factor costs, too, are constantly changing (and usually increased in the 1950's); this affects marginal costs—shifts the position of the marginal-cost curve for the enterprise involved. Thus the farm operator in the fast-changing twentieth century is forever changing his resource mix—as product prices change, as technology changes, and as factor prices change—to obtain profit maximizing factor combinations in each enterprise. Good management in agriculture now demands a high order of skill, ability, and enterprise.

REFERENCES

Boulding, Kenneth E., *Economic Analysis,* rev. ed., Chapters 22 and 24. New York: Harper & Brothers, 1948.

Heady, Earl O., "Basic Economic Considerations and Welfare Aspects of Farm Technological Advance," *Journal of Farm Economics,* (May 1949).

————, and Harald R. Jensen, *Farm Management Economics,* Chapter 4. Englewood Cliffs, N.J.: Prentice-Hall, Inc., 1954.

Malone, Carl C., *How to Make Your Farm Pay,* Chapter 3. Ames, Iowa: Iowa State College Press, 1950.

Wilcox, Walter W., "Effects of Farm Price Changes on Efficiency in Farming," *Journal of Farm Economics,* (February 1951).

POINTS FOR DISCUSSION

1. What kind of information does a production function provide? How is this information to be obtained? How is such information used to help determine the proper allocation of resources on the farm?

2. What is meant by diminishing returns, or diminishing marginal productivity? What do we mean by marginal analysis?

3. How is a marginal cost curve constructed? What does a marginal cost curve describe? In what sense is a marginal cost curve a supply curve?

4. What is a farm budget analysis? Why is it used in practice, instead of marginal analysis?

5. When are the total returns of a multiple enterprise firm maximized?

6. What have been the important technological changes in agriculture since the middle 1930's? How have these changes limited the usefulness of static marginal analysis?

7. What is a farm technological advance? Define, and give some illustrations. Indicate the effect of one of your illustrations on marginal costs and the commodity supply curve.

CHAPTER 5

Costs, Returns, and Size of Farm

COST OF PRODUCTION is a much used and much abused term. In the previous chapter, we saw how the profitable limits to expanding production were determined by rising marginal costs. In this chapter, we hope to explain the different meanings that are given to the term "cost of production" and show which costs affect farmers' short-run responses to changes in market demand and which affect only their long-run responses. We also will examine the popular dictum "to make higher profits one must 'reduce expenses.' " The way in which costs per unit of output fall as the size of farm is increased also will be noted.

Fixed and variable costs. Total costs of farm operation may be grouped in a number of different ways, each method of grouping having its advantages for particular purposes. We are particularly interested in a method which will reflect economic incentives for changing production plans. From this standpoint, two major groups, fixed and variable costs, are particularly significant. The term "fixed costs" is often used interchangeably with "overhead costs" to identify costs that do not vary with the level of output during the time period under discussion, for example, one year. Thus, the real estate taxes are a fixed expense or cost that will not change with the level of production on the farm in any particular year.

Variable costs on the other hand, as the name indicates, vary with the level of output. As more fertilizer is applied to increase crop yields total fertilizer costs increase. The significance of this particular classification is evident when one considers why farmers change their production plans. Marginal cost is a pure expression of variable costs, measuring the costs associated with variations in the use of a factor input. It is the additional cost per unit of additional output. We found in the preceding chapter that as long as the cost of an additional unit of output is less than its selling price, it pays to continue expanding output. Conversely, whenever additional variable or marginal costs per unit of output are not covered, losses may be minimized by reducing production. Fixed costs do not affect the short-term level of production. The real estate taxes and other fixed costs are incurred, regardless of whether or not any production takes place. Fixed costs per unit of output continue to decline as long as output is expanded, whereas marginal costs and average variable costs increase as output is expanded (Table 5-1 and Figure 5-1).

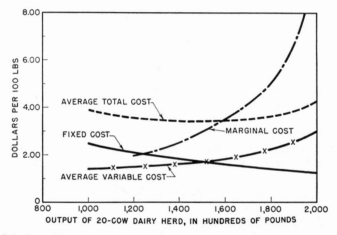

Fig. 5-1. Cost per 100 pounds for producing milk, twenty-cow dairy herd. Data in this figure are based on a range of 100,000 to 200,000 pounds of total milk produced, or 5,000 to 10,000 pounds per cow. Fixed costs include maintenance, feed and labor, housing, and interest and depreciation on the dairy herd and on equipment used. Variable costs included are, primarily, feed and labor, in addition to maintenance. The rising variable and marginal costs are due to the increasing quantities of feed required per pound of milk at higher levels of input. (See note under Table 5-1.)

In the early days when farming was largely self-sufficient, almost all costs fell into the fixed, or overhead, category. The farmer planted his own seeds, using his own labor and horse power. He increased production by using his labor and horse power more intensively. On the family farm, the living expenses of the family are a part of the overhead costs of the farm business. Family living costs, taxes, and interest on money borrowed were almost all the cash expenses farmers incurred in early Colonial days. Obviously, a drop in the price of wheat or hogs had little effect on the farmer's production activities under such circumstances. He could not reduce his cash costs by reducing his output.

As farming has become more commercialized, variable costs in farming have increased relative to fixed costs. Variable costs today are a higher proportion of total farming costs than in any previous period. Studies of family farming conducted by the Agricultural Research Service, U. S. Department of Agriculture, show that in recent years variable costs on most family farms have reached about one-third of total costs.

If a dairy farmer has a 20-cow dairy herd housed in a conventional dairy barn, the fixed or overhead costs of maintaining and sheltering the dairy herd might be $2,500 a year, regardless of the level of their milk production. The most important method of varying the level of milk output from these 20 dairy cows in a brief period, say twelve months, is to vary the level of feeding. By increasing the rate of feeding above body-maintenance levels, milk production can be increased with each additional input of feed until a level is reached where the cows go off feed or fail to consume additional concentrates placed before them. The data in Table 5-1 and the curves in Figure 5-1 are based on experimental data indicating the increased quantities of milk output which are associated with increased inputs of concentrates for a 20-cow dairy herd.

TABLE 5-1*

Average Fixed, Variable, Marginal, and Total Costs per 100 Pounds of Milk†

Output (in pounds)	Fixed Costs	Variable Costs	Marginal Cost	Average Total Cost
100,000..............	$2.50	$1.40	—	$3.90
120,000..............	2.08	1.50	$2.00	3.58
140,000..............	1.78	1.65	2.55	3.43
160,000..............	1.56	1.90	3.65	3.46
180,000..............	1.38	2.25	5.00	3.63
200,000..............	1.25	3.00	9.75	4.25

* See legend under Figure 5-1. Fixed costs are estimated at $125 per cow, or $2,500 for a 20-cow herd. It is estimated that at an output level of 100,000 pounds of milk, or 5,000 pounds per cow, it takes an average of 70 pounds of feed to produce 100 pounds of milk. At 200,000 pounds of milk for the herd, or 10,000 pounds per cow, an average of 150 pounds of feed are required, above maintenance needs, per 100 pounds of milk produced. Feed is estimated to cost $2 per 100 lbs. Marginal costs are computed by dividing the increase in total cost by the increase in total milk produced between the different levels of output.

† Output of a 20-cow herd, varying from 100,000 to 200,000 pounds.

Variable cash expenditures versus unit production costs. The typical advice to a young couple about to start farming is to "keep expenses down," if they wish to make financial progress. Yet an examination of the recommendation that production per acre or per animal unit be expanded until marginal costs equals the value of the marginal unit of output indicates that up to this point profits are increased by increased cash expenditures. The typical farmer, starting his spring farming operations with his own labor, a fixed acreage of land, and a standard set of machinery, must decide from time to time throughout the season what quantity of variable production supplies to combine with these fixed (or relatively fixed) factors in the year's farming operations. How much fertilizer should he purchase? How much should he invest in improved seeds and breeding stock? How much in insecticides? How much extra labor should he hire to improve the timeliness of his operations or to permit more intensive use of labor and machinery in preparing and cultivating the land? How much should he spend on protein and mineral supplements to improve his livestock rations?

If he followed the old dictum and kept expenses for these items at a minimum, his total production would be low. Total costs, both fixed and variable would be low, but as long as the value of increased production exceeds the cost of additional fertilizer, net income is increased by increasing expenditures for fertilizer. The farmer who decides not to use commercial fertilizer on his corn may have total production costs per acre of $40 and get a yield of 40 bushels, that is, have unit costs of $1 per bushel. His neighbor, with the same production costs other than fertilizer, spends $4 per acre for fertilizer, increasing his costs to $44 per acre, and gets a yield of 50 bushels per acre. He has increased his cash expenses, but his average cost per bushel (unit cost) is only $.88.

In other, and more technical, words the returns to an enterprise are never maximized (or losses are never minimized) until marginal costs have turned upward. More specifically, returns to an enterprise are maximized at that point where marginal cost is equal to marginal revenue (and under competitive conditions marginal revenue is constant and equal to price). These complex relationships are illustrated in Figure 5-2. Below point C in Figure 5-2 the cost of each additional unit of product is less than the selling price of the unit of output. Hence, there is an incentive to expand output to point C. Beyond point C, the cost of each additional unit of product exceeds the selling price of the product. Hence there is an incentive to reduce output to point C. The maximum profit position of the firm at point C is described by the rectangle $ABCD$ (net return per unit of product [CD] times the number of units of product [BD]). In the common case, then, where the selling price of the product is high enough to cover average total unit costs a producer will continue adding inputs of the variable factors, thus expanding output, until marginal costs are greater than average total unit costs.

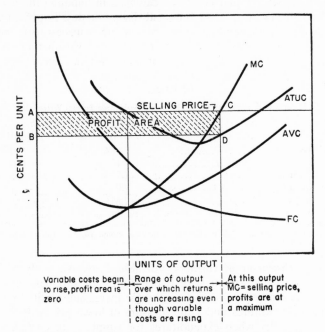

Fig. 5-2. Determining the most profitable level of production.

Summaries of farm accounts indicate that cash expenditures are higher on farms with the higher net incomes (Table 5-2). All increases in cash expenditures in farming operations do not increase cash income, but in the farming community, farmers do not use as much of specialized production supplies as would be profitable. When farmers with the highest net incomes from farming in a community are studied, one finds that they have higher cash expenses than the average, with higher expenditures for fertilizer, purchased feeds, insecticides, improved strains of seeds, and similar output-increasing items. The profitable adjustment for most individual farmers is not to reduce expenses, but, rather to increase those that will bring in even more income.

The advice, "keep expenses down," had more point in the earlier years, when there were few specialized supplies available to increase output per acre or per livestock unit. It also has merit today when applied to some types of farm-business expenditures and when applied to family living. Carelessness in handling farm machinery leads to excessive repair costs. Carelessness in handling the livestock may lead to high veterinary bills and disease losses. Expenses which can be avoided without affecting output are unnecessary expenses. A few farmers in each community fail to make satisfactory incomes because they incur extra expenses from careless management practices.

TABLE 5-2

Cash Income and Expenses on High- and Low-income Farms, Wisconsin, 1948

	High-Income Farms	Low-Income Farms
Total acres	186	180
Acres of crops	123	116
Cash income	$21,735	$14,641
Cash operating expense	9,057	7,865
Net Cash Income	$12,678	$ 6,776

Source: Annual report (1948), Northeast Wisconsin Cooperative Farm Management Association, Extension Service, College of Agriculture, Madison. The high-income farms were the 20 per cent with the highest net incomes out of a total of 55 in this size group. The low-income farms were the 20 per cent with the lowest net incomes in the same size group.

Unique character of farmers' variable costs. An analysis of the effect of particular supplies, or expenditures for supplies, on output indicates that there is little possibility for increasing profits by reducing these expenditures under the pressure of lower prices. Production drops so rapidly when expenditures for supplies are curtailed that, even though prices are relatively low, the value of the reduction in output is usually greater than the cost of the supplies.

In Chapter 4, we noted that, in years of fair-to-good moisture in North Carolina, increasing the nitrogen application on corn from 80 to 120 pounds increased average yields 8 bushels per acre. Another 40-pound application would only increase yields an additional 2 bushels. There is the danger that applications in excess of 120 pounds may reduce the yield. This will happen if there is not quite enough moisture. Under these conditions the good farmer will apply only 120 pounds of nitrogen per acre under the most favorable price relations. And since the marginal cost of the additional corn produced by the extra nitrogen application is low, relative to the selling price up to this point, he will not have an economic inducement to change his fertilizer practice unless the price of corn falls precipitously.

Similarly, the good farmer is now using high-yielding hybrid seed corn; he is using a rotation including deep-rooted legumes to maintain high crop yields and conserve his soil resources; he is practicing weed control with modern cultivation and chemical sprays. If the corn borer is a problem, he may be dusting his corn to reduce borer damage. Using marginal analysis, he equates the cost of each of these specialized supplies, in the amounts commonly used, with the expected value of the increase in yield associated with them. And he finds that, if he plans to grow corn, it will pay him to continue to use each of these specialized supplies in approximately the same amounts as he did before. The explanation for this lack of flexibility lies in the relatively large increase in output, relative to the cost of each of these practices. It is possible that, having more information on technical responses, farmers would find it profitable to vary fertilizer application rates, the number of applications of insecticides, and similar production practices as the price of the product changes.

Until our knowledge of technical production responses increases considerably, however, progressive farmers, following improved practices to obtain high levels of output, will continue these practices, for the most part, irrespective of the price received for their product. If the price of potatoes relative to dry beans or sugar beets drops, they may shift from growing potatoes to growing one of these relatively more profitable crops. If they are livestock farmers they may change their livestock numbers in response to relative price changes for the different livestock products. But within the limits of practical farm management, they find it profitable to use the improved technology in each line of production undertaken, regardless of price levels.

Average production costs versus opportunity costs. We must now examine the nature and significance of average total costs per unit of output, or average unit costs in contrast to opportunity costs. The Agricultural Research Service and the state agricultural experiment stations have made many studies of the cost of producing farm products. These studies were made mostly in the 1920's, but a few continue to be made each year. A condensed statement of the cost of producing corn and soybeans in Illinois in 1946 is presented in Table 5-3 for illustrative purposes.

Average production costs on the 23 farms studied varied from $.24 to $.53 per bushel for corn and from $.67 to $1.58 per bushel for soybeans. The variation from farm to farm in unit costs was so great that the data for each farm were reported separately, rather than presented as averages for all farms in the study. *Average production costs have limited significance, because of their great variation from farm to farm. From the standpoint of economic analysis, they have even greater limitations.* By far, the greater part of the total costs of producing a bushel of corn or a bushel of soybeans is not cash costs for the period of the growing and harvesting season.

The man labor is furnished by the operator and his family. The tractor and other machinery are used for many operations, in addition to growing corn and soybeans each year, and last for ten to fifteen years. Only the seed, fertilizer, and fuel costs are directly chargeable to the corn and soybeans. In cost-accounting studies, such as that from which the data in Table 5-3 are taken, labor is charged against a particular product at average hired-labor wage rates. Annual tractor and machinery costs are pro-rated to the individual products at uniform rates per hour of use, and taxes and interest on investment in the land are pro-rated on an acre basis to the different crops grown.

TABLE 5-3

Cost of Production of Corn and Soybeans, Illinois, 1946

	Corn	Soybeans
Labor per Acre		
Man hours	6.0	4.4
Tractor hours	5.0	3.0
Cost items per acre:		
Growing cost		
Man labor	$ 3.00	$ 2.80
Tractor use	1.80	1.40
Machinery, seed, etc.	7.70	5.90
Total growing cost per acre	$12.50	$10.10
Harvesting cost	5.40	2.90
Taxes and interest on land	9.40	8.40
Total cost per acre	$27.30	$21.40
Yield per acre (bushels)	85	23
Cost per bushel	$ .32	$ .93

Source: *Complete Costs and Farm Business Analysis on 24 Farms in Champaign and Piatt Counties* (Mimeo.) (Urbana, Illinois: College of Agriculture, University of Illinois, 1946). This is a study of the median costs of 23 growers (one farm was not included).

This uniform method of allocating total farm costs to individual products has been adopted as an accounting procedure because it is difficult to allocate costs in line with the joint, supplementary, and complementary relationships described in the previous chapters.

Using these cost allocations, it is possible to compute the net profit per acre of growing different crops. This has been done in Table 5-4. Without a knowledge of the complementary and supplementary relations among these crops, one would conclude that farmers would increase their profits by putting all their land in corn. But nothing could be farther from the truth. Profits from corn, in large part, depend on growing corn in rotation with legumes. Unit-production costs, relative to market prices, cannot be used to guide the selection of enterprises because of the accounting procedures used. The average imputed costs do not correspond with the economic motivations. For example, if oats are not seeded in combination with new legume seedings, the farmer gets little or no crop from the land that year. He will grow oats with his legume seedings until he finds another more profitable crop to replace legumes in the rotation, regardless of the relation between computed production costs per bushel and the selling price of oats.

TABLE 5-4

Market Price, Unit Production Cost, Profit Per Unit and Per Acre, Illinois Farm Products, 1946

	Corn	Soybeans	Oats	Alfalfa
Price per unit....	$ 1.20	$ 2.30	$ .80	$24.50
Cost per unit....	.32	.93	.37	14.90
Profit per unit....	$ .88	$ 1.37	$ .43	$ 9.60
Yield per acre....	85 bu.	23 bu.	46 bu.	2.9 ton
Profit per acre....	$74.80	$31.50	$19.78	$27.84

Source: *Complete Costs and Farm Business Analysis on 24 Farms in Champaign and Piatt Counties* (Mimeo.) (Urbana, Illinois: College of Agriculture, University of Illinois, 1946).

In contrast to these average unit-production costs arrived at by arbitrary allocation of overhead costs, we have a non-accounting concept of opportunity costs. This concept is particularly useful in analyzing what goes on in a farmer's mind in deciding how much of each product to produce from the group of resources available to the farm. His land, labor, machinery, and breeding stock, in any given year, are, to a large extent, fixed and he must plan his operations within these limitations. If a farmer devotes a greater acreage to soybeans, he has to use fewer acres for some other crop. If he uses more labor and machinery on one crop he is forced to use less on another. *When the resources employed are not purchased in the market, the significant economic cost is the income given up by not using the resource in its next most profitable use.* The cost that a farmer has in mind when he makes his decision to use his labor on one enterprise rather than on another is the cost to him of losing an opportunity to make an income from another, neglected enterprise. Although the loss to the farmer, from being unable to exploit all opportunities cannot be measured by accounting methods, except on an individual farm basis, consideration of the loss influences the farmer when he makes managerial decisions. The farmer is using the usual marginal analysis when he arrives at decisions by considering opportunity costs.

Costs as affected by size of farm. Thus far we have centered our attention on costs as affected by the choice of methods and technology. Costs per unit of output also are affected by the scale of production. Costs decline as the scale of operations increase, primarily because of the use of larger and more specialized machinery and buildings. A farmer with 200 acres of cropland to prepare and cultivate finds it profitable to buy and operate a larger tractor and more specialized equipment than is economical for a farmer with 50 to 100 acres of cropland. Labor and power costs per acre, or per unit of output, are lowered by the use of this larger machinery. Operators of large farms obtain a more efficient combination of labor, power, and equipment than operators of small farms find possible. A detailed analysis of 238 accounting farms in northwest Illinois for 1946 indicates that as the size of the farm increases from less than 121 acres to 360 acres, there are both lower investment and lower production costs per acre (Table 5-5).

TABLE 5-5

Investment in Buildings and Machinery; Building, Power and Machinery, and Labor Cost Per Acre by Size of Farm, Illinois, 1946

	Acres in Farms			
	Less than 121	*121 to 200*	*201 to 280*	*281 to 360*
Investments:				
Buildings per acre	$24.90	$21.45	$19.59	$13.93
Machinery per acre	18.11	15.45	12.55	10.76
Annual costs:				
Building cost per acre	$ 2.38	$ 1.93	$ 1.69	$ 1.28
Power and machinery cost per crop acre	$16.00	$13.57	$12.00	$11.02
Labor cost per crop acre*	$25.70	$19.83	$17.05	$14.57

* Includes operator and family labor.
Source: Illinois Farm Economics (Urbana, Illinois: University of Illinois, July-August 1947), Table 8.

Labor, power, and machinery costs per crop acre on the 281- to 360-acre farms are only 60 per cent as high as on the farms with less than 121 acres. The annual cost of buildings per acre is small, although the cost per acre on the larger farms is only a little over 50 per cent as high as on the farms under 121 acres.

Scoville,[1] in a study of production costs on 4 sizes of corn-livestock farms in northeastern Nebraska, concluded that labor and capital costs per unit of output declined very little as the size of farm was increased beyond 440 acres in size. He observed that while the net returns available to operators would increase substantially

[1] Orin J. Scoville, "Relationship Between Size of Farm and Utilization of Machinery, Equipment, and Labor on Nebraska Corn-Livestock Farms," *Technical Bulletin 1037* (U.S.D.A., 1951).

as the size of the farm increased, most of the increase would result from the division of the net income from the total acreage among fewer operators. Savings arising from increased production efficiencies contributed only 10 per cent of the estimated increase in the net income of the farm operator on a 1,760-acre farm as compared with the net income of the operator on a one-man, 220-acre farm. He reports that reductions in machinery costs per acre become relatively insignificant for corn-livestock farms larger than a two-man unit.

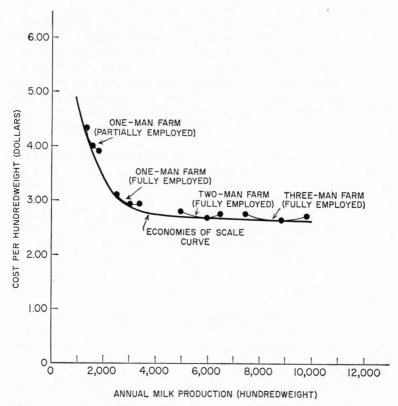

Fig. 5-3. Cost per hundredweight of milk produced on four New England farm models under specified harvesting and labor assumptions when feed concentrates are fed at varying rates.*

* Assumed situation: (a) Seasonal labor receives $0.75 per hour. Regular hired labor receives $1,500 annually. Labor and management return to the operator is $2,000. (b) Long hay on one-man farms. Field chopped hay and grass silage on two- and three-man farms. (c) Concentrates are fed at the rate of 500, 2,000, and 3,500 pounds annually per cow.

Source: Bulletin 285 (Storrs, Connecticut: Storrs Agricultural Experiment Station, 1952), Fig. 6.

Wilcox and Rauchenstein[2] found that cost reductions in milk production in the Midwest in the late 1940's were only 5 to 10 per cent as the size of the milking herd was increased beyond 15 cows.

Fellows, Frick, and Weeks[3] concluded that in New England in the early 1950's, if they used modern technology, dairy farmers with fewer than 35 cows needed less than one full man-equivalent in labor resources. Costs per hundredweight of milk declined rapidly as the farm size was increased to this level with a production of about 3,000 hundredweight of milk a year. If the farm size should be increased beyond this level, the unit cost reductions would be small.

We developed an economies-of-scale curve for New England dairy farms (Figure 5-3) which is comparable to the theoretical long-run cost curve presented in general economics texts. This economies-of-scale curve indicates how average, total unit costs of producing milk in New England fall as land, buildings, and dairy herd are increased over a period of time from a small unit (for example, fewer than 35 cows and a small acreage) until the combination of land, buildings, equipment, and dairy herd is large enough to employ three workers on a full-time basis.

It will be noted that average costs, as indicated by the economies-of-scale curve are somewhat lower for the two-man than for the one-man dairy farm. There is no further reduction in average costs, however, on the three-man, as compared with the two-man, dairy farm.

In computing average costs, the authors assumed that on each size of farm the buildings, equipment, and the size of the dairy herd were appropriately adjusted to each other. The small curves imposed on the economies-of-scale curve and tangent to it are short-period, average-cost curves which assume all factors to be fixed during that time except the rate of feeding concentrates to the dairy cows (see footnotes to Figure 5-3).

Economic basis of family farms. By far, most of the business units in agriculture are family farms. In most lines of farming, especially those involving livestock production, economies arising from the scale of operation are rather completely realized on the medium to large commercial family farms. Power and machinery adapted for farm use now permit a family on a farm of one of these sizes to use most of the cost-reducing equipment that a large-scale farming corporation would employ. Large-scale farming operations appear to have been successful where large gangs of hand workers are required, such as in vegetable and sugar-beet production. One-crop farming, such as wheat production, also lends itself well to large-scale units, although

---

[2] *Journal of Farm Economics,* Vol. 30 (1948), pages 721-722.

[3] *Bulletin 285* (Storrs, Connecticut: Storrs Agricultural Experiment Station, 1952).

it is doubtful if large-scale wheat farms, with several sets of machinery, have any lower costs than large family units employing one full set of modern machinery. Another example of a large-scale farming unit is the farm which has developed large market outlets for specialized products. In such cases as this, the scale of production is often adapted to supply a uniform product to the market outlets, rather than because of any advantage in lower production costs.

The rapid technological advance in agriculture, including the rapid rise in capital requirements in recent years for efficient, low-cost production, creates real problems for the typical or average farm family. It obviously will have increasing difficulty in maintaining a low-cost producing unit. An efficient two-man crop and livestock farm in the Midwest in the late 1950's often represented an investment of $100,000 or more. It seems highly probable that the capital requirements imposed by an advancing technology will increase faster than the capital accumulation of most farm families. It is entirely possible that capital requirements for low-cost farm production, including improved quality control and increased standardization of the products will become so great that corporations increasingly may replace family farming enterprises in the future. Developments in this area will depend on many factors, including especially the ability of families to obtain and use credit wisely and the ability of families to transfer their farms from father to son as financially solvent and efficient operating units.

Turning our attention to the small farms, we must find out why the smaller farming units persist, considering that larger family farms can achieve large cost reductions in their operations.

Why haven't the operators of small farms been forced out of business? The answer is that farming is a way of life, as well as a business. Farm families can and do continue in farming even though they realize very little net cash income for their efforts. Farm families with low earning ability, either in farming or in nonfarm occupations, compete actively for the rental of small, poor farms.

The active demand for small, low productivity farms by these families who are looking for a home as much as a source of income forces rental rates for these properties higher than is justified on an income-earning basis. When such conditions exist, commercial farmers cannot afford to consolidate these low-productivity units into larger farming enterprises. They cannot pay the rentals or the purchase price for such farms out of the net income produced on them. The families who do rent these low-productivity units find it possible to pay the rentals only by maintaining very low levels of living.

Essentially the same competitive condition exists with respect to the small farms owned by farm families. The ownership of a farm, no matter how small, is held in such high esteem by many families that they will pay much more for a little land with a house on it than a family living nearby can afford to pay in order to add the land to their commercial farming operations. There are still a large number of small farms because people wish to live on the land in seeking a means of existence, as is pointed out in more detail in Chapter 19.

REFERENCES

Brewster, John M., "Technological Advance and the Future of the Family Farm," *Journal of Farm Economics,* Vol. 40 (1958), pages 1596-1609.

Fellows, I. F., G. E. Frick, and S. B. Weeks, "Production Efficiency on New England Dairy Farms," *Bulletin 285.* Storrs, Connecticut: Storrs Agricultural Experiment Station (1952).

Heady, Earl O., and Harald R. Jenson, *Farm Management Economics,* Chapter 15. Englewood Cliffs, N.J.: Prentice-Hall, Inc., 1954.

Scoville, Orin J., "Relationship Between Size of Farm and Utilization of Machinery, Equipment, and Labor on Nebraska Corn-Livestock Farms," *Technical Bulletin 1037,* U.S.D.A. (1951).

POINTS FOR DISCUSSION

1. Make a list of the different cost items in producing the leading farm product in your community. Classify them as either fixed or variable costs.
2. Obtain information from the agronomist in your state on the yield of cotton, tobacco, corn, wheat, or legumes as different quantities of fertilizer are applied per acre. Assume that the cost of the land, labor, and machinery is $25 an acre. Construct a table and chart showing the relation of cost per unit to level of output as the rate of fertilizer application is varied.
3. Make a list of the current farm practices that should be modified and those that should not be modified if the price of the leading farm product in your community drops 33 per cent.
4. Give examples of excessive expenditures by farmers in your community. What are the reasons for them?
5. Explain why cost of production cannot be used to determine "fair" selling prices.

CHAPTER 6

The Aggregate Supply Response in Agriculture

FARMERS IN their efforts to maximize returns are adopting new and improved technologies in one farm enterprise after another. This is clear from the discussions in Chapter 4. These farm technological advances are reducing costs and expanding supply in one enterprise after another. Thus, our general picture is one of commodity-supply relations in most commodity lines shifting to the right under the relentless pressure of farm technological advance. But does this picture of individual commodity behavior properly portray the supply response of the farm firm as an aggregate and of the agricultural industry as an aggregate? In a way it does, but in another way it is misleading. To understand fully the aggregate supply behavior of the agricultural industry, one must understand the supply behavior of farm firms, in contradistinction to enterprise behavior, because the industry aggregate is a summation of the firm aggregates.

The aggregate supply relation of the farm firm. The aggregate supply relation of the farm firm describes the total supply behavior of the firm in response to price. It describes how the total output of the firm varies as price, or price level, varies, all other variables held constant. Since the typical farm firm is a multiple-enterprise operation, this means that total output is composed of several commodities and the relevant price concept is a level of prices. Hence, the price-quantity variables in this concept must assume an index-number form. This is necessary to reduce several different commodity prices into a single series, and to convert several different commodities into a single measure of output. This statistical problem complicates the supply concept involved, but it in no wise invalidates the concept. It is of critical importance to gain a good understanding of the aggregate supply concept.

Understanding of the aggregate supply concept in agriculture is furthered by considering the supply behavior of three categories of farms: (1) low-production family farms, (2) commercial family farms, and (3) larger-scale commercial farms. We will concentrate on the supply behavior of small farms with inadequate production resources (with gross sales below $2,500 in 1954) in category (1), of the common family-type farm where the family provides the management and most of the labor required (with gross sales between $2,500 and $25,000 in 1954) in category (2), and of the large-scale operation largely dependent on hired labor and specialized management (with gross sales above $25,000) in category (3).[1]

Supply behavior of low-production family farms. The principal productive resources—land and labor—are fixed in the typical low-production farm. Lacking access to sources of financing and having limited contacts with the commercial world, the typical farmer in this category treats land and labor as given, producing as much product as he is able with those given resources. His limited capital resources, too, are typically of a "sunk" type (that is, antiquated machinery and buildings with low salvage values). Thus, we conclude that the typical and principal resource inputs on these farms do not vary in use with the return to them; for practical purposes, the supply of the various inputs is highly or perfectly inelastic.

Because family members on low-production farms often seek and take off-farm employment, it should not be concluded that the supply of family labor is elastic. Off-farm employment does not vary with the return to labor, which is shockingly low at all times on these farms; it varies with off-farm employment *opportunities*. When off-farm employment opportunities of a suitable nature are good, family labor on low-production farms leaves agriculture at a rapid rate. But with any given set of off-farm employment opportunities the family labor supply on low-production farms is highly inelastic.

A fixed cost, or fixed input, model best describes the supply behavior of low-production farms. The costs of fixed resources run on whether they are used on not, or whether they are used partially or fully. The optimum use of resources on a farm with fixed resources is, thus, a full use of resources. The farmer produces as much as he can with his often limited managerial ability and with his available

---

[1] These categories are consistent with and follow the groupings employed by J. V. McElveen in "Family Farms in a Changing Economy," *Agricultural Information Bulletin 171* (U.S.D.A., March 1957) and by C. Brice Ratchford in "The Nature of Income Problems of Farmers," *Policy for Commercial Agriculture,* Joint Committee Print, Joint Economic Committee, 85th Congress, 1st session (November 22, 1957).

resources and there he stops. He does this because the more he produces the lower his unit costs become. Hence, he maximizes his return or minimizes his losses by producing to the limit of his capacity —albeit a limited capacity in this case.

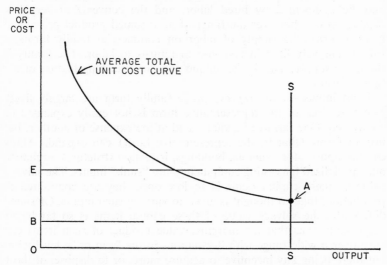

Fig. 6-1. The supply relation for a typical low-production family farm.

This type of supply behavior is illustrated in Figure 6-1. Unit costs fall, where resources are fixed in the farm, as total output increases. Thus, the fixed resources are utilized as fully as possible, and output is pushed to the maximum. Total output is pushed to point *A,* and there it holds constant, regardless of price. More cannot be produced because of resource limitations, and less will not be produced regardless of the level of price, or prices. At point *A,* profits are maximized with a price of *OE,* or losses are minimized with a price of *OB.* Thus, the aggregate supply curve of the low-production farm may be conceptualized as line *SS* in Figure 6-1.

Since, as is implied, there is no change in management ability within the production period and the resource inputs of land and capital are severely limited as well as fixed on these low-production farms, the output from such farms is small as well as inelastic. By definition, the gross output per farm is valued at less than $2,500 in 1954 prices.

Supply behavior of commercial family farms. We find two classes of inputs on commercial family farms: (1) those that are typically varied, and (2) those that are not. Let us consider the second category first. The most important input that is held fixed for the farm as a whole is labor. Typically, the family supplies all or most of the labor on family farms, as operations on such farms are adjusted to the size, composition and abilities of the family labor supply. At very high product prices, hence high labor returns, the family labor supply may be augmented by hired labor, and the converse at very low product prices, but over the range of accustomed product prices and labor returns, the supply of labor on commercial family farms is varied relatively little in response to returns to labor. The family is the labor supply. This is the unique and distinguishing feature of the family farm.

Land inputs on the *representative* family farm are largely fixed. The land area of the representative farm is not easily expanded or contracted. One farm can acquire land at the expense of another, but not all farms (that is, the representative farm) can expand.[2] Many capital inputs—for example, buildings, irrigation structures, orchards, and specialized harvesting equipment—are "sunk" inputs. The salvage value of these capital items is so low once they are committed to production, that no thought is given to varying such inputs. Or stated differently, the salvage value of these capital items is so far below acquisition costs that the marginal value product of such items can vary over a wide range with fluctuations in the farm price level without there being any incentive to acquire more, or to dispose, of those already acquired. Finally, feed supplies on representative farms tend to be fixed in the short run (although inter-temporal substitution under government storage programs modifies the fixed input argument somewhat with regard to feeds).

But some inputs can be and are varied on commercial family farms. Typically they are inputs acquired from the nonfarm sector. Fertilizer is the classic example. Other such inputs might include veterinary services, pesticides, plant disease control, and the repair of machinery and equipment. The use of these resource inputs does vary with the level of product prices, hence with the return to them.

The supply curve for one enterprise of a commercial family farm, *where the price of the commodity in question and the price of each other commodity produced on the farm varies in the same proportion and where the supply of each resource employed is perfectly inelastic,* is presented in Chart A of Figure 6-2. The curve *SS* in Chart A describes the price-output behavior for the commodity in question when all produce prices rise and fall together (that is, when the price level

---

[2] The expansion in the average size of farms operated in the United States in recent years is offset by the fact that there are smaller numbers of larger farms. There have been no net additions to the land in farms.

confronting the farm firm varies) and the imputed returns to the factors rise and fall with the produce prices. Since factor costs rise and fall identically with product prices, there is no incentive to expand, or contract, the output of the commodity. The supply relation for this commodity, and each other commodity produced on the farm is perfectly inelastic, as portrayed by the curve *SS* in Chart A. When the supply curves of the factor inputs involved are perfectly inelastic, the cost structure of the firm simply slides up and down with product prices in a parallel fashion.

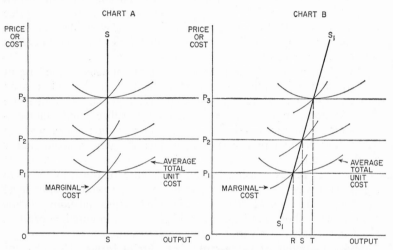

Fig. 6-2. The supply relation for a typical commercial family farm. (The marginal and average curves in the charts are illustrative only; they are not drawn with mathematical precision.)

The aggregate supply relation for the farm firm, granted the above assumptions, is the summation in index terms of the curves *SS* for each enterprise on the farm. And since the curve *SS* is perfectly inelastic for each commodity enterprise, the aggregate relation for the farm firm is perfectly inelastic. It will be recognized at once, that should the price of one commodity move relative to the others in the total farm operation, then the marginal curve in Chart A (not the curve *SS*) describes the output behavior of that commodity, and becomes the relevant supply curve for that commodity enterprise. But such would be a relative price change, with individual commodity supply consequences, and we are not concerned with relative price problems in this chapter. We are concerned with the aggregate supply behavior of the farm firm.

We have already observed, however, that some inputs are varied on commercial farm firms (that is, that supply curves of these inputs are not perfectly inelastic). These inputs are usually acquired from the nonfarm sector, and the prices of such inputs do not vary directly with farm product prices. The supply curve S_1S_1 in Chart B of Figure 6-2 illustrates this more elastic case. The supply curve S_1S_1, like supply curve SS, describes the relation of output to price for one commodity where the price of that commodity and the prices of all other commodities involved vary directly and proportionately. But in the case of S_1S_1 in Chart B, it is assumed that the prices of certain inputs (for example, fertilizer) do not rise as the commodity price rises from P_1 to P_2 to P_3. Hence, more of these variable inputs are used, and the output of this commodity increases from OR to OT as its price rises from P_1 to P_3.

The aggregate supply relation of the farm firm again is the sum of the S_1S_1 commodity enterprise curves for the farm, expressed in index number terms. This aggregate firm supply relation exhibits some slope —certain nonfarm resources (for example, fertilizer, and plant disease control) flow into agriculture with rising product prices, and out with falling product prices. But it remains a highly inelastic supply relation, because the preponderance of factor prices ride up and down with product prices causing the cost structure of the firm to move in a general way, if not exactly parallel, with the product price level confronting the firm. Most factor prices in commercial family farms (land, family labor, and sunk capital prices) are imputed to product prices and simply move with those product prices.

Supply behavior of large-scale commercial farms. This class of farms differs from commercial family farms in one important respect: labor is a highly variable input factor on large-scale farms. It is hired and fired as profit maximization dictates. When low or falling product prices make the intensive use of labor on a large-scale farm unprofitable, some labor is sent packing down the road. When high or rising product prices render the intensive use of labor profitable, additional labor is recruited in urban areas or outside the country (in Mexico, for example).

Thus, we would expect the aggregate supply relation for the large-scale farm firm to be more elastic than that for the family farm firm in comparable situations. In other words, we would visualize the S_1S_1 curve in Chart B of Figure 6-2 to be more elastic for the large-scale farm than for the family farm, the reason being that, the important input, labor, is varied on large-scale farms.

Certain inputs, however, tend to remain fixed even on large-scale farms. The land area of the *representative* large-scale farm is not readily increased. And numerous capital inputs become sunk inputs and nonvariable on large-scale farms as well as on family farms (for example, buildings, orchards). To some degree, then, the cost structure of large-scale farms must float with the price level, and this action tends to reduce the incentive to expand, or contract, the total output of the farm.

The aggregate supply relation for the agricultural industry. The aggregate supply relation for agriculture is the summation of all farm firm supply relations. In concept, the industry supply relation states how the total output from agriculture varies in response to changes in the level of farm prices, all other influencing factors held constant. The slope and elasticity of this industry aggregate relation should be a matter of empirical fact. But problems of statistical estimation make available estimates of its elasticity the subject of considerable controversy. The results of estimating work done in the past by one of the authors suggests that the aggregate supply relation for agriculture is perfectly inelastic.[3] Estimates by other workers suggest that the elasticity of this relation may approach 0.3.[4]

On the basis of the foregoing logical discussion, it seems improbable that the true aggregate supply relation for agriculture could be perfectly inelastic. In 1954, large-scale commercial farms accounted for about 31 per cent of the gross sales of agricultural products and commercial family farms for about 60 per cent. And since we have argued that the typical firm supply relation in each of these classes of farms is not perfectly inelastic, then the industry supply relation could hardly be perfectly inelastic. On the other hand, some 60 per cent of total market sales are accounted for by firms—commercial family farms—with high inelastic aggregate supply relations. Thus, it is the judgment of the authors that the aggregate supply relation for agriculture probably has an elasticity falling somewhere between 0.0 and 0.3. The aggregate supply relation for agriculture is highly, but not perfectly inelastic.

Short- and long-run considerations. So far, the discussion in this chapter has focussed on short-run supply. The relations discussed describe how much the output of the firm or industry may change from one season to the next, or one production period to the next, in response to a given price change. And price change here, although almost impossible to measure, refers to the change in price from the past production period to the forthcoming period. (The price change

---

[3] Willard W. Cochrane, "Conceptualizing the Supply Relation in Agriculture," *Journal of Farm Economics, Proceedings Number* (December 1955).

[4] Zvi Griliches, "The Demand for Inputs in Agriculture and a Derived Supply Elasticity," *Journal of Farm Economics* (May 1959).

involved is some sort of an expected price change that varies from one farmer to the next, and hence is difficult to quantify.) Thus, changes in firm supply, that we have been discussing, relate to those changes in resource use that can be made from one production period to the next.

In the long run—that is, in a length of run in which *all possible* resource adjustments in response to a given price change can be made, but in which all other influencing factors hold constant—the firm supply relations under consideration would probably become more elastic. Particularly at very high and very low product price levels, the relationships would become more elastic. This increased elasticity of firm supply, for the long run, is deduced from the logic that at very high prices capital formation in agriculture would occur more generally and more intensively in the long run than in the short, and at very low product prices some capital that wears out would not be replaced. Some further adjustments in the use of hired and family labor might occur in the long run. But the important long-run adjustments would probably occur through capital formation and destruction.

We should be clear about what we mean by *long run,* however. The long-run concept under discussion here, and common to economic analysis, refers to Marshallian time—to nondated time. It is an abstraction to permit the analyst to conceptualize and visualize the complete resource adjustments to a given price change, *where all other influencing forces are conceived to be constant.* In the world of reality the full and complete resource adjustments to a given price change can rarely be observed. All other things do not hold constant in the real world. We get changes in technology, changes in institutions, changes in consumer tastes, war and peace, and so on. The authors, therefore are inclined to minimize the implications of long-run economic analyses, and concentrate on the short-run relations, and shifts in those relations, that generate real world prices, quantities and incomes.

Output of and inputs in agriculture—the historical record. The total output of agriculture increased about 50 per cent between 1938 and 1958 (see Table 6-1). A stationary aggregate supply function with an elasticity of less than 0.3 is obviously incompatible with this great increase in farm output. Some part of the concept of supply is missing, or incorrect. Some further reflections on the concept of supply make it clear that the great increase in farm output between 1938 and 1958 cannot be explained by a stationary aggregate supply relation no matter how elastic it is conceived to be. In the first place, farm product prices did not increase relative to nonfarm prices over the 20-year period in question; hence there was no relative price increase to induce greater farm output. The relative increase in farm prices which occurred in the 1940's was entirely lost in the 1950's. And in the second place, farm product prices actually declined relative to nonfarm prices in the 1950's. The only kind of a stationary supply curve that could explain the increased farm output of the 1950's with declining prices is one with a negative slope.

TABLE 6-1

Total Output and Gross Production of Livestock and Crops, United States, 1935-59

(1947-49 = 100)

Year	Total Farm Output	All Livestock and Livestock Products*	All Crops†
1935	72	72	76
1936	65	77	64
1937	82	76	88
1938	79	79	83
1939	80	85	82
1940	83	87	85
1941	86	92	86
1942	96	102	97
1943	94	111	90
1944	97	105	96
1945	96	104	93
1946	98	101	98
1947	95	100	93
1948	104	97	106
1949	101	103	101
1950	100	107	97
1951	103	112	99
1952	107	112	103
1953	108	114	103
1954	108	117	101
1955	112	120	105
1956	113	122	106
1957	113	121	106
1958‡	124	125	118
1959‡	125	129	116

* Includes clipped wool, mohair, and for 1940 to date, honey and beeswax.
† Includes production of hay seeds, pasture seeds and cover-crop seeds, and some miscellaneous crop production. Coverage of production of seed and miscellaneous crops is more complete for 1940 to date than for prior years.
‡ Preliminary.

The riddle of agriculture supply, in an aggregate sense, is first deepened and then cleared away by a careful look at resource use in agriculture. It is clear that the cropland base of agriculture has not widened since 1938. The index of cropland used for crops stood at 98 in 1938 and at 94 in 1958; in that time period, the index fluctuated between 94 and 102. Thus, the total input of cropland held almost constant over the period in question.

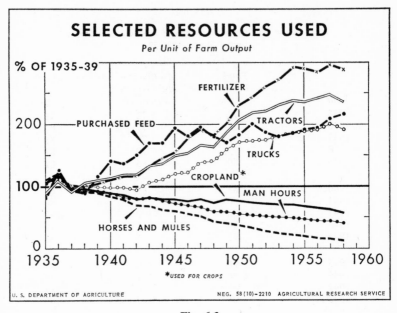

Fig. 6-3.

The total input of labor in agriculture declined significantly between 1938 and 1958. The index of man-hours of labor used in farm work declined from 120 in 1938 to 80 in 1958—or by 33 per cent. In contrast, inputs of almost every capital item used in agriculture increased over this period. Farmers have substituted all kinds of capital for human labor while holding the over-all size of the physical plant constant since the 1930's. This is the picture of resource use in absolute terms. But output has increased since the middle 1930's. Thus, in terms of resources used per unit of output, nonfarm-produced capital has substituted for both land and labor, as well as horses and mules (see Figure 6-3).

One might hypothesize that the increased use of all kinds of nonfarm-produced capital has just about offset the decrease in labor employed in agriculture in an absolute sense, and offset the decrease in *land and labor* used in a per unit sense. And this hypothesis squares with the best available estimates of the use of total resources in agriculture over the period in question. An index of total farm inputs, developed by the U. S. Department of Agriculture,[5] indicates that total resources used in agriculture increased 7 per cent between 1939 and 1958 (see Table 6-2). In other words, total inputs in agriculture probably increased moderately between 1938 and 1958, but did not nearly approach the amount that total farm output increased.

TABLE 6-2

Aggregate Farm Output, Total Inputs, and Output per Unit of Input, United States, 1939-58

(1947-49 = 100)

Year	Aggregate Farm Output	Total Farm Inputs	Output per Unit of Input
1939	79	94	84
1940	82	97	85
1941	85	97	88
1942	96	101	95
1943	94	101	93
1944	97	101	96
1945	95	99	96
1946	98	99	99
1947	95	99	96
1948	104	100	104
1949	101	101	100
1950	101	101	100
1951	104	104	100
1952	108	104	104
1953	109	103	106
1954	109	102	107
1955	113	102	111
1956	114	102	112
1957	114	100	114
1958	124	101	123

Source: Agricultural Outlook Charts '60 (U.S.D.A., Agricultural Marketing Service), Table 1, Page 50.

---

[5] The index is computed by considering the combined volume of farm labor, land and service buildings, machinery and equipment, fertilizer and lime, purchase of feed, seed and livestock, and miscellaneous production items in constant dollars.

What did happen between 1938 and 1958 is this: output per unit of input in agriculture increased greatly—productive efficiency soared. This we see in Table 6-2; output per unit of input increased from 84 on the index in 1939 to 123 in 1958. Farmers were getting more output out of the resources committed by them to production in 1958 than in 1939—about 46 per cent more.

Sources of increased productive efficiency. There are several ways by which output per unit of input could have increased between 1938 and 1958: (1) through a tendency for more farm operators to approach the minimum points on their respective long-run planning curves in 1958 than in 1938; (2) through increased regional specialization; (3) through the adoption of improved production practices, and (4) through the increased skill of the labor force. Technically, any one of these avenues to increased efficiency means that the firm's production function shifts, hence the supply curve of the firm shifts. Thus, all these avenues could have contributed to the expansion of the aggregate supply relation in agriculture between 1938 and 1958. But some of the ways probably contributed more to increased efficiency than others, and certain interactions were involved too. Consequently, we will investigate these various sources of increased efficiency briefly.

The authors see no obvious reason why more farmers should be at the minimum point of their respective long-run planning curves in 1958 than there were in 1938. In fact, there are grounds for arguing that farmers generally may be farther from such minimum points in 1958 than they were in 1938. These grounds are: the world of production techniques is more dynamic in 1958 than it was in 1938, and the task of effecting optimum long-run adjustments is more difficult in 1958 than it was in 1938. In any event, the authors are not inclined to believe that this source contributed significantly to increased productive efficiency in agriculture.

Regional specialization in agricultural production continued to evolve over the period 1938-58—cotton spread onto the high plains and into the irrigated valleys of the West; potatoes moved out of general farming in the Midwest and into concentrated production areas; and the soybean found a new home in the Midwest. All this certainly contributed to increased production efficiency. But much of this industry relocation and specialization resulted from the availability of new, improved techniques, such as new plant varieties, improved plant-disease control, and new tillage practices. In turn, the adoption of new techniques is associated with the skill and intelligence of the human agent. The effective use of new techniques often requires highly skilled labor, and skilled, intelligent operators seek out and adopt improved techniques.

There is interaction all along the line among these three sources of increased productive efficiency. Increased specialization, the adoption of new techniques, and enhanced operator skill combine and interact to increase output per unit of input in agriculture. In the drive to increase efficiency in the dynamic production process in agriculture it is difficult, if not impossible, to separate these three efficiency-generating forces into separate causal strands; they are inextricably combined in practice. Thus, we are inclined to wrap the total process— increased specialization, the adoption of new techniques, and enhanced operator skill—into one package and call it farm technological advance.

Thus the great increase in total farm output since 1938 is fundamentally the result of farm technological advance in the inclusive sense, given above. Total farm output increased only modestly, if at all, as the result of the increased employment of resources committed to agricultural production by farmers. And the change-in-scale argument (that is, that there is movement to more optimal positions on long-run planning curves) is not persuasive. The principal explanation for the great increase in total output in agriculture since the middle 1930's must be the occurrence of rapid and widespread farm technological advance. Rapid and widespread technological advance in agriculture has shifted the enterprise production functions on most commercial farms. This, in turn, has expanded firm supply relations, with the final result that the aggregate supply function for the industry has shifted to the right—increased.

Of course, farm technological advance, as we shall discuss in Chapter 17, is not a free good. It occurs, and only occurs, as resources are devoted to it. It costs money to develop new techniques through research; it costs money to extend those techniques to farmers through informational services; and it costs money to educate farm workers and improve their productive skills. But the resources employed in the above activities are not committed there solely by farmers, or solely to maximize profits. Resources employed in research, extension, and teaching that result, in some part, in farm technological advance are committed to those activities by all of society and for various reasons. Thus, resources employed in research, extension, and teaching are not expanded and contracted, except indirectly, as farm price levels or general price levels change. The society of the United States has supported and continuously expanded research and educational activities because it places high values on the results of those activities.

The shifting aggregate supply relation. The riddle of the aggregate supply problem is solved. It is possible for the firm and industry supply relations to be severely inelastic and for the total output of agriculture to increase. It can and has occurred through expanding shifts in these relations; farmers in the aggregate have stood ready to offer more supplies on the market at a given price level in almost every year since 1938 (this action is illustrated in Figure 6-4). Aggregate farm output has increased through shifts in the aggregate supply relation rather than through a movement along such a relation. And these shifts in the aggregate supply relation have been powered by persistent and widespread farm technological advance.

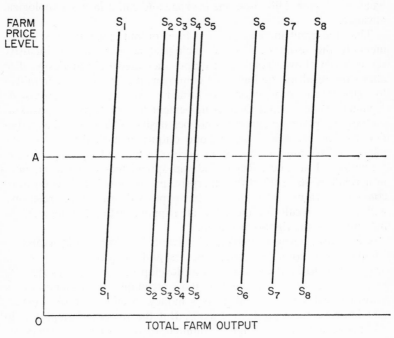

Fig. 6-4. The shifting aggregate supply relation in agriculture.

Our ideal construct of the aggregate supply relation for agriculture is then as follows—*a short-run, highly inelastic relation expanding through dated time in an irregular but persistent fashion* (see Figure 6-4). For obvious reasons, the aggregate supply relation does not expand in a regular cadence: the chance occurrence of important new technologies (for example, the gasoline motor, hybrid seed corn), the bunching of new technologies, and the financial position of farmers. But the outpouring of new technologies in agriculture has been along a sufficiently broad front and the financial position of farmers generally has been sufficiently strong since 1938 to insure almost continuous and widespread adoption of new techniques at the farm level. Hence, the aggregate supply relation has shifted to the right in terms of Figure 6-4 in almost every year since 1938.[6]

The financial position of farmers is, of course, related to the level of farm prices. The financial position of farmers generally is strong when the farm price level is high and stable. Thus, we would always expect to find a more rapid rate of farm technological advance with a high and stable level of farm prices than with the converse.

One final point needs to be made with respect to the industry supply relation. Logic suggests that the rightward shifting action of the industry supply relation is not reversible. Technological advance shifts the industry supply relation to the right, as marginal and average unit costs on individual farms are lowered. It is to the advantage of farmers to hold on to such techniques once adopted, whether prices turn high or low.[7] If prices are falling, the farmer can minimize his losses by continuing to employ the cost-reducing techniques already adopted, and he, of course, can maximize his profits by pursuing the same course of action. Thus, once a farmer has adopted a new cost-reducing technique there is *no* logical reason why he should want to give it up, except to substitute a still better technique for it.

In longer run situations, if farm prices hold at an extremely low level, fixed capital investments in agriculture may not be replaced as they wear out and labor saving equipment may not be substituted for the labor which shifts to other industries. In the shorter run situations, however, including periods as long as several years, we find no logical basis for a contracting aggregate supply relation in agriculture. Farm operators who fail to replace their worn-out capital investments in these shorter periods of low prices are more than balanced by others who adopt new cost-reducing production technologies in order to lower production costs.

There is no evidence of a contraction in the aggregate supply relation in agriculture going back as far as 1929. The historical data indicate that the aggregate supply relation in agriculture did not contract, did not shift to the left, between 1929 and 1932, when farm prices fell disastrously. The aggregate supply relation in agriculture

---

[6] For an empirical view of the aggregate supply relation for agriculture refer to Chapter 15.

[7] Typically, the new technique involves a capital investment which, once made, serves for a number of years or involves the use of new output-increasing supplies, such as a feed supplement, which costs so little in relation to its contribution to increased output in the new production function that it is profitable to continue its use as long as the enterprise is continued on the farm.

appears to have held constant in a perfectly inelastic position from 1929 to 1936. And when the farm price level fell by about 25 per cent between 1951 and 1955, the industry supply did not contract; in fact, the industry supply curve continued to shift to the right in the face of this farm price level decline. Thus, what we seem to have is an industry supply relation for agriculture that expands irregularly but persistently over time, *but which does not contract*. At least it has not in modern historical experience.

REFERENCES

Cochrane, Willard W., "Conceptualizing the Supply Relation in Agriculture," *Journal of Farm Economics,* Proceedings Number (December 1955).

Johnson, D. G., "The Nature of the Supply Function for Agricultural Products," *American Economic Review* (September 1950).

Johnson, Glenn L., "Supply Function—Some Facts and Notions," *Agricultural Adjustment Problems in a Growing Economy,* Earl O. Heady, Howard G. Diesslin, Harald R. Jensen, and Glenn L. Johnson, editors. Ames, Iowa: Iowa State College Press, 1958.

"Changes in Farm Production Efficiency: A Summary Report," *Statistical Bulletin 233,* U.S.D.A., (August 1958, and more recent annual issues).

POINTS FOR DISCUSSION

1. How does the concept of a firm-supply relation differ from that of a commodity-enterprise relation?
2. Compare the supply relation with respect to elasticity for different categories of farms: low-production farms, commercial family farms, and large-scale farms. If there are differences in elasticity, explain why.
3. What effect does the length of run have on the elasticity of firm supply?
4. Is the great increase in farm output over the period 1938-58 incompatible with a highly inelastic industry-supply relation? Explain and rationalize.
5. How does the aggregate supply relation for agriculture behave through time?

PART TWO

Marketing Farm Products

CHAPTER 7

The Farm Marketing System— What Is It?

A COMPLEX and elaborate set of practices, processing and handling facilities, and commercial "know-how" have come into being over the past hundred years to move the products of our farms to consumers. All this we call "marketing," or sometimes "distribution," when the emphasis is on the broad aspects of the problem. In brief, marketing comprises "those business activities involved in the flow of goods and services from production to consumption."[1]

But there is more to the marketing of farm products than the transfer of the raw products of the farm to the consumer. We don't eat wheat; we eat bread. We don't eat hogs; we eat pork chops. And we don't wear cotton lint; we wear cotton shirts. Further, we don't consume the entire apple crop at the time of harvest, and we don't smoke up the entire tobacco crop during the months of harvest. Farm products must be processed into a form that consumers can use; the supply of these products must be released to consumers in an even flow, in order to span the interval between one surplus producing period and the next. It is the function of our marketing or distribution system to undertake these operations: processing, storage, orderly dispersement. Thus, we usually say that the act of production creates form utility and the act of marketing creates time and place utility. But this is not strictly correct, for when wheat is processed into flour and cotton fiber is spun into thread, form utility is created.

Developing needs for a marketing system. The need for a special-

---

[1] From the "Definition of Marketing Terms" by the Committee on Definitions of the National Association of Marketing Teachers, *The National Marketing Review* (Fall 1935).

ized and, in this case, highly complex system for marketing farm products is very often poorly understood. In the early 1800's, an American farmer hauled his wheat crop to the local miller, had the wheat milled into flour, and hauled the flour back to his farmstead for the use of his family during the coming year. Payment to the miller was probably made in kind, in flour. In this self-sufficient situation, there existed little need for a system for marketing flour; there existed little in the way of a marketing problem. And in primitive societies, in which a few goats (or cows) are driven around the producers' milk route and milked before the door of each customer, the marketing problem is reduced to its most simple form. But we know that self-sufficiency has not been the way of American agriculture. We have seen already how certain areas and farms in those areas specialize in the production of those products for which they have the greatest advantage. And once individual areas and farmers specialize in the production of certain commodities, we have a marketing problem. Producers in one area now have a *surplus* of certain commodities that they *must* trade for the surpluses of producers in other areas in order to obtain the goods that are required to maintain a balanced living.

This tendency toward specialization and the production of surpluses for trade, area by area, began early in our national life. We remember how the Pennsylvania farmers, even prior to 1800, were raising surpluses of rye and corn in the more fertile limestone valleys of the Appalachians, converting these grains into whiskey, and marketing their grain to the outside world in this form. Before the coming of the railroads, settlers in the broad stretches of the Ohio Valley fed their surplus grains to cattle and hogs, sometimes floating their hogs down the Ohio and Mississippi rivers to the New Orleans market, sometimes driving their cattle overland, via the Cumberland and the Mohawk Valley routes, to the eastern markets. And far on the west coast, surpluses of barley and wheat were loaded into sailing ships and carried around the Horn to English markets before the steamship and the steam locomotive reached that new area of settlement. Out of these early tendencies in American agriculture toward specialization and surplus production grew a need for methods of collecting the produce of many producers and, in turn, dispersing these products in modified form to many and distant consumers. "Middlemen," in the broadest sense of the term, entered the picture to undertake such activities as collection, transportation, storage, processing, and retailing in order to move these surplus products from producing areas to consuming areas.

Marketing needs of commercial agriculture. In the highly commercialized agriculture of the present time, the need for an effective marketing system has reached its greatest intensity. Where wheat production is concentrated on highly commercialized farms on the Great Plains to the extent that not even a garden or chicken or milk cow is maintained in many cases, where fruits and vegetables are produced in factories in the field in California and certain southern states, and where corn and hogs have become the dominating enterprises of the rich prairie lands of Iowa and Illinois, it is clear that the organization and services involved in moving those commodities to consumers form an indispensable part of our economic life. For if these area surpluses are not moved to consuming centers, they become almost valueless. What would Kansas do with all the wheat it produces if it could not trade it for goods and services produced elsewhere?

Distribution and concentration of population. Marketing problems created by surplus-producing areas are intensified by the distribution and concentration of population. The marketing problem is not simply that of trading back and forth between surplus producing areas. We must recognize that our population is not uniformly distributed state by state. Rather, it is heavily concentrated in the industrial states. Some 36 per cent of the total population of the United States in 1955 was concentrated in the six industrialized states: New York, New Jersey, Pennsylvania, Ohio, Michigan, and Illinois. Into this area of population concentration must move the principal farm surpluses of our specialized producing areas. Another area of population concentration is developing on the Pacific Coast. Thus, we see the picture: specialized producing areas scattered over the country with the core located in the Mississippi Valley and two centers of population concentration, one in the Northeast and one on the Pacific Coast. In one case, we have surplus farm products; in the other, we have food and fiber deficits. It is the job of the marketing system to move the surpluses to the deficit areas and, in that way, satisfy the needs of producers for a market and the needs of urban consumers for supplies. In the United States, no master planner sits at the head of this system, directing and controlling each individual action, in an effort to match demands with supplies. Still, that is the very problem that must be solved in our present day, interdependent, specialized economy, and we rely upon the marketing system to do this.

The complexity of the marketing system. It is difficult to describe the farm-marketing system, because of the diversity of activities and complexity of business relations found therein. The variety of services, practices, and agencies found in the marketing of cotton lint is portrayed in Figure 7-1. As complex as Figure 7-1 may appear,

MARKETING CHANNELS FOR COTTON LINT

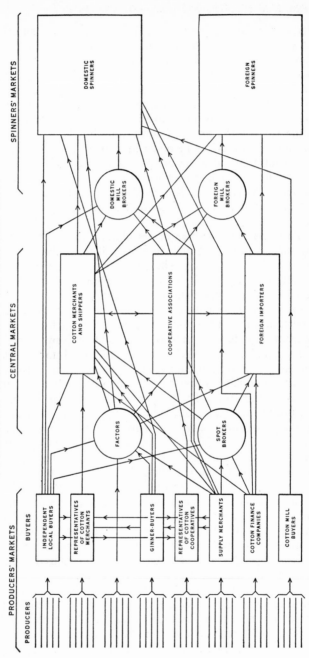

RECTANGLES INDICATE MARKETING FIRMS ACQUIRING TITLE TO THE COTTON.   CIRCLES INDICATE FIRMS ACTING IN THE CAPACITY OF AGENT.

U.S. DEPARTMENT OF AGRICULTURE   NEG. 33492   BUREAU OF AGRICULTURAL ECONOMICS

Fig. 7-1.

however, it is not complete; it does not tell the full story. In the first place, we do not get any picture of the volumes handled. In the second place, we do not get a picture of the number of firms and the size of firms engaged in the various activities. In certain instances, there may be a few firms, in other instances, many firms. In some cases, the operation may be dominated by one or two large firms and, in other cases, there may be many small firms. All this we do not see. The information that Figure 7-1 conveys is that of the number and type of *activities* involved in moving cotton lint from the producer to spinners' markets.

But even with regard to the presentation of activities, Figure 7-1 is not complete. Certain activities must be imagined. For example, the financing services provided by individual firms in the transfer of the product are not shown. Neither are the informational services of the various governmental agencies nor the regulatory operations of the various governmental agencies indicated in Figure 7-1. And, of course, that part of the market from the spinners to the retail outlets is missing.

Marketing channels. Although it is important to have an appreciation of the complexity of the farm-marketing system, the purpose of any field of study is to explain, to point out, the significant relationships hidden in a maze of raw information. Such is our purpose in studying the marketing of farm products. One of the useful ways of describing the farm-marketing system is in terms of *flows* of products from producers to consumers. These flow processes may be likened to pipelines conducting food and fiber products from the producer to the consumer. To these pipelines we commonly give the more elegant name "marketing channels." And these channels, if properly marked out, provide us with information as to the direction of product movement and volume of product movement.

A highly simplified, yet descriptive, flow chart for wheat is shown in Figure 7-2. We see that the principal marketing channel for wheat moves directly through country elevators, on to terminal elevators, and, thence, to the processing mills. At the mills, the main channel forks into several lesser channels: one leading direct to retailers, a second leading to retailers via the wholesalers, and a third leading to retailers via the bakers. We lose some of the activities and agencies involved in the marketing process in the pictograph of Figure 7-2, but we gain importantly concerning direction of movement and volume of movement. It is interesting to note that more pounds of wheat products (42.6 billion) reached consumers in 1939 than left the farm (35.3 billion). The ingredients added in processing and baking, of course, explain this increase.

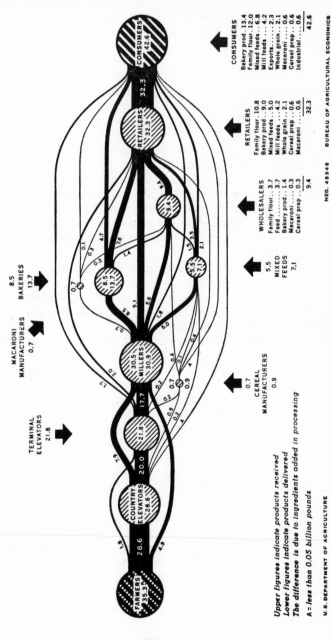

MARKETING CHANNELS AND UTILIZATION OF WHEAT AND WHEAT PRODUCTS, UNITED STATES, 1939

(ALL FIGURES ARE IN BILLIONS OF POUNDS)

CONSUMERS	
Bakery prod.	13.4
Family flour	12.0
Mixed feeds	6.8
Mill feeds	4.2
Exports	2.3
Whole grain	2.1
Macaroni	0.6
Cereal prep	0.6
Industrial	0.6
	42.6

RETAILERS	
Family flour	10.8
Bakery prod.	9.0
Mixed feeds	5.0
Mill feeds	4.2
Whole grain	2.1
Cereal prep	0.6
Macaroni	0.6
	32.3

WHOLESALERS	
Family flour	3.7
Feed	3.7
Bakery prod.	1.4
Macaroni	0.3
Cereal prep	0.3
	9.4

MIXED FEEDS	
	5.5
	7.1

CEREAL MANUFACTURERS	
	0.7
	0.9

Upper figures indicate products received
Lower figures indicate products delivered
The difference is due to ingredients added in processing

A = *less than 0.05 billion pounds*

U.S. DEPARTMENT OF AGRICULTURE

NEG. 43346   BUREAU OF AGRICULTURAL ECONOMICS

Fig. 7-2.

94

Although schematic flow charts describing the principal marketing channels have been worked out for most farm products, we do not have the time to work through the marketing system commodity by commodity. We will only point out that these flow charts describing the principal marketing channels become considerably more complex in the case of livestock. In contrast, the flow chart for the marketing of eggs is a rather simple affair.

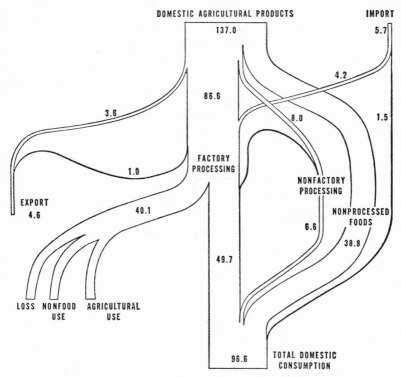

Fig. 7-3. Flow of foods in the United States: 1935-39 average tonnage in millions of tons.

The flow of food products from producers to consumers, measured in tons, may be seen in Figure 7-3. We see that only about one-third of the consumer's food supply reaches the consumer in an unprocessed state. Also, a goodly portion of the total domestic production of food products is lost to domestic consumers as those food products move through the marketing channel—"lost" as exports, or through physical loss, or by diversion to nonfood uses.

The concentration and dispersion process. We have gained some insight into the complexity and nature of the farm-marketing system in the previous sections. But the bulge of marketing activities, appearing in the graphic presentations between the producer and the consumer, may have warped our perspective. In reality, the marketing system consists of a great concentration process on one hand, and a great dispersion process on the other. Business firms early in the marketing system are engaged in the collection of products from

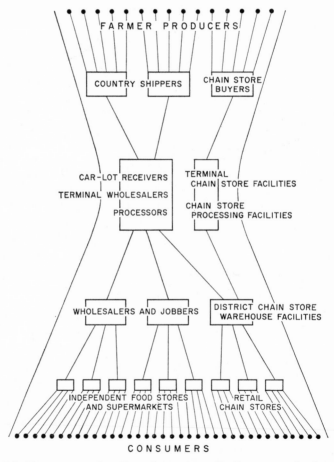

Fig. 7-4. The concentration, dispersion, and equalization process for farm food products.

some 4.8 million farmers; in the next phase, firms are engaged in the concentration of those products at strategic points, such as processing points or carlot receiving points; and lastly, firms are engaged in the dispersion of those products to 180 (and more) million consumers.

This total process might be likened to the figure of an hourglass. That is the picture, in any event, that emerges in Figure 7-4, where the concentrating and dispersing processes for a large city are illustrated. Across the upper opening of this hourglass, we must imagine many thousand individual producing units. The products of these units are reduced and moved through the hands of only a few thousand country shippers. The flow is further reduced as the products concentrate into the hands of processors, manufacturers and carlot receivers. There, the trend toward concentration is reversed, and the dispersion process begins. The original products, processed, packaged, or broken into smaller lots, are now dispersed to a greater number of wholesalers, jobbers, and manufacturer's representatives. The dispersion process continues as these food products move on to the shelves of many thousand retail stores. And from these numerous stores, these food products move into the many thousand homes of our mythical city.

These processes of concentration and dispersion are highly important for food and agriculture. We say this, first, because farm products are produced in relatively small quantities on many, many producing units; second, because the farm units engaged in producing particular commodities are not distributed uniformly over the country, but rather are to be found in specialized producing areas; and third, because centers of population do not lie close to specialized producing areas. Thus, the problem, which the marketing system solves satisfactorily in most cases, but not so satisfactorily in others, is that of concentrating products from many producing units, directing those products to centers of population, and there dispersing them to many consumer units.

The equalization process. What do we mean by equalization? By this we mean the process whereby the supply of a farm product is fed to consumers as they require that product. It is the adjustment of supply to demand on the basis of time, quantity, and quality. The seasonal flow of farm products to market bears little reference to the continuous needs and demand of consumers. Most farm commodities are produced over a climatically determined period, are harvested at a given time, and come to market in a rush. Even products such as milk and eggs, which are produced the year around, have flush periods of production. In sum, commodities are produced on the farm for the market (in the general sense of the word market), not for the filling of orders at the retail level.

Further, farm products rarely come to a specific market in the quantity or quality demanded in that market. For example, the supply of fluid milk forthcoming from the milkshed surrounding a particular city may not be adequate to meet the requirements of that city the year around. Or the supply of wheat from the area around a milling center may be adequate, as far as quantity is concerned, but lacking in the particular types of grain needed to yield the quality of flour in demand. Now the process of equalizing or adjusting supplies to demand is carried out, for the most part, in wholesale markets. These markets may be looked upon as great reservoirs into which farm products flow in varying amounts and varieties; and here they are held until the demand for them by consumers brings about their dispersion. *Equalization is the great service provided in wholesaling,* involving the acquisition of products of the qualities demanded, the accumulation of products demanded seasonally, the storage and dispersement of products produced seasonally, and the taking up of slack between currently changing volumes of output and consumption.

A market. We have alluded to the term "market" above, but what exactly is a market? A market is not an easy thing to define. It can be a specific place ("a meat market," "a produce market," "a livestock auction"), but it need not involve space or occupy a geographic location. It may, for instance, be organized or integrated around the telephone or telegraph. But there is one thing that always occurs in a market, the thing for which a market is organized, namely, *the exchange of title to a particular product.* Markets are organized to facilitate transfers of ownership. Hence, we think of a market as a place or a sphere in which buyers and sellers get together to arrange sales, to effect transfers of ownership.

We find markets in the economic system wherever one group of individuals finds it convenient to dispose of its products and another group finds it convenient to acquire those goods. Thus, at country shipping points we often find a market; a place where producers who do not know how to ship and handle the product efficiently wish to sell and dealers who do know how to ship and handle the product efficiently wish to buy.

A market is thus a sphere within which price-making forces operate. We have the forces of demand represented by the buyers and the forces of supply represented by the sellers. Out of the interaction of these forces, the price of the product in question is determined. The size of a market is described by the number of firms engaged in buying and selling who are subject to the common forces of demand and supply. In other words, any group of buyers are in the same market when the action of one affects all others; the same is true of suppliers.

We once said that the size of a market is limited to that area or sphere in which one price prevails. But where product differentiation is the rule, the single price criterion does not correctly delimit the market. There can be as many different prices prevailing in a market as there are differentiated products in the market. Thus, the critical criterion of a market becomes the common influence of demand and supply, not a single uniform price.

Classes of markets. The markets in which farm products are handled and exchanged in the flow from farm to city may be divided into three principal classes: (1) local markets, (2) central markets, and (3) retail markets.

Local markets lying close to producing areas constitute the first step in the concentration of farm products. These markets provide a convenient place for producers to sell their products; hence, they contribute to the collection of products from many small producers for economic handling and shipment. In the performance of this basic service, local markets usually provide facilities for weighing, storing, grading, packaging, and loading.

Buyers and shippers operating in local markets furnish a ready and, in most cases, a cash outlet for growers. They constitute the link between many producers, on one hand, and wholesale markets on the other. It is their task to establish those numerous and intricate business relations with dealers in the wholesale markets, on one hand, and with producers, on the other. There are four principal classes of middlemen operating in local markets: (1) private resident buyers, (2) local farmers' cooperatives, (3) traveling buyers, and (4) local auctions. Of course, the proportion of product shipped by each class of middlemen will vary with the market. For example, oranges produced in California typically enter the marketing channel through a farmers' marketing cooperative. Grain more often enters the marketing channel through a private elevator. And an increasing number of meat animals are entering the marketing channel by sale to local truckers who ship them direct to interior packers.

But farmers sometimes dispose of their products through other local outlets. Producers, in some cases, sell directly to consumers, either by peddling their products from house to house or from roadside markets. On occasion, farmers sell directly to chain stores, restaurants, and institutions. On other occasions they sell directly to manufacturers or make direct shipments to commission merchants

in wholesale markets. Thus, the four classes of local agencies described above do not constitute the only ways by which farmers dispose of their products. To repeat, however, those four types of agencies constitute the principal ways.

Central markets in food and agriculture are pre-eminently concerned with the broad processes of concentration, equalization and dispersion. These are the markets to be found in cities, located strategically between producing and consuming areas, in which the means of transportation converge as in a spiderweb. Chicago, Kansas City, and Buffalo are representative of these important central wholesale markets. Grain from the Northwest pours into Buffalo and is dispersed from there, either as grain or milled flour. Livestock from the Midwest converges on the great, central, wholesale markets of Chicago and Kansas City for slaughter, processing, and dispersion to areas of population concentration.

First, then, these central wholesale markets must be the focal point of the major transportation facilities. This is clearly the case with Chicago where most railroads find a terminus, where water transportation meets the rails, and where good highways lead trucks in increasing numbers. Here also are to be found the great storehouses, credit agencies, commodity exchanges, and other institutions requisite to successful marketing. Because of their strategic location, their improved facilities and the large volume of consumption in the immediate area, buyers come to look upon these markets as basic sources of supply. The bulk of farm products flow through these narrow points; hence, buyers and sellers concentrate at these points to conduct their business. These markets represent the final point of concentration and the initial point of dispersion. And in these markets, with their splendid and important storage and financing facilities, the basic equalization decisions are made.

In the literature of marketing, two other types of wholesale markets are described: (1) secondary wholesale markets and (2) jobbing markets. Secondary wholesale markets typically receive farm products from central markets and disperse those products to processors. Jobbing markets receive farm products that do not require processing from central markets (also directly from the country) and disperse those products to retailers. Now, clearly, the role of these markets is different from that of the central wholesale markets. Middlemen operating at this level are engaged primarily in dispersing a supply, already concentrated, among a fixed clientele. And as we shall see later, markets at this level are fast losing an independent status.

The retail market forges the final link in the marketing process.

The service of retailing is often looked upon from the point of view of the consumer. The retailer, in this view, is the purchasing agent of the consumer. He anticipates consumer needs, assembles the products that the consumer desires, and serves them up in quantities that the consumer can use. The farmer tends to overlook this final act in the flow of products from farm to city. He tends to ignore this step, concentrating his attention on marketing steps closer to him. But to ignore the retailing link may constitute a major error. The cost of retailing is by far the largest single item in the total marketing spread. For some commodities, it absorbs half of all marketing charges, and retailing costs, on the average, amount to nearly 40 per cent of total marketing charges.

Commodities may be sold at retail in several ways: (1) through the retail store, (2) through a mail-order house, (3) from house-to-house, (4) by automatic vending. We could discuss each of these ways at some length, but we wish to concentrate on the modern, retail food market, whether chain or independent. Private grocery chains made a tremendous growth in the 1920's. It is estimated, for example, that the Great Atlantic & Pacific Tea Company increased its number of stores from 5,217 in 1922 to 15,737 in 1931. To survive the intense competition offered by chain systems in the 1930's, independents banded together in voluntary or contract chains to reap the benefits of large-scale buying and national advertising. The growth of voluntary chains in the 1930's and '40's was almost as spectacular as the earlier chain store development. By 1948, voluntary chains were handling about the same volume of business as the private chains— each about one-fourth of total food sales in the United States.

But as George Mehren of the University of California has said— the issue in the 1950's is not chain versus independent.

The issue is that a few large retailers in all parts of the United States, comprising less than one-tenth of stores, are doing almost two-thirds of the business . . . [and] . . . there are a large number of small stores— nearly 70 per cent of the total—which do less than 10 per cent of the total retail business.[2]

Marketing functions. In the foregoing discussion of markets, we met certain of the functions undertaken in the marketing system. Whatever mention was made of these functions, however, was fragmentary and incomplete. Hence, it seems useful at this point to set forth in outline those services, often referred to as marketing func-

---

[2] "Market Coordination and Buyers' Requirements," *Policy for Commercial Agriculture,* Joint Committee Print, 85th Congress, 1st Session (November 22, 1957).

tions, that business firms undertake in the marketing system. Much thought has been given to the analysis of the marketing functions, and it is possible to classify these functions in different ways, depending upon the purpose of the study. In fact, many different classifications may be found in the literature dealing with marketing. But some classification must be settled upon, and the following one would seem to be inclusive and useful for our purposes:

Marketing Functions

A. Exchange functions
    1. Buying
    2. Selling
B. Physical handling functions
    1. Assembling
    2. Standardizing and grading
    3. Storing
    4. Transporting
    5. Dividing and packaging
C. Facilitating functions
    1. Financing
    2. Risk-bearing
    3. Providing market information
D. Processing[3]

Let us now discuss each of these functions briefly. It is important to see how and where each of these functions forms an integral part of the total farm marketing system.

Exchange functions: buying and selling. One is tempted to say that buying and selling are simply different sides of the same transaction, for in every transaction in which goods and services are exchanged there must be a buyer and a seller. But in marketing, the function of buying differs considerably from the function of selling. Let us consider the case of a small independent grocer in New York City. The function he performs in buying is quite different from that of selling when he arises early in the morning and goes down to the Washington Street terminal market to purchase fresh fruits and vegetables to sell in his retail establishment during the day. He goes to the Washington Street market, first, with the aim of purchasing fruit and vegetable items that his clientele wants, and second,

---

[3] There is some debate as to whether processing should be included here; whether it is, in fact, a marketing function. Perhaps it is not a true marketing function since it is concerned with the provision of form utility, rather than time and place. But we include it here, because it plays such an important part in the moving of farm produce from the farm to the consumer.

to acquire them at a price that will permit him to make a net return on each item handled. Thus, he moves through the market looking, selecting, and purchasing in a discriminating way to acquire just those items at the prices that will move them through his store during the day at a profit.

Now let us observe this independent grocer in his selling function. In the first place, he has acquired a volume of fruits and vegetables that he must sell. He displays these fruit and vegetable items and prices them in such a way as to make them move. Further, he reminds his customers that certain items are in stock, that they are of good quality, and that they represent economical buys. In short, he does everything within his power to move that stock during the day, even to the possible extent of revising prices.

The transaction between wholesaler and retailer and the transaction between retailer and customer each represents an identity: in each case, the seller receives in money exactly what the buyer gives up, and conversely, for the goods. But certainly our retailer has performed a different service in his purchasing operations than he has in his selling operations. In the American economy, the impetus to exchange goods falls, in large part, on the seller. Hence, throughout the marketing process, we find that the selling function assumes an aggressive and driving character, whereas the buying function tends to be selective and discriminatory. At all stages in the marketing process, we find salesmen relentlessly seeking out prospective purchasers and purchasers hanging back, seeking better conditions of sale, better quality at the same price and lower prices. In sum, different motives are at work in the selling function than in the buying function, and different services are provided.

Assembling. Assembling is concerned with the gathering together of farm products at a central point, in the country or city. Assembling at country points often occurs because an individual grower does not have enough produce to fill out a freight car or truck. By assembling the output of several farms, cars may be filled immediately and shipped to distant markets. Assembling at country points is also necessary to bring together sufficiently large quantities of a product to interest buyers in coming to that local point. Shipping point auctions, for example, are organized for the primary purpose of collecting at one point sufficient produce to meet buyers' demands, thereby attracting those buyers.

Wholesale markets in large cities require a constant supply of a wide variety of products. These products must be assembled from diverse producing areas to provide retailers with a certain source of supply of the wide variety of commodities demanded by their customers. The process of assembling is also performed by retailers, who assemble a wide variety of food products in one store so that consumers may make all of their food purchases in one place. Thus, assembling commodities occurs at all stages of the marketing process, *and we should not confuse the function of assembling with the broader process of concentration and dispersion.* Assembling takes place in the early process of concentration *and in the later process of dispersion.*

Standardizing and grading. This function has to do with such activities as the establishment of standards, the maintenance of standards, and the sorting of products into lots conforming to established standards. The latter two of these activities are often referred to as grading. It is evident, however, that all three activities are closely related and have as their objective the realization of those advantages to be derived from marketing standardized products: the marketing of products of which the characteristics of each unit in a particular lot are uniform.

When products are graded into uniform lots, in accordance with defined standard grades, they can be bought by sample or even description. In these cases, it is not necessary for a buyer to inspect all of a lot of produce to know what he is getting. Graded products may be sold by description over the phone or by letter, thereby facilitating the marketing process.

Grading also enables agencies and individuals in the marketing process to obtain the grade of product they seek. Some groups may want only high-quality products and are willing to pay for that quality. Others may seek lower quality products in order to obtain them at lower prices. Graded products make it possible to satisfy both groups, whereas ungraded products would satisfy neither.

Some grading is done for almost every farm product. Produce that is obviously spoiled or is otherwise unfit for consumption must be removed from the lots in which they are found. To be most effective, however, grading must be carried out in accordance with well-established standards. Grade specifications have been established for practically all of the important agricultural products by the United States Department of Agriculture and the various state departments of agriculture. The grade specifications exist; it is simply for the farmer to decide whether or not it will pay to grade his product.

Storing. Wherever farm products are assembled for sale, we find storage facilities. At country shipping points, we find all types of storage facilities: grain elevators, potato warehouses, cotton warehouses, fruit packing warehouses, vegetable packing sheds, and refrigeration rooms in creameries. Wholesale houses must have storage facilities, and retailers, of course, have their stores in which they stock, display, and move their goods. From one end of the marketing system to the other we find storage facilities. No other type of facility is so omnipresent. And by reason of these storage spaces, vast and small, the marketing system is able to engage successfully in that complex process of equalization. These storage spaces, which are continuously filled and drained, make possible the physical adjustment of supplies to demand.

Storage permeates every nook and cranny of the marketing system and is involved in practically every operation undertaken in the marketing system. Once produced, products spend most of their time "setting" in storage awaiting some new operation: handling, processing or transporting. Storage is the great matter-of-fact function in the marketing system providing time utility.

Transporting. Transportation provides place utility. By means of transportation we place products where we need or want them. The development of modern means of transportation has permitted specialization in production. And specialization in production has given rise to the modern, interdependent economy. Thus, we might say that the development of cheap transportation is, in fact, responsible for the highly complex marketing system that we have today.

Railroads have had an important influence on the location of production in agriculture and upon the marketing of farm products. The development of refrigerated railway cars in the 1890's represented a tremendous innovation in transportation, with far-reaching consequences for agriculture. Prior to this, perishable products could be produced only within the immediate areas surrounding large centers of population. With the development and use of refrigerator cars, it became possible to locate the production of perishable products in areas best suited to their production. Tomatoes and lettuce could be produced in the Imperial Valley of California and transported to the eastern seaboard. The location of fruit and vegetable production has moved far from the centers of urban population to the South and Southwest. The development of refrigerator cars also made it possible to establish meat-packing plants in the Midwest closer to the supply of animals, with the result being that fresh meat rather than live animals is shipped East.

Highway transportation in the United States in the past 30 years has been revolutionized and, as a result, so has much of the marketing system. Improved highways and the motor truck have had a greater influence on the farm marketing system in recent years than any other single factor or combination of factors that might be mentioned. The motor truck reduces transportation costs to the farmer, especially in local hauling to nearby assembling points and markets. Further, the motor truck has made it more convenient for the farmer to market his products in smaller quantities, with the result that he markets his products at several different times during the season. With the reductions in cost on one hand, and the greater convenience on the other, the institutions of marketing have changed. Local livestock shipping associations, which assembled livestock for rail shipment, have disappeared and direct trucking to terminal markets and to interior packing houses now flourishes. More farmers produce milk for fluid consumption, eggs are delivered more frequently, and purchased supplies are delivered on call. Everywhere you turn in the farm marketing system the motor truck has made itself felt.

Dividing and packaging. It has already been pointed out that products must be assembled at different stages in the marketing system for efficient movement and for the convenience of buyers. The final consumer, in most cases, makes purchases in small lots or quantities. Therefore, we have the marketing function of dividing and packaging as a counterpart to assembling. Division into wholesale lots, we remember, was one of the major services provided by operators in central wholesale markets. And jobbers in smaller markets have as their principal function the breaking down of carlot shipments into smaller lots: into lots that retailers can use. For example, it is the principal function of wholesalers and jobbers in fruit and vegetable terminal markets to divide carlot shipments into the smaller portions that retailers are able to sell through their stores in one day (or other brief period).

But in the retail store, the function of dividing and packaging reaches an apex. We pointed out earlier that the individual grocery store is engaged in assembling a variety of products for the convenience of its patrons. But the local grocery store, to an even greater degree, is engaged in dividing and packaging. The local store purchases potatoes in 100-pound lots and sells those potatoes to its customers in 5- to 10-pound lots. The same is true for any commodity that we may wish to consider. The retail store finds its reason for being in: (1) the purchase of relatively large lots and (2) the sale of relatively small lots.

The service of dividing and packaging, just as with assembling, is to be found at almost every stage in the marketing process. However, while assembling finds its greatest importance at the local shipping point and the central wholesale markets, dividing and packaging finds its greatest importance in jobbing markets and at the retail level.

Financing. From the time products leave the farm until they reach the consumer, someone's funds are tied up in them. Farmers could finance the entire marketing operation by waiting to be paid until after their products were sold to the final consumer. But this is impracticable and undesirable from the farmer's point of view. On sending his product to market, the farmer wants to get his money as soon as possible and ordinarily he does not have to wait long. The local grain elevator usually pays him in cash, the creamery sends him a check once a month, and he is paid at the time of sale in local livestock auctions.

It is the middleman who bears the brunt of financial operations. It is he who purchases farm products, places them in storage, and feeds them out as demand requires. And it is this accumulation and maintenance of inventory which creates a financing problem. For during the period that stocks are held in storage, the middleman has his funds tied up in those stocks. But middlemen usually do not possess sufficient free funds to finance such inventory operations. They obtain their funds from banks and other sources of credit. Thus, interest on funds tied up in stored products becomes a necessary and unavoidable marketing cost. Financing is a service indispensable to the holding of stocks, but financing is attained only at a cost: the cost of money borrowed to finance the purchase and the holding operations.

Risk-bearing. Whoever takes title to products moving through the marketing processes also takes risks. The farmer runs a risk when he buys livestock to feed, or when he stores potatoes in his cellar. He does not know what will happen to price between the current date and the time of sale.[4] It is possible, too, that uncertain weather will interrupt his feeding operations, or that his potatoes will spoil. In short, there are many types of physical risks that the farmer, or any operator who takes title to products in the marketing process, must consider. But it is the price risk that causes the most trouble. This type of risk permeates the entire marketing system. Prices are forever changing or fluctuating, and there is little that any one individual operator may do to influence these price changes, although we should be clear in our minds that prices can go up as well as down. During periods of falling prices, middlemen may realize losses that cause them financial difficulty and even bankruptcy. But during periods of rising prices, profits accumulate on goods held in storage through no effort on the part of the middleman.

Various devices are used to shift or spread risk. For certain commodities, such as wheat and cotton, farmers can get government nonrecourse loans. Here the government bears the full cost of protecting farmers against price declines. Farmers redeem the loans and sell the

---

[4] It is assumed here that prices are not fixed or supported by government.

product when prices are good, but permit the government to take title to the commodity at the loan maturity date when market prices are below the loan rate.

Another device is to sell products for later delivery. A wheat miller may sell flour to bakeries for later delivery at the price prevailing when he bought the wheat. The deferred delivery period might be thirty days to six months, depending on buyers' needs and willingness to run the risk of falling prices.

A more widely used device is the buying and selling of futures contracts on commodity exchanges. All individuals or firms holding agricultural commodities for which futures markets are available may guard—"hedge"—against price changes in that way. Essential marketing services are performed by the people who run a futures exchange and enforce its trading rules, the brokers who act as agents on the floor of the exchange, and the speculators who assume the risks and thus make hedging possible.

Providing market information. Decisions to buy and sell are based on market information, good or bad. Thus, an important function in marketing is the collection and interpretation of market information. By this we mean the collection of information dealing with quantities moving in trade, market price quotations for the previous hour, previous day, previous week, or other periods, weather conditions, governmental operations, and other factors. Some individuals base their decisions on information collected by themselves or on personal hunches. And some firms pay private agencies to collect information of an exclusive nature for them. But most individuals, farmers and middlemen, operating in the market, depend upon the Federal government for their basic market information. The United States Department of Agriculture maintains a far flung system of crop reporting and market news reporting on which everyone in the market relies. Periodically, the department issues reports describing the condition of crops and storage holdings on hand, and daily it releases to radio stations and newspapers current information on prices received in the various markets and quantities moved to these markets. This is the basic information used by farmers and middlemen in making their decisions to buy and sell.

Processing. Processing is, in effect, manufacturing. For some reason, we describe those operations in food and agriculture concerned with changing the form of agricultural products by the term processing, whereas in other fields we describe the operation that changes the form of the product as manufacturing. But in either case, it is the form of the product that is changed. This is in contrast to the functions discussed above. All those were concerned with the creation of time and place utility, with the movement of farm products through space and through time. Hence, some people argue that processing, since it is not concerned with the creation of time and place utility, is not properly a marketing function.

But however we wish to classify processing, two facts stand out. Processing is important in the preparation of food for human consumption, and processing stands squarely in the track of the marketing process. Some farm products reach the consumer in much the same form as they were produced on the farm: eggs, apples, and cabbages are examples. But these products, too, may be processed. We now have dried eggs and frozen eggs. Apples are canned, dried, frozen, or processed into cider and other products. And cabbage, we know, sometimes ends up in sauerkraut. Thus, processing is important for even those commodities that we usually do not think of as being processed.

Processing arises, in part, from the obvious fact that we cannot consume most farm products in the form in which they come from the farm. This, clearly, is the case for such farm products as livestock, wheat, and cotton. It is the perishability of farm products, however, that gives rise to much of the processing. It is the perishability of milk, of fruits and vegetables, and of meat products that forces some type of processing in each of these cases. Since farm products often do not come to market at the time when consumers need them, they must be stored and fed into the market as consumer demand develops, which means that perishable food products must be processed. Thus, the characteristic quality of all foods, namely perishability, makes processing an indispensable part of those activities to be found in the moving of products from farm to city.

Frozen foods are an outstanding example. The production of frozen fruit, vegetables, poultry, meats, seafoods, fruit juices, and specialties increased twelvefold between 1938 and 1953. In 1953 the entire output of frozen foods was about 5 billion pounds, 3.4 billion pounds of it produced by 1,400 commercial packers and more than 1.5 billion pounds in 11,000 frozen-food locker plants. A spectacular expansion has occurred in the production of table-ready meats, processed cheeses, canned citrus juices, frozen concentrate juices, prepared cake mixes, baby foods, and precooked frozen and canned specialties. Factory production of canned fruit and vegetable juices has more than trebled since 1938. Half of the orange crop and nearly one-fourth of the commercial meat production in the United States in 1952 were processed in the form of ready-to-serve canned, and cooked, cured, dried, or frozen products.

The factory prepares an almost complete menu of foods for

children—more than 50 pounds for every child under 3 years of age in 1952, as compared with 2 pounds in 1935 and almost none in 1930.

The firm in the marketing process. The impression may have been formed from the preceding discussion that the marketing system, in some vague way, undertakes to provide the various services necessary to effective marketing. If that is true, we have fostered a false impression. The various services described above must be provided, but the loose structure we call the marketing system certainly does not *undertake* the provision of these services. Individual business firms, operating within the marketing system, *undertake* the provision of these services. The provision of service (perhaps storage, perhaps financing, perhaps selling) represents the "product" of these firms. These marketing services are provided at a cost and, in the usual case, add value to the product. We must remember that the provision of such services as assembly, storage, or transportation create value, create utility just as certainly as the original productive act of form creation. Apples grown in the state of Washington are not consumable apples to New Yorkers, until they are transported to New York and dispersed to those consumers. So we get the picture: business firms constitute the operating units in the marketing system; it is they who *undertake* to provide the services necessary to effective marketing; in doing so they incur costs and create value in the products handled by them.

The analysis of the marketing firm is the same as that presented for the farm firm in Chapter 4. The marketing firm seeks to maximize its profits at all times. To this end it is continually varying the factors of production under its control in an effort to realize, not the least cost output, but the maximum profit output. In a rigorous sense, the firm achieves this goal by applying units of a variable factor of production (for example, day laborers) to the fixed combination of factors (such as the building, storage space, equipment and fixtures, business office, management), to that point at which the cost of the added output just equals the selling price of the last unit of product. Or in a more flexible sense, the firm balances off expected increases in cost against expected increases in income from the employment of some variation of past production methods. And when the firm finds the change to be advantageous, it adopts the new practice.

Two dissimilarities between the farm firm and the marketing firm do, however, need to be pointed out. In the first place, as already noted, the "product" of the marketing firm is usually a service rather than form creation. Hence, it is difficult to apply a marginal analysis to the marketing firm, the *output* of which is not readily measurable. The output of the farm is easily measured in bushels or pounds, or some other standard measure, but how do you measure the output of a service, such as selling or storage? Certainly not in terms of the number of units of product handled. Those units represent the product of the farm firm and a cost to the wholesale firm. The output of the wholesale firm may be measured only in terms of the *value added* to the units handled, for the *services* provided. But this leaves us without a physical measure of output.

In the second place, a relatively large proportion of the costs of the farm firm are fixed costs, whereas a relatively large proportion of the costs of a merchandising firm are variable, out-of-pocket costs. Most of the costs of a merchandising firm vary directly with the volume of product handled; labor and inventory charges vary directly with the volume of business. Thus, marketing firms that buy and sell produce tend to have high mortality rates.

Marketing firms operating at the wholesale and retail levels usually apply some "rule of thumb" markup to each batch of merchandise purchased. This markup is designed to cover average unit costs, plus some measure of profit, but it cannot be maintained when it comes into conflict with competitive price relationships. If the firm has paid too much for its produce or prices fall, the firm will be forced to sell at the competitive price regardless of the desired markup. Thus, one or two bad business decisions or market reverses, which send cash costs soaring above cash receipts, may put the firm out of business.

It is our point that marketing firms constitute the operating units of the marketing system. Through these operating units flow two streams: the goods stream and the receipts stream. The decision by a wholesale firm to purchase a given quantity of a farm product moving in the marketing channel acts to propel that quantity of product forward to the consumer and money receipts backward to the farmer. The original consumer expenditure becomes cash receipts for the retailer, who holds out a small portion as income for services rendered by him, and he, in turn, by the decision to buy inventory from a wholesaler, makes payment to that wholesaler of most of the expenditure made by the consumer. The wholesaler takes a slice of those receipts as income for the services provided by him and by a decision to purchase products from a farmer directs the remaining receipts back to the farmer. So the simple pipeline approach, with a goods stream moving in one direction and a money stream in the other, must be modified. These streams move through operating units—marketing firms—and the flows are maintained only insofar as transactions are made.

REFERENCES

Black, John D., and Neil T. Houston, *Research in Resource-Use Efficiency in the Marketing of Farm Products,* Harvard Studies in Marketing Farm Products, No. 1-H. Cambridge: Harvard University Press, 1950.

Clark, Fred E., and Carrie Patton Clark, *Principles of Marketing,* Chapters 1, 2, 4, 5, 14, and 16. New York: The Macmillan Company, 1942.

Kohls, R. L., *Marketing of Agricultural Products,* Chapters 1 and 2. New York: The Macmillan Company, 1955.

Shepherd, Geoffrey S., *Marketing Farm Products,* 3rd ed. Chapter 1. Ames, Iowa: Iowa State College Press, 1955.

POINTS FOR DISCUSSION

1. What do we mean by "marketing"?
2. Why is marketing unimportant in primitive economics?
3. What are the causes of the highly complex farm marketing system in the United States?
4. What do we mean by concentration, equalization, and dispersion? In what sense are these processes particularly important in agriculture?
5. What is a market?
6. What kinds of markets are encountered in the movement of farm produce from the producers to the consumer?
7. List the principal marketing functions. Are all these functions necessary, or could some of them be dispensed with? If the latter is the case, which ones could best be eliminated? Would you say that storage and transportation, which provide time and place utility, are less important than production, which creates form utility?
8. Who undertakes to provide these functions in the marketing system? What is the "product" of the marketing firm?

CHAPTER 8

The Farm Marketing System— An Atlas

PRESENTED IN the following pages is an "atlas of marketing," which points out the problems of marketing selected farm products: feed grains, livestock, sugar, cotton, and dairy products. Some of these commodities are widely grown; others are restricted to highly specialized areas of production. Some are produced the year around; for others the whole year's supply comes on the market in a few months. Some are highly perishable, others can be stored from one year to the next. Some come off the farm ready to be eaten, and others require extensive processing. Each of these commodities requires its own types and locations of markets, its own methods of handling, its own marketing agencies, facilities, and channels. This atlas portrays these unique characteristics.[1]

Feed grains.[2] Feed grains are marketed principally through livestock and livestock products. The cash sales of the four feed grains—corn, oats, barley, and the sorghum grains—are comparatively small; they make up only about 5 per cent of the gross income of farmers. But cash receipts from the livestock and poultry that are produced from the feed grains and forages account for more than 50 per cent of the total farm income.

The surplus feed-grain producing area of the Midwest has become the center of the livestock industry, particularly hogs and beef, which

---

[1] This atlas is adapted from materials presented in pages 402-489 of the 1954 *Yearbook of Agriculture* entitled "Marketing." For greater detail, and reference to other agricultural commodities, see the 1954 *Yearbook of Agriculture.*

[2] Original statement prepared by Malcolm Clough and James W. Browning of the U. S. Department of Agriculture.

can be processed and shipped to major consuming areas more economically than feed grains.

Some livestock products, notably milk, eggs, and poultry, are produced in quantity near the areas of consumption, particularly the Northeast, which depends largely on Midwest feed.

The production of feed grains has increased steadily since the early part of the nineteenth century. The improvement of the plow for turning the prairie sod was later followed by mechanical power for cultivating and harvesting feed grains. Those developments made possible greater production and released about one-fourth of the production of feed grains, which had been fed to work animals, for use in producing meat, milk, and eggs. The extension of railroads into the Midwest facilitated the movement of grain and livestock to consumers in the East and to the coast for export. The rapid growth of trucking has been important more recently in the transportation of feed grains, livestock, and livestock products. Another factor in the increase of feed grains was the improvement in seed, including the development of corn hybrids and new varieties of grains that are adapted to the various regions.

The acreage in feed grains reached a record high in 1932, but has declined since then. In 1948-1952 the acreage was about one-eighth smaller than 20 years earlier, but production, reflecting higher yields to the acre, increased nearly one-fourth.

Grains and the byproduct feeds ordinarily provide nearly one-half of the total feed for livestock. Pasture, hay, and other forages furnish a little over one-half. Corn makes up about 60 per cent of the total grain and the byproducts fed to livestock, but only about one-fourth of the total feed, including forages. Hogs and poultry are produced almost entirely from grains and byproduct feeds, but cattle and sheep depend heavily on pasture and other forages.

The North Central States produce approximately 75 per cent of the national output of the feed grains. They are especially important as a source of commercial supplies of feed grains, providing about 85 per cent of the corn and more than 80 per cent of the oats going into commercial channels.

The normal flow of feed grains is from the Midwest to the East, South, and West. But because each region is a producer as well as a consumer of feed grains, the movement is not uniform or continuous. Year-to-year variations in production and feed requirements in the various regions result in local surpluses or deficits, which change the magnitude of the flow or reverse it. In abnormal years, such as 1936 and 1947, the pattern of movement changes materially, and it may even be reversed as drought areas of the Corn Belt become deficient in production of feed grains. In 1949-1950, a fairly typical marketing year, farmers in North Central States sold about 28 million tons of feed grains, of which 8.3 million tons were shipped out of the region by rail and barge—a little over 40 per cent to the North Atlantic region; about one-half to the South Atlantic and South Central regions; and less than 10 per cent to the Western States. An additional tonnage moved out by truck, for which data are not available.

Commercial marketing of grain begins at country elevators, which have facilities for marketing, conditioning, and storing grain.

The cost of receiving the grain by truck, placing it in the elevator, and moving it from the elevator at the close of the storage period usually is $.03 to $.08 a bushel, depending on the kind of grain and the state or area in which the elevator is located. The usual yearly charge for storage is $.10 to $.20 a bushel.

Country elevator operators have many outlets for their grain. They sell some locally to stockmen, dairymen, and poultrymen. They sell and ship large quantities to millers, feed manufacturers, and feeders in deficit producing areas. But most of the grain handled in country elevators goes to terminal markets.

Terminal markets provide weighing and inspection services, drying and storage facilities, market quotations, services of commission merchants, and services of financing, insurance, and forwarding agencies. Farmers, country elevator operators, or others who wish to ship grain to a terminal market may either sell their grain to a cash-grain firm, consign it to the market for sale by a commission merchant, or to a terminal elevator or warehouse for storage. The charges for receiving grain into the storage elevator by rail or water and loading it out into cars range from about $.02 to $.03 a bushel. The storage charge is approximately the same as for the country elevators.

Marketings of feed grains by farmers are seasonally heavy during and just after harvesting.

Marketings of corn are greatest during November-January, after the harvest in the Corn Belt. The prices are seasonally low during November and December. They normally advance during the rest of the season, reaching a seasonal high in August. The seasonal pattern of marketings, cost of storage, and loss of grain in storage are all basic to the seasonal rise in prices. The seasonal rise in the average price to farmers is greater than that in the market price of a specified grade, as the farm-stored corn loses moisture and usually improves in quality during the year. Average prices received by farmers normally rise from a seasonal low of 91 per cent of the yearly average in November to a high of 112 per cent by August. The seasonal range

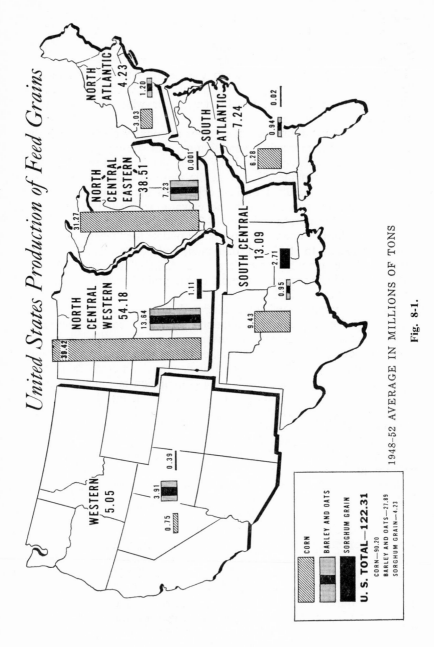

United States Production of Feed Grains

NORTH ATLANTIC 4.23
3.03
1.20

SOUTH ATLANTIC 7.24
6.28
0.94
0.02

NORTH CENTRAL EASTERN 38.51
31.27
7.23
0.001

NORTH CENTRAL WESTERN 54.18
38.42
13.64
1.11

SOUTH CENTRAL 13.09
9.43
2.71
0.95

WESTERN 5.05
3.91
0.75
0.39

CORN
BARLEY AND OATS
SORGHUM GRAIN
U. S. TOTAL—122.31
CORN—90.20
BARLEY AND OATS—27.89
SORGHUM GRAIN—4.23

1948-52 AVERAGE IN MILLIONS OF TONS

Fig. 8-1.

Movement of Corn and Other Feeds
MILLIONS OF TONS
(Corn Equivalent)

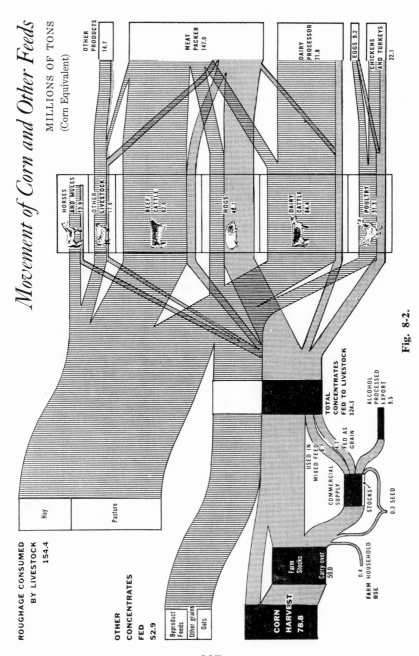

Fig. 8-2.

117

in price of No. 3 Yellow corn at Chicago, however, is usually about 95 to 108 per cent of the yearly average.

Marketings of oats and barley follow a somewhat similar pattern. Heaviest marketings occur during July-September, the period of seasonally low prices. Marketings decline in the winter and spring and the prices advance, usually reaching a seasonal high in April or May.

In the commercial channels of distribution, feed grains are practically always bought and sold by grade. The United States Grain Standards Act requires that in all interstate trading in which grains are bought or sold by grades, the grades used shall be those established by the Secretary of Agriculture. At country points the buyer determines the grade, but at large terminal markets grains are graded by inspectors licensed by the Department of Agriculture, but employed usually by the state or by the grain exchanges located in such markets.

Storage of feed grains from one year to the next has, in the past, been comparatively small. The bulk of the storage is from harvest until the grain is used later in the marketing year. About 10 to 15 per cent of the production has been carried over at the end of the year, and part of it as normal working stocks. More than 85 per cent of the carryover stocks of corn and oats ordinarily are held in the North Central Region.

Under government price support programs during the 1950's there was, however, a great build-up of feed grain stocks. The carryover at the end of the year increased each year following 1952—rising from 27 million tons in 1952 to 68 million tons in 1959. The estimated carryover of feed grains in 1959 amounts to well over one-half of one year's total utilization.

This build-up in feed grain stocks did not result from a decline in the total utilization of feed grains during the 1950's. On the contrary, the total tonnage fed to livestock increased from 99 million tons in 1954-55 to around 124 million in 1958-59. Exports in the three-year period also increased. Even so, total utilization ran around 9 million tons below total production (plus imports) in 1958-59, bringing carryover stocks up to the record of around 68 million tons.

Farm sales and imports, which have been fairly important for oats and barley in recent years, make up what is considered the commercial supply of feed grains. Farmers sold about one-fourth of the corn and oats, 60 per cent of the barley, and two-thirds of the sorghum grains produced in 1947-1951.

A little less than one-third of the corn sold by farmers is purchased by processors for making food and industrial products. The wet-processing industry converts corn into starch, sugar, and syrup. Dry processors produce cornmeal, hominy grits, flour, and prepared cereals. Distillers use corn in producing alcohol, distilled spirits, and other alcohol products. Usually a little more than half of the corn sold is bought for livestock feed, and includes that going directly to livestock producers and that purchased by feed manufacturers. Thus, including the corn fed on farms, about 90 per cent of the total corn produced is fed to livestock.

About 12 per cent of the oats sold and 3 per cent of the total production is used for making oatmeal. Nearly one-fourth of the commercial oats supply is bought for seed. Most of the remainder is bought for livestock feed.

A little more than 50 per cent of the barley sold in 1947-1951 was used in making malt, which in turn is used principally in producing malt liquors, alcohol, and distilled spirits. About one-fourth was bought for feed. Most of the remainder was exported.

The bulk of the sorghum grains entering the commercial channels is bought for livestock feed or exported. In 1947-1951 about 40 per cent of the quantity marketed by farmers was bought for feed and about 45 per cent was exported.

Foreign trade in feed grains in most years is comparatively unimportant, as the bulk of our feed grain is produced and consumed within our own country. Although total exports in 1948-1952 were larger than in any comparable period since 1900, they averaged only about 4 per cent of the total production and 15 per cent of the total sales by farmers. Exports of corn averaged 109 million bushels, or about half of the total tonnage of feed grains exported. They accounted for a little more than one-tenth of the total sales, and about 3 per cent of the total production of corn.

Imports of feed grains are generally of minor importance. Except in the drought years of 1934 and 1936, imports of corn have been practically negligible. During World War II and in some years since, substantial quantities of oats and barley were imported from Canada. Except in the drought years, imports have never exceeded 3 per cent of our total production of feed grains.

Livestock.[3] Meat is the most important item in the food budget. Expenditures for meat amount to 25 per cent or more of the total cost of all food of the American people. The retail value of the per capita meat consumption in 1958 was about $90. For that sum, the consumer got in terms of carcass weight (before shrinkage resulting from cutting, trimming, and evaporation) 66 pounds of pork, 80.5

---

[3] Original statement prepared by Charles A. Burmeister and Harold F. Breimyer of the U. S. Department of Agriculture.

pounds of beef, 7 pounds of veal, and 4 pounds of lamb. Actual purchase weights were less.

About $.56 out of every dollar consumers spend for meat goes back to the livestock producer. To the income he receives from the meat is added that from hides, pelts, fats, and other byproducts. Together, cash receipts of $11,178 million were returned to farmers for the meat animals they marketed in 1958. This was almost one-third of farmers' receipts from all sources.

Most of the beef, veal, lamb, and mutton reaches the consumer within a short time after slaughter. Much of the pork also is sold quickly, although several pork products are cured and then moved along more slowly. Peak loads of meat in commercial freezer and cooler storage seldom amount to more than 2 per cent of the annual commercial output of beef and veal, 2 per cent of lamb and mutton, and 4 per cent of pork—the equivalents of only 5, 7, and 15 days' supplies of the respective meats.

Considerable amounts of meat—although a small part of the total supply—are made into sausages, frankfurters, sandwich meats, and other products. More of them go into cans now than a few years ago. From an annual rate of 300 to 500 million pounds before the war, the output of canned meat jumped to 2 billion pounds in 1943. It was 1,651 million pounds in 1958. The total production of carcass meat was 26 billion pounds that year.

Range, pasture, and hay are primary feeds for raising sheep and cattle. Corn and other concentrate feeds are the diet for hogs, and they will put finish on cattle and sheep.

First-ranking grazing and pasture area is that large territory known as the Great Plains, which slopes east from the Rockies and is bracketed on the north by Canada, on the south by the Gulf of Mexico, and on the east by the western edge of the Corn Belt (about the 97th meridian). The region is primarily a breeding ground. Each year it sends hundreds of thousands of feeder cattle and sheep east. It also feeds many animals to part or full finish, slaughtering some locally but shipping more of them east or west for slaughter. In January 1959 the six States from North Dakota to Texas had 27 per cent of the nation's cattle, 29 per cent of its sheep, and 13 per cent of its hogs.

The mountain West has a similar position as a cradle for feeder cattle and sheep as well as a producer of many grass-fat and some grain-fed animals, but its carrying capacity is below that of the Plains. In 1959 it had 11 per cent of all cattle and 32 per cent of all sheep. Few hogs are raised there.

The area ranking first in raising hogs and feeding cattle and sheep is the Corn Belt. The 8 states from Ohio to Minnesota produced 65 per cent of the United States corn crop. In 1958 those states raised about 70 per cent of all the pigs. On January 1, 1959, they had 52 per cent of all the cattle and 34 per cent of all the lambs that were on feed in feed lots. Those states also have large numbers of cattle and sheep for breeding. In 1959 they had 15 per cent of all the beef cows.

Progress toward more productive pastures and better adapted breeds has boosted the cattle industry of the South and Southeast. Large acreages of cropland in the area have been shifted from cultivated crops to grassland. The region ships out a few feeder cattle but the greater part of its production is slaughtered locally as grass-fat cattle. It ranks next to the Corn Belt in production of hogs. It has 22 per cent of the population of the United States, but it has 19 per cent of the cattle, 6 per cent of the sheep, and 18 per cent of the hogs. Inshipment of beef is not so great as the figures suggest; people in the South eat less beef per capita than do those in other regions, but more pork.

The Northeastern States comprise the big deficit region into which meat pours, chiefly from the Midwest. With 25 per cent of the population and an above-average income per person, the states from Maryland to Maine have 15 per cent of the country's cattle and calves.

On the Pacific Coast a growing cattle industry has failed to keep up with an even faster growing population. The region in 1959 with 10 per cent of the population had only 7 per cent of the nation's cattle. It had 9 per cent of the sheep. Both range and irrigated land are used in the production of cattle and sheep. There is much dry-lot feeding on beet pulp, barley, and a variety of other feeds that substitute for the Corn Belt's plentiful corn.

The quantity of meat produced varies both seasonally and from year to year. Not all the ingenuity of man has erased fully the synchronism of the seasons and the life cycle in livestock production. Spring still is the time of most births, summer of grazing, and fall and winter of intensive feeding. More pigs are born in March and April than in any other months. Crowded into three months, November to January, is almost one-third of the year's total hog slaughter. A second slaughter peak occurs in early spring. Slaughter of all cattle, considered together, is fairly evenly distributed throughout the year because feeding operations act as a leveler of supplies, withdrawing cattle marketed off grass in the fall and delivering them for slaughter the next spring. But in this process the composition of slaughter and the beef supply changes greatly. In the fall more grass cattle are slaughtered and the lower grades of beef are in more plentiful supply. In the spring and summer well-finished cattle and Choice and Prime beef are more abundant.

The annual production of hogs and output of pork rise and fall irregularly, largely in response to changes in the size of the corn crops. The ratio between prices of hogs and prices of corn, alternately favorable and unfavorable to hog production, is the mechanism that keeps the hog production in line with the corn supply. When corn-loan programs are in effect, however, the production of hogs and of pork is less closely tied to the size of each year's corn crop. It is governed more by the relation of demand for pork to loan or release prices for corn.

The production of cattle and output of beef go through long cyclical variations. Because of the heavy investment required for raising cattle and the long life span of the species, changes in demand for beef or in the supply of range, pasture, and crop feed are manifest in slow and prolonged upswings and downswings in cattle numbers and beef supply.

Sheep production and annual output of lamb also experience cyclical fluctuation, chiefly according to altering conditions in producing areas and shifting competitive relationships.

Meat is a heterogeneous commodity. Red meat comprises beef, veal, lamb, mutton, and pork, each of which is retailed in a wide assortment of cuts. Meats also vary over a range of grades, since they are derived from live animals varying greatly in quality, conformation, and finish. Standard grade names established by the Department of Agriculture have provided an identification terminology for transactions in all livestock except hogs, even though actual sales usually are made by inspection of each lot offered. New grades were set up in 1952 for hogs, but these animals still are sold more according to weight than by grade. There also are Federal grades for meat. Any inspected and some noninspected packers can have meat graded by Federal graders by asking for and paying the costs of the service. Substantial quantities of all meats except pork are so graded. Much meat is sold by description alone rather than by personal inspection at the time of sale.

Grades for livestock and meat, as for all farm commodities, differentiate the products in a way that facilitates trade and rewards the producer who supplies the kind and qualities desired by consumers. The increasing consumer preference for lean over fat pork, for instance, can be reflected back to producers of hogs only if a distinction is made between fat and lean hogs and a higher price paid for the leaner ones. Selling hogs by the new live hog grades is one proposed method for doing that. Another is selling by carcass grade and weight, a system whereby the return to the producer for each hog is determined from the value of its carcass.

Finally, meat comes from numerous suppliers. About 4 million farms and ranches produce cattle and 2 million produce hogs. A little more than 350,000 produce sheep. The slaughtering industry has considerable concentration among a few large packers and several dozen firms of intermediate size, but even so it includes a total of 952 wholesale slaughterers, 1,810 local smaller concerns classed as slaughterers, and 11,000 still smaller operators designated as butchers. Meat wholesalers are many and retailers legion.

Livestock marketing agencies are equally diverse. Notwithstanding many changes in the livestock marketing system over the years, terminal public markets still are of considerable importance. In 1950 federally inspected packers reported that they obtained 75 per cent of their cattle, 57 per cent of their calves, 40 per cent of their hogs, and 57 per cent of their sheep and lambs at the 65 stockyards markets operating under Federal supervision.

Direct buying of livestock has grown in volume and is the predominant means of marketing hogs in many areas of the North Central States.

Livestock auctions experienced a spectacular expansion after 1930, until they numbered about 2,400 in 1949. In the South and Southeast about two-thirds of the livestock is sold at these auction markets. In addition to these outlets, local markets and local dealers and buyers probably numbering in the tens of thousands are available in all parts of the country.

Sugar.[4] Each person in the United States consumes an average of about 95 pounds of cane and beet sugar each year. The major use of sugar is to sweeten foods such as ice cream, baked goods, beverages, and candy. A small amount of sugar is consumed directly as such.

The total annual consumption of refined sugar in the United States amounts to about 7.6 million tons. The sources are the sugar beet regions of the Midwest and West, the sugar cane areas of Louisiana, Florida, Puerto Rico, and Hawaii, and the foreign sugar cane areas, principally Cuba and the Philippines. Continental and off-shore domestic areas supply about 53 per cent of total consumption; the rest is imported.

A fairly complex marketing structure carries sugar in its final form to the consumer from the farms where sugar cane and sugar beets are grown.

---

[4] Original statement prepared by Marshall E. Miller of the U. S. Department of Agriculture.

Cane sugar, which forms the bulk of domestic consumption, undergoes two refining processes before distribution to end users. The first refining process is done by factories in production areas where raw sugar is made from sugar cane. In a few instances, the second refining operation is done at the same plant, but most raw sugar is further processed by large refineries in major port cities in the United States. Thus sugar cane is sold by farmers to raw-sugar mills, which manufacture raw sugar from the cane and sell their output to refineries. Refiners perform the final processing necessary and act as primary distributors of sugar to industrial users, who use sugar in their operations, and to wholesale and retail buyers, who sell sugar to institutional and household consumers.

The development of the separate phases of processing and marketing came about for several reasons. The manufacture, by mills located in production areas, of raw sugar from cane, which is seasonally produced, extremely bulky in relation to value, and highly perishable, permits the second refining operation to be performed on a volume year-around basis by a relatively few large-scale refineries located in consuming areas. The complete manufacturing process performed at one factory would require great capital outlay, highly skilled labor, and adequate fuels. In the infancy of the sugar industry, those requirements were lacking in some of the production areas. Some marketing advantages accrue also to the location of refiners, who are primary distributors, in consuming areas.

Processing of beet sugar, because of the nature of the extraction methods, is an integrated operation at the factory located in the beet-growing region. Those processors are faced with the problem of seasonal use of costly facilities, but they have the advantage of location in areas where most of the beet sugar is consumed.

Another factor contributing to the complexity of the marketing structure is the way sugar is used. More and more manufactured sugar-containing products are being bought; consequently there is a decline in direct sugar purchases by consumers for use in baking, canning, and other home uses. The industrial use of sugar has increased since 1935 from about 28 per cent of total sugar marketed to slightly more than 51 per cent in 1953. Conversely, sugar purchases for household, restaurant, and institutional usage have shrunk from about 72 per cent of total marketings to about 49 per cent.

Increased industrial use has been particularly notable in the beverage, baking, ice cream, canning, bottling, and frozen-food industries. Considerable quantities of sugar, most of which has already undergone two refining processes, consequently enter other manufacturing processes. The shift to industrial usage has come about because of the willingness of consumers to pay for additional marketing services embodied in finished products.

The greatest problem faced by domestic producers and processors over the years has been the achievement of relatively stable prices high enough to maintain a healthy industry.

The most important external factor contributing to that problem has been world market conditions. Sugar is one of the commodities on which many governments have placed tariffs, internal taxes, certain controls of supply, consumer subsidies, and other trade restrictions. Some countries have set up the restrictions for revenue purposes. Others use them to protect high-cost domestic industries. Uncertainty as to supplies in wartime motivates to a large extent the maintenance of sugar industries by many countries through various control measures. Sugar production is an industry that has a high capital investment and heavy fixed costs. Output cannot be adjusted readily to changes in demand and price. These also are factors which occasion the establishment of controls.

International trade barriers have two major effects on marketing sugar. The amount of sugar exported to countries or areas in which it enjoys no preference amounts to only about 10 per cent of the world's total production and consumption of sugar. This limited amount constitutes the world free-sugar market, to which Cuba is the chief supplier. It more nearly represents a residual supply, which completes the requirements of deficit-supply countries not filled by producers within the protective systems of such countries. This characteristic leads to instability in the world sugar market and makes prices in that market highly susceptible to the full inflationary and deflationary effects of changes in world production and consumption. Even small changes have significant effects because of the narrowness of the free world market.

High tariffs, internal taxes, and other barriers have resulted in high prices to consumers in many countries. In many instances they bear no relationship to prices received by exporters of sugar. High retail prices have tended to restrict consumption. Although per capita consumption in the United States is relatively high while prices to consumers are relatively low, the reverse situation prevails in many countries.

Some protection has been given the United States sugar industry against the instability of the world market. For many years a tariff system applied to sugar imports. Its net result was to encourage domestic production, while at times Cuba, the principal supplier, was obliged to reduce her export prices to disastrously low levels. Recurrent market crises led to the adoption of the Jones-Costigan

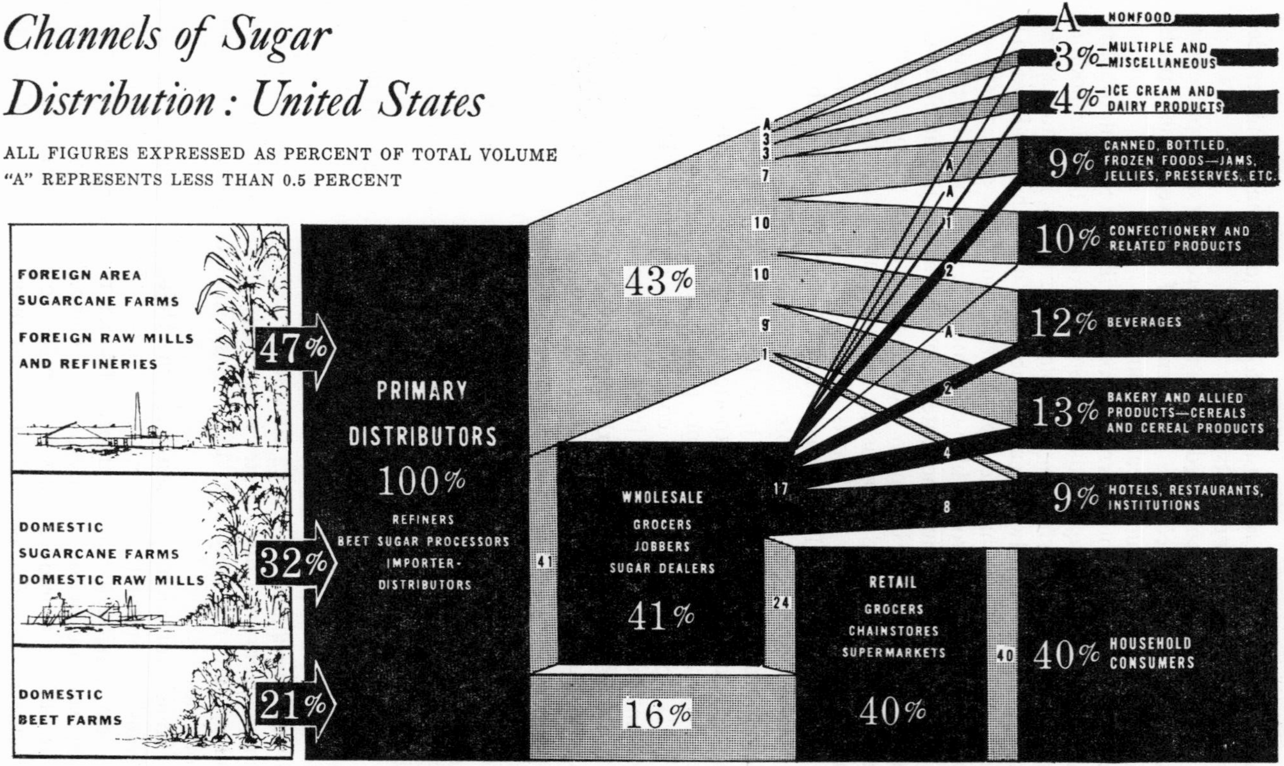

Channels of Sugar
Distribution : United States

ALL FIGURES EXPRESSED AS PERCENT OF TOTAL VOLUME
"A" REPRESENTS LESS THAN 0.5 PERCENT

A NONFOOD

3% MULTIPLE AND MISCELLANEOUS

4% ICE CREAM AND DAIRY PRODUCTS

9% CANNED, BOTTLED, FROZEN FOODS—JAMS, JELLIES, PRESERVES, ETC.

10% CONFECTIONERY AND RELATED PRODUCTS

12% BEVERAGES

13% BAKERY AND ALLIED PRODUCTS—CEREALS AND CEREAL PRODUCTS

9% HOTELS, RESTAURANTS, INSTITUTIONS

40% HOUSEHOLD CONSUMERS

PRIMARY DISTRIBUTORS 100%
REFINERS
BEET SUGAR PROCESSORS
IMPORTER-DISTRIBUTORS

43%

WHOLESALE GROCERS JOBBERS SUGAR DEALERS 41%

16%

RETAIL GROCERS CHAINSTORES SUPERMARKETS 40%

FOREIGN AREA SUGARCANE FARMS
FOREIGN RAW MILLS AND REFINERIES 47%

DOMESTIC SUGARCANE FARMS
DOMESTIC RAW MILLS 32%

DOMESTIC BEET FARMS 21%

Fig. 8-3.

126

Sugar Act in 1934. The Sugar Act of 1948, as amended, still maintains the general features of the first sugar act.

The Sugar Act is designed to maintain a healthy and competitive domestic sugar industry of limited size and to improve our import trade. As stated in the act, the objective is to achieve prices that will not be excessive to consumers and will fairly maintain and protect the domestic industry.

Provisions are included in the act to insure that a fair share of the consumer's dollar goes to growers and to workers in the beet and cane fields. To achieve these objectives, sugar requirements of consumers for the following year are determined by the Secretary of Agriculture each December; quota provisions for foreign and domestic areas to fill the requirements are in operation; and conditional payments are made to domestic growers. The act contains an amendment to the Internal Revenue Code providing for an excise tax of $.005 a pound, raw value, on the manufacture or importation of sugar. Tax collections have exceeded payments to growers by $15 to $20 million a year.

It would be just about impossible, short of rigid controls, to isolate the United States sugar market from the world market, but the Sugar Act has reduced the impact of world market conditions on domestic prices. Since its inception in 1934, United States sugar prices have been much more stable, which has been beneficial to the domestic industry, and have shown a much less proportionate increase than have the prices of most other food products which has benefited consumers.

While sugar legislation provides a buffer against world-market conditions, it is not a substitute for efficient marketing practices nor is it a cure-all for problems affecting price which are prevalent in all phases of the domestic marketing structure.

Cane and beets have to be marketed and processed shortly after harvest. Farmers must sell their crop at harvest-time with only moderate regard for price. To pay the growers, raw mills market the bulk of their raw-sugar production during and shortly after the processing season. Heavy volume of selling during this period in the past often has depressed prices more than if more orderly marketing methods were followed.

Farmers and mills therefore adopted a variety of settlement methods. Average prices for periods of 2 weeks to 12 months, depending on area and individual contractual arrangements, are used often in settlements between cane growers and processors. The common settlement practice for sugar beets is on the basis of net proceeds from sugar sales. As to raw cane sugar, many mills have attempted to hedge average settlements by corresponding arrangements to sell raw sugar. For example, sales of raw sugar often are made on various average price bases. This in effect removes such sellers from a bargaining position and reduces the volume of sugar as well as the number of sellers acting as a register of raw sugar values. There are indications that the raw-sugar market has become quite narrow, and at times small isolated transactions in raw sugar have a significant effect on the raw-sugar price level. Thus, these attempts to reduce market risks have given rise to other problems.

Cotton.[5] The marketing of an average United States cotton crop involves the distribution and utilization of some 6 or 7 billion pounds of fiber and 10 or 11 billion pounds of seed produced on about 1,100,000 farms in 17 or 18 states. It includes hundreds of processes and thousands of consumer items used by every individual and every segment of industry in this country and by many in foreign lands.

The fiber provides about 70 per cent of the textile products manufactured in the United States, and sizable proportions of those in Europe, Japan, and other foreign areas. The seed provides nearly one-third of the nation's requirements for edible vegetable oil, one-fifth of the protein feed consumed by our livestock, and large amounts of raw material for the domestic chemical industry.

No other agricultural product involves so many separate qualities, end products, and separate marketing phases or steps. Consequently, the marketing of cotton takes a larger share of the consumer's dollar and leaves to the farmer a much smaller share than for most farm products.

The first important steps in the movement of cotton fiber and seed from farmers to final consumers take place at the cotton gin. There the seed cotton goes through a series of mechanical processes, which separate the fiber from the seed. From the gins fiber and seed move mostly through separate steps and channels and into widely different markets and uses. As the fiber, or lint cotton, is six to seven times as valuable as the seed sold, even though it is equivalent to less than 60 per cent of the weight of the seed, it is given primary attention.

The various marketing transactions and services relating to American cotton fiber and fiber products are often included under five groups: Merchandising of the raw fiber; manufacturing of yarns and fabrics; manufacturing of fabricating apparel, household, and other consumer items; wholesaling; and retailing.

The transactions and services considered here as merchandising cover such services as marking or tagging, weighing, compressing,

---

[5] Original statement prepared by Maurice R. Cooper and Frank Lowenstein of the U. S. Department of Agriculture.

storing, loading and transporting, sampling for and determining quality, buying and selling, assembling, financing, and hedging. Many of them are done by or at the direction of cotton merchants or shippers, and account for the designation of merchandising, but merchandising also includes the services of many other business organizations and of a few Government agencies. The activities collectively are concerned with the movement of hundreds of different qualities of lint cotton, from our 7,300 gins to 1,600 domestic spinning and weaving mills and to many such mills abroad.

After the lint cotton reaches the spinning mills, many of which are also weaving mills, it goes through a series of complicated manufacturing processes that convert the raw fiber into yarn. The types, sizes, and qualities of yarns produced determine the number of processes involved and the quality of fiber that can be used most advantageously. For single or unplied yarns, the number of processes range from 4 to 16; most yarns require 8 to 12 processes. The processes in the order in which the fiber moves through them are: opening, cleaning, carding, or carding and combing, drawing, roving, spinning, spooling or winding, and warping or beaming.

The weaving of cotton yarns into fabrics also involves a number of processes. Ordinarily they include: slashing and drawing in the warp, combining the warper beams into a single sheet for weaving, coating the yarns with sizing, and the actual weaving. Because of differences in the type of weave, width of fabric, warp and filling ends to the inch, and the size and quality of yarns used, there are thousands of different constructions and qualities of woven cotton fabrics. Woven fabrics are usually rolled automatically by the loom into large rolls, which may be sewed into even larger rolls. The fabrics are then cleaned and inspected, after which they are either transferred directly to the finishing plant or baled for shipment.

Some 5 to 10 per cent of the cotton yarn produced in the United States goes into knit goods. Knit goods are made by the formation of connected loops produced on a series of needles. Variations in the types of machines, needles, and knitting principles used and the variations in the sizes and types of yarns result in hundreds of different kinds and qualities of knitted cotton products.

Most cotton goods come from the looms or from the knitting machines as gray goods and in most instances are subsequently dyed or otherwise finished before they are ready for the ultimate consumer. Some fabrics are made entirely or partly of dyed yarns and may or may not be used without additional finishing. The chief methods of finishing gray goods include bleaching, mercerizing, dyeing, and printing. The several hundred separate establishments engaged in dyeing and finishing textiles provide a wide variety of designs, styles, and finishes, which are performed by a diversity of processes. Many fabrics require a dozen or more separate operations.

Cotton textiles are used in a large number of products, which can be divided into three broad groups—clothing or apparel, household, and industrial. For such household items as sheets, pillowcases, and tablecloths, relatively little further processing is involved. For products generally included in the industrial-goods group, which includes fabrics or cords for such things as machinery belts, tarpaulins, bags, upholsteries, tires, and footwear, additional processing is usually done by firms outside the textile industry.

Probably the largest amount of cotton fiber goes into cutters goods, which are used mainly for wearing apparel and household items produced by the textile establishments that cut and sew purchased fabrics. Their methods of fabricating cotton textiles vary considerably. Some of the key steps include: cutting the material; sewing or joining the parts; pressing and folding; and boxing for shipping. In making dresses and other items of women's apparel, one of the important and expensive steps is designing.

Most cotton-fiber products are distributed through a big number of wholesaling and retailing agencies.

Even though many manufacturers provide their own wholesaling services, large proportions of the products move through separate wholesalers. Wholesale services include: storage; assembling and delivering the types, sizes, and quantities of items desired by retailers and others; and financing the movement of the goods.

Retailing is the final stage in the marketing of raw and processed cotton fiber. A retailer's functions include assembling of varied stocks of goods, storage, financing, selling, and (in some instances) delivery and consumer credit. Through his direct contacts with consumers, the retailer also collects and passes back to processors and other distributors information on the consumers' desires, preferences, and practices, which serves as guides for future production.

The costs of moving the raw and manufactured cotton fiber from the farm to the ultimate consumer in this country represent a large share of the consumer's dollar.

For cotton clothing and household items, which account for almost three-fourths of domestic consumption, it is estimated that on the average about $.85 to $.90 of the consumer's dollar go for marketing services, including less than $.01 for ginning. The remaining $.10 to $.15 represent the share going to farmers for the raw fiber.

A further breakdown shows that, of the five groups of services

involved, merchandising of raw fiber and wholesaling of the manufactured goods received the smallest proportions of the consumer's
dollar. The other three broad phases—manufacturing, dyeing, and
finishing of the yarns and fabrics; manufacturing or fabricating the
apparel and household goods; and retailing—each accounted for much
larger proportions and collectively represented about four-fifths of
the dollar.

THE UNITED STATES CONSUMER'S COTTON DOLLAR

WHERE IT GOES, BY PERCENTAGES

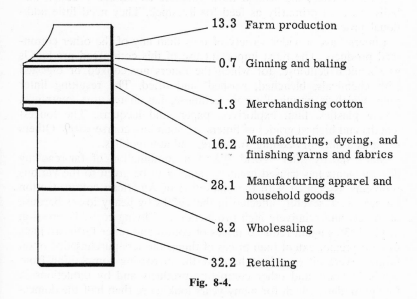

13.3 Farm production

0.7 Ginning and baling

1.3 Merchandising cotton

16.2 Manufacturing, dyeing, and
finishing yarns and fabrics

28.1 Manufacturing apparel and
household goods

8.2 Wholesaling

32.2 Retailing

Fig. 8-4.

The costs for cotton in industrial products are so completely inter-
twined with costs of other materials and services that it is difficult
to determine the farmer's share or any other division of the consumer's dollar. There is no question, however, but that the cost of the
raw cotton also represents a small proportion of cotton's part of the
final consumer's products.

Unlike cotton fiber, most of the cottonseed is sold by the farmer
to the ginner, who in turn sells it directly to cottonseed processors.
At the processing plants the seed is cleaned, delinted, and hulled,

and the resulting flaked meat is separated from the hulls. These processes give two of the four original products obtained from cottonseed—linters, the short fuzz or fibers remaining on the seed coat after ginning, and hulls, the stiff outer coating of the seed. The other two products—oil and cottonseed cake or meal—are obtained from the flaked meat through mechanical or solvent extraction processes.

Oil is by far the most valuable of the cottonseed products. After it is extracted, it is processed mainly into such edible products as shortening, cooking oils, salad oils, salad dressing, and margarine. The major processing steps are: refining, bleaching, winterizing, hydrogenation, and deodorization.

Meal or cake, the second most valuable cottonseed product, and hulls are used primarily as feed for livestock. They need little additional processing.

Linters have a wider variety of uses than any of the other cottonseed products. The most important use of this cottonseed product is as chemical cellulose, for which the linters are cooked or digested with chemicals, bleached, washed, and dried. The resulting linter pulp, which is practically pure cellulose, has many uses, mainly in rayon, plastics, film, explosives, paper, and lacquers. The longest lengths and highest grades of linters are spun into coarse yarns. Others serve as a filler in bedding, furniture, and automobiles.

Since shortly after World War I a combination of far-reaching developments has caused greater attention to be given to the various problems associated with the marketing of American cotton. Cotton farmers were severely affected in the 1920's by heavy losses because of insects and relatively high production and living costs. Depression in the 1930's again reduced prices of cotton and other farm products to a far greater extent than prices of things farmers purchased. Cotton farmers were hit especially hard by the increasing competition from synthetic fibers and other competing products and by reductions in foreign outlets, which for many years took more than half the domestic production of lint cotton.

Since the middle 1920's few promising means of improving the situation have been left untried. The losses in markets and the accumulation of surplus stocks meant that greatest effort was directed toward improving the market situation. Among the developments were: additional and more timely market information, including Government estimates of the quality of the crop and the carryover; research to improve ginning services; research to develop and encourage more efficient marketing methods, procedures, and processes and to provide new and expanded uses; market price supports, acreage allotments, and marketing quotas; and loans, grants, and other aid and assistance to foreign countries to strengthen the export markets.

Most groups directly concerned with cotton have been giving special attention to the various properties of cotton and how they can be utilized to better advantage. As a result, the precision measurements of fiber fineness and strength are now used commercially to a considerable extent in the marketing of cotton.

Despite the large amount of effort that has been made to improve and utilize more effectively the various fiber properties and to increase the efficiencies and reduce the costs of the ginning, merchandising, manufacturing, and other marketing services involved, American cotton has been barely holding its own in the battle for domestic and foreign markets. The total domestic mill consumption of cotton has tended to increase since 1930, but when reduced to a per capita basis, it has not shown an upward trend. During this period, the favorable influence of increasing economic activity and higher consumer incomes on per capita consumption of cotton has been counterbalanced by per capita gains in consumption of synthetic fiber, paper, and plastics. As a result, consumption of cotton per person in 1952 was only slightly higher than it was in the late 1920's.

Exports of our cotton have declined since 1930 because many of the same competitive forces in our own markets are found also in foreign markets, because of increased competition from other exporters and because of efforts of other countries to conserve dollars by limiting imports.

Dairy Products.[7] One-sixth of every food dollar spent by nonfarm consumers is for dairy products. A little less than half of that outlay goes to the marketing and processing agencies and the rest goes to farmers.

Milk is produced in nearly every county of the United States. About 3,200,000 farmers were milking at least one cow at the time of the 1954 census; 1.5 million of them reported sales of dairy products, and the rest used all the milk at home. Sales of whole milk were reported by 934,000 farms and sales of farm-separated cream by 540,000.

In the fifteen years ending in 1958, farm milk production in the United States ranged from 113 billion to 126 billion pounds. To obtain that huge amount, farmers milked 20 to 25 million cows twice a day, and got an average of about 5,400 pounds a year from each cow.

---

[7] Original statement prepared by Herbert C. Kriesel and Max K. Hinds of the U. S. Department of Agriculture.

The annual production is somewhat more than 700 pounds of milk for each person in the United States—*about 100 pounds per capita less than a decade earlier.*

Fresh milk is a favorable medium for bacterial growth if it is not carefully handled. The earliest governmental regulation in the milk industry was primarily concerned with protecting consumers against fraud and adulteration, but the realization of the dangers of infected milk led to the broadening of the scope of regulation to cover factors influencing health and sanitation.

A standard milk ordinance was requested from the United States Public Health Service in earlier years to overcome the wide variations among local regulations. The first ordinance was published in 1924, and an accompanying code was published in 1927. The ordinance had been adopted by 1,575 municipalities and 405 counties by March 1, 1954. It is used as the standard of milk served on interstate carriers and has been incorporated into Federal specifications. An important effect of the standard is to facilitate the shipment and acceptance of milk from one area to another.

In earlier days, when most families had a cow or two, the location of milk production varied directly with the distribution of the population. Specialization in production of milk and factory dairy products brought important regional differences in production. Since 1925 the East North Central Region has consistently marketed a larger proportion of the nation's milk than any other region. In the last ten years these states have marketed over one-third of the milk and cream delivered to plants and dealers in the United States. Next in importance are the North Atlantic States, with nearly one-fourth of the marketings. Other regions accounted for the following percentages: West North Central, 12 to 16 per cent; the Western States, 13 per cent; the South Central States, 10 per cent; and the South Atlantic States, 5 per cent.

Because milk for fluid use is perishable and bulky, consumers tend to obtain it from nearby sources. In any given area milk for fluid consumption has first call on the available supply because it brings the highest average price. The greater the distance from major markets, the greater the tendency for the milk to be used in production of a high value product per unit of weight. Accordingly, 70 per cent of the manufactured dairy products come from the North Central States.

With a larger population in comparison to the milk supply and a higher average consumption of liquid milk per person, there has been an increase in the percentage of total milk used in fluid outlets. Of the milk and cream produced by farmers in 1958, 48 per cent was used by consumers in liquid form, a gain of 8 per cent over 1935. The change lowered the proportion of milk used in making factory products from about 55 per cent in the 1920's and 1930's to about 50 per cent in later years.

Milk production usually shows substantial seasonal variation but fluid milk consumption is about the same in all months. Therefore, some city markets must bring in fluid milk from surplus producing areas (for example, Minnesota) during months of lowest production, usually late fall and early winter. Inter-regional shipments of milk, however, are comparatively small, partly because of the high freight rate in relationship to the value of the product.

Because the production of milk varies seasonally and factory uses of milk absorb the excess over fluid needs, there is pronounced seasonal variation in the total production of manufactured dairy products. But the consumption of the products is rather steady throughout the year. Most processed dairy products may be stored only from the seasonal surplus—spring and summer—to the following winter. Manufacturing and storing dairy products is a problem to operators of marketing and processing agencies. It is hard for them to gage demand and supplies so as to establish prices that will give a desirable balance between production and accumulation in storage during the into-storage season and consumption of stored products during the deficit out-of-storage season of the year.

The consumption of fluid milk and cream per person in the United States changed little until the 1940's. During World War II, because of shortages of some other foods and the relatively low retail prices of whole milk, the use of fluid milk went up substantially. The consumption of fluid cream declined after the war, but the consumption of liquid skim milk and other liquid products made from skim milk increased.

Consumption of milk fat per person declined from 32 pounds annually during the late 1930's to 28 pounds in the late 1950's. The amount consumed through different dairy products shifted far more than the figures indicate. Except for 3 per cent fed to calves, all the milk fat produced is used as human food. Consumption of milk fat in butter declined from around 14 pounds in most years before 1940 to less than 7 pounds per person in 1958. Nearly half the decline in butterfat consumed as butter was absorbed through the increased consumption of fluid milk, cheese, and ice cream. Butter now takes about 25 per cent of the milk fat produced in the United States, compared with about 42 per cent two decades earlier.

In the period that per capita consumption of butter has declined over 50 per cent, consumption of margarine more than quadrupled, but consumption of the two items combined is only slightly greater than consumption of butter alone in earlier years. Among the many reasons for the increase in the use of margarine were the removal of Federal taxes on its production and distribution and the removal of restrictions governing its sale in individual States. Other considerations in the decline in demand for butter were an apparent general lessening in demand for table spreads and a conscious effort on the part of consumers to eat less fat.

The consumption of solids-not-fat increased from 40 pounds a person in the 1930's to 50 pounds in 1946; then it declined slightly. The consumption of all dairy products which contain solids-not-fat increased over pre-World War II levels; these include: whole milk, skim milk drinks, cottage cheese, cheese, ice cream, and nonfat dry milk solids. Sales of nonfat dry milk solids in consumer packages, generally 1 pound each, increased from 2 million pounds in 1948 to 169 million pounds in 1958. This pattern of consumption is significant: Whereas solids-not-fat and milk fat are produced in a rather fixed ratio, the trend in milk fat consumption is downward, while the trend in consumption of solids-not-fat is upward.

Of the nonfat portion of milk, a large percentage is still used for nonfood purposes. Much of it is retained on farms and therefore does not enter commercial channels. A substantial increase occurred, however, in the proportion of this component of milk marketed. More than 75 per cent of the production has been used for food in recent years, compared with 50 per cent two decades earlier.

Milk used in manufacturing is produced under two different circumstances. A substantial part is produced near city markets as an excess over current fluid milk requirements. In some markets less than one-half of the milk meeting sanitary requirements for fluid purposes is channeled to that outlet; the balance is sufficient to produce more than one-third of the total of manufactured dairy products in the United States. Items made from this milk consist mainly of ice cream and bulk condensed milk; some part of it is made into butter and dried milk during one season or another. The other milk used in manufacturing is supplied by farmers who have only a manufacturing outlet or whose milk is not eligible for anything except use in manufacturing.

Of the milk fat used in making creamery butter, a little over one-third is still supplied by farm-separated cream. Cream sold by farmers declined nearly 66 per cent from the mid-1930's to 1958. The decline reflected a reduction in milk output in the farm-separated cream areas of the country and an increase in sales of whole milk by farmers in most states. Most of the solids-not-fat produced on farms selling cream does not get into commercial channels but is used for feeding hogs, poultry, and other livestock.

While the North Central States account for about 70 per cent of the total United States quantity of milk used in manufacturing, there is substantial variation among the products as far as the contribution of each region is concerned.

The North Central Region in 1957 produced 75 per cent of the country's cheese, 85 per cent of the creamery butter, 74 per cent of the dry whole milk, 78 per cent of the nonfat dry milk, and 47 per cent of the evaporated milk. The contribution of the region to the United States total of each product (except evaporated milk and cheese) was larger in 1957 than in 1929. Because of its bulky nature and strict requirements for refrigeration, production of ice cream is concentrated near the consuming areas. Regional shifts in output of ice cream therefore have followed geographical changes in population.

Dairy products are manufactured in about 10,000 plants that are scattered throughout the states. Many individual plants are operated by one parent firm. The largest concentration of ownership exists in the evaporated milk industry, and probably the least in the manufacture of butter and nonfat powdered milk.

The numbers of creameries and cheese factories declined considerably. A striking change in the structure of the dairy-processing industry was the rapid increase in number of plants making nonfat dry milk solids during World War II. Production of nonfat dry milk solids increased from 366 million pounds in 1941 to 643 million in 1945, and in 1958, approached 1.7 billion pounds.

In pricing, milk offers an unusual problem among livestock products because of its perishability, the frequency of its marketing, and its widely dispersed sources of supply. Market prices for butter and nonfat dry milk solids have made milk fat the more valuable component of milk. Milk as produced contains on the average 2.25 pounds of solids-not-fat for every pound of fat. Milk fat from 100 pounds of milk has been worth two to three times as much as the nonfat, but because of the increasing trend in use of solids-not-fat, greater emphasis has been given to that component in pricing of milk. This component of milk offers consumers a cheap source of high-quality protein and some other food nutrients. Consumers, however, buy individual dairy products for the particular want-satisfying qualities of the product, rather than for the quantities of the different milk solids contained in it.

Regardless of whether milk is sold for manufacturing or for fluid use, it must be sold by a prearranged pricing procedure, as raw milk does not lend itself to dealing on an "offer and acceptance" basis.

Firms making processed dairy products base their purchase prices for milk largely on the basis of returns for the finished products that they sell nationally.

Wholesale markets for most dairy items are scattered over the country. Even in the largest wholesale markets, trading is light in relation to the total supply. But prices established through a series of adjustments tend to approximate an equilibrium so that the total national supply normally moves into consumption. Manufactured dairy products are not so perishable as to prevent shipment between important wholesale markets. Through such shipments, the prices in the individual wholesale markets tend to be the same except for customary freight differentials.

Pricing milk used in fluid consumption is more difficult than pricing the product used in manufacturing. Several price-making bodies or procedures govern the pricing and marketing of fluid milk. They include: (1) simple negotiations between dealers and farmers or between dealers and representatives of farmers, (2) State milk-control agencies, which may set prices at various stages of distribution from farmers to consumers, and (3) Federal milk-marketing orders, which establish only minimum prices to producers.

After World War II there was a shift to the use of pricing formulas that employed more general types of economic indicators. The specific formulas were introduced after long study by economic technicians, and the Federal marketing orders using them were promulgated after public hearings. Regardless of the pricing procedure used, the returns to farmers invariably are based on prices for milk in the different classifications of use.

The Federal Government first began pricing fluid milk in 1933 and 1934, issuing licenses regulating the handling of milk in about 50 markets. Following passage of the Agricultural Adjustment Act of 1935, the role of the Federal Government in pricing milk was conducted through the establishment of milk-marketing orders. Forty-nine milk-marketing orders were in operation by 1953 and in mid-1959 there were 77. Prices and other conditions for sale of milk by producers were established thereby in the marketing areas covered. Marketing orders may be issued only after petitions of dairy farmers, public hearings, and approval by at least two-thirds of the dairy farmers affected by the order. The order may be amended by a two-thirds vote of the dairy farmers affected by it, or can be terminated if requested by 50 per cent of the producers and the producers supplying 50 per cent of the milk. Approximately one-third of the milk consumed in fluid form is channeled through markets with Federal orders and a substantially greater proportion of the nation's milk supply for fluid use is indirectly affected by the orders.

Flow of Milk and Dairy Products, 1956 (In millions of pounds)

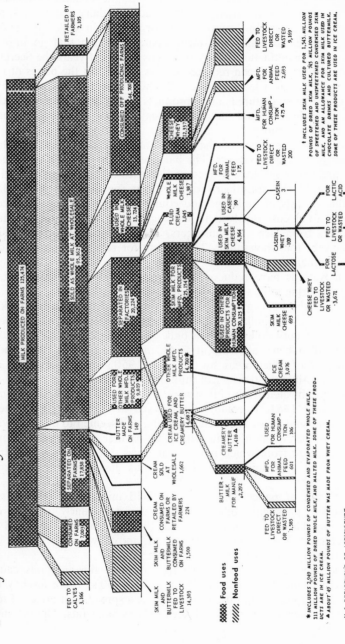

Fig. 8-5.

U.S. DEPARTMENT OF AGRICULTURE

At various times since the early 1930's, the Federal Government has intervened in the pricing of manufactured dairy products. A purchase and diversion program was organized in order to achieve higher prices for milk and farm-separated cream that go into the making of manufactured dairy products. In recent years the Secretary of Agriculture has been required by law to support the prices of milk and butterfat at a level between 75 and 90 per cent of parity. Purchases of manufactured dairy products under this program tend to stabilize prices of fluid milk as well as those of the entire manufacturing milk category.

About 45 per cent of the expenditures by consumers for dairy products goes to producers. The balance goes for marketing, processing, and other services. Wages and salaries take between 20 and 25 per cent of the consumer's dollar spent for the four major dairy products; costs of buildings and equipment take around 6 per cent. Of the total cost involved in moving the annual quantity of dairy products from farms to consumers, 11 per cent goes for processing, 4 per cent for wholesaling, 23 per cent for retailing, and 6 per cent for all other marketing costs, including transportation.

Innovations have reduced the costs of handling, transporting, or manufacturing milk and dairy items.

One is the bulk-tank method of storing and transporting milk. It involves use of a bulk-type tank on the farm where the milk is cooled and stored until collected by a bulk type of milk truck. The method was used first in California in 1938, in Connecticut in 1948, and in a number of other areas by the early 1950's. It reduces costs and makes possible the delivery of milk of higher quality.

A concentrated fresh milk was made available to several fluid-milk markets in 1951. It could be processed in surplus milk-producing areas and sold in areas of deficit supply, and seemed to offer a saving. In a number of markets in which it was first introduced, however, the raw milk from which it was made was priced the same as fresh milk used for fluid consumption, thus lessening the economic advantage.

The use of paper containers for fluid milk is the predominant method of packaging milk in many areas, particularly for store distribution. Their per-unit cost exceeds that for glass but they need not be returned. Milk keeps better in them, and they permit a wider distribution of milk from processing points.

The substitution of vegetable fats for milk fats in foods caused concern in the dairy industry in the early 1950's. There already had been a sharp decline in use of milk fat as a spread, and prices of milk fat were high in relation to prices of vegetable fats. Opportunities appeared for reducing the costs of food by substituting the lower cost product. A few states permitted the production and sale of "filled" milk, evaporated milk in which milk fat is replaced by vegetable fat. Frozen desserts resembling ice cream also use vegetable fat in place of milk fat and have become a significant factor in a number of markets. The practice of substituting vegetable fat for milk fat in such products promises to grow even more rapidly than has the substitution of margarine for butter. That is to be expected, for the decision to substitute vegetable fat for milk fat in these foods is made by a limited number of food processors rather than by millions of individual consumers.

Our imports of dairy products, measured on a fat-solids basis, have seldom exceeded 1 per cent of the domestic production. Exports normally have been smaller than imports, so that there has been a slight net import balance. During World War II and for several years after, however, the pattern was reversed, as exports under various aid programs reached 6 per cent of domestic production and took one-half or more of dry milk. Exports by 1952 had declined to the lowest level since 1940 and imports had increased so that there was a small export balance. Imports recently would have been greater had there not been import controls on individual dairy products.

REFERENCES

Agricultural Outlook Charts, U.S.D.A., for recent years—refer particularly to the section on Farm Commodities.

The Outlook Issues of such *Situation Reports* as *The Feed Situation, The Dairy Situation, The Livestock and Meat Situation, The Cotton Situation,* U.S.D.A. for recent years.

"Marketing," *The Yearbook of Agriculture,* U.S.D.A. (1954).

"The United States Sugar Program," *Agricultural Information Bulletin 111,* U.S.D.A. (July 1953).

POINTS FOR DISCUSSION

1. How do the marketing systems and problems for two commodities such as cotton and feed grains compare?
2. Milk is often said to be a complex commodity that moves through an even more complex marketing system. Can you give some reasons, or an explanation, for this complexity?

3. What are the unique aspects of the commodity sugar? How does the marketing system for sugar differ radically from that of the other commodities studied?

4. Livestock production is sometimes described as "a way of marketing feed grains." What is meant by this statement? What are the difficult problems in the production and marketing of livestock, if any?

CHAPTER 9

The Changing Structure
of Farm Markets[1]

THE FARM-MARKETING system, and the structure of markets within that system, has been changing in America since the earliest Colonial times. All the components of economic development— population growth, migration between economic sectors and geographic areas, technological development and adoption, territorial expansion, and changing human wants and the ability to satisfy those wants—acting and interacting have produced a state of continuous change in the farm marketing system. And we can expect the working of most of these same forces to give rise to further changes, probably rapid and dramatic changes, in the farm marketing system in the second half of the twentieth century. Thus, we should not conclude that the institutional and structural changes of the 1940's and 1950's, that are considered in this chapter, are unusual or unique. They have been and are important, but they are simply the most recent in a continuum of important changes.

It is also difficult to isolate the important current developments, and appraise the significance of such developments. Hence, all observers would not describe and evaluate the changing farm-marketing system in exactly the same way, or as we have done. But the big issues and the causal forces in the drama of change are laid out for all to see; perhaps the interpretation is open to debate.

Concentration at the retail level. Numerous writers, particularly Mehren, Collins, Mueller, and Davis, have pointed out that some exciting and far-reaching changes have occurred during the past ten

---

[1] This chapter is adapted from the article by Willard W. Cochrane, "Changing Structure of the American Economy: Its Implications for the Performance of Agricultural Markets," *Journal of Farm Economics* (May 1959).

years, and continue to occur, in the farm-marketing system. Many of these changes have occurred at the retail level, but certainly not all. And it may be that, after the excitement of current developments has died away, the most dramatic changes will appear to have occurred near the farm level. But it is the thesis of this chapter that the key, causal changes in the food-marketing system are occurring at the retail level. And it is the task of this chapter to describe these causal changes at the retail level, and trace their consequences through the rest of the farm marketing system.[2]

Some 10 per cent of all grocery stores did 67 per cent of the grocery business in 1957; these were the supermarkets,[3] chain and nonchain, with sales per store averaging over $1 million per year.[4] When all supermarkets and superettes are aggregated we find that 32 per cent of all grocery stores made 92 per cent of the total grocery sales in 1957. This left 68 per cent of all stores, the small stores, with 8 per cent of the market. This dramatic concentration of food sales is relatively recent. As late as 1952, supermarket outlets had only 43 per cent of the total market and small stores 22 per cent. And in 1940 the supermarkets had no more than 25 per cent of total grocery sales.

In this concentration process, chains have not gained relative to independents; chains versus independents has not been the point at issue in this structural change. The chains had 37 per cent of the total grocery sales in 1941, 34 per cent in 1956, and 38 per cent in 1957. The battle line is drawn between large and small stores. Sales in those supermarkets doing over $2 million per year, increased by more than 20 per cent in 1957 over 1956. During the same time, sales in stores doing less than $75,000 decreased by 3 per cent. And this pattern of change, with minor variations, has occurred every year since the late 1940's. Likewise, the number of small stores declined from 285,000 units in 1952 to 203,000 units in 1957—a decline of

---

[2] Much of the argument and many of the analytical points of this and the following section grow out of the work of George L. Mehren and Norman R. Collins. See particularly the article by Mehren entitled "Market Coordination and Buyers' Requirements," *Policy for Commercial Agriculture,* Joint Committee Print, 85th Congress, 1st Session; and the article by Collins and Jamison, "Mass Merchandising and the Agricultural Producer," *Journal of Marketing* (April 1958).

[3] See *Progressive Grocer* (April 1958), page F-6, for the definitions which are used throughout this book. The following definitions are given therein: *Supermarket*—any store, chain, or independent, doing $375,000 or more per year; *Superette*—any store, chain or independent, doing from $75,000 to $375,000 per year; *Independent*—an operator of 10 or less retail stores; *Chain*—an operator of 11 or more stores.

[4] *Progressive Grocer* (April 1958), pages 58-81.

approximately 29 per cent. In contrast, the lion's share of the market, 67 per cent of total sales, was shared almost equally between 14,300 independent supermarkets and 14,500 chain supermarkets in 1957.

It might be reasoned that some sort of an oligopsonistic market model, with the resulting less-than-competitive equilibrium prices and quantities for producers (that is, farmers), and excessive profits for the buyers (such as firms of supermarkets), could be used to describe the performance of markets falling between farm and retail. But such a model does not seem to fit the facts of the situation for several reasons. First, the foremost plank in the market policies of large-scale retail grocery firms is *increased volume*—increased volume is viewed as the direct avenue to profit maximization. All readily observable market practices are geared to sales expansion—not to supply control, nor to market restrictionism.

Second, although a great concentration process has been going on in the retail food trade in recent years—the market structure of the trade most certainly cannot be characterized as "competition among the few." In 1954, there were some 34,000 retail firms with two or more establishments, and this number could not have changed greatly since that year. Furthermore, the relative gains of chains (that is, firms with 11 or more units) since 1941, in terms of the proportion of total food sales, would not suggest that a few giant chains were just about to take over the food trade. It will be recalled that the proportion of total sales made by chains since 1941 has held almost constant at 37 per cent.

Third, the product flows, the marketing channels, from farmer-producer to food-retailer are so complex and so diverse that monopsony power cannot easily be brought to bear on suppliers. The bottleneck situation into which product flows converge, around which a formal market develops, and in which implicit, or explicit, collusion leads to monopsonistic buying practices, to the disadvantage of the supplier, is hard to find in the farm marketing system.

The product flow combinations and diversifications which exist in the farm-marketing system may be illustrated if we consider what happens to eggs, a relatively uncomplicated product to market. First, some proportion of all eggs produced are consumed on farms. Another small, but observable share is peddled by producers directly to consumers. Some eggs move up through dairy and other marketing cooperatives as a side line, and are sold to other marketing agencies at various levels of the marketing system. An important share of the supply of eggs moves through egg-marketing cooperatives, sometimes as a differentiated, trademarked, item for consumer selection, sometimes to be sold to various marketing agencies at different levels of the marketing system. Some eggs are sold by producers to local, private buyers—often truckers, who in turn sell them to different marketing agencies. Some producers sell directly to retailers, or chains. Other eggs go back to hatcheries and so on. The possible flow and outlet combinations appear to be limitless. In this situation, the large-scale retailer must find it virtually impossible to pursue monopsonistic pricing policies; such policies vigorously pursued over any length of time would eliminate his source of supply.

Retail procurement policies and changes in market structure. An independent food retailer with about six supermarkets, each grossing $1 million a year, *does, however, have market power*. And a retail chain with one hundred such supermarkets *has even greater market power*. This power grows out of the fact that such firms provide an important market outlet for a given product supplier. The supplier *wants* to place his product on, and hold it on, the store shelves of such important market outlets. This is a matter of survival to the supplier in the competitive struggle for product space on the limited shelves of the self-service store. Out of this market situation the retailer derives power, albeit limited power; and based on this limited power the retailer develops and pursues independent procurement policies. This, according to Mehren, is the pre-eminent development in retailing in recent years.[5]

The question before us, then, is—What does such limited market power and resulting policies convert into with respect to marketing practices? This can best be answered by inquiring into the merchandising goal, or goals, of the food retailers in question. The obvious answer is profit maximization. But this general goal is not analytically helpful; we must be more specific. The overriding goal of modern large-scale food retailers is *increased volume*. The retailer seeks to expand sales as a means of increasing profits, and he seeks to do this in the cultural setting of great consumer mobility, one-stop shopping, self-service, and convenient visual inspection of food products. The means open to the retailer to expand sales in a highly competitive situation, where the possibility of price reductions are limited, are essentially two: (1) to present a product which by its taste, texture, coloring, packaging, or by a combination of these qualities, impels the consumer to pick it up and place it in her basket, and (2) to present that eye-catching product regularly. A product, though desirable in quality and appearance, is next to worthless from a merchandising point of view if it is not offered to the consumer in a timely context (that is, regularly).

It follows, then, from the nature and objectives of the merchan-

[5] *Op. cit.,* page 291.

dising operation that procurement policy must be aimed at acquiring a certain and regular supply of a product with desired quality attributes. The market power of large-scale food retailers is used to gain control over two variables—(1) time and conditions of delivery and (2) quality and appearance attributes of the product. Food retailers insofar as they are able (that is, insofar as their power in the market permits) seek to, and do, specify the content of these two product variables to suppliers.

The brunt of these procurement policies by retailers, of course, falls on the wholesalers with whom the retailers deal most directly. The wholesaling function has in no wise been eliminated, or reduced, in recent years, but it has been more closely integrated with the retailing function—usually upon the initiative of retailers. Food retailers have acquired wholesaling facilities, joined cooperative wholesaling groups, and entered into contracts with private wholesaling firms in the furtherance of required procurement policy, namely, control over the product variables—time and conditions of delivery and quality and appearance attributes. And this, of course, is what we mean by "vertical integration": the coordination of the decision process in two or more stages of production through management action, rather than through the market.

In other words, the wholesaling function in the food trade has become rather completely integrated into the retailing function. In the language of the trade, wholesaling has made a "good adjustment" to changing market conditions. What this euphemism means, of course, is that wholesaling as an independent, profit-seeking venture is disappearing, as the function is increasingly made a part of the retail organization.

It may be argued that too much emphasis is placed on modern procurement policy above, as an explanation of the demise of the independent food wholesaler. A. C. Hoffman,[6] for example, argues that the integration of the wholesaling function into the large-scale retailing operation is to be explained largely in terms of the resulting gains in efficiency in handling the product. Perhaps the Hoffman interpretation is the correct one; certainly he has been close to the development and is a keen observer of marketing phenomena. But it is possible that what the businessman, even the economist-turned-businessman, calls gains in efficiency "by reason of a closer tie-in between successive marketing stages," under vertical integration (for

---

[6] See his paper entitled *The Changing Scene in Marketing and What Producers and Marketing Agencies Must Do to Meet It,* presented before the 1957 National Marketing Workshop, Memphis, Tennessee (November 1957), pages 4 and 5.

example, the elimination of the undependable routeman; the establishment of warehouse facilities conveniently adjacent to retail store outlets) also subsume under what we could call an effective prosecution of modern procurement policy. In other words, unit costs of achieving a certain and regular supply of a product with specified quality attributes are reduced through vertical integration where, for example, the haphazard order-taker is eliminated, or warehouse facilities are more conveniently located; this may be called a gain in efficiency, or the effective pursuit of procurement policy, depending upon your preference.

The great integration battle in the food trade is currently being waged between the large-scale retailers and the national processors and packers. The question at issue is: Who is going to integrate whom? There is no question in either camp as to the desirability, or survival value, of product differentiation, quality control, and product eye appeal. The national packers and processors recognize that survival in an independent status rests on their ability to hold their national brands before the consumer. The large-scale retailers, on the other hand, recognize that control of their merchandising policy rests on the establishment of their own private brands and the specification of the quality attributes of their products, which means in turn the reduction of processors to the passive status of present-day wholesalers. Thus, the issue is joined and the outcome is in doubt. And, although it seems to the authors that a strategic advantage lies with the retailers in this power struggle, namely, control over the product outlet to consumers, it is not necessary to the argument of this chapter to pick, or even to know, who the final victor will be. Further, it is possible, perhaps even probable, that the combatants will accept a policy of "live and let live" in order to restrict the range of the battle and limit potential losses. In any event, the remaining large-scale independent marketing agents will push integration, and for identical reasons—the twin imperatives of procurement policy: control over time and conditions of delivery, and control over the quality and appearance attributes of the product.

The question may now be asked: Why is the vertical integration of wholesaling and processing activities into the retailing organization essential to the control over the two product variables in question? Why cannot market price effect the necessary integration with respect to these variables? Collins and Jamison provide the answer in general terms:

. . . The complexity of the demand function plus the uncertainty surrounding interfirm relationships in general make it difficult, if not impossible, for the producer to translate a price quotation (particularly if this is only an estimate of a future price at time of harvest) first into the set of product characteristics that is implied and then in turn into a set of production operations to achieve this result.[7]

More specifically, first because of the uncertainty that attaches to future farm product prices, second because market prices fail to adequately evaluate and report desired and undesired quality attributes of a commodity, and third because quality and appearance attributes are assessed and valued differently among different retail firms, market prices do not, and cannot, effect the integration between production stages required by modern retail merchandising policy. In other words, the process of acquiring through open markets a product with desired quality and appearance attributes and the required time specifications turns out to be an inefficient, costly business, as far as many agricultural commodities are concerned. Thus, to gain as complete control as possible over the two variables in question, large-scale retailers have acted, and continue to act, vigorously to integrate the wholesaling and processing functions into the retail organization.

Markets, providing a nexus between wholesaler and processor on one hand and retailers on the other, have never been noted for their formal structure or institutionalized procedures. But markets of an informal sort have existed in this marketing area. Wholesalers and processors historically have published price lists, and on the basis of such lists orders have been sought and taken. But even such informal markets are withering away under the impact of vertical integration. Purchase of facilities, merger, cooperative affiliation and contracts are replacing the order-taker. The operator of a few or a chain of supermarkets feels that he cannot afford to wait and order what the order-taker may have in stock when he comes around. Aggressive merchandising requires that the operator take the initiative to acquire and maintain in stock products that the consumer cannot resist plucking off the shelves and stuffing in her basket. In this milieu the "open" market is passing out of existence.

Changes in market structure at the farm level. Let us now inquire into the extent to which retailer-initiated integration is bypassing local farmers' markets, to encompass farmers as well as middlemen. But first, we must recognize that vertical integration has long existed between the processor and the farmer in certain vegetable-canning crops, and it has come into prominence between the processor and the chicken farmer in broilers in recent years. In these, and other instances that could be cited, the initiating force has come from the

---

[7] *Op. cit.*, page 364.

processor, or first-handler, and for the very same reasons as those outlined for retailers. Processors have long felt the need for quality control during the complex production and processing operations and the pressure to acquire a certain and regular source of supply of these products. Control over these variables by processors was a prerequisite to the establishment of national brands, and the widespread distribution of a product of a given quality. Thus, whether the large-scale retailers or the large-scale packers and processors win the integration battle, it seems clear that the production activities of farmer-producers will be increasingly integrated into the processing stage of marketing.

But to return to the question under consideration: Is the integration of marketing activities, initiated by retailers, bypassing local markets and reaching farmer-producers? Although the vertical integration process comes unhinged to a great degree at the processing stage, at the present time—with many integration strands running from retailer to processor and fewer, different, strands running from processor to farmer—large-scale retailers are beginning to integrate their procurement activities all the way back to the farmer, involving, most often fresh fruits and vegetables, but also eggs, poultry, and red meats. It is occurring wherever retailers have acquired their own handling or processing facilities, or where they clearly dominate small private processors. And it is facilitated at the farm level by large-scale producers, areas of product concentration, and an effective farmers' marketing cooperative.

The extent to which more farmer-producers are tied to processors and first-handlers through integration, and the extent to which the operations of those farmer-producers are more closely integrated into the operations of processors and first-handlers depends upon at least two sets of factors: (1) those on the producer side, and (2) those on the processor-handler side.

The willingness of farmers to work under a contract rather than for an open market will depend upon their need for capital, which in turn will depend upon the general prosperity of agriculture. (It is assumed here that the contracting firm is able to supply the capital, since, if it could not, it would not be in business.) Also, it will depend upon the effectiveness of the contractual arrangement to reduce, or minimize, price and income risks to farmers. These factors will set the stage and determine the reception that forgers of the final link of integration will receive from farmers.

The initiating forces, as usual, will come from the supply procurement side and in large measure for the same old reasons. The imperatives of (1) a certain and regular source of supply and (2) control over quality and appearance attributes will force the issue. And the greater the need to control these variables at the farm level, the greater will be the push to integrate the production activities of farmers with those of the processor or first-handler.

But other considerations may enter from the processor-handler side. If there are great opportunities to reduce product costs, or to produce an eye-appealing product, through fundamental and complex changes in technological or institutional practices, processor-handlers may be expected to initiate such changes through integration. This, of course, is what has happened in processing broilers and, to a lesser extent, turkeys and may be in the offing for hogs. Where a technological revolution in production gives promise of greatly reducing costs, or yielding a superior quality product, and farmers generally lack the capacity to organize and prosecute that revolution, then processors and first-handlers may be expected to initiate the changes through integration.

No one can read the future with certainty, and certainly not the authors. But it seems reasonable to expect that in the not too distant future the operations of much of the farm marketing system will be integrated through contractual and ownership arrangements. The integration process will be broken in places and will be informal in places for some products; but in fruits and vegetables and the many animal products it will be commonplace. In many cases the initiating action will come from large-scale retailers, and production activities will be integrated from retailer to farmer; in other cases the initiating action will come from processors and farm supply companies (for example, feed dealers), and integration will run through the processor from farmer to retailer; and in some cases farmers' cooperative marketing associations may integrate forward to the retailer. In this context, institutionalized auction markets and less formal local markets, too, will wither away. In this context, farmers typically will not produce a product of any quality for any time of delivery to an open market. Instead, most farmers will produce a product to quality specifications for specific times of delivery.

The role of farmers' cooperatives. Cooperative associations have played many roles on the agricultural scene: forcing competition, providing previously non-existent marketing services, purchasing supplies, and bargaining. Some of these ventures have been highly successful—in those cases where the need was great, adequate financing was achieved, competent management was secured, and farmer-members understood the real problems confronting the association. Where these ingredients in some proportions have been lacking the ventures have been less successful. But it is possible that farmers' cooperatives have yet to play their greatest role—as the business organizations representing independent farmers in the negotiation of —in the bargaining over—contracts with marketing organizations integrated from retailer down in many cases, and from processor down in still others. We hasten to add, however, that we attach no probabilities to this outcome (that is, the widespread seizure of this bargaining role by farmers' cooperatives). Institutional developments along this line will depend upon the extent to which farmers generally and clearly appreciate the nature of the marketing problem confronting them, and, more importantly, upon the extent and generosity of Federal credit policies to farmers' cooperatives in the future.

Whatever the ultimate success of this institutional development, the cooperative prototype, at first, is likely to be similar to the bargaining association which has been developed to confront sugar-beet processors and vegetable processors. But it is not likely to remain such a simple organization for very long. In some cases it may develop its own processing facilities as in the case of fluid milk, and in some others it is likely to develop distributive facilities as in the case of the Sunkist Growers, Inc. Negotiation or bargaining will remain the central function of cooperatives, but to negotiate effectively they may have to establish product-handling, storing, and processing facilities.

On what kinds of issues will the cooperative be able to represent independent farmer-members effectively in negotiations with vertically integrated marketing organizations? There are many issues, but they group nicely under two headings, our same two variables: (1) time and condition of delivery, and (2) quality and appearance attributes. With respect to the first variable, the following items must go into every contract in some form: the time schedule of delivery, method and schedule of payment, point of delivery, who supplies the harvesting and cartage equipment, and so on. With respect to the second variable, the following points must be settled: variety of seed or breeding stock, feeding rates and rations, disease and pest control, who controls the harvesting schedule, and premiums and discounts for variations in quality and appearance.

Negotiation over these variables may seem unglamorous to economists and disappointing to farmers, but there are many points to be negotiated with respect to each, and the *net* effect of these many decisions can be important to the farmer's pocketbook and to his self-respect. And in theory at least, an intelligently managed and loyally supported farmers' cooperative should be able to negotiate effectively on these issues, because no single issue is likely to be as important to the purchasing firm as the continued receipt of supplies from the cooperative in the desired time and quality dimensions. The large-scale retail organization with heavy demands for a product of given quality and delivery specification has an important stake in any particular source of supply that can, in fact, deliver the specified product. The cooperative gains limited power in the market —power to negotiate effectively with purchasing firms over issues of time and conditions of delivery and quality and appearance—as it becomes an important supplier to a purchasing firm of a product with given time and quality specifications. Thus, size achieved through collective action at the farm level brings with it some limited power to bargain.

There is another set of issues, however, on which local, state or even national marketing cooperatives are not likely to be strong bargainers. Those issues relate to prices received by farmers. It is reasonable to assume that every produce-buyer comes to the contract negotiation table with an upper price limit in mind—a reservation price based on all known supply and demand conditions. And it is reasonable to assume that a skillful and experienced cooperative negotiator could approximate the buyer's reservation price. But, the moment the cooperative pushes its selling price above the buyer's reservation price, the cooperative will have pushed itself out of that market. This follows from the fact that the purchasing firm can obtain its supplies from another cooperative, a large private producer, or by entering into agricultural production itself. Locating a new, desirable source of supplies would certainly prove annoying, and in all probability would involve some extra costs, but it could be done; that is the important point in this context. A higher-than-going price, or readily acceptable price, can only be made to stick where the purchaser does *not* have alternative sources of supply. And unless some general scheme of supply control is embraced by farmers with the aid of government, the typical integrated buyer will have many sources of supply for many years to come. Thus, the bargaining power of farmers' cooperatives, unless buttressed by state action as in the case of fluid milk, has been and will continue to be weak with respect to price. In the typical case, a farmers' cooperative cannot control supply; it is as simple as that.

Mueller has stated the proposition even more strongly:

. . . Once and for all let us recognize that vertical integration per se does not give a cooperative or any other firm market power. Market power is built of different stuff. It depends upon a high degree of horizontal concentration or product differentiation. . . .[8]

---

[8] "Vertical Integration Possibilities for Agricultural Cooperatives," *The Frontiers of Marketing Thought and Science,* Proceedings of the December 1957 Conference of the American Marketing Association, Philadelphia.

Referring to such vertically integrated associations as Sunkist Growers, Inc., Sun Maid Raisin Growers and Diamond Walnut Growers, each of which has marketed as much as 70 per cent of its industry's supplies, Mueller goes on to say:

> . . . None has the essential prerequisite of market power, the ability to limit supply. . . . Market power depends upon control over the supply of the product passing through the system, not just on ownership of the marketing facilities through which it passes. . . .

We have, prior to this section, been describing a situation in which vertical integration is pushing its way back to the farmer, deriving the strength to do this from the operational goals and the capacity of large-scale retailers to control the two merchandising variables. In this changing structure the open, auction type of market is becoming a casualty. Production activities are, more and more, being integrated through contractual and ownership arrangements, rather than through open markets. But in the last stage of integration, at the farmers' level, we witness the emergence of a new power, *a countervailing power,* in the form of farmers' cooperative action. This power is limited, as is the power at the retail level, which, it is the thesis of this chapter, started the whole integration business.[9] Market power is not absolute at either end of the line, nor can the agents involved control price at either end of the line. But farmers, acting through their cooperative associations—associations that we see existing already in fruits and vegetables and being talked about and initiated in hogs and other animal products—can use their limited market power to moderate and blunt, hence influence, actions taken by purchasing firms with respect to the variables of time and conditions of delivery and of quality and appearance attributes of the product.

A new type of market is, thus, beginning to take shape at the farm level, a bargaining market, in which farmers are using in some instances, and are learning to use in other instances, the limited power of cooperative action to countervail against the typically greater, but still limited power of large-scale, vertically integrated purchasing organizations. It will remain a market so long as farmers remain independent agents. And they will remain independent agents in the tide of vertical integration so long as they manage and run their cooperative bargaining associations wisely.

Some larger questions related to changing market structure. In bringing this discussion to a close, let us touch briefly on two larger

---

[9] The fact that vertical integration appears on the historical scene earlier at the processor level does not spoil the argument. It occurred at the processing level for the same reasons that it is occurring at the retail level. But integration stemming from retailer action is the general, classical case.

questions raised by the broadening and deepening of vertical integration. First, will the rational allocation of resources be impaired by the eroding away of open markets and the overt prices generated in such markets? And second, will the farm surplus problem pass away, as a general problem, under the institutional complex envisaged above?

Some kind of a pricing system, market or accounting, that accurately describes the rates at which commodities are being traded one for another, and therefore describes the true alternatives open to the maximizing decision-maker, is basic to the operation of a rational economic system. And in our economy market prices generated in open markets have typically provided this basic information. But, where products and services move through an integrated system under contractual and ownership arrangements, open markets disappear, and market prices are not generated. Or they are formed on such a thin portion of the supply that the prices so generated are not representative, that is, they do not describe the true situation. (This has been the case in open butter and egg markets for several years.) Hence, it is sometimes concluded that a rational allocation of productive resources is not possible in integrated sectors of the economy.

But this is not necessarily the case; accounting prices can serve as a basis of resource allocation. If, in the integrated farm-marketing system, farmers cooperatives would regularly report their contract prices, this would provide a part of the information required for the rational use of resources. If, further, the government collected and regularly reported supply information, including production, quantities contracted, and inventory data, all the price-quantity information prerequisite to rational resource allocation would be available. In the world of vertically integrated production activities, accounting prices *actually used* must take the place of market prices *actually generated*.

It has been argued on occasion that the general and chronic surplus problem of American agriculture would cease to exist in a vertically integrated farm-marketing system. Perhaps so, but probably not. If our picture of the ultimate farm-marketing system were one of three or four giant chains doing all the retail grocery business, with clean, integrated strands of productive activity stemming back from each retailer through the wholesaling and processing operation to the farmer in each food line—then, perhaps the surplus problem would be solved. Each of three or four large retail chains in this world could accurately gauge the total market for a food product and its (the firm's) share of the total market, and transmit this knowledge back through the system in the form of contracts to farmer-producers to yield the quantities necessary to fill out their shares of the market.

In other words, where a few retailers share the total food market, they can know and stabilize their own shares and contract for just those quantities required to satisfy their shares. In this neat world there can be no surplus problem; other problems yes, but no surplus problem.

But is the farm-marketing system likely to become so structured in the decade of the 1960's or even the 1970's? It seems doubtful. The farm-marketing system seems destined to become integrated to an important degree through contractual and ownership arrangements within a decade or so. But it can remain a somewhat complex, disorderly affair under the dominance of such institutional arrangements. Certainly there are going to be several thousand retail firms for a long time to come. Some of these retail firms are going to integrate back to the farm level, others are not. Some independent processors and packers with well integrated operations seem destined to stay in the picture. And some farmers' cooperatives are going to push toward the retailer with integrated operations.

In this institutional complex, market shares cannot be known, hence total contracted quantities cannot equal total retail sales in any given period except by chance, or through inventory accumulation or de-accumulation. (It is assumed that supply control, and sales quotas under governmental sponsorship do not exist.) In the context of market uncertainty with regard to shares of the market at all stages, farmers may be expected to produce on their own account, cooperatives will accept supplies not contracted for, and purchase contracts will remain flexible with respect to total quantities, in the event that sales in a particular commodity, or through a given firm, turn out to be greater than prior operational estimates.

In a context of market uncertainty all agents in the marketing system will remain "flexible" in regard to quantities, and farmers will continue to produce in the hope of finding a market outlet. In this context, burdensome surpluses are a distinct probability, where the government seeks to support farm income. And if it does not, returns to farmers can be expected to be disastrously low for a long time to come, since one of the important by-products of vertical integration will certainly be a speed-up of an already revolutionary rate of farm technological advance.

REFERENCES

"Marketing," *The Yearbook of Agriculture*, U.S.D.A. (1954), pages 60-75, 224-237, 238-253.

"Contract Farming and Vertical Integration in Agriculture," *Agricultural Information Bulletin 198*, U.S.D.A. (July 1958).

Mehren, George C., "Market Coordination and Buyers' Requirements," *Policy for Commercial Agriculture: Its Relation to Economic Growth and Stability*, Joint Committee Print, Joint Economic Committee, 85th Congress, 1st Session (November 22, 1957).

Progressive Grocer, monthly and annual summary issue.

Collins, Norman R., and John A. Jamison, "Mass Merchandising and the Agricultural Producer," *The Journal of Marketing* (April 1958).

POINTS FOR DISCUSSION

1. What dramatic changes have taken place in food-retailing in the 1950's? How have these changes affected procurement policies of retailing firms? What influence have these new procurement policies had on the structure of markets?

2. Why are large-scale retailing firms so anxious to control the merchandising variables: (a) time and conditions of delivery, and (b) quality and appearance attributes of the product?

3. What specifically is happening to wholesalers, and wholesale markets?

4. What is the major point at issue in the economic battle between the large-scale processors and the large-scale retailers? How is the battle turning out currently (that is, at the time you are studying the problem)?

5. What new role is being thrust upon farmers' cooperatives by market integration? How well are such cooperatives meeting the challenge?

6. Can comprehensive integration in food production and marketing solve the "surplus" problem in agriculture?

CHAPTER 10

Marketing Services
and Costs

IT IS often noted, sometimes with a note of despair, but more commonly with implied criticism, that charges for marketing take a large share of the consumers' food dollar—about 60 per cent in the late 1950's. It is, further, noted that the marketing and processing charges on a basket of given food items have increased since World War II, while the farm value of those food items has declined. These developments are disquieting to many people—particularly farmers and farm leaders. In this chapter we will examine these trends and analyze the factors responsible for them.

Employment in production and distribution. The expanding role of distribution (marketing and processing) in the operating economy is reflected in the increased employment of workers in the distributive trades. In 1870, more than three-fourths of the laboring force of 13 million workers was engaged in the production of physical goods, and less than one-fourth was engaged in distribution and service activities. Agriculture alone, at that time, absorbed 7 million workers, or more than one-half of the total laboring force.

By 1929 the employment picture had changed dramatically and by 1956 it had turned upside down. Employment in agriculture had declined to 29 per cent by 1929 and to 13 per cent by 1956. Total employment in the production of physical goods (agriculture, mining, manufacturing and construction) stood at 59 per cent in 1929 and 49 per cent in 1956. The distributive trades and services (trade, transportation, finance, services and government) on the other hand employed 41 per cent of the total laboring force in 1929 and 51 per cent in 1956. Employment in trade alone increased from 15 per cent in 1929 to 19 per cent in 1956.

These changing proportions in the employment of the total laboring force establish a well-defined trend. A smaller and smaller proportion of the nation's laboring force is needed to produce raw materials and manufactured products and an increasing proportion is needed in transporting and distributing these goods and in providing personal services.

The expanding role of marketing is shown more clearly in Table 10-1. Workers engaged in retailing and wholesaling activities increased almost threefold from 1910 to 1957, which is a much greater increase than that occurring in manufacturing. Although the subtotal in Table 10-1, average number of workers in wholesale and retail, does not include all workers engaged in marketing, it does include the bulk of the workers so employed. Thus, there is ample basis for the conclusion that employment in marketing activities increased rapidly between 1910 and 1957.

TABLE 10-1

Distribution of the Labor Force, 1910-1957

	1910	1920	1930	1940	1950	1957
Total number of gainful workers*	(*Thousands*)					
	37,370	42,434	48,830	57,742	59,015	64,000†
Average number of workers in						
Manufacturing	8,750‡	10,534	9,401	10,780	14,967	16,800
Agriculture	13,590§	12,730§	12,497	10,979	9,342	7,649
Wholesale and retail	3,900¶	4,623	6,064	6,940	9,645	11,543
	(*Per Cent*)					
Per cent of workers in						
Manufacturing	100	120	107	123	171	192
(Per cent of 1910)						
Agriculture	100	94	92	81	69	56
(Per cent of 1910)						
Wholesale and retail	100	119	155	178	247	296
(Per cent of 1910)						

* 1910-1930, persons ten years old and over; 1940-1957, persons fourteen years and over.
† Extrapolated on the basis of relationship of gainfully employed series to civilian labor force series.
‡ Extrapolated on basis of those gainfully employed in manufacturing.
§ Extrapolated on basis of those gainfully employed in agriculture.
¶ Extrapolated on basis of those gainfully employed in marketing.
Source: Statistical Abstract of the U.S. (1958), Tables 252, 254, and 261.

The changing role of the home. Distribution is more important today than it was in 1870, because so many activities, once carried on in the home, are now undertaken in factories. Spinning and weaving have long since left the home. The ready-made clothing industry has, in large measure, taken the place of home-sewing. The canning and preserving of fruits and vegetables and the baking of bread and pastries have been transferred from the home to the factory. The role of the home has changed; factories have displaced homes as producing units. And with this changing role, the number and extent of activities between the farm producer and urban consumer have increased.

Instead of selling the housewife staples, such as flour and sugar, to be processed into bread and pastries in the home, the retail grocer today must carry in stock a wide variety of *finished* products (5,000 to 6,000 items in a modern supermarket) from which the housewife makes her selections. Most of these finished products, too, are purchased in small quantities by the homemaker. And the cost of marketing a variety of finished products in small quantities is greater than merchandising yard goods or 100-pound sacks of flour.

The crowding of families into small city apartments with little or no storage space has made the dividing and packaging of foodstuffs an important phase of marketing. The emphasis on the hygienic preparation of food has further contributed to the packaging service, hence, to the higher cost. The grocer no longer sticks his hand into the pickle jar and fishes out a dill or two. On the contrary, dill pickles come in pairs, safely encased in a cellophane wrapper. Today, then, we find the kitchen cupboard scantily stocked, with neat cartons of rice, sugar, coffee, and macaroni, encased in air-proof wrappings. Beside these cartons, we find the canned goods packed in conveniently small tins. Add to this a refrigerator stocked with a variety of fruits and vegetables, both fresh and frozen, and numerous small cuts of meat and the picture is complete. But to concentrate this variety of foodstuffs in the home in convenient and attractive packages, merchants and distributors have had to assume new risks, accept new tasks, and incur additional costs.

The revolution in the kitchen. As family incomes in the 1950's have risen, as families have pushed into and beyond the $5,000-$6,000 income range, they have changed their food habits. They spend their food dollars differently. They eat more expensive foods, of course; but what is significant to agriculture and to the marketing system is that they also begin demanding and buying a lot of processing, packaging and special services in their food. Instead of buying a whole chicken to be cut up and apportioned at home, they buy a package of frozen chicken breasts, or better still go out for a chicken dinner. And instead of buying a bushel of apples to be stored in the basement, they buy six beautifully colored apples in an attractive carton. The modern American family wants not only good food, *but convenience built into that food as well.*

The relentless pursuit of convenience items has been the most dramatic change in the food market since 1946. Most of the food purchased today is prepackaged. And an important share has been precooked and apportioned as well.

The American housewife substitutes these conveniences built into food items for nonexistent kitchen help and loathsome hours spent in the kitchen. Thus, the purchase of services or conveniences built into food products is now enabling the housewife to follow the cook and the maid in their flight from the kitchen.

Selling the consumer. The creation of demand, selling the consumer, becomes increasingly more important as finished goods are produced by mass production. Unit costs of production are reduced through mass production only when large volumes are, in fact, produced and sold. Hence, the incentive to produce in large quantities and to realize low unit costs continually drives the businessman to expand his sales, to enlarge the market for his product, to convince more and more consumers that only his product is good. In broad terms, the consumer has permitted himself to be convinced, with the result that the material level of living has improved, as the fruits of mass production have been realized.

To understand the problems of marketing in a modern, interdependent economy, we must consider, not only the *volume* to be marketed, but the *nature* of new things to be marketed. The things which people want today are not necessarily things that the consuming public demanded on its own initiative. The automobile, the radio, elaborately packaged foods, and the current style in women's clothing are not goods that consumers first wanted and that later were produced to their specification. On the contrary, those goods were first conceived and pioneered by producers and then the demand for them was created by aggressive sales methods. This does not mean that producers can present anything they wish and induce the public to demand those commodities by an aggressive sales campaign. When new products are suited to their times, such as quick-frozen and packaged foods for families in small apartments, they have proved successful. Demand can be created and must be created for new products by selling activities, but success, in the sense of creating and expanding the market for a new product, is not achieved in every case, in fact, in only a relatively few cases.

Someone has to guess what to produce. In the usual case, consumers do not know and are not concerned with what their new wants may be and cannot tell manufacturers and distributors what they are. It is the task of innovators in manufacturing and marketing to seek out new wants and create products and services that satisfy the wants. It is in this sense that demand is created. And for the individual business firm, the problem is not one of filling the demand for cereals, clothes, or soap; it is a problem of creating demand for a specific kind of cereal, a specific brand of clothes, and a specific kind of soap. This type of demand creation is necessarily costly, but it goes hand in hand with the development of mass production techniques. Thus, sales promotion becomes an important and indispensable part of marketing when low unit costs of production are dependent on wide markets.

Competition and service. Competition in production has most often had the effect of decreasing costs. But competition in distribution more often leads to increased costs. Success very often comes to the manufacturer and distributor who spend the most on advertising, packaging, delivery, and other expensive personal services. And efforts to cut costs are restricted by the inherent difficulties of mechanizing and standardizing marketing methods. Thus, competition in the marketing process does not tend to take the form of price competition. Competition in the marketing and distribution process, instead, often takes the form of the provision of additional services. Merchants seek to attract customers by offering additional services.

The consumer is the victim, as well as the beneficiary, of modern merchandising. He appreciates improved service and is attracted to those retail outlets that provide the greater service, but greater service entails greater costs. Thus, the consumer, as indicated above, is responsible, in part, for the higher distribution costs that have resulted from the competition for his favor. It is true, however, that merchants and distributors have led the consumer on, led him to expect more and more services through advertising and promotional efforts. The consumer does not usually seek additional services, he simply succumbs to the temptation of greater convenience and service continuously thrust before him by the competition for his favor.

Food processing.[1] The production of manufactured food products in the United States was about 13 per cent greater in 1956 than was the average during 1947-49, according to the Federal Reserve Board index of production. The average annual rate of increase between 1947 and 1956 was 1.3 per cent, slightly less than the rate of growth in the population. The output of all manufactured products increased by 44 per cent between 1947-49 and 1956. Thus, although food processing increased in the 1950's, industries manufacturing food

---

[1] Adapted from Forrest E. Scott, "The Food Marketing Industries—Recent Changes and Prospects," *Marketing and Transportation Situation* (U.S.D.A., Agricultural Marketing Service, November 1957).

products have a less prominent place in the economy in 1957 than they did in 1947. To illustrate, 2.5 per cent of the national income originated in the food manufacturing industries in 1956, compared with 2.9 in 1947 and 3.1 in 1939.

The increase of 13 per cent in the output of manufactured foods is a composite of widely varying rates of change for individual products. Indexes in 1956 for the major product groups varied from 98 for bakery products (1947-49 = 100) to 133 for the meat products and canned and frozen foods. Variation between indexes for individual products was considerably wider—from 84 for wheat flour to 151 for beef.

Other products for which changes in production diverged widely from the average for food products are flour mixes and ready-to-serve cereal breakfast foods, which experienced increases in shipments of 32 per cent and 30 per cent, respectively, between 1947 and 1954; but shipments of other cereal breakfast foods decreased 12 per cent.

Many of the products that are rapidly becoming popular are comparatively new. In spite of this, they are still relatively unimportant in the total output of the food-manufacturing industries. Furthermore, their growth has been partly offset by a reduction in the output of other products. The increase in the output of flour mixes, for example,

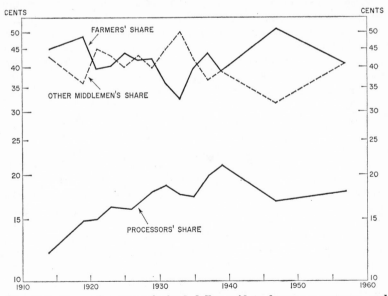

Fig. 10-1. **Share of consumer's food dollar paid to farmers, processors, and distributors, 1914-1954.**

was considerably smaller than the decrease in the production of white flour.

The consumer's food dollar can conveniently be broken down into three parts: (1) that going to farmers, (2) that going to processors, and (3) that going to other middlemen, in payment for the services rendered in providing consumers with food. The increase in services rendered by processors over the long period 1914-1939, is reflected in the increased share of the consumer's dollar going to processors. It is estimated that the processor's share increased from $.12 in 1914, to approximately $.21 in 1939 (see Figure 10-1). The principal change indicated in Figure 10-1 is the long-run increase in the processor's share prior to 1939. Following 1939, the processor's share, as well as that going to other middlemen, dips sharply; this results from the great increase in prices received by farmers, and returns to farmers, in the World War II period. Between 1947 and 1957 the processor's share held relatively constant, as the shares going to farmers and other middlemen reverted to their pre-World War II positions. The behavior of the processor's share following 1947 is consistent with the previous findings, namely, that the annual rate of increase in the production of manufactured food products has been about equal to the rate of population growth.

Price spreads between farmers and consumers. In order to measure changes in the spread between retail prices of food, on one hand, and payments to farmers, on the other, the Agricultural Marketing Service combines all farm products into what is known as the family "market basket." This market basket measures the average quantity of domestic farm foods bought per family by urban wage-earner and clerical-worker families in 1952. These families had an average of 3.3 members in that year. With the quantities in this basket fixed, the cost of the basket changes as prices or costs change. Changes in food prices at retail, at farm market levels, in food-marketing charges (that is, the farm retail spread), and in the farmer's share of the consumer's food dollar *of this market basket* over the period 1913-58 are presented in Table 10-2. A review of the data presented here brings to the fore several interesting relationships. First, the farmer's share of the consumer's dollar changes in a direct relation with fluctuations in business activity. We see that the farmer's share of the consumer's dollar rose during World War I to $.51, dropped during the 1920's and stabilized in the neighborhood of $.40, tumbled again with the onset of the Great Depression, reaching a low of $.32 in 1932, and then rose gradually during the 1930's, and hit a new peak of $.53 in the war year 1945. Thereafter the farmer's share has declined, leveling off at around $.40 in the late 1950's. It would seem that the farmer's share of the consumer's dollar did not trend upward nor downward over the period 1913-58, but simply rose and fell with business fluctuations and war and peace.

If, however, we examine the data presented in index number form under the columns headed Farm-Retail Spread and Farm Value in Table 10-2, we obtain a somewhat different impression. Marketing charges rose rapidly during the period of World War I, paralleling the rise in the retail cost of the market basket. But during the 1920's and 1930's, marketing charges did not fall as much as the farm value of the market basket. For example, in 1932, the farm value of the market basket was less than the farm value of that same basket in 1913, whereas the marketing charges in 1932 remained significantly above those of 1913. It would seem that marketing charges are stickier than farm prices. Once marketing charges increase, they do not come down easily.

TABLE 10-2

The Market Basket of Farm Food Products: Indexes of Retail Cost, Farm Value, Farm-Retail Spread, and Farmer's Share of Retail Cost, 1913-58*

Year	Retail Cost	Farm Value	Farm-Retail[†] Spread	Farmer's Share
		(1947-49 = 100)		(per cent)
1913	40	37	43	46
1914	41	37	45	45
1915	40	35	45	44
1916	48	43	53	45
1917	66	62	71	47
1918	69	69	68	51
1919	77	74	80	48
1920	85	73	97	43
1921	64	51	77	40
1922	61	48	74	40
1923	62	49	75	40
1924	61	49	73	40
1925	67	56	77	42
1926	67	56	79	42
1927	65	53	77	41
1928	66	55	76	42
1929	66	55	76	42
1930	64	49	78	39
1931	51	36	66	35
1932	43	27	59	·32
1933	42	27	56	32
1934	47	32	59	34
1935	52	40	61	39
1936	53	42	63	40
1937	55	45	64	42
1938	50	38	61	39
1939	48	37	59	38

TABLE 10-2 (*Continued*)

The Market Basket of Farm Food Products: Indexes of Retail Cost, Farm Value, Farm-Retail Spread, and Farmer's Share of Retail Cost, 1913-58*

Year	Retail Cost	Farm Value	Farm-Retail† Spread	Farmer's Share
		(*1947-49 = 100*)		(*per cent*)
1940	48	38	58	40
1941	53	46	59	44
1942	62	58	65	48
1943	69	71	69	51
1944	68	70	70	52
1945	69	74	70	53
1946	79	83	78	52
1947	97	100	94	51
1948	104	107	102	51
1949	99	93	104	47
1950	98	93	103	47
1951	109	107	111	49
1952	110	103	116	47
1953	107	96	118	44
1954	105	90	119	43
1955	103	85	121	41
1956	103	84	123	40
1957	107	86	127	40
1958	113	91	135	40

* Data for 1947 and later years apply to farm food products representative of those bought by urban families in 1952. For the years before 1947, the series were weighted by quantities of food products bought per family in 1935-39. Index numbers were computed by "linking" the two series at 1947. The dollar figures for the group, which are published quarterly in *The Marketing and Transportation Situation*, can be converted to index numbers by the following 1947-49 average: Retail cost, $940.13; farm value, $465.15; farm-retail spread, $474.98.

† The farm-retail spread was adjusted to exclude processing taxes in 1933-35 and to include Government payments to processors in 1943-46.

Source: "Farm-Retail Spreads for Food Products," *Miscellaneous Publication 741* (U.S.D.A., Agricultural Marketing Service, Marketing Research Division).

The farm-retail spread did not decline following World War II either. In fact the spread, between the retail cost and the farm value of the market basket (that is, marketing costs), has increased in every year except one since 1945. Thus, perhaps a second important generalization is in order. Marketing charges do not come down easily, but they do rise easily. The farm value of the market basket has, however, declined steadily since 1951. And with this decline in the farm value of the market basket, the farmer's share of the consumer's food dollar in 1958 is down to 40 per cent, or where it stood in 1940. The fact that the farmer's share of the consumer's food dollar stands at 40 per cent once again in 1958, does not prove that the representative farmer is either suffering or prospering financially, or that the whole long development in marketing is either good or bad. It does suggest one important thing, however; the farmer is the residual claimant of the consumer's food dollar.

The total marketing bill. Marketing-bill data are sometimes confused with the market-basket data, but the two sets of data describe different phenomena. Marketing-bill statistics relate to the total quantity of farm foods purchased annually by all civilian consumers, whereas the market-basket statistics describe the average quantity of domestic farm foods bought per family by urban wage-earner and clerical-worker families. The marketing-bill data measure year-to-year changes in the cost of marketing the actual quantities of the various groups of farm products. Market-basket data in contrast measure changes in the cost of marketing a constant set of food items.

The total bill for marketing farm-food products has increased steadily since 1940 (see Table 10-3). In 1958, it was $37 billion—about four times greater than in 1940. Further increases are in prospect in both the near and distant future. This bill includes charges for processing and distributing to civilian consumers domestically produced farm foods, including food sold in the form of restaurant meals. Gross returns to farmers have increased by about the same proportion as the marketing bill since 1940. However, returns to farmers have not risen steadily. They advanced each year except one from 1940 to 1951, declined in 1952-55, and increased through 1956-58.

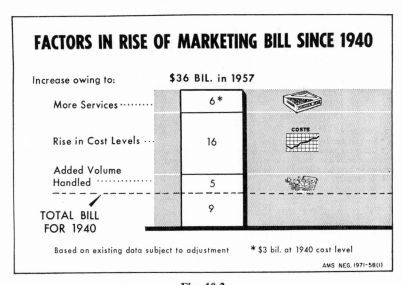

Fig. 10-2.

TABLE 10-3

**The Bill for Marketing Domestic Farm Food Products
Bought by Civilian Consumers, 1929-58***

Year	Civilian Expenditures for Farm Food	Farm Value	Total† Marketing Bill
	(Billion Dollars)		
1929	16.9	7.2	9.7
1930	16.2	6.3	9.9
1931	13.3	4.7	8.6
1932	10.9	3.4	7.5
1933	10.9	3.6	7.3
1934	12.1	4.3	7.5
1935	12.6	5.0	7.3
1936	14.0	5.8	8.2
1937	14.1	6.0	8.1
1938	13.6	5.2	8.4
1939	13.8	5.2	8.6
1940	14.7	5.6	9.1
1941	17.0	7.1	9.9
1942	21.0	9.3	11.7
1943	23.8	11.4	12.6
1944	24.4	11.6	13.3
1945	26.8	12.6	14.9
1946	33.5	15.7	18.3
1947	39.4	18.7	20.7
1948	42.2	19.3	22.9
1949	40.8	16.9	23.9
1950	41.5	17.6	23.9
1951	46.4	20.0	26.4
1952	48.2	19.9	28.3
1953	48.3	19.0	29.3
1954	48.8	18.4	30.4
1955	50.5	18.3	32.2
1956	52.7	18.7	34.0
1957	55.1	19.5	35.6
1958‡	57.7	20.8	36.9

* See text for description of data.
† Difference between retail-store cost (or civilian expenditures) and farm value, except that Federal processor taxes have been deducted for 1933-35 and allowances for Federal government payments to processors have been added for 1943-46.
‡ Preliminary.

Price inflation was the major factor in the $27 billion increase in the marketing bill between 1940 and 1957. Increases in *per unit* marketing costs of 120 per cent account for $16 billion of the total $27 billion increase between 1940 and 1957 (see Figure 10-2). The volume of food marketed rose about 50 per cent; this increased the

1940 marketing bill by an additional $5 billion in terms of 1940 prices. The remaining $6 billion represents charges for increased services provided by the food marketing system. These latter charges include costs and profits to firms providing such increased services as prepared dinners and other built-in maid services.

Components of the marketing bill. The bill for marketing farm-food products has increased in every year since 1939 as the result of persistent increases in all principal components of that marketing bill. Each of the components—labor, transportation, corporate profits and other costs—have more than tripled since 1939 (see Figure 10-3).

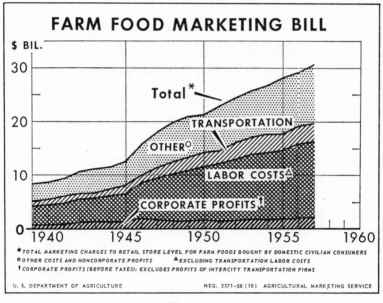

Fig. 10-3.

The upward trend in labor costs since 1940 has been caused in part by the increase in the number of persons employed in processing and distribution activities; more workers have been required to handle the increasing volume of products and to provide the additional services required in the processing and distribution of semi-prepared and prepared foods. In addition, an increasing number of technical, clerical, professional, and sales personnel was employed by marketing firms in selling more products. It is estimated that the full-time equivalent of 5.2 million workers were employed in processing and distribution in 1956. This is approximately 33 per cent more than in 1940.[2]

Between 1940 and 1957 the spread of unionization in food-processing and distributing industries established a workday and workweek with provision for overtime payments, higher wage rates and numerous fringe benefits. In addition, state and Federal legislation provided for increasing kinds and amounts of fringe benefits. Part of these higher labor costs has been offset by the greater productivity of labor during the 16-year period. The best available estimates indicate that *unit* labor costs have increased by only 140 per cent whereas total labor costs have gone up by approximately twice that amount (see Figure 10-4).

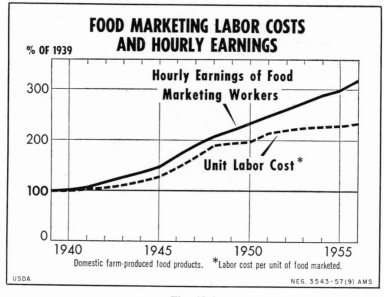

Fig. 10-4.

Transportation rates and charges have followed the same trend as labor costs because transportation services in the main reflect labor usage. There are a number of contractual limitations between labor

---

[2] This discussion is based upon the article by D. B. DeLoach, "Costs of Marketing Major Farm Products," *Policy for Commercial Agriculture: Its Relation to Economic Growth and Stability,* Joint Committee Print, 85th Congress, 1st Session (November 22, 1957).

and management in the transportation industry that restrict the cost benefits that might be gained from new technologies. These and other institutional factors may have to be changed before any sizable improvement can be expected in transportation costs and efficiency.

Corporate profits of food-processing and distributing firms have ranged between 5 and 11 per cent on invested capital, before taxes, since 1940. Such profits amounted to about $1.8 billion in 1956, which exceeded the previous high of $1.7 billion in 1946, and were 38 per cent higher than the average of $1.3 billion for 1947-49. Generally speaking, profits in the food industry have been lower than the average for all manufacturing industries. Regardless of this, profits cannot be considered an inconsequential item in the food marketing bill.

Does distribution cost too much? This is a difficult question to answer. A study undertaken by the Twentieth Century Fund in 1939 concludes that the answer is yes, distribution does cost too much. The conclusion is also advanced in that study to the effect that:

. . . there is little evidence of general high profits being made in the field of distribution considered as a whole. Some firms, it is true, and some of the newer branches of distribution, have been conspicuously profitable. But for every outstandingly successful and profitable organization there are many that barely break even and some which operate at a loss, even in good years.[3]

The basis for the conclusion that distribution (marketing and processing) costs too much, thus, must rest on grounds other than exorbitant profits. The affirmative conclusion would seem to depend upon such factors as duplication of services and functions and the insidious drive to provide consumers with more and more service. In other words, the basis for the conclusion that distribution costs too much rests upon a second conclusion, namely, that services are provided and costs are incurred, *which really are not to the advantage of the consumer,* to expand sales.

We are inclined to take a somewhat opposing view. We recognize that services are foisted on consumers, in certain cases, and additional costs are incurred when, in fact, consumers do not want those additional services. But we know that when real incomes of consumers are rising, as they have been in the United States for many, many years, consumers desire to spend those additions to income, not entirely for new and more products, *but, rather, on additional*

---

[3] Paul W. Stewart, and J. Fredrick Dewhurst, with the assistance of Louise Field, *Does Distribution Cost Too Much?* (New York: The Twentieth Century Fund, 1939), page 335.

services. And the competition for new customers through the provision of greater services, which must add to the cost of distribution, succeeds only because consumers desire to spend their rising real incomes for greater convenience and more service. Thus, we conclude that costs of distribution are high and, with the exception of the war period, are rising because consumers seek greater services. Merchants, realizing this, compete to provide these greater services with the result that distribution costs are high and increasing. Consequently, we take the view that distribution does not cost too much. If consumers desire to allocate their incomes in such a way as to spend a larger proportion of their income on service (packaging, credit, delivery, convenience) who is to say that such an allocation is improper or costly?

We are not saying that the food distribution system is perfect or highly efficient. Inefficiencies may be found in the system in almost any direction that we care to look: in the antiquated fruit and vegetable terminal markets of the East, in the shrinkage of livestock on their way to terminal markets, in the inequitable payment practices to be found in country cotton markets. But a comparable list of inefficiencies could be set forth for any sector of the economy: manufacturing, professional services, government administration. We are inclined to doubt that the extent and magnitude of inefficient practices is any greater in food processing and marketing than in other areas that we might care to examine. And we do not feel that the growing list of marketing services, which consumers demand and pay for, should be treated as unwarranted or exorbitant costs. Very simply, consumers are purchasing services as well as products.

REFERENCES

Cochrane, Willard W., "Some Additional Views on Demand and Supply," *Agricultural Adjustment Problems in a Growing Economy.* Ames, Iowa: Iowa State College Press, 1956.

Davis, John H., and Ray H. Goldberg, *A Concept of Agricultural Business,* Division of Research, Graduate School of Business Administration. Boston: Harvard University, 1957.

De Loach, D. B., "Costs of Marketing Major Farm Products," *Policy for Commercial Agriculture: Its Relation to Economic Growth and Stability,* Joint Committee Print, Joint Economic Committee, 85th Congress, 1st session (November 22, 1957).

"Farm-Retail Spreads for Food Products," *Miscellaneous Publication 741,* U.S.D.A., Agricultural Marketing Service (November 1957).

1. How did the distribution of the laboring force, as among agriculture, manufacturing, and the distributive trades, change over the long period 1870 to 1956? What explanation can you offer for the changing proportions?

2. Make a list of the services that were undertaken in the home in 1870, but which now are provided in the marketing system. Does the transfer of these services from the home to the marketing system, with the increased costs of marketing, mean that the economy is more or less efficient?

3. What form does competition most often take at the retail level: price competition or service competition? Why?

4. What has been the long-run trend with respect to the distribution of the consumer's food dollar among farmers, processors, and other middlemen? Do you expect the share going to processors to increase in the future? If so, why?

5. How does the "market-basket" concept differ from the "marketing-bill" concept? What do the marketing-bill data measure that the market-basket data do not?

6. Why has the total marketing bill for domestic food products increased so greatly since 1940? Indicate sources of the increase.

7. Which of the following developments best explain increases in food- and clothing-marketing costs over the last century: (1) excessive profits, (2) duplication and inefficiency, (3) the provision of new services, and (4) greater processing and manufacturing outside the home? Do you think that the trend toward increased marketing and distribution costs is an undesirable trend? If so, what should we try to do about it?

CHAPTER 11

Consumer Needs, Wants, and Demands

THE CONSUMER has long been eulogized in economics texts. Very often we find statements such as: the consumer is the prime mover of the economy; all economic activity is undertaken to satisfy consumer wants; the people who direct business firms only execute what is prescribed for them by demands of consumers. But, just as often, writers of these statements have promptly forgotten the consumer and the role he performs and turned their attention to the complexities of production and exchange. More recently, however, economists have been paying more attention to consumer behavior. For it is recognized that consumer decisions to spend or save, when lumped together in a national total, have significant implications for the operating economy. Further, the manner in which consumers allocate their limited incomes between different lines of expenditure has important price-output consequences for the goods and services involved. Here we will try to follow more recent thinking and emphasize the role of the consumer in shaping farm production and marketing activities.

The consumer in the marketing process. As suggested in Chapter 7 it is sometimes useful to take a channel or "pipe line" approach to the marketing process. Let us, therefore, visualize the marketing process in food and agriculture as a broad channel carrying food and fiber along from farm-producers to consumers. And within this broad channel, we may picture many smaller channels carrying this particular farm product and that. But this flow of food and fiber is not forthcoming automatically. Neither are the total flow and its component parts fixed and unvarying in size. It is the consumer, injecting purchasing power at the end of the channel, who *pulls* farm products along through the marketing channel. It is, further, the behavior of consumers, in the allocation of their purchasing power between different food and fiber products, that causes a strong pull to be exerted in one line and a weak pull in another.

This mechanistic view of the marketing process is, however, rather complicated. We have food and fiber products flowing toward the consumer and purchasing power flowing toward the producer, a goods stream, on one hand, and a purchasing power stream, on the other. And neither of these streams flows automatically. The purchasing power stream grows out of the consumer's income, which is injected by him in the act of making purchases for food and clothing. In the other stream, the goods stream, food and fiber products move toward the consumer only as a result of initial purchases by consumers and secondary purchases by handlers in the marketing channel.

Now it may be argued that all important changes in the goods stream do not result from consumer action. This we do not deny. Innovations, such as the development of new products (concentrated quick frozen orange juice), or the development of cost reducing techniques (the self-service supermarket), are usually initiated by producers or business firms. Changes in the method of handling or in the form of a product are almost always pioneered by enterprising businessmen who have studied the market and believe a new product or a new marketing service will better meet the needs of consumers. Nonetheless, it is the consumer at the end of the marketing process, who, by making purchases or withholding them, makes the final decision as to the acceptability of a new product or service.

Consumer needs. The discussion turns logically at this point to an explanation of the behavior of consumers in their strategic position at the end of the marketing process. It seems proper, therefore, to begin with a discussion of the basic needs of consumers. By basic needs we mean that consumption necessary to life itself; that consumption rooted in the physiological requirements of the human body. This physiological drive plays an important role in the consumption of food and fiber products. We must eat regularly or we starve, and, in many climates, we must wear clothing or we freeze. With respect to food consumption at least, the basic physiological requirements of the body lend themselves to scientific inquiry wherein the needs may be tested and measured. As a result of much scientific research into basic food needs, there have been established certain objective standards (or dietary allowances) necessary to the maintenance of good health.

The Food and Nutrition Board of the National Research Council

TABLE 11-1

Recommended Daily Dietary Allowances for Selected Age Groups

Family Members	Food* Energy (Calories)	Protein (Grams)	Calcium (Grams)	Iron† (Mg)	Vitamin A (I.U.)‡	Thiamine (Mg)	Riboflavin (Mg)	Niacin (Mg)	Ascorbic Acid (Mg)	Vitamin D (I.U.)
Children under 12 years:										
1-3 years (27 lbs.)....	1,300	40	1.0	7	2,000	0.7	1.0	8	35	400
10-12 years (79 lbs.)....	2,500	70	1.2	12	4,500	1.3	1.8	17	75	400
Women (128 pounds):										
25 years	2,300	58	0.8	12	5,000	1.2	1.5	17	70	§
45 years	2,200	58	0.8	12	5,000	1.1	1.5	17	70	§
65 years	1,800	58	0.8	12	5,000	1.0	1.5	17	70	§
Men (154 pounds):										
25 years	3,200	70	0.8	10	5,000	1.6	1.8	21	75	§
45 years	3,000	70	0.8	10	5,000	1.5	1.8	20	75	§
65 years	2,550	70	0.8	10	5,000	1.3	1.8	18	75	§

* Calorie allowances apply to individuals usually engaged in moderate physical activity. Persons engaged in heavy labor will have larger requirements, but the allowance probably need seldom be increased more than 25 per cent above the standard allowance.

† Milligrams.

‡ International Units.

§ For persons who have no opportunity for exposure to sunshine and for elderly persons, the ingestion of small amounts of vitamin D may be desirable.

Source: "Recommended Dietary Allowances," revised 1958, Publication 589 (Washington, D.C.: The Food and Nutrition Board of the National Academy of Sciences, National Research Council, 1958).

issues reports, from time to time, setting forth in precise terms the amounts and kinds of nutrients required by the human body to maintain the body in good health. We present in Table 11-1 the recommended daily dietary allowances specified by the National Research Council for selected age and weight groups. A quick glance at the table makes it clear that these recommended dietary allowances are not set forth in measures common to everyday living. These requirements are presented in terms of the kinds of nutrients that the human body assimilates out of foods consumed. For example, the human body requires, according to the age of the person and his weight, a certain amount of food energy measured in terms of calories. But calories, fuel which motivates the body, are not enough. We require other types of nutrients: protein, calcium, iron, and various types of vitamins.

Three points should be made regarding Table 11-1. First, it is clear that persons in different age and weight groups require different amounts of the various nutrients. For example, a moderately active woman of 25 years and 128 pounds requires 2,300 calories a day to maintain her health, whereas a man of 25 years and 154 pounds requires 3,200 calories. Growing children in the age group, 10 to 12 years, require 70 grams of protein a day, whereas a moderately active woman only requires 58 grams. Second, although the data presented in Table 11-1 appear fixed, they should not be considered the ultimate in dietary requirements. These recommended allowances have changed over the years as the state of nutritional knowledge has advanced, and we must expect them to change in years to come, as the state of nutritional knowledge continues to advance. Third, these recommended allowances are designed to provide the human body with quantities of nutrients well above minimal requirements. It is perhaps too strong to say that the recommended allowances represent optimal quantities, but they are designed to support desired body growth and repair, and good health.

With some knowledge now at our command of the basic physiological requirements of the human body, let us look around the world at the consumption of these nutrients by various peoples. In 1952, the Food and Agricultural Organization of the United Nations released the *Second World Food Survey,* presenting estimates of food consumption and requirements for most peoples of the world. Broad caloric comparisons may be studied in Table 11-2.

The high-calorie areas include most of the Western World, all of North America, most of Western Europe, and such countries as Australia, New Zealand, and Argentina. The low-calorie areas include most of Asia, parts of the Middle East, all of Central

TABLE 11-2

Calorie Supplies Measured Against Requirements

Region and Country	Recent Level*	Estimated Requirements	Difference of Requirements
Europe:	(Calories)		(Per Cent)
Belgium-Luxembourg	2770	2620	+ 5.7
Denmark	3160	2750	+ 14.9
France	2770	2550	+ 8.6
Greece	2510	2390	+ 5.0
Italy	2340	2440	− 4.1
Netherlands	2960	2630	+ 12.5
Norway	3140	2850	+ 10.2
Sweden	3120	2840	+ 9.8
Switzerland	3150	2720	+ 15.8
United Kingdom	3100	2650	+ 16.9
USSR	3020	2710	+ 11.4
North America:			
Canada	3060	2710	+ 12.9
United States of America	3130	2640	+ 18.5
Latin America:			
Argentina	3190	2600	+ 22.7
Brazil	2340	2450	− 4.5
Chile	2360	2640	− 10.6
Colombia	2280	2550	− 10.6
Cuba	2740	2460	+ 11.4
Mexico	2050	2490	− 17.6
Peru	1920	2540	− 24.4
Uruguay	2580	2570	+ 0.4
Venezuela	2160	2440	− 11.5
Near East:			
Cyprus	2470	2510	− 1.6
Egypt	2290	2390	− 4.2
Turkey	2480	2440	+ 1.6
Far East:			
Ceylon	1970	2270	− 13.2
India	1700	2250	− 24.4
Japan	2100	2330	− 9.9
Pakistan	2020	2300	− 12.2
Philippines	1960	2230	− 12.1
Africa:			
French North Africa	1920	2430	− 20.9
Mauritius	2230	2410	− 7.5
Tanganyika	1980	2420	− 18.2
Union of South Africa	2520	2400	+ 5.0
Oceania:			
Australia	3160	2620	+ 20.6
New Zealand	3250	2670	+ 21.7

* In most cases 1946-49; in some cases 1949-50.
Source: Second World Food Survey (Rome: Food and Agriculture Organization of the United Nations, November 1952).

America, and most of South America and Africa. Countries and areas with calorie levels averaging around 3,000 also had the well-balanced diets. In these countries and areas, the consumption of cereals, in relation to that of other foods, was relatively low, whereas the consumption of milk and meat was relatively high, giving a supply of animal protein of about 50 grams. And when we compare these rough *averages* for the high calorie areas with the nutrient requirements of Table 11-1, we see that actual consumption compares favorably with the scientifically prescribed nutrient requirements.

This general dietary pattern contrasts sharply with those of countries in which the average caloric intake is 2,000 or less. In these countries, a high proportion of total calories was obtained from cheap foods, such as cereals and tubers. It would seem that a vicious cycle develops in the case of these peoples who subsist at such low calorie levels. Restricted diets lead to poor physique and low-energy output (ability to work), and these, in turn, contribute to low worker productivity, contracted food output, and restricted diets.

It is evident from this food survey that much of the world's population was subsisting in the immediate post-World-War-II years at a level of food consumption not high enough to maintain normal health, allow for normal growth of children, or furnish enough energy for normal work. Fortunately for those of us in the United States, consumers, on the *average,* maintain their food consumption at levels that satisfy the basic needs of the human body. But these are *averages,* and even in the United States there are many, many people who do not, either from lack of income or lack of knowledge, or both, consume foods at a level and in amounts that satisfy their physiological needs.

Science has provided a guide to good nutrition in terms of calories, proteins, minerals, and vitamins. These allowances are in terms of the nutrients that *need to be ingested daily.* But in our daily lives, we do not consume nutrients as such; we consume foods that provide our bodies with nutrients. A real problem arises in translating these nutrient requirements into the kinds and amounts of specific foods that, in fact, satisfy those requirements. Many different combinations of foods will satisfy the basic requirements set forth by the National Research Council and, of course, many combinations of foods that we might wish to consume do not satisfy these requirements. It is possible, for example, to specify a nutritionally adequate diet plan, composed largely of wheat flour, navy beans, cabbage, and evaporated milk, which no one would want to eat. It is also possible to suggest a combination of high-cost foods heavily weighted with sugars and fats, that does not satisfy the requirements stated in Table 11-1. Consumers, then, are confronted with a continuing problem of translating basic nutrient requirements into the kinds and quantities of foods that, in fact, satisfy those requirements.

The Agricultural Research Service of the U.S. Department of Agriculture has undertaken to convert these physical requirements into realistic diet plans at two levels of cost; low-cost and moderate-cost. In Tables 11-3 and 11-4, the kinds and quantities of food that satisfy the nutrient requirements of Table 11-1 are presented at two levels of cost for identical age and weight groups.

The low-cost plan relies heavily on the cheaper foods: potatoes, dry beans and peas, flour, and cereals. This plan also places greater emphasis on the selection of cheaper foods within certain groups: for example, less expensive cuts of meat and lower priced fruits and vegetables. The moderate-cost plan allows for larger quantities of more expensive foods, such as meat and eggs. It also allows for more higher priced cuts of meats and certain out-of-season foods. As the plans appear in Tables 11-3 and 11-4, we cannot see the extent to which higher priced cuts of meats are included in the moderate-cost diet and lower cost cuts in the low-cost diet. We can, however, see how quantities vary by food groupings. For example, a man 25 years of age would consume 3.75 pounds of meat per week under the low-cost diet, whereas it is recommended that the same man consume 5.5 pounds of meat per week under the moderate-cost diet. In the case of citrus fruits and tomatoes, we see that the 25-year-old man would consume 2.25 pounds per week in the low-cost diet, whereas he would consume 2.75 pounds per week in the moderate-cost diet. In the category, potatoes and sweet potatoes, our same man would consume 3.25 pounds per week under the low-cost diet, but only 3 pounds under the moderate-cost plan.

Thus, it is clear that the combination of foods consumed can vary considerably and still satisfy the basic nutrient requirements. The suggested quantities of specific foods in the two diet plans under consideration are quite different. And diet plans for families not restricted in the amount of money that they can spend on food could change still further. More liberal plans, with respect to cost, would include larger quantities of meat, dairy products, and fruits and vegetables. Although a family may have an unlimited amount of money to spend for food, this is no guarantee that it will have an adequate diet. Care must always be taken to include sufficient quanties of such foods as milk and fruits and vegetables.

We have dwelt at some length on physiological needs as a factor determining the selection and consumption of food. We have done

TABLE 11-3

Master Food Plan at Low Cost: Weekly Quantities of Food (as Purchased) for Selected Age Groups

Family Members*	Leafy Green and Yellow Vegetables (lb.)	Citrus Fruit, Tomatoes (lb.)	Potatoes, Sweet Potatoes (lb.)	Other Vegetables, Fruit (lb.)	Milk† (qt.)	Meat, Poultry, Fish (lb.)	Eggs (no.)	Dry Beans, Peas, Nuts (lb.)	Flour, Cereals‡ (lb.)	Fats, Oils (lb.)	Sugar, Syrups, Preserves (lb.)
Children under 9 years:											
under 1 year	.12	1.50	.50	1.00	5.5	1.00	5	—	.75	.06	.12
1-3 years	.25	1.50	.75	2.25	5.5	1.25	5	.06	1.25	.12	.12
7-9 years	.50	2.00	2.00	4.25	5.5	2.00	6	.25	2.25	.38	.50
Boys:											
10-12 years	.50	2.25	2.50	5.00	6.5	2.25	6	.38	3.00	.50	.75
Girls:											
10-12 years	.50	2.25	2.25	4.75	6.5	2.25	6	.25	2.75	.38	.62
Women:											
21-34 years	.75	2.00	2.00	5.00	3.5	2.50	5	.25	2.50	.38	.62
35-54 years	.75	2.00	1.50	4.50	3.5	2.50	5	.25	2.50	.25	.62
55-74 years	.75	2.00	1.25	3.50	3.5	2.50	5	.25	2.25	.25	.38
Men:											
21-34 years	.75	2.25	3.25	5.50	3.5	3.75	6	.38	4.25	.75	1.00
35-54 years	.75	2.25	3.00	5.00	3.5	3.50	6	.38	3.75	.62	.75
55-74 years	.75	2.25	2.50	4.75	3.5	3.25	6	.25	3.50	.62	.62

* Quantities of food suggested here are based on growth and activity levels believed to fit average conditions in the United States.
† Fluid milk or the calcium equivalent of milk products.
‡ Weight in terms of flour and cereal; count 1½ pounds of bread and baked goods as 1 pound of flour.
Source: "Family Food Budgets," revised 1957, *Family Economics Review* (U.S.D.A., Agricultural Research Service, October 1957).

TABLE 11-4

Master Food Plan at Moderate Cost: Weekly Quantities of Food (as Purchased) for Selected Age Groups

Family Members*	Leafy Green and Yellow Vegetables (lb.)	Citrus Fruit, Tomatoes (lb.)	Potatoes, Sweet Potatoes (lb.)	Other Vegetables, Fruit (lb.)	Milk† (qt.)	Meat, Poultry, Fish (lb.)	Eggs (no.)	Dry Beans, Peas, Nuts (lb.)	Flour, Cereals‡ (lb.)	Fats, Oils (lb.)	Sugar, Syrups, Preserves (lb.)
Children under 9 years:											
under 1 year	.12	1.50	.50	1.50	6.0	1.25	6	—	.75	.06	.12
1-3 years	.25	1.50	.75	2.75	6.0	1.75	6	.06	1.00	.12	.12
7-9 years	.50	2.25	1.75	4.75	6.0	3.00	7	.12	2.00	.50	.75
Boys:											
10-12 years	.75	2.50	2.25	5.50	6.5	4.00	7	.25	2.75	.62	.88
Girls:											
10-12 years	.75	2.50	2.00	5.25	6.5	4.00	7	.12	2.50	.50	.75
Women:											
21-34 years	.75	2.50	1.50	5.75	3.5	4.25	6	.12	2.25	.50	.88
35-54 years	.75	2.50	1.25	5.25	3.5	4.25	6	.12	2.00	.50	.75
55-74 years	.75	2.25	1.25	4.25	3.5	4.25	6	.12	1.75	.38	.50
Men:											
21-34 years	.75	2.75	3.00	6.50	3.5	5.50	7	.25	4.00	1.00	1.25
35-54 years	.75	2.75	2.50	5.75	3.5	5.25	7	.25	3.50	.88	1.00
55-74 years	.75	2.75	2.25	5.50	3.5	5.00	7	.12	3.25	.75	.88

* Quantities of food suggested here are based on growth and activity levels believed to fit average conditions in the United States.
† Fluid milk or the calcium equivalent of milk products.
‡ Weight in terms of flour and cereal; count 1½ pounds of bread and baked goods as 1 pound of flour.
Source: "Family Food Budgets," revised 1957, *Family Economics Review* (U.S.D.A., Agricultural Research Service, October 1957).

this because much nutritional information is available in an objective form. But when we turn to fiber products we cannot be so specific and so definite. It is clear that in extremely hot climates the body needs to be covered to prevent heat exhaustion and a burning of the skin. It is even more evident that in cold climates man must protect himself from freezing and frostbite by covering his body in some way. It is difficult, however, to develop objective standards and measures of the amount of covering that man must have in these varying situations. It is technically possible to specify weights and kinds of clothing that best satisfy physical need, and, in fact, such is common practice in military organizations in which the wearing of clothing is uniform. But in everyday life we do not do this. The most we can say is that some clothing is necessary.

Consumer wants and desires. Consumer wants and desires are more inclusive than physiological need. This was evident in the discussion of translating a schedule of nutrient requirements into diet plans. We do not consume nutrients as such. We do not consume food as such. We want and select specific kinds of food to satisfy the basic needs of our bodies. In some way, wants and desires for specific things come into being. These wants and desires are broader than need, but, in the case of food and fiber products, they grow out of physiological need.

In broad outline, wants, the variation in wants, and the almost unlimited aspects of these wants come into being: (1) because of personal characteristics, some physical, some psychological, and (2) because of the nature of the social and physical environment. In other words, a person wants (or doesn't want) a particular food because it *tastes* good (or bad) to him and because it *looks* good (or bad) to him. And a person wants a particular food because it is customary in his society to eat that kind of food. Or he may want a wide variety of foods because that is customary. It is customary, for example, in America, to want a variety of foods on the table. It lends prestige to the family to have out-of-season foods on the table. It widens the experience of the family to have exotic foods on the table. And since prestige and wide experience are valued in our society, a basis is established for wanting a variety of foods. In another direction, it has, in the past, been sociably acceptable and even socially desirable among certain peoples for one man to eat another. The willingness, yes, desire, to consume human flesh in one society and the repugnance of the idea in another, illustrates forcefully the power of social environment in determining food wants. The physical environment, too, influences wants. In South China, people learn to eat rice as children and continue to eat rice throughout their lives because rice grows well in South China. In North China, people want wheat products because wheat grows well in North China. So many things contribute to the diversification of wants.

We cannot live in any social group without feeling the need for a tremendous number of goods and services that are not necessary for bare existence, but that are, nonetheless, important to our happiness and welfare. Although we need clothing, in some form, to protect us from the elements, our desires for such protection are more often dominated by the cultural demands of the season. In short, it is the ornamental value of clothing that usually determines the nature of a selection made. We conclude, therefore, that the culture in which we live is most important in determining the structure of the individual's wants. But we must recognize that wants take a personal twist, because each individual is a personality unto himself. The average individual wishes to conform to socially accepted patterns of conduct, but he also wishes, by reason of his distinct personality, to vary in some degree from socially accepted norms. Thus, the total environment imposes on each of us a structure of wants that are more or less accepted. But each individual continuously nibbles away at socially accepted patterns of conduct as he varies his consumption from those patterns. Hence, in time, the structure of wants changes.

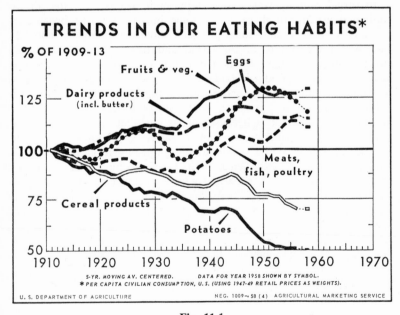

Fig. 11-1.

The changing structure of food wants is illustrated in Figure 11-1. In the long run, we see that food consumption habits have changed markedly. For whatever reason, change in food production and processing, change in the state of nutritional knowledge, change in the real income of consumers, change in food superstitions, consumers in the United States are eating differently in 1958 than they did in 1910. Consumers in the United States in the late 1950's want different kinds of food than they did in 1910. They want more fruits and vegetables and more dairy products; they want fewer grain products and fewer potatoes. And within each of these food groupings, changes have, of course, occurred. Consumers give evidence of wanting beef cuts more than they once did. They also give evidence of wanting citrus products more than they once did. So the structure of wants shifts within the various food groupings.

The central problem of choice. The elements of the central problem confronting every consumer begin to emerge. First, the consumer has almost an infinite number of wants, conditioned and created by physiological need, personal characteristics, social and physical environment. Even when we narrow the area of discussion to food and fiber products, consumer wants are varied and numerous. Second, the consumer has only a limited income with which to satisfy this myriad of wants. It is a rare consumer indeed who has sufficient income to satisfy his many and varied wants, either in total or in the narrower field of food and fiber consumption. Consequently, each consumer is faced with the problem of choosing and selecting from his list of wants those that he must or will satisfy through the purchase and consumption of specific goods and services. His is a continuing problem of choice—choice among many alternative lines of consumption, where personal income is limited.

The question now arises: What criteria does the consumer use in making his choices? Certainly he must be guided by some motive or goal in his behavior as a consumer. The consumer, like the firm, is engaged in trying to maximize his total material well-being. The farmbusiness firm, we have seen, is engaged in maximizing its total profits. Resources are combined and recombined, always with the goal of maximizing total profits. The consumer unit or household is comparable, in many respects, to the farm-business firm. The consumer unit or household is not engaged in maximizing profits. Its activity leads to the spending of income, not acquiring it. But the consumer unit or household is engaged in maximizing total satisfactions. Each of its decisions in choosing and spending is taken with the objective of increasing its total satisfaction.

This concept of total satisfaction is a little hard to understand, because satisfactions are not measurable. Still the concept is useful.

In the selection of goods and services, each consumer unit or household seeks to maximize its total satisfaction. If a dollar spent for milk today provides more satisfaction, all things considered, than a dollar spent for bread, consumers will purchase milk instead of bread. For by adding the quarts of milk that a dollar will purchase, total satisfaction will be greater than by adding the loaves of bread that a dollar will purchase. But as more and more milk is purchased, the usefulness of the additional milk falls; its capacity to satisfy wants falls. We might arrange the wants for milk in a descending order: to drink, to use in cooking, to feed to the cat. In this schema, we see that milk wants are limited, and some are lower than others. Thus, consumers do not indefinitely expand their consumption in any one line.

Even though the satisfaction derived from a dollar spent on milk exceeded that derived from a dollar spent on bread at one point in time, continued purchase and consumption of milk leads to smaller and smaller satisfaction. Continued consumption in one commodity line must, assuming that consumption in other lines is constant, leads to diminishing marginal utility for the consumer with respect to the commodity in question. Hence in the milk-bread example, we reach a point at which the satisfaction derived from a dollar purchase of milk is no greater than that to be derived from a dollar purchase of bread. At this point, the consumer ceases to expand his consumption of milk, for further milk consumption now provides less satisfaction than a dollar purchase of bread.

From the reasoning above we can set forth a famous principle: the *equimarginal principle*. Consumers, in dividing a fixed quantity of income among different lines of expenditure, will apportion that income among different uses, so as to cause the gain involved by transferring a unit of income into one use to be just equal to the loss involved in the use from which the unit of income is withdrawn. Here we have a principle of great importance. The ideal apportionment of consumer income is clearly that in which there is nothing to be gained by transferring a marginal unit of income from one use to another. For if some additional satisfaction could be gained by such a transfer, the previous situation would not have been ideal. Total satisfaction could and would be increased, for example, by taking $.25 out of milkshake consumption and adding $.25 to hamburger consumption, when $.25 spent for hamburgers provides more satisfaction than $.25 spent on milkshakes.

The way in which consumers allocate their scarce funds at different levels of income may be seen in Table 11-5. Many important relationships are revealed in the data presented there, but we will point

Table 11-5

Expenditures for Current Consumption, As a Percentage of Disposable Income, United States Urban Families, 1950

Income Class	Family Characteristics		Average Expenditure as Per Cent of Disposable Income										
	Family Size	Disposable Income	Total Expenditure	Food and Beverage	Housing	Fuel, Light, Refrig.	Household Operation	Furniture and Equipment	Clothing	Transportation	Medical Care	Personal Care	Recreation
Under $1,000	1.5	$ 614	208	72	39	16	10	9	13	15	15	4	7
$1,000-$2,000	2.1	1,532	115	42	18	7	5	6	11	9	6	3	4
$2,000-$3,000	2.7	2,534	107	37	14	5	4	7	11	12	6	3	5
$3,000-$4,000	3.2	3,487	102	34	12	4	4	7	11	14	6	2	6
$4,000-$5,000	3.4	4,462	100	31	11	4	4	7	11	14	5	2	6
$5,000-$6,000	3.6	5,449	96	29	10	4	4	7	12	15	5	2	6
$6,000-$7,500	3.7	6,618	91	27	9	3	4	7	12	14	6	2	6
$7,500-$10,000	4.0	8,434	84	24	8	3	5	5	11	13	4	2	6
$10,000 and over	3.7	15,914	67	17	7	2	6	6	10	9	3	1	5

Source: Study of Consumer Expenditures, Incomes, and Savings. Vol. XVIII (University of Pennsylvania, 1957).

TABLE 11-6

Annual Per Capita Consumption of Food in the United States by Family Income Classes in 1955

Food Groups	Under $1,000	$1,000-$1,999	$2,000-$2,999	$3,000-$3,999	$4,000-$4,999	$5,000-$5,999	$6,000 and over
				*Family Income Class**			
				Retail Weight in Pounds			
Milk or its equivalent........	490.7	477.0	507.1	520.1	563.6	565.5	573.3
Potatoes and sweet potatoes....	99.2	110.7	114.2	117.8	112.4	106.2	106.1
Dry beans, peas, and nuts	19.7	18.6	18.0	14.4	13.6	13.4	12.4
Tomatoes and citrus fruits	74.2	81.1	93.7	102.0	114.3	128.5	147.6
Leafy green and yellow vegetables	86.5	85.8	83.9	80.9	83.0	87.3	92.7
Other vegetables and fruits	149.4	175.9	187.0	193.6	202.0	205.3	235.1
Eggs	44.6	44.5	43.7	44.7	43.6	45.2	47.6
Meat, poultry, and fish	121.2	145.7	160.3	162.2	173.9	183.5	193.9
Flour and cereal	218.0	180.2	162.6	147.6	134.2	134.6	123.5
Fats and oils	54.6	51.5	49.1	47.7	46.1	46.4	47.3
Sugar and other sweets	117.6	119.3	109.3	109.7	102.2	100.7	101.6

* Family income after taxes.
Source: Computed from *Household Food Consumption Survey, 1955* (U.S.D.A.).

out only three. First, at low levels of income, consumers tend to spend more than they receive, but as their incomes rise, they spend smaller proportions on consumer goods and services and save more. Second, at low levels of income, expenditures for foods are relatively large, running up to 70 per cent of the total expenditure at the lowest income level. But as we ascend the income scale, the proportion of income allocated to food expenditure falls importantly. Third, for all levels of income between the highest and lowest, expenditures for clothing remain almost constant in the budget, close to 11 per cent.

We see in some detail the food choices of consumers in Table 11-6. It will be observed that consumers at low levels of income use relatively large quantities of sugar, fats, flour and cereals, potatoes and sweet potatoes, and dry beans, peas and nuts. And they go easy on fresh vegetables and fruits, milk, meat and eggs. In short, they fill up on cheap, energy foods. They choose those cheap foods where their funds go farthest, in terms of quantity. But as consumer incomes rise, consumers are inclined to, or more properly, can afford to satisfy more and more varied food wants. The pattern of food choices reflecting the pattern of income allocation is modified as we ascend the income scale. The consumption of flour and cereals actually declines; the consumption of such foods as sugar and fats does not change; but the consumption of meat, milk, and fresh fruits and vegetables increases in important proportions.

We conclude then, that when incomes are low, consumers maximize their total satisfaction by purchasing and eating large quantities of cheap, low-resource-using foods. When incomes are high, consumers maximize their total satisfaction by consuming less of these low-resource-using foods and by expanding their purchases and intake of high-cost animal products and fruits and vegetables.

Consumer demand. By consumer demand we mean how much the individual consumer will take of a particular commodity under certain conditions. We mean the quantity of a particular commodity that a consumer wants and is prepared to purchase. Consumer demand is customarily measured in one of two ways. We can relate the quantity of a particular commodity that the consumer *stands ready to take* to his income. The resulting measure, when quantity is related to income, is called a *consumption curve*. Or we can relate the quantity of a particular commodity that the consumer *stands ready to take* to the price. The resulting measure, in this case, is called a *demand curve*.

Let us look first at the *consumption curve* as a measure of consumer demand. In Figure 11-2, consumption curves for three food commodities (beef, white flour, and fats and oils, excluding butter) are presented. The consumption curve for any one of these commodities states a relation between pounds of that commodity consumed and average incomes of United States families in 1955. The measure tells us how the consumption of beef, for example, might be expected to vary as family income varies.

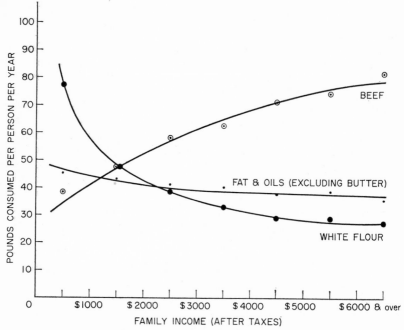

Fig. 11-2. Food consumption for selected commodities, United States, 1955.

The curves presented in Figure 11-2 illustrate the different income-consumption relationships to be found in the world of food and agriculture. The consumption of beef increases at a decreasing rate with rising incomes, the consumption of white flour falls sharply and then levels off with rising incomes, and the consumption of fats and oils is not influenced much one way or another by changes in income. The consumption curve for white flour is something of an exception. Only a few foods are consumed in smaller amounts by consumers with high incomes than by those with low incomes. The typical curve will assume a shape falling within the limits of the two commodity-consumption curves for beef, and fats and oils. It is important to notice, however, that the consumption of each of the three commodities shown in the figure changes only modestly in amount once the middle-income class is passed. Changes in income, once the upper-income brackets are reached, usually have only a small effect on the amount of food consumed.

Providing nothing disturbs the relationships presented in Figure 11-2, we know what consumption response to expect from a change in family income. But these curves can and do change in configuration and position with the passage of time. Changes in taste, changes in fashion, changes in knowledge, commonly influence these income-consumption relationships. A growing preference for beef, for example, would have the effect of raising the curve presented in Figure 11-2. And an upward shift in the curve would mean that, for any given income class, more meat would be consumed than now is indicated. These modifying influences do not render the concept of a consumption curve useless; they simply mean that we must make costly and inclusive budget studies periodically.

We turn now to the demand curve. In Figure 11-3, a hypothetical consumer demand curve (*DD*) for chicken is presented. This curve is constructed from the following hypothetical, but nonetheless realistic, information:

Price per Pound	Per Capita Consumption (in pounds)
$.75	15
.65	18
.55	23
.45	30
.35	40

This curve (*DD*) states a relation between the number of pounds of chicken consumed per year per person and the price of chicken per pound. This measure tells us how the average per capita consumption of chicken might be expected to vary as the price of chicken varies.

It will be observed that the demand curve for chicken is negatively inclined; it slopes downward and to the right. When the price of chicken rises, the number of pounds consumed declines, and when the price falls, the number of pounds consumed increases. This is a perfectly logical relationship and one we would expect to find for most food items. As we consume more and more of a product, the amount of utility or satisfaction derived from additional amounts of consumption declines. The willingness of consumers to pay for

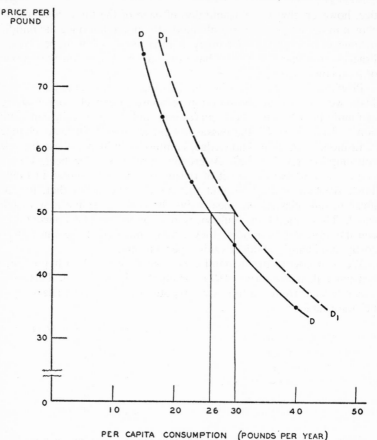

Fig. 11-3. Consumer demand curves for chicken.

additional amounts of that commodity falls. Hence, increased amounts of a particular commodity may be sold to a consumer only at lower prices.[1]

At this point, it would seem wise to distinguish between two commonly used phrases: *change in demand* and *change in the amount demanded*. By a *change in demand* we have in mind a shift in the demand curve itself: a shift from position *DD* to D_1D_1 in Figure 11-3. By reason of that shift, the consumption of chicken increases from

---

[1] The rationale for the demand curve sloping downward and to the right can be presented in strictly behavioristic terms (rather than in utilitarian terms), as will be done in Chapter 13.

26 pounds per year per person to 30 pounds at the price of $.50. And that is what we mean by a change (in this case an increase) in demand. If *at any given price,* the consumer stands ready to buy more chicken, the demand for chicken may be said to have increased. With a decrease in demand, the consumer stands ready to buy less chicken *at any given price.*

By a change in the amount demanded we mean a movement along one curve, along curve *DD* in Figure 11-3. When the price of chicken falls from $.55 to $.45, we read off curve *DD* and discover that the consumption of chicken increases from 23 pounds to 30 pounds. And this is what we mean by a change in the amount demanded.

A word or two about the hypothetical character of our demand curve for chicken is perhaps in order. The demand curve *DD* in Figure 11-3 does not represent an actual measurement; it is illustrative only. We did not present a statistically derived consumer demand curve in Figure 11-3, because such curves are terribly hard to come by. It is difficult to obtain a measure of the quantities of chicken (or any other commodity) that a particular consumer stands ready to take at varying prices, at any one time. Hence, the few statistically derived demand curves that we do have are complex, sophisticated, and difficult to present. But the concept of a consumer-demand curve is straightforward and highly useful, so we have illustrated the concept with realistic, yet hypothetical, data.

Market demand. The market demand for a particular commodity is the summation of all individual demands for that commodity. The market demand curve sums up the amounts that individual consumers stand ready to take at each price in the price-quantity schedule. The consumer demand curve *DD* for chicken in Figure 11-3 may be converted to a market-demand curve by multiplying the average per capita consumption at each price by the total population. Assuming the population of the United States to be 170 million, we obtain the following price-quantity schedule:

Price per Pound	Total Consumption (in millions of pounds)
$.75	2550
.65	3060
.55	3910
.45	5100
.35	6800

The market demand curve is an analytical tool of great power. It tells us how much of a commodity, chicken in this case, all consumers will purchase at varying prices. If, then, we are able to derive statistically the demand curve for a *given commodity,* we are able to predict how much of that commodity will move into consumption at a particular price, or with a change in price. The idea of consumers exerting a pull on particular goods in the marketing channel now gains in precision. We do not visualize consumers aimlessly tossing coins down the marketing channel. On the contrary, we have a precise concept of demand that tells us how much consumers will spend on a commodity, on chicken, at various prices. Thus, our measure of the pull exerted by consumers on a specific good in the marketing channel is the market-demand curve for that good.

We should never forget, however, that our measure, the market-demand curve, can shift: expand or contract. This possibility does complicate the problem. An expansion in market demand, for example, means that all consumers stand ready to take more at the same price. So our measure is not easily derived and is not to be used carelessly. But when properly applied, it is most useful.

REFERENCES

Boulding, Kenneth E., *Economic Analysis,* rev. ed., Chapter 29. New York: Harper & Brothers, 1948.

Cochrane, Willard W., and Carolyn Shaw Bell, *Economics of Consumption: Economics of Decision Making in the Household,* Chapters 5, 7, 10, 16, and 17. New York: McGraw-Hill Book Co., Inc., 1956.

"Food Consumption of Urban Families in the United States: with Appraisal and Analysis," *Agricultural Information Bulletin 132.* U.S.D.A. (October 1954).

"Food Consumption of Households in the United States," *Household Food Consumption Survey, 1955, Report No. 1.* U.S.D.A. (December 1956).

Second World Food Survey. Rome: Food and Agricultural Organization of the United Nations (November 1952).

POINTS FOR DISCUSSION

1. In what sense is the consumer sovereign?
2. Why are we able to state precise, physiological requirements with respect to food, but not with respect to fiber? How do these requirements vary with respect to sex, age, and weight?
3. What problems are encountered in the conversion of nutrient requirements into kinds and quantities of food? How do tastes and preferences enter into the problem?

4. What do we mean by the central problem of choice? How does the limitation of income act to create a problem of choice?

5. By what principle do consumers allocate their income between different lines of expenditure? How does the concept of diminishing marginal utility relate to this principle?

6. What is a consumption curve? What variables are related in the consumption curve?

7. What is a demand curve? What variables are related in the demand curve? What is the difference between a change in demand and a change in the amount demanded?

PART THREE

Toward an Understanding of
Farm Prices

CHAPTER 12

The Price-Income Structure
of Agriculture

FARM PRICES are constantly on the move, and that movement is often extreme in character. This we must recognize. Farm people often have the idea that there is such a thing as a normal price or a just price. The price they usually have in mind is a pleasant recollection from some favorable historical period. But farm price behavior is not one of stability. Rather, it is one of change, fluctuation, and sharp movement. It is this evolving pattern of farm prices in the United States, sometimes called the *structure* of farm prices, that we wish to portray.

The farm price level. It is often useful to speak of a price level, for example, the general price level, the farm price level, or the retail food price level. When we speak of a price level, in this case the farm price level, we have in mind an average of the prices of all farm commodities. Such an average, with its changes from month to month or from year to year, that sums up the behavior of all farm prices, is useful in situations in which we wish to speak of total agriculture. Now it may be readily seen that this device is a meaningful one if all farm prices move up and down together. But if some prices are rising, some falling, and others holding stable, the concept becomes devoid of meaning and may even convey a false impression. Fortunately, since prices of individual farm products tend to move up and down together, the concept of the farm price level is a handy one.

The use of index numbers. To measure changes in the farm price level, or any other price level, we make use of a concept known as an index number. An index number measures the level of farm prices at any one time, not by measuring any particular price, but by representing the whole structure of prices. If, for example, a large number of prices are plotted over a series of years on chart paper, one gets the impression of a badly frayed and raveled rope (see Figure 12-1). There are many loose strands, *yet a central core exists,* and the whole pattern follows the bends of that core. The index number becomes our measure of that central core, rising and falling with it through time.

An understanding of the computation of an index number helps in the understanding of the meaning of an index number. Suppose that we decide to use the period 1935 through 1939 as a base for measuring the rise in farm prices during the war and postwar years. To simplify the problem, we assume that there are only three farm commodities: wheat, hogs, and cotton. From the following information we can compute a simple index number to represent the movement of the farm price level:

Commodity	U.S. Price 1935-39 Average	U.S. Price in December 1949
Wheat	$ .83 per bu.	$ 1.93 per bu.
Hogs	8.38 per cwt.	14.80 per cwt.
Cotton	.103 per lb.	.265 per lb.

The price of each commodity in 1949 is expressed as a percentage of the average price for 1935-39. The average percentage is then computed to obtain the index value of the farm price level in 1949.

Commodity	Per Cent of 1935-39	Per Cent in 1949
Wheat	100	233
Hogs	100	177
Cotton	100	257
Average	100	222

The index value for 1949, then, equals 222, and we have a measure of the rise in the farm price level between 1935-39 and 1949.

One fault with the index number just computed is that it gives equal importance to each commodity. One way (out of many) to correct this obvious imperfection is to *weight* each commodity by the average total cash income received by producers of that commodity in the base period 1935-39, as follows:

Commodity	Total Cash Income, United States, 1935-39	Per Cent of Total
Wheat	$2,261,071,000	23
Hogs	4,278,211,000	44
Cotton lint	3,249,927,000	33
Total	$9,789,209,000	100

Since hogs are the most important source of income, the price of hogs is given the most weight. And wheat, the least important source of income, is given the least weight.

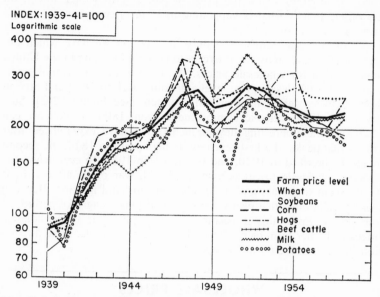

Fig. 12-1. Indices of prices received by farmers for all commodities and for selected commodities, United States, 1939-57.

Let us now compute a *weighted* index number of the farm price level.

Commodity	Weight	1935-39 Weight × Per Cent	1949 Weight × Per Cent
Wheat	23	23 × 100 = 2300	23 × 233 = 5359
Hogs	44	44 × 100 = 4400	44 × 177 = 7788
Cotton	33	33 × 100 = 3300	33 × 257 = 8481
Total	100	10000	21628
Dividing the totals by 100 we get........................		100	216

The *weighted* index value for 1949 is 216. Our measure of the rise in the farm price level between the period 1935-39 and 1949 is thus reduced from 222 to 216 by reason of the fact that we have assigned more importance to hog prices and less to wheat prices in the second calculation than we did in the first.

Now let us be certain that we know what an index number means. The index number of 216 for 1949 tells us, assuming that agriculture produces only three commodities, that the level of farm prices rose from 100 in the base period 1935-39 to 216 in 1949. It does not tell us anything about the price level of the total economy, on one hand, or anything about the price of No. 2 hard winter wheat, on the other. It tells what is happening to farm prices when we put all farm products in one basket.

Long-run price trends. The only information we have which describes price-level movement over a long period of time in the United States is that for wholesale prices. We have a measure (index numbers) of the wholesale price level extending back to 1800 and broken down between farm and nonfarm products (see Figure 12-2). Surveying wholesale price-level movements from 1800 to 1960, we can observe some interesting developments. We have experienced four great price peaks, the first reaching its high point in 1814, the second in 1864, the third in 1920, and the fourth in 1951. In every case, the peak in wholesale prices is associated with war or its aftermath. It would seem that wars and price inflations go hand in hand. Between these precipitous price peaks, we have had long troughlike periods of low prices. From this it becomes exceedingly clear that wholesale prices (whether farm or nonfarm) have not been stable. Price fluctuations have been the normal thing.

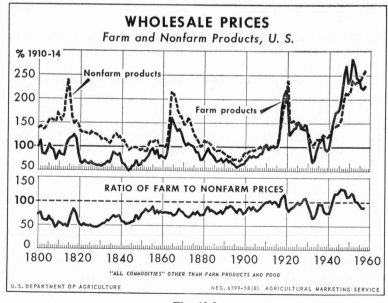

Fig. 12-2.

Another interesting trend emerges from Figure 12-2. We see that the amplitude of farm price swings has become greater over the years. In the early 1800's, the wholesale price level for farm products exhibited greater stability than the nonfarm level. But in more recent years the wholesale price level of farm products has shown the greatest variation. In the very long run, farm prices have also been rising relative to nonfarm prices at the wholesale level (see the ratio of farm to nonfarm prices at the bottom of Figure 12-2). Finally we observe that farm prices in the 1950's, even though supported by government action, have once again sagged.

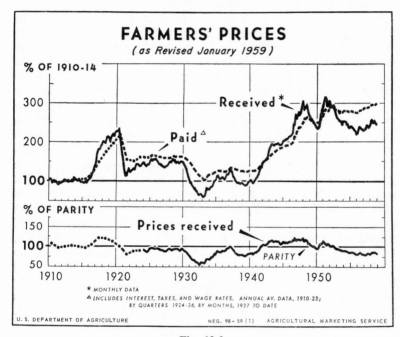

Fig. 12-3.

In Figure 12-3, two well-known and commonly used farm price series appear: (1) the index of prices received by farmers, and (2) the index of prices paid by farmers, including interest and taxes. The first of these series tells us the level of prices farmers received for the products they sold over the period 1910-58. The second tells us the level of prices farmers had to pay for production supplies and consumer goods over the period 1910-58. And since the two series are based on the same period, 1910-14, a comparison of them, for any given year, tells us whether farm products have a lower or higher purchasing power in terms of nonfarm products as compared with 1910-14.[1] This comparison is made in the lower chart, where the line expressing the comparison is below the 100 per cent parity line whenever the prices-paid index exceeds the prices-received index. It needs to be pointed out carefully, however, that the prices received by farmers and the prices paid by farmers were not identical in 1910-14. As in our index problem, we simply let both the prices received and the prices paid in that period equal 100. Incidentally, the prices farmers received then were relatively high; 1910-14 is often referred to as the "golden age" of American agriculture.

It will be observed from Figure 12-3 that the prices received by farmers moved up to high levels during and immediately after World War I and then fell, in one swift movement, in 1921. Farm prices steadied in 1922 and remained on something of a plateau during the glittering 1920's, although not too high a plateau. They broke again with the onset of the Great Depression and remained at relatively low levels during the 1930's. The prices that farmers had to pay for the things they purchased also fell in 1921, but not nearly to the extent that the received prices fell. Hence, the position of two series is reversed, and, for the next 20 years, the price level for those things that farmers bought remained substantially above the farm price level: the index of prices received by farmers. Now this does not mean that the price of a cookstove was greater than the price of 100 pounds of hog, or that the price of butterfat was less than the price of gasoline. These index values tell us nothing about prices of specific items, and such information would be meaningless if it did, for the commodity units are not comparable. We learn from Figure 12-3 that, over the 20-year period, 1921 to 1941, the prices paid by farmers were high, relative to the prices they received. In other words, the *real income position* of farm people declined in the years between World Wars I and II, relative to the base period 1910-14.

In 1942, however, prices received by farmer-producers began to rise, and they rose spectacularly over the period 1942-48. We discovered something about the extent of that rise in our little index problem. Prices received by farmers rose relatively too—relative to prices paid by farmers. The prices-received series shot past the prices-paid series in the early years of World War II and held that preferred position down to 1949. Thus, the *real income position* of farmers improved during the war years.

The 1950's are suggestive once again of the 1920's and 1930's as far as farmers are concerned. Prices received by farmers thrust up-

[1] The meaning and significance of the parity ratio is explained in Chapter 27.

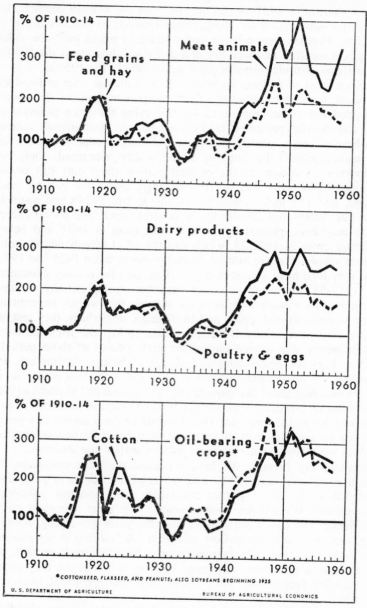

Fig. 12-4. Prices received by farmers for selected commodity groupings, 1910-1958.

ward sharply in 1951 in conjunction with the Korean conflict. But they did not hold. After 1952, prices received by farmers began to decline. Furthermore, relative to the index of prices paid, the index of prices received has been low and depressed throughout the 1950's. The terms of trade turned against agriculture in the 1950's.

Since most of us have an interest in a particular crop or livestock product, let us look at some of the component items of the prices-received index (see Figure 12-4). Surveying the price behavior of the commodities presented, feed grains and hay, meat animals, cotton, oil-bearing crops, poultry and eggs, and dairy production, one point is made indelibly: the similarity of commodity price trends. Only two important exceptions to the over-all pattern stand out: (1) cotton prices, in the early 1920's, rise strikingly above the general price trend, and (2) meat-animal prices, in the late 1920's and again in the late 1950's run counter to the general trend. The cotton exception may be explained by a very short crop in 1921 and below average crops in 1922-23, which had the effect of reducing the total world supply. The rise in meat animal prices between 1925 and 1929, the very high meat animal prices in 1951, and the counter movement in 1957-58, would seem to stem from the great prosperity of those periods. When workers have spare money, they switch from bread and potatoes to pork chops and beef steaks, or perhaps, they just eat more chops and steaks. But it takes time to increase livestock numbers; supply was limited during the early phases of those periods, hence livestock prices advanced sharply. These variations are important, as are the multitude of smaller variations that escape us in these sweeping trend-like movements. The central and important point to be made, however, is the similarity to be found in commodity price movements in the long run. The structure of farm commodity prices trends up and down in the extreme, but the individual commodity prices maintain a rather uniform pattern within that structure.

Influencing factors. We have observed the wide swings in the farm price level since 1910 and the tendency for farm price-level movements to be of greater magnitude than nonfarm price-level movements. We will now look at some of the more important forces or factors that have been at work over the years influencing, actually causing, these dramatic price-level swings. A first step in any analysis of prices, whether it be hog prices at a local livestock auction, the world wheat price, or the farm price level, is to sift out the various influencing factors and place them under two principal headings: *demand* and *supply*.

On the demand side of the price problem, there are several factors to be considered. The income of consumers is an important consideration, perhaps the most important. The tastes or preferences of consumers is another. And the ability of consumers to substitute one product for another must also be considered. In other words, these forces are always at work, influencing the amount of total food and the various kinds of food that consumers demand (want and have the money to buy).

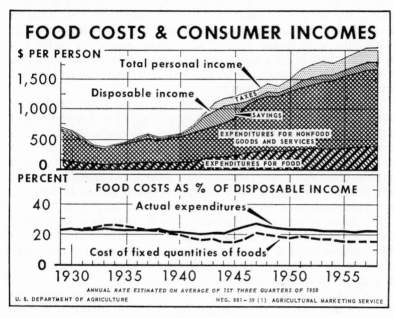

FOOD COSTS & CONSUMER INCOMES

$ PER PERSON
Total personal income
Disposable income
TAXES
SAVINGS
EXPENDITURES FOR NONFOOD GOODS AND SERVICES
EXPENDITURES FOR FOOD

1,500
1,000
500
0

PERCENT
FOOD COSTS AS % OF DISPOSABLE INCOME
Actual expenditures
Cost of fixed quantities of foods

40
20
0

1930   1935   1940   1945   1950   1955

ANNUAL RATE ESTIMATED ON AVERAGE OF 1ST THREE QUARTERS OF 1958

U. S. DEPARTMENT OF AGRICULTURE   NEG. 881 – 59 (1) AGRICULTURAL MARKETING SERVICE

Fig. 12-5.

The farm price level, as measured by the index of prices received by farmers, moves up and down with any measure of consumer or national income we wish to take. Referring to Figure 12-5, we see that personal incomes in the United States fell in the early 1930's, rose modestly in the late 1930's, turned up sharply during the war years, and advanced persistently in a great period of national prosperity from 1945 to 1958. The volume of consumer expenditures varies directly with variations in personal incomes. A brief reference to Figures 12-3 and 12-5 indicates the close correlation that exists between movements in income and the farm price level. We don't say that changes in income alone caused those price movements. We can't say that, for other factors must be considered, the supply of farm products for example. But it is obvious that the personal incomes of all people in the United States provide the bulk of the purchasing power out of which farm products are purchased. Hence, changes in the income received by individuals influence expenditures for food and in turn the demand for farm products and the prices at which they sell.

The total amount of food consumed by individuals and all consumers together changes very little with changes in tastes and preferences. We require so much food to ward off hunger and maintain a good state of health; those requirements are physiological. But within the total basket of food demanded, consumers prefer this food item to that; they prefer beefsteak to navy beans, for example. Consequently, changes in tastes and preference influence the demand for individual commodities in the total basket.

When consumers come to care less for a particular commodity than previously was the case, their expenditures for that commodity are likely to fall and the price of that commodity falls. Potatoes are a case in point. Consumers have steadily been cutting down on their consumption of starchy foods over the long period 1900-1960, which means, of course, fewer potatoes. This in itself has acted to contract the demand for potatoes and to depress potato prices. In contrast, consumer preference for oranges increased over the period 1920-50. This change in preference, in itself, acted to strengthen the demand for oranges and to strengthen orange prices. So we find in this determinant of demand (changes in consumer tastes and preferences) a reason for commodity price trends changing their position relative to one another in the structure of commodity prices.

But potato prices do not fall indefinitely and orange prices do not rise indefinitely. They do not for one very important reason. When potato prices fall, consumers tend to eat more potatoes and less of other kinds of food; they substitute potatoes for other foods. In this way, the demand for potatoes is strengthened and the price of potatoes stops falling. With oranges, we have the opposite situation. As the price of oranges rises, some people find oranges too expensive and substitute other fruits and/or vitamin pills for orange juice. Thus, the demand for oranges is weakened and the price of oranges stops rising.

It is on the supply side of the price problem that we unearth some unusual relationships. We are aware that *total* agricultural output has increased steadily over the years (see Figure 12-6). But if we were to remove the upward trend from the agricultural production series, we would discover that *total* output does not change much from year to year. When farm prices were shooting skyward during World Wars I and II, total agricultural production increased, but not much faster than the long-run trend. And when farm prices fell sharply and remained low during the interwar period, total agricultural production leveled off, but did not decline. This behavior on the part of agricultural production is in sharp contrast to the behavior of industrial production. On the nonfarm side, production varies directly with changes in the price level. When industrial prices move up, so does total output, and when prices move down, so does total output.

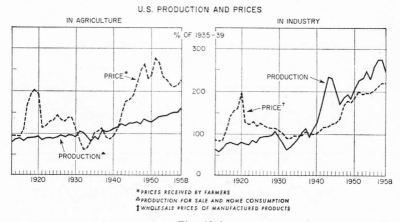

U.S. PRODUCTION AND PRICES

*PRICES RECEIVED BY FARMERS
△PRODUCTION FOR SALE AND HOME CONSUMPTION
†WHOLESALE PRICES OF MANUFACTURED PRODUCTS

Fig. 12-6.

This relationship in industry and the lack of relationship in agriculture has important implications for the price-level movements. The expansion in total industrial output associated with a price rise tends to modify that rise; more goods come off the assembly lines to ease the pressure on prices. And the contraction in total industrial output associated with a price decline tends to modify that decline; the fewer goods on retail shelves act to strengthen prices. But in agriculture, we do not find this price-dampening influence of output. Total output pours forth largely without regard to price-level movements. This pouring forth of a relatively constant volume of food and fiber products when the price level is falling simply acts to push prices to lower levels. Carry-overs pile on top of average crops and the combined supplies provide a persistent downward pressure on farm prices. In an upward price movement, just the opposite occurs. Greatly expanded supplies of food and fiber do not materialize even though demand is increasing and prices are rising; hence, consumers bid wildly for what they believe are short supplies and prices keep rising; total agricultural output, like "Old Man River," just keeps rolling along.

Cyclical price movements. Although the long, wide price swings, that we have been considering, are undoubtedly of the greatest importance to them, American farmers are confronted with other types of price movements which also are important to them. In the day-to-day and month-to-month operation of the farm, producers are faced with short-run price movements that are more or less regular in character and that last more than one year. These we call cyclical price movements.

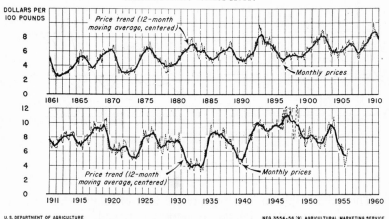

HOGS, HEAVY: PRICES AT CHICAGO BY MONTHS, 1861–1956
(ADJUSTED TO 1910-14 PRICE LEVEL)

U. S. DEPARTMENT OF AGRICULTURE   NEG. 3554-56 (9) AGRICULTURAL MARKETING SERVICE

Fig. 12-7.

Both the production and prices of some types of livestock move up and down in a somewhat regular, cyclical pattern. In Figure 12-7, we see this wave-like price movement for hogs: the hog price cycle. We observe a fairly regular cyclical pattern that takes between 4 and 5 years to complete itself. Hog prices go up for about 2 years and down for about 2, and this cycle repeats itself over and over again for the 95-year period under review. Sometimes the number of years required to move from one price peak to the next extends to 5 or 6 years and sometimes drops to 3. And some cyclical movements are more intense than others; some are deep and some are shallow. But a persistent wave-like movement of about 4 years in duration emerges, that is clear.

Two forces generate the hog cycle. One is the supply of corn. When the supply of corn is large, the farmer's best alternative use for most of it is feeding hogs. When it is short, a decrease in the number of hogs fed is required to make the available corn go around. The second force is a change in the price of hogs and the farmer's attempt to respond to that price change. Farmers try to expand production when hog prices are high and contract production when prices are low. (Although we have observed that the total output of agriculture is stable in the short-run, the production of individual commodities often varies and importantly so, from year to year.)

The hog-corn ratio puts these two forces in one formula, and helps explain the cyclical movement in hog production and prices. The ratio is computed by dividing the price of 100 pounds of hog by the price of a bushel of corn. The ratio tells us how many bushels of corn are required to buy 100 pounds of hog. A high ratio means that hogs are high-priced in relation to corn, that putting corn into hogs is a profitable way to market corn. But it takes time to raise hogs, hence, an increase in the market supply of hogs does not occur until more than a year after farmers first started to expand production. And one year later, the situation is likely to be changed: hog numbers will have outrun corn supplies and corn prices will be high, whereas hog supplies will have increased and hog prices fallen. Thus, the hog-corn ratio falls, and producers contract production. This sequence of events gives rise to the hog price cycle.

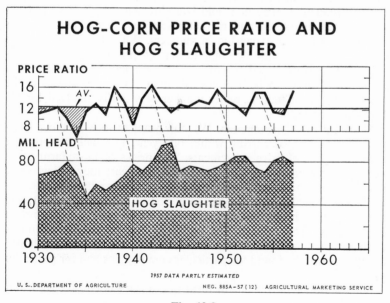

Fig. 12-8.

The effect of changes in the hog-corn ratio on the number of hogs marketed is shown in Figure 12-8. The upper part of the chart shows hog-corn ratios as they move above and below the average line of slightly over 12. The lower part of the chart shows the cyclical movement in hog slaughterings. Comparing the upper chart with the lower, we see that the number of hogs slaughtered always reaches a peak about two years after the hog-corn ratio has reached a peak. We see, on the other hand, that a low hog-corn ratio, when the ratio falls below the average, causes a decrease in marketings a year or two later. Once started, the hog cycle, with respect to prices and production, moves endlessly on.

Let us turn to another commodity, beef cattle, that also exhibits a cyclical pattern with respect to prices and production. A market cycle, averaging about 14 years in length, is apparent, with respect to both the number of beef cattle on farms and the prices received for beef cattle. Although somewhat irregular in length, the cycle is smoother and more pronounced than that for hogs.

Fluctuations in feed supplies and attempts by farmers to respond to price changes generate a beef cycle. The elapse of time between breeding and marketing is, however, much longer for beef cattle than for hogs. Cattle are not as prolific as hogs. Considering that cattle have a longer life cycle, as well, this means that it takes longer to increase and decrease beef production. When farmers start to increase production, they first hold back breeding stock. This reduces the numbers marketed and market prices rise. These higher prices encourage a further expansion in numbers. When increased supplies of beef cattle eventually do come to market, prices drop and farmers begin to liquidate breeding stock. Thus, we have a cycle for beef cattle with respect to both prices and numbers that is similar to the hog cycle, except that a greater number of years is involved for the beef-cattle cycle.

Seasonal price movements. We now want to look at those time-price movements, occurring within one year, to which we give the name of *seasonal* price movements. The prices of most farm products do not remain constant throughout the year; they follow some seasonal pattern. Usually prices are lowest during harvest and immediately thereafter (or during the period of flush production), and then they rise throughout the remainder of the year, reaching their highest point just prior to the period of harvest or the period of flush production. This is the common seasonal pattern, although exceptions may be found for particular commodities and for particular years.

This seasonal movement in farm prices does not result from any imperfections in, or manipulation of, the market. The price of a farm product can be expected to rise over the year as costs of storage and handling accumulate, or as current supplies are reduced because production of such commodities as eggs and milk slacken off in the winter months. On the other hand, we would expect prices to be lowest in that period of the year when agricultural products come to market directly and costs of storage and handling are at a minimum.

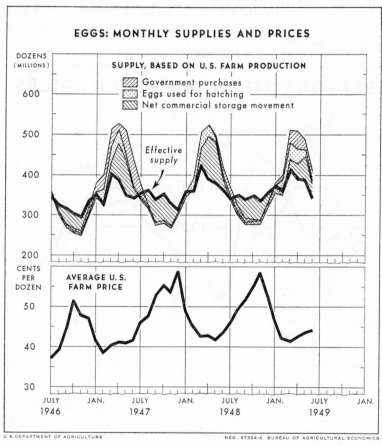

Fig. 12-9.

The seasonal pattern in prices and production is highly pronounced for eggs. This marked seasonal pattern may be seen in Figure 12-9. It will be observed that the production of eggs reaches a high point in March, April, and May and reaches the low in September, October, November, and December. Egg prices move directly opposite to the seasonal production pattern. When farm production is high, prices received for eggs are low, and when production is low, prices received for eggs are high. A large proportion of the eggs produced during the flush season moves into storage and then moves out during the slack season. This tends to even out the supply over the season and modify the seasonal price movement. We would not, however, expect the seasonal pattern in prices to be eliminated, even with a perfect storage program, because costs of storage must increase as the season advances.

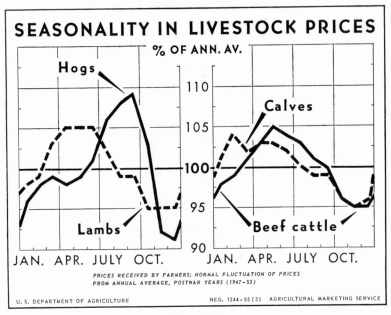

SEASONALITY IN LIVESTOCK PRICES

% OF ANN. AV.

Hogs

Calves

110

105

100

95

Lambs

Beef cattle

90

JAN. APR. JULY OCT.   JAN. APR. JULY OCT.

PRICES RECEIVED BY FARMERS; NORMAL FLUCTUATION OF PRICES
FROM ANNUAL AVERAGE, POSTWAR YEARS (1947-53)

U. S. DEPARTMENT OF AGRICULTURE   NEG. 1244-55(3)   AGRICULTURAL MARKETING SERVICE

Fig. 12-10.

Seasonal patterns in production and prices are important for such other commodities as butter, corn, hogs, lambs, cattle, fluid milk, and fruits and vegetables. But we will not look into the precise seasonal pattern of each of these commodities. The seasonal price pattern for different classes of livestock may, however, be observed in Figure 12-10.

Farm income. Gross farm income in 1958—the sum of cash receipts from farm-marketings, the value of food produced and consumed on the farm, the rental value of farm dwellings and direct government payments—is estimated to be $38 billion. This figure is well above the level of $33 to $34 billion grossed by all farmers in the United States each year from 1954 to 1957, and represents the first substantial increase in gross income experienced by farmers after 1951 (see Table 12-1). Looking once again at the year 1958, we see that total expenses of production are estimated at $25 billion, which leaves an estimated $13 billion as realized net income from agriculture. This sharp increase in net income—about 20 per cent above 1957—brings to light an important income relationship in agriculture: net farm incomes are at the crack end of the whip. Production expenses tend to be sticky: rising more slowly than gross farm income and falling more slowly. Consequently, net farm income rises rapidly in good years, as in the periods 1940-47 and 1950-51, but in the bad years a squeezing action comes into play as production expenses remain high and relatively constant, and gross farm incomes decline. This is the cost-price squeeze so common to American agriculture, which has been experienced by farmers throughout the middle 1950's and is in prospect for the 1960's.

TABLE 12-1

Gross and Net Income of All Farm Operators from Farming, United States, 1910-58*

Year	Realized Gross Farm Income†	Production Expenses	Realized Net Income
		(million dollars)	
1910	7,477	3,531	3,946
1911	7,183	3,581	3,602
1912	7,663	3,833	3,830
1913	7,919	3,973	3,946
1914	7,718	4,029	3,689
1915	8,060	4,167	3,893
1916	9,643	4,836	4,807
1917	13,310	6,092	7,218
1918	16,447	7,507	8,940
1919	17,825	8,331	9,494
1920	15,907	8,837	7,070
1921	10,521	6,634	3,887
1922	11,009	6,608	4,401
1923	12,119	7,046	5,073
1924	12,736	7,436	5,300
1925	13,667	7,334	6,333
1926	13,256	7,356	5,900
1927	13,295	7,441	5,854
1928	13,553	7,727	5,826
1929	13,895	7,631	6,264

TABLE 12-1 (*Continued*)

**Gross and Net Income of All Farm Operators from Farming,
United States, 1910-58***

Year	Realized Gross Farm Income†	Production Expenses	Realized Net Income†
		(*million dollars*)	
1930	11,432	6,909	4,523
1931	8,385	5,499	2,886
1932	6,371	4,443	1,928
1933	7,081	4,314	2,767
1934	8,541	4,670	3,871
1935	9,666	5,061	4,605
1936	10,712	5,574	5,138
1937	11,329	6,097	5,232
1938	10,101	5,828	4,273
1939	10,556	6,162	4,394
1940	11,038	6,749	4,289
1941	13,828	7,675	6,153
1942	18,767	9,942	8,825
1943	23,362	11,487	11,875
1944	24,412	12,195	12,217
1945	25,772	12,922	12,850
1946	29,706	14,483	15,223
1947	34,352	17,048	17,304
1948	34,914	18,857	16,057
1949	31,821	18,032	13,789
1950	32,482	19,297	13,185
1951	37,323	22,165	15,158
1952	37,016	22,600	14,416
1953	35,265	21,366	13,899
1954	33,865	21,664	12,201
1955	33,332	21,862	11,470
1956	34,626	22,594	12,032
1957	34,389	23,371	11,018
1958	38,291	25,152	13,139

* Excluding net changes in farm inventories.
† Including direct government payments.
Source: The Farm Income Situation. (U.S.D.A., Agricultural Marketing Service, July 1959), Fig. 174.

If we compare Table 12-1 with Figures 12-2 and 12-3, we discover that gross farm incomes and, to a lesser extent, net farm incomes vary directly with the farm price level. Both gross and net farm incomes were very low in the 1930's when farm prices were extremely low. When, however, the farm price level shot up sharply during World War II, gross farm incomes also turned up sharply. Then declining and low farm prices during the 1950's put farm incomes on the skids once again. In other words, gross farm income varies directly with those wide swings in the farm price level that we observed earlier, and, after taking into consideration the somewhat sticky movement in the production expenses, we can say that net incomes of farm operators also follow the farm price level.

It is clear that net incomes of farm operators have fluctuated in the extreme since 1910—from $1.9 billion in 1932 to $17.3 billion in 1947. But when we compare variations in net income from agriculture with variations in total national income, we discover that agriculture's share of the total national income has remained more stable than would be imagined. Agriculture's share of the net national income for the period 1940-58 is presented in Table 12-2.

TABLE 12-2

Relation of Total Net Income from Agriculture to National Income, United States, 1940-58

Year	Total National Income* (million dollars)	Total Net Income from Agriculture† (million dollars)	Farm Income as Per Cent of National Income‡ (per cent)
1940	77,638	6,340	8.2
1941	95,406	8,753	9.2
1942	124,105	12,717	10.2
1943	153,950	15,139	9.8
1944	167,648	15,282	9.1
1945	168,590	15,995	9.5
1946	170,178	19,416	11.4
1947	185,455	20,034	10.8
1948	210,098	22,425	10.7
1949	206,081	17,141	8.3
1950	221,665	18,175	8.2
1951	253,304	20,793	8.2
1952	268,805	19,879	7.4
1953	281,587	17,632	6.3
1954	280,070	16,939	6.0
1955	302,493	15,965	5.3
1956	320,024	15,993	5.0
1957	333,856	16,018	4.8
1958§	333,863	18,751	5.6

* This total is approximately equal to the Department of Commerce series on personal income less transfer payments plus undistributed corporate profits.

† Including net income of farm operators, farm wages, interest on farm mortgage debt, rent to nonfarm landlords, and government payments.

‡ All series adjusted to comparable basis, see annual July issues of *The Farm Income Situation*, U.S.D.A.

§ Preliminary.

Source: *The Farm Income Situation*. (U.S.D.A., Agricultural Marketing Service, July 1958), Fig. 169.

Over the decade of the 1940's, agriculture's share of the total national income varied from 8.3 to 11.4 per cent. In some respects that is an important variation. But there is no discernible trend over the period, hence one might conclude that agriculture's share of total national income held reasonably constant at 10 per cent over the decade. But in the decade of the 1950's agriculture's share dropped off sharply. It is clear that in the 1960's agriculture's share of total national income will be no more than 5 per cent, and probably below that percentage. Agriculture is truly becoming a small segment of the national economy.

Income comparisons. The average income of persons engaged in agriculture runs consistently below the wage income of *employed* industrial workers, as the averages show:

Year	Average Net Income per Agricultural Worker	Wage Income per Employed Factory Worker
1920	$ 660	$1,368
1925	583	1,267
1930	456	1,209
1935	423	1,047
1940	484	1,310
1945	1,515	2,308
1950	1,698	3,085
1955	1,725	3,979
1957	1,793	4,284

In appraising farm-nonfarm incomes such as these, we must remember that unemployment was heavy in urban areas between 1930 and 1940, and those without income are not averaged into the wage income of *employed* factory workers shown above. Thus, the average income position of nonfarm folks is not as favorable as these data would indicate at a first glance. Further, the data indicate a favorable trend as far as agriculture is concerned during much of the 1940's. Between 1940 and 1948, the average income of agricultural workers rose much more rapidly than did the wage income of factory workers. In fact, if we put the two series into index-number form with a 1910-14 base, the incomes of agricultural workers rise above those of industrial workers for the period 1945-48, indicating that the income position of farm people was more favorable in those years than it was even in the so-called "golden age of agriculture."

But the situation reversed itself in the 1950's. Per capita income of agricultural workers rose little in the 1950's, whereas per capita incomes of factory workers climbed substantially—by some $1,200— during the same period. In index-number terms (1910-14 = 100), agricultural worker incomes increased from 502 to only 530 over the period 1950-57, while factory worker incomes rose from 557 to 773. Here again we observe the failure of agriculture to share in the national prosperity of the 1950's.

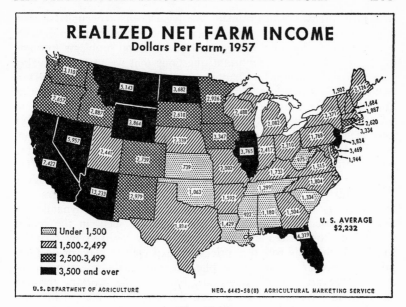

Fig. 12-11.

Not all of the interesting income comparisons are to be made between the farm and the nonfarm segments of the economy. There are some important income variations within agriculture (see Figure 12-11). For example, the annual net income of farm operators in 1957 varied from $13,200 per year per operator in Arizona to $739 per operator in Kansas, when the U. S. average was $3,232. (Interestingly, the average figure for the U. S. in 1945 was $2,250. The average farm operator did not make much progress incomewise from farming over the period 1945-57.) No other state average approaches the Arizona figure of $13,200 in 1957; California is second with an average operator income of $7,400. But at the other extreme we find a number of states in which average operator incomes approach $1,000: Kansas, Mississippi, West Virginia, Oklahoma, Alabama, and Tennessee. Thus, we find a geographic distribution of income in agriculture, with a low, broad base, that tails off on the high side in one or two states. And we must remember that each farm operator's income in a state such as Mississippi did not average $922, the state average. There were many large operators whose incomes greatly exceeded the state average. Hence, many people in the rural South in a year of great material prosperity such as 1957 must have experienced incomes of less than $922 per year.

Price and income problems. We have not as yet inquired into how farm prices are determined. We have been preoccupied with a presentation of the structure of prices and incomes in agriculture, with a presentation of a setting for questions and problems to come later. Now one of the important questions that we want to develop in a thorough fashion in Chapter 13 is that dealing with the determination of farm prices. Why is one price high and another price low? And what causes one commodity price to rise and another to fall? These are questions to which we must provide answers, for we have seen that farm prices do rise and fall, often in an extreme fashion. But we don't want answers so narrow in scope that they fit only the one situation under investigation. We want to develop a method for analyzing the price-making process that can be used in any situation.

Probably the most important question asked by producers and consumers is: what functions do prices perform in a dynamic society? We are all familiar with and we have seen, in the recent discussion, how prices influence the incomes received by farmers. But is this the only role that prices are expected to play, or do farm prices play other and more complicated roles in the operating economy? These are not idle questions. Farm people, working through the Federal government, have been tinkering with the pricing system for years, and they seem determined to continue to do so. But to tinker without an appreciation of the consequences involved is dangerous. Thus, a thorough understanding of the function performed by prices becomes imperative.

After we understand how the price of a particular commodity is determined and what the function of commodity prices are in the operating economy, we must inquire in more detail into an explanation of farm price-level movements in the United States. Why is it that all farm prices seem to travel the same tortuous road together? What is the explanation for the extreme movements in the farm price level? We have observed the extreme behavior of the farm price level, and we have seen some of the implications for farm incomes. But what can be done to reduce the amplitude of these price-level movements? What can be done to prevent the level from fluctuating so widely? Here is the heart of the farm-price problem.

After we have built, bit by bit, an understanding of farm price behavior—commodity prices and the price level—we will analyze current governmental programs and alternative proposals for dealing with the problem. For we must provide some help in trying to answer the question: how may we best support farm prices and farm incomes? But, it is vital to understand the functioning of the price system before trying to answer this important problem.

REFERENCES

Agricultural Outlook Charts. U.S.D.A. (1958 and current issues).

The Farm Income Situation. U.S.D.A. (July 1958, September 1958, and current issues).

Report of the Governor's Study Commission on Agriculture, Minnesota, 1958, pp. 97-150.

Waite, Warren C., and Harry C. Trelogan, *Agricultural Market Prices,* 2nd ed. Chapters 2, 9, and 10. New York: John Wiley & Sons, Inc., 1951.

POINTS FOR DISCUSSION

1. What do we mean by the general price level and farm price level?
2. How do index numbers measure a price level?
3. Construct an index of food prices for these items on sale in your local grocery store: bread, fluid milk, round steak, eggs, oranges, and coffee. What weights will you use?
4. How do farm prices behave in wartime? What are the important causes of this behavior on the demand side, on the supply side?
5. How does the process of substitution operate to moderate commodity price movements?
6. What is the hog price cycle? How is the hog-corn ratio related to the hog price cycle?
7. Does net income from agriculture fluctuate in a more extreme fashion than national income? What has happened to agriculture's share of the national income in recent years?
8. Do farm workers on the average or urban workers on the average receive the higher incomes?
9. In which geographical areas of the United States are farm incomes the highest, the lowest? What was the range in incomes in 1957?

CHAPTER 13

How Farm Prices Are Determined

WE INQUIRED into the nature and problems of agricultural production in Part I. From that discussion we gained some insight into the way in which the supply of a commodity is determined: how farmers decide what to produce, how much to produce and at what cost. In Part II we inquired into the nature of demand: how consumers decide what food and fiber products they want and in what quantities. Further, the movement of farm products to the consumer through the complex marketing system was investigated. Now we want to bring these ideas together in an explanation of *How Farm Prices Are Determined*. The economic forces arising on the farm, under the category *supply,* and the economic forces arising in the household, under the category *demand,* command our attention in the price-making process.

Price, that is, the price of a particular farm commodity, provides a neat focal point for studying the economic system. Most of the important economic forces come into focus in a study of the price-making process. Thus, we seek a full explanation of price determination, not only to understand how the price of a bushel of wheat is arrived at, but also to provide an explanation of the operating economy.

Demand. The demand of an individual consumer for a particular product may be defined as the amounts of that product that the consumer stands ready to take at varying prices (refer to the discussion of demand in Chapter 11). The market demand for this particular product is the sum of the individual consumer demands. Thus, the demand for a product in a particular market may be

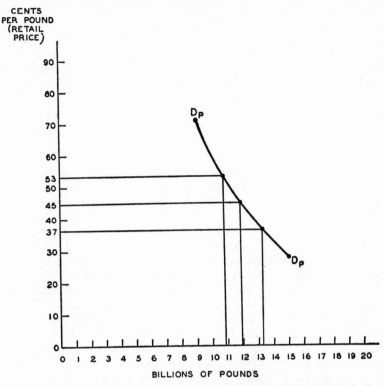

Fig. 13-1. Hypothetical demand curve at the consumer level for pork, including lard, by carcass weight equivalent in the United States market.

defined as the amount of that product that all consumers stand ready to take at varying prices.

The demand for pork in the United States' market is illustrated in Figure 13-1.[1] We see at once, in this hypothetical, but nonetheless realistic, example, that the amount of pork demanded increases as price declines: at a price of $.53, all consumers stand ready to take 10.8 billion pounds of pork; at a price of $.45 they stand ready to take 11.9 billion pounds, and so on down the scale. For a century or more, economists have explained this phenomenon by an appeal to

---

[1] To simplify the discussion, we treat the United States as one market, which, in fact, it is, but we assume away geographic price differentials arising out of different transportation costs. Further, we assume that pork is one homogeneous product. And lastly, we ignore the relatively small amount of foreign trade in pork products.

personal experience. As each of us consumes additional pounds of pork, the satisfaction (the utility) derived from each additional pound consumed declines, *when all other things remain constant, unchanged.* Or to take a more exciting example, the satisfaction (the utility) derived from a piece of pie, say the tenth in a pie-eating contest, is somewhat less than that derived from any of the previous pieces, and much less than that derived from eating the first. And perhaps the twelfth piece has a negative utility, that is, it makes us sick. Now this explanation as to why we value additional units of a product less and less was and remains a useful and meaningful explanation. But it has certain limitations. This concept of utility is a nebulous thing. It cannot be measured directly; and whether the utility of the second piece of pie was greater for you than me, we have no way of knowing.

Economists, in explaining the slope of the demand curve in more recent years, have moved toward a behaviorist type of explanation: one which says less about why and more about how. The consumer will take more pork at a lower price for two reasons: (1) When the price of pork goes down and the prices of other food products do not, pork has become relatively cheaper; hence, it pays to *substitute* pork for other food commodities. (2) When pork is an important item in the budget, a decline in the price of pork increases the real income of the consumer and out of this increase he may buy more of all products including pork. The first of these reasons is known as the *substitution effect,* which describes the behavior of consumers in substituting lower-price food items in the diet for more expensive items. The second reason is known as the *income effect,* which describes the behavior of consumers in purchasing more goods and services, when their real income has been increased by a price decline in one of the principal items of their budget. The advantage of this explanation exists, then, in the fact that we can observe these actions and measure them. In reality, the two types of explanation, the old and the new, complement one another and render more complete our understanding of the concept of demand.

Very often we need some measure of the change in quantity demanded (taken), associated with a change in price. Now the problem is just a little more complicated than it might seem to be at a glance. A measure that tells us that pork consumption expands by 1 billion pounds with a price decline of $.08 provides some information. But it raises the questions: "1 billion pounds starting from where?" and "$.08 starting from what price?" What we need is a measure that relates two rates of change: the change in quantity taken on its base (or a 1 billion pound increase on a 10 billion base) *with* the change in price on its base (or an $.08 price decrease on a $.45 base). Our name for this measure is the *elasticity of demand,* which may be defined concisely as the ratio of the proportionate change in the quantity taken to a proportionate change in price. With this concept, we derive appropriate measures of change in price and quantity along the demand curve.

The concept of elasticity, strictly interpreted, refers to infinitesimally small changes from point to point along the demand curve.[2] But in the economic world, price-quantity data most often occur in discrete jumps, as indicated by the observation points along the demand curve in Figure 13-1. Now to derive a measure of elasticity between the price points, $.45 and $.37, on the market-demand curve for pork, we use the following formula:

$$E = \frac{\dfrac{q_1 - q_2}{q_1 + q_2}}{\dfrac{p_1 - p_2}{p_1 + p_2}}$$

Substituting in this equation, we get:

$$E = \frac{\dfrac{11.9 - 13.2}{11.9 + 13.2}}{\dfrac{45 - 37}{45 + 37}} = \frac{\dfrac{-1.3}{25.1}}{\dfrac{8}{82}} = -0.53$$

This measure of elasticity ($E = -0.53$) means that the rate of increase in the amount of pork taken is .53 of the associated rate of decrease in the price of pork. Stated approximately, the percentage increase in the quantity taken is one-half the percentage decrease in price. And the minus sign before the estimate -0.53 indicates that the demand curve is negatively inclined as all good demand curves are supposed to be. When the measure of elasticity is less than one, it is common usage to describe the demand curve as being inelastic; when the measure of elasticity is greater than one, as being elastic; and when the measure of elasticity is equal to one, as unity.

But the question may be asked—does not the demand curve D_pD_p in Figure 13-1 shift as economic conditions change? The

---

[2] The formula is given by:

$$E = \frac{dq}{q} \div \frac{dp}{p}$$

where q = quantity, p = price, dq = infinitesimal change in q, and dp = infinitesimal change in p.

answer, of course, is yes. Three classes of forces operate to cause the demand curve to change its position in the short run. These forces (or determinants of demand) may be listed as follows: (1) changes in consumer tastes and preferences, (2) changes in consumer incomes, (3) changes in the prices of competing commodities. And in the long run, the size and composition of the population may be added as an important determinant.

When a change in tastes and preferences is running against a commodity, as would seem to be the case with pork, we would expect the demand curve to shift to the left, to contract. And by contract we mean, very specifically, that the quantity taken *at any given price,* say $.45, is reduced. In contrast, an expansion in consumer incomes would have the effect of shifting the demand curve to the right, and in the years immediately following World War II, the expansive effects of rising consumer incomes overrode the modest, contracting influence of a change in preference. The third determinant is the most difficult to measure and handle. The prices of close substitutes are changing all the time, and the combinations are almost limitless. But we must recognize that a change in the price in some commodity, such as beef or chicken, is going to have an important influence on the quantity of pork demanded.

Our analytical tool, the demand curve, is forged. We have an explanation for its slope, and we have a method for measuring that slope. Finally, we know what factors determine the position of the demand curve and cause it to shift.

Supply. The supply of an individual producer of a given product may be defined as the amounts of that product the producer is willing to produce and sell at varying prices (refer to the discussion of commodity supply in Chapter 4). Thus, we have a supply curve for an individual producer comparable to the demand of the individual consumer. It happens that the supply curve of a producer of a particular commodity, say pork, is identical with the marginal cost curve of the pork enterprise of that farm firm. This is so because the marginal cost curve describes the additional costs associated with the production of one additional unit: the cost of producing the sixty-ninth pig over the sixty-eighth. Now if we know the cost of producing the marginal pig, the sixty-ninth, we know the price that the farmer must receive to call forth the extra production (that is, a price that covers the cost of producing the sixty-ninth pig). Hence, the marginal cost curve of the individual producer is, in fact, the supply curve of the hog-pork enterprise on his farm.

Very simply, the market supply for a particular product, in this case pork, is the sum of the individual supplies. Thus, the supply in a particular market may be defined as the amount of that product that all producers in that market are willing to produce and sell at varying prices.

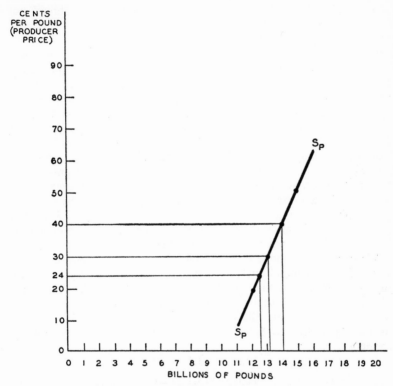

Fig. 13-2. Hypothetical supply curve at the producer level for pork, including lard, by carcass weight equivalent in the United States market.

The supply of pork in the United States' market is illustrated in Figure 13-2. We see that the supply curve is positively inclined, slopes upward and to the right, which tells us that amounts offered on the market increase as price increases. Reading off the supply curve, S_pS_p, in Figure 13-2, we obtain the following information: at a price of $.24 (producer price), farmers will supply the market with 12.6 million pounds of pork; at a price of $.30, a supply of 13.1 billion pounds is forthcoming; at a price of $.40, a supply of 14 billion pounds is forthcoming, and so on. In other words, *when all other things are constant, unchanged* (for example, prices of competing products, costs of production), we can set forth the general principle that producers will produce and sell a larger volume as the price of that product rises. And that, of course, is what the hypothetical supply curve, S_pS_p, describes.

This relationship between price and amount offered should not come as a surprise. It squares with our everyday experience. To induce most people to put forth more effort and produce a greater supply, a greater reward must be offered. In most cases, they will produce more at higher prices. In a more rigorous sense, the supply curve slopes upward and to the right because it represents the sum of the marginal-cost schedules of all firms producing hogs. And as we already know, the schedule of marginal costs will be rising in each instance, indicating the additional costs involved in producing one more pig, or 100 additional pounds of pork. The commodity-supply curve may, however, be more gently sloped than the marginal-cost curves of individual firms, because new firms enter production at higher prices. At higher prices, the outputs of newly attracted producers of hogs must be added to the market supply. Thus, the market-supply curve may possess some slope, as in Figure 13-2, even when the marginal-cost curve of the hog-producing enterprise is highly inelastic (nearly vertical in position).

We measure the slope of the supply curve in exactly the same way as we do the demand curve. We seek a measure that compares two rates of change: (1) the rate of change in quantity, with (2) the rate of change in price. The concept of price elasticity provides us with this measure. For example, the price elasticity of the supply curve, S_pS_p, over the arc $.24 to $.30 may be obtained by substituting in the formula:

$$E = \dfrac{\dfrac{12.6 - 13.1}{12.6 + 13.1}}{\dfrac{24\cancel{c} - 30\cancel{c}}{24\cancel{c} + 30\cancel{c}}} = \dfrac{\dfrac{-0.5}{25.7}}{\dfrac{-6.0}{54}} = 0.17$$

This measure of elasticity ($E = 0.17$) means that, relative to the existing price and quantity, the increase in the amount supplied is only 17 per cent as great as the increase in price. Over this price range, the hypothetical supply curve for pork may be described as highly inelastic.

As in the case of the demand curve, the supply curve can and does shift positions. Even if the hypothetical supply curve, S_pS_p, is properly constructed and positioned as of, say, 1958, there is little reason to assume that it will hold the same position in 1965, or that it held that position in 1955. But the determinants of the position of the supply curve are not the same as those determining the position of the demand curve. In fact, the determinants of the supply curve, the factors that fix its position and cause it to shift, are of an altogether different nature than those discussed in connection with demand.

The position of the supply curve is determined by *cost* relationships. Money costs of the agents of production combined in the production of hogs influence the position of the schedule of marginal costs, as do technological innovations. A technological innovation that increases the productivity of the hog enterprise or reduces the money prices of productive agents has the effect of lowering marginal costs, which, in turn, cause the supply curve to expand to the right. This follows from the fact that hog farmers may now produce any given volume of hogs at a lower cost than before, which is the same thing as saying that producers may now offer the same amount at a lower price. The latter condition describes and defines an expansion in supply. In the opposite direction, when the prices of productive agents rise, we find that marginal costs rise and the supply curve shifts to the left; that is, it contracts.

A perfectly competitive market. Before we come to grips with the problem of price determination, we need some knowledge of the market in which price is to be determined, and of the behavior of individuals in that market. We could describe the nature and operation of some specific market, as for example, the terminal livestock market in Chicago or a local livestock auction. We will not follow that procedure, however. We will abstract from our knowledge of and experience with the operation of *competitive* markets and define the conditions that must be satisfied in order that a market be perfectly competitive. It is the determination of price in a *perfectly competitive* market that we will inquire into first.

The concept of a perfectly competitive market is a stilted concept, and certainly most markets do not satisfy the rigorous conditions imposed by this concept. But we make use of it, because the price-making process can most clearly be described in such a synthetic market. Later we can relax some of the conditions imposed by the concept of a perfectly competitive market.

The nature of a perfectly competitive market may be described by three conditions:

(1) The sales and purchases of firms and households are so small, relative to the total volume of transactions in the market, that each exerts no perceptible influence on the price of the product it sells or purchases.

(2) There are no restraints to the free operation of the market, and the mobility of resources is not restricted in any way.

(3) All units operating in the market have equal access to information, and that information adequately describes the operation of the market.

We must consider one more element: the behavior of individuals or economic units operating in the market. We make the fundamental assumption that every individual or economic unit in the market behaves *rationally*. And rational economic behavior implies that the individual in all economic actions seeks to "maximize his gains and minimize his losses." In other words, the individual undertakes those activities that increase his net income, or net return, or material well-being, and refuses to engage in activities that decrease them. Critics often claim that this maximizing assumption is unrealistic and point out that individuals often behave irrationally in the economic sense; they are often careless, charitable, or listless, rather than vigilantly acquisitive. And insofar as these criticisms are valid, our theoretical explanation of price determination does not hold. Still an appeal to personal experience reveals the general validity of this assumption: as producers and consumers, we seek, in general, to maximize our gains and minimize our losses. And as we shall see, this assumption regarding the behavior of market participants proves most useful in developing a theory of prices.

Derived demand and supply. It may have been observed that our market-demand curve for pork exists at the consumer level: quantities demanded are related to retail prices. And the market supply for pork exists at the producer level: quantities supplied are related to producer prices. Thus, for mechanical reasons, we may not combine on the same chart the demand and supply curves in their present forms. They do not have common vertical axes.

If, in this pork example, it is our decision to explain the determination of price at the consumer or retail level, we must *derive* a supply curve that incorporates marketing and processing charges. Such a derived supply curve we may then relate to the presently constructed demand curve. However, if we wish to explain the determination of price at the producer level, we must *derive* a demand curve for pork out of which marketing and processing charges are subtracted. Such a derived demand curve we may then relate to the supply curve at the producer level. Technically, either method is correct, and we could apply either with propriety. We will not, however, use either method. Rather, we will derive both the demand and the supply curves to obtain schedules representative of those existing in the central wholesale markets for hogs. In Figure 13-3, the derived demand and supply curves for hogs (carcass-weight equivalent), both at the wholesale level, are presented. With the aid of these derived demand and supply curves, we will inquire into the price-making process at the wholesale level.

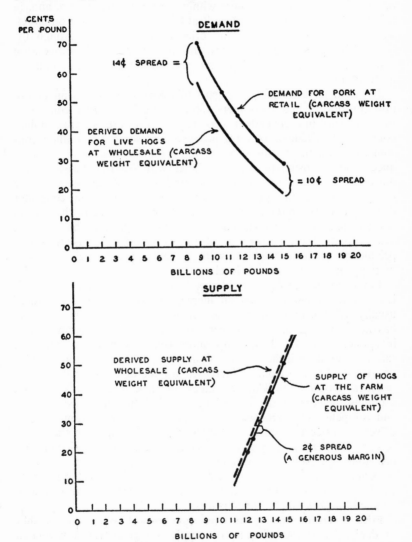

Fig. 13-3. Derived demand and supply curves for pork in the wholesale market.

We follow this mechanical procedure for good, analytical reasons. The source of demand is to be found in consumer decisions. The source of supply is to be found in producer decisions. But original consumer demand rarely meets original producer supply to determine price; the marketing system intervenes. The basic determination of price takes place somewhere within the marketing system, and, in this hog-pork example, we place it at the wholesale terminal market. The basic determination of the price of pork occurs through the competitive action of producers and producer representatives, on one side, and packers and packer representatives at the wholesale level, on the other.

It would be a mistake to regard this pork example as an exception. Producers and consumers rarely come into direct contact in the modern, interdependent economy. There are several million commercial producers of farm products and some 175 million consumers of them. In this context, most transactions involving producers and consumers are negotiated with intermediaries in the marketing system, and it is to the central wholesale markets that we turn to observe the price-making process. Changes in consumer demand and/or producer supply work themselves out in the central markets and result in changed central market prices. The initiating price-making forces grow out of the decisions of consumers and producers, but the tangible results, as far as prices are concerned, first appear at the wholesale level.

For example, an increase in the demand for pork first manifests itself at the retail level, in an increase in sales. The local grocer usually will not mark up his price. If his competitor down the street has not done so, the first grocer would cut his sales by increasing his price. Thus, retail store operators generally prefer to follow a safe course and sell more at the same price. In this way, they realize an increased return from an increased volume of turnover. But when the local grocer and all other retailers increase their orders for pork products, dealers in the central market feel the increased demand and compete more vigorously for supplies. The competition for hogs drives the price upward at the wholesale level, and, when the grocer receives his next delivery of meats, he discovers that the price of pork has gone up. Now the local grocer and his competitors add their customary margin to the new, higher, wholesale meat price with confidence and consumers reap the consequences of their increased demand for pork: higher retail prices.

Price determination in the wholesale market. When the schedule of demand and the schedule of supply are given for a particular product, as is the case in Figure 13-4, the theoretical determination of price is easily accomplished, although the actual process in the market may be involved and somewhat indeterminate. In Figure 13-4, the derived demand curve, DD_p, intersects the derived supply curve, DS_p, at the price (wholesale) of $.275. This price we call the equilibrium price. It is the only price that is stable, showing no tendency to move. It is the only price that clears the market. At a price of $.275, the amount demanded is equal to the amount supplied. At $.275, buyers in the market will take 12.8 billion pounds of pork and sellers will supply 12.8 billion pounds of pork. The price is stable, and the market is in equilibrium.

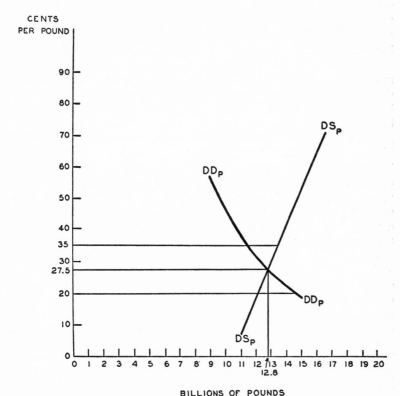

Fig. 13-4. Determining the price of pork at wholesale under competitive conditions.

But these conclusions are in the nature of assertions. Can we demonstrate that with a price of $.275 and a quantity of 12.8 billion pounds "the price is stable, and the market is in equilibrium"? We think we can. A price of $.35, for example, is not stable. At $.35, the amounts supplied exceed the amounts demanded: 13.4 billion pounds are supplied and 11.4 billion pounds demanded. In a free market, where men are motivated by profit (income maximization) and information concerning the market situation is adequate and widely distributed, a price of $.35 cannot hold. Buyers will hold off, waiting for the price to fall. Sellers will be forced to lower the offering price, in order to make sales. Thus, the price will be driven toward the equilibrium price of $.275. A price of $.20 is also unstable. Demand exceeds supply at a price of $.20. In this situation, sellers will hold back and buyers will bid up the price in an effort to obtain supplies. Hence, the price will be driven toward the equilibrium price, $.275. Competitive forces are continuously operating in a free market to drive the actual price toward the equilibrium price.

Does this mean that every transaction in a market will take place at the equilibrium price? No. At a price of $.35, for example, buyers demand 11.4 billion pounds of pork. Now if market information is imperfect or inaccurate, or possibly for other reasons, some of these buyers may enter into transactions to buy pork at $.35 a pound. This price is sometimes called a *false* price. But we should not get the idea that only a few transactions are negotiated at a false price of say $.35 or $.30 or $.29. The more closely we approach the equilibrium price, the more transactions will be entered into. This occurs because market information is not perfect. We must remember that dealers operating in the market are not so fortunate as we. They do not have a neat chart, as that in Figure 13-4, telling them the exact level of the equilibrium price.

Dealers are feeling their way toward equilibrium by adroit and artful higgling in the market. As the price declines from $.35, in our example, many buyers may enter the market and purchase supplies of hogs at $.29, thinking that equilibrium had been reached. Hence, a large volume of transactions takes place at $.29. But the price does not stabilize there; it must fall on to $.275, to clear the market. For at $.29, all the hogs offered on the market will not be taken. The final, firm price is $.275, but in the wake of this equilibrium price we have a series of false prices. In practice, then, we would expect to find a cluster of prices ringing the equilibrium price, where transactions actually took place. These transaction prices are the market price quotations that we read in the newspaper and hear on the radio. And the more perfect the information in the market, the tighter the cluster of transaction prices we would expect to find ringing the equilibrium price.

The price of $.275 is determined by the well-known forces of supply and demand. And the determination of this price has taken place at the terminal wholesale market for hogs, where the forces of consumer demand and producer supply are given expression in the decisions of dealers in the market. The price in the retail market now becomes this $.275, plus the marketing margin, which we estimate to be $.115. Thus, the price of pork to the consumer is $.39 per pound and, at this price, all consumers in the United States take 12.8 billion pounds (see Figure 13-1). To obtain the price received by producers at the farm level, we subtract $.02 from the wholesale equilibrium price of $.275, which yields of price of $.255.

These prices, at the producer level and consumer level, will hold until the wholesale price changes once again, *changes because at the producer price of $.255 and the consumer price of $.39, producers and consumers make decisions that cause the amount demanded and the amount supplied at wholesale to change, consequently changing the equilibrium price.* The forces which change the equilibrium are thus initiated at the consumer and producer levels, but when the marketing system intervenes, the price-making process occurs at the wholesale level and the price changes effected there will naturally reverberate forward to the consumer and backward to the producer.

A price change. The equilibrium price at the wholesale level will change whenever consumer demand changes (*the curve shifts*), or whenever producer supply changes (*the curve shifts*). The derived curves at the wholesale level change correspondingly and we obtain a new equilibrium price. Thus, to explain a change in the equilibrium price at wholesale and, with it, the whole structure of pork prices, we must explain the causative shift in either the consumer-demand curve or the producer-supply curve. Happily, we have already provided this explanation. Shifters of the demand curve are to be found in the determinants of demand: (1) incomes of consumers, (2) tastes and preferences of consumers, (3) prices of close substitutes, and (4) size and composition of the population.

When one (or some combination) of these determinants changes, the demand curve shifts. Shifters of the supply curve are to be found in the factors that determine the position of the marginal-cost curve: (1) price of productive agents and (2) introduction of new technologies. When one of these factors changes, the supply curve shifts.

Certain of these determinants operate slowly and others quickly. Changes in the tastes and preferences of consumers, size and composition of the population, and introduction of new technologies usually take place slowly. In contrast, changes in the prices of close substitutes and productive agents take place quickly and fairly often. And, as we know, changes in consumer incomes occur cyclically and secularly.

In the hog-pork example that we have been using, one determinant on the supply side, the price of productive agents, is particularly volatile. The total production of corn, the principal raw material of pork, varies considerably from year to year. And in a free market, the price of corn varies inversely with the total supply. Hence, we have changes in the price of corn that influence the supply of hogs (the hog-corn cycle). On the consumption side, the price of beef and other protein foods, relative to pork prices, has an influence on the amount of pork demanded at any particular price. The state of consumer incomes, however, is probably the most important determinant of the demand for pork. When consumer incomes are high, the demand for all meat (including pork) is large, but when consumer incomes are depressed, the demand for meat falls off rapidly.

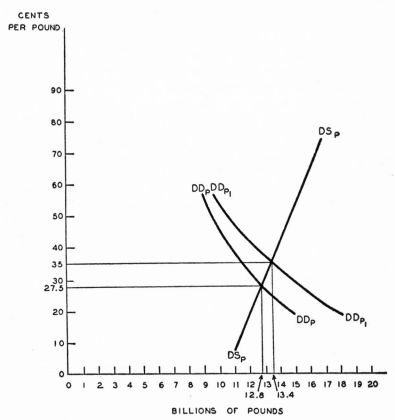

Fig. 13-5. Determining the price of pork at wholesale when the demand
increases.

In Figure 13-5, the effects on price of a change in (1) consumer incomes and (2) tastes and preferences, are illustrated. Here we see the derived demand curve, DD_p, and the derived supply curve, DS_p, the intersection of which yields an equilibrium price of $.275 and a quantity of 12.8 billion pounds (the same as in Figure 13-4). Now let us assume that (1) the incomes of all consumers increase as the national income expands, and (2) the preference of consumers for pork over beef, or beef over pork, becomes less pronounced (consumers become increasingly indifferent as to the type of red meat consumed). The effect of the increase in income is that of expanding the demand for pork. At any price, consumers will stand ready to take more pork than previously. The effect of the change in preference is to make the demand curve more elastic. Because of the increased indifference on the part of consumers as between pork and beef, when pork prices fall, consumers more readily substitute pork for beef, and, when pork prices rise, they more readily substitute beef for pork. The greater willingness to substitute gives rise to a more gently sloping demand curve. The result of these influences is to push the demand curve for pork to the right and into a more elastic position, as indicated by the curve, DD_{p_1} in Figure 13-5.

The intersection of the expanded demand curve, DD_{p_1}, with the old supply curve, DS_p, yields a new price-quantity solution. The new equilibrium price is $.35; the new equilibrium quantity is 13.4 billion pounds. We see clearly the consequence of the expansion in demand: more is taken and at a higher price than was previously the case. Of course, a contraction in demand has the opposite effect.

The new equilibrium price of $.35 will soon make itself felt throughout the marketing system. Deliveries made to retailers after this price rise are marked up accordingly. Hence, the consumer finds that the price of pork has risen approximately $.075. Producers, too, feel the effects of the price rise. In a perfectly competitive market, which is still our assumption, competition among packers for hogs will drive up the price at the farm level by approximately $.075. So the price changes, which came into being at the wholesale level, reverberate through the marketing system, affecting all concerned: producers, middlemen, and consumers.

Imperfect competition. The discussion of price determination, to this point, has been in terms of a perfectly competitive market. But the rigorous requirements of perfect competition are not easily satisfied in the business world. In the first place, the imperfect state of knowledge, information, in most markets, goes a long way toward making those markets imperfect. But a more critical element is that of the number of buyers and sellers in the market. If the number of buyers or sellers in a market are few, the action of anyone will have a discernible influence on price. In this context, a dealer can no longer assume that a purchase or sale action by him will have no influence on market price; on the contrary, he must consider the price consequences of his action and the possible retaliatory action of competitors. Clearly, when this condition prevails, we have passed out of the realm of perfect competition. We have passed over into that broad and vague land, variously described as imperfect competition or monopolistic competition, lying between perfect competition at one extreme and perfect monopoly at the other. And we define imperfect competition in a negative way: it is a market in which the rigorous requirements of a perfectly competitive market are not met in full, but where some competition exists, in that the market is not monopolized by one buyer or one seller.

Now the concept of imperfect competition may lack precision, but this lack of precision does not stem from the fact that it is an exceptional case. *On the contrary, the vagueness of the concept grows out of the multitude of cases which exist, each different in some respect.* Practically all durable goods, household appliances, clothing, and personal effects are sold under brand names. Each firm produces and sells a differentiated product, a product differentiated by appearance, name, and advertising. Hence, we no longer have a situation in which many firms produce and sell the same product; rather, we have as many products as firms. For each product, we have a market demand, and this demand confronts the single firm producing the product. Competition takes place through the substitution of one differentiated product for another. This is the classic case of monopolistic competition.

But a growing number of imperfect markets are to be found in food and agriculture; most processed foods are now branded. We do not ask for oatmeal; we are conditioned to ask for Quaker Oats. We do not ask for frozen spinach; we ask for Birdseye Frozen Spinach. And at the wholesale level, we think of imperfectly competitive conditions in the fluid milk and livestock markets, specifically, and all of agriculture, insofar as governmental price-supporting operations are engaged.

But what is the point of all this for our discussion "How Farm Prices Are Determined"? The point is this: when the market is imperfectly competitive, the equilibrium price will differ in some respect from the solutions shown in Figures 13-4 and 13-5. We cannot make a general statement as to the nature of the difference, for the imperfections take many forms and may occur on the buying side, the selling side, or both. But let us examine some possible cases under our hog-pork illustration.

If the market imperfection takes the form of imperfect knowledge, we would expect to find an expansion of the cluster of false prices around the equilibrium price. Further, the tendency for transaction prices to move toward the equilibrium price would be weakened. If the market imperfection should take the form of a national co-operative marketing organization that controlled the total supply of hogs moving to market, we might find the supply curve contracted in certain situations, to support prices, and expanded in others, with the result that wholesale prices would fluctuate less than in a perfectly free market.

Or, if the market imperfection should take the form of four large packers and many smaller ones, *as once was the case,* we might find that market price would be determined by the largest packer (the price leader), and it and the remaining three large packers would take their "fair" and constant percentage shares of the volume offered by all producers at that price. In support of this practice, George E. Putnam of Swift and Co. had this to say:

. . . It should be observed that the general practice among intelligent competitors of respecting one another's position need not be a matter of "tacit understanding." *In the case of Swift and Company it is an individual, commonsense policy arrived at independently, not to invite retaliation and trade wars by using overaggressive tactics.* [Swift] has deliberately tried to avoid cut-throat competition wherever it was legally possible to do so.

The same policy will always be followed by intelligent men. Purely as a matter of self-interest, no intelligent and successful business man wants to destroy his competitors. He knows that he himself may not survive the competitive struggle. Or if he should survive that struggle and become a monopolist, he knows that private monopoly, in these days of democratic government, will invite public ill-will and destructive legislation. It is clearly a matter of sound business policy to avoid cut-throat competition, but, unfortunately, there are times when the tactics of a competitor may become intolerable and in the interests of self-preservation one must have recourse to the same tactics. Thus a trade war may be provoked by an overaggressive policy on the part of one competitor.[3]

The situations mentioned above illustrate certain of the imperfections to be encountered in price-determining markets. But we should be clear on the fact that the number and variety of situations to be

---

[3] George E. Putnam, *Supplying Britain's Meat* (London: Geo. G. Harrap & Co., 1923), pages 124-26.

encountered in this vague land of imperfect competition are almost infinite. It needs, also, to be pointed out that the basic forces of supply and demand are not altered significantly by different forms of market organization. The force of demand arises out of decisions of consumers, and the force of supply arises out of decisions of producers. Dealers in the market, few or many, must operate within the conditions of that demand and supply. In our case, for example, consumers have, in a general way, decided how much pork they will take at various prices, and producers have decided how much they will supply. If there were but one meat packer, the perfect monopolist, he could not ignore these determining forces. He might manipulate them a bit to his advantage, but he could not control them in a free society.

There is one imperfection in agricultural commodity markets, which is becoming more generally accepted and which does not derive *directly* from private actions, that we should note: namely, the support of farm prices at some specified level of parity. Insofar as farm prices are supported by government action, market prices will differ from equilibrium prices. The forces that we have grouped under supply and demand do not cease to operate; government counteracts the operation of those forces by reducing supplies, in the usual case, by the amounts necessary to hold market prices at the announced support prices (the methods and consequences of price-supporting operations will be treated thoroughly in Part VI).

What we have here is price-making in political markets, rather than in economic markets. What prices of farm commodities *ought to be* are determined by political action in the Congress, rather than by economic action in markets. We do not say that such a development is bad, but it does represent a market imperfection in the technical sense.

A generalizing statement. We have developed only one commodity illustration in this chapter. We have followed this technique to maintain the *continuity* of the discussion in a difficult and vital area of economics. But is the price-making process that we have described applicable to other agricultural commodities? In a broad and general way, the answer is yes. We have outlined the process and the principal determinants within that process whereby a commodity price is determined. And the broad outline is as applicable for cotton and potatoes as it is for pork. But each commodity has peculiar and differentiating characteristics of its own. Hence, an analysis of cotton prices will take a somewhat different form than an analysis of potato prices, and the latter analysis will vary in some degree from the hog-pork case. The over-all framework of analysis is established, but the form of the analysis will vary commodity by commodity, as the market organization varies and as the supply-price and demand-price relationships vary.

REFERENCES

Boulding, Kenneth E., *Economic Analysis,* rev. ed. Chapters 4, 5, and 27. New York: Harper & Brothers, 1948.

Samuelson, Paul A., *Economics: An Introductory Analysis,* 3rd ed. Chapters 19 and 20. New York: McGraw-Hill Book Company, Inc., 1955.

Waite, Warren C., and Harry C. Trelogan, *Agricultural Market Prices,* 2nd ed. Chapters 3, 4, and 5. New York: John Wiley, & Sons, Inc., 1951.

POINTS FOR DISCUSSION

1. How do the twin concepts of the *substitution effect* and the *income effect* explain the negative slope of the demand curve?
2. What do we mean by the elasticity of demand? Derive a measure of the elasticity of demand for pork when the price rises from $.45 to $.53 per pound and the quantity taken declines from 11.9 billion pounds to 10.7 billion pounds. Is the demand for pork over this price range elastic or inelastic?
3. How do we derive the market supply curve for any commodity, say pork? What basic principle explains the positive slope of the supply curve (why does it slope upward and to the right)?
4. How do we define a perfectly competitive market? Why do we make use of such an unreal, abstract formulation?
5. Demonstrate that the price indicated by the intersection of the demand curve with the supply curve is stable, that it shows no tendency to move.
6. Assume that consumer incomes rise: what will happen to the demand for pork, what will happen to equilibrium price?
7. Suppose the price of corn rises: what will happen to the price of hogs? Why?
8. What do we mean by imperfect competition? Where in the agricultural industry are we most likely to find examples of imperfect competition? What form will these "imperfections" most likely take?

CHAPTER 14

The Role
Farm Prices Play

EVERYONE IS interested in farm prices: the farmer, the economist, the politician, and the consumer. To appreciate this continuing interest, we must understand what farm prices do, the role that they play. In some cases, this role is so obvious that economists are prone to overlook its importance. In other cases, it is so complex that laymen and economists alike find it difficult to understand thoroughly. Our goal here, then, is to describe clearly the role (or roles) that farm prices play.

The over-all integrating role of prices. Every economic society, whether it be a military dictatorship, a communistic dictatorship, free and perfectly competitive, or mixed capitalism (compounded of perfectly competitive markets, imperfectly competitive markets, and governmental intervention, as represented by the United States), must meet and solve in some way three fundamental economic problems:

(1) What goods and services shall be produced and in what quantities?

(2) How shall those goods and services be produced, that is, by whom, with what resources, and in what technological manner?

(3) For whom are they to be produced, that is, who is to consume and enjoy the goods and services produced?

These three questions are fundamental and common to all economies and to every segment of each economy. For as a rereading of these questions will indicate, their solution determines how well each of us lives, how each of us is employed, and what each of us lives by. These are determinations that vitally concern people everywhere.

It should not be inferred that these are the only questions of importance confronting an economic society. The employment problem, the level of economic activity, is a problem of great importance not included here.

Important for this discussion is the fact that the automatically operating pricing system in a free and perfectly competitive society solves, or is tending to solve, these three questions simultaneously. In such a competitive system, no individual or organization is consciously concerned with the solution of these three basic questions. Thousands of different kinds of goods and services, produced by millions of geographically scattered workers, are moved around and distributed to other millions of consumers, in a relatively orderly fashion, under the unconscious direction of the pricing system. In a mixed, capitalistic system, the automatic price mechanism continues to provide this basic integrating function, but not perfectly, and it gets some help from the government. In other words, business firms, when they can, and government, when it intervenes, provide some conscious direction in the way of price control and administration. Still, the automatically operating price system carries the main load. In this over-all integrating role, farm prices, of course, play their part. They knit the various parts of food and agriculture together in a whole fabric and they integrate agriculture with the rest of the economy in an organic fashion.

We have worked through the theory and mechanics of price determination for a single farm commodity (Chapter 13). The question now arises: how does the automatically operating price *system* integrate the total economy; how does it fit all the parts of the economy together in a meaningful and effective pattern? In the first place, everything has a price: each consumer good has its price, each service has its price, each producer good has its price, each kind of labor has its price (wage rate), and even the commodity money has its price (the interest rate). Everyone receives a money income for what he sells: the producer, a gross income on the product sold; the laborer, a net income (wages) for services rendered; the stockholder, a net dividend on funds invested. And each receiver of this money income, in a free society, uses it to purchase what he needs or wishes. If all consumers demand more lettuce, orders at retail and at wholesale rise, market price rises, and eventually more is produced. In contrast, if there are more eggs supplied than consumers will take at existing prices, the prices of eggs are forced down through competitive action. At lower prices, consumers will consume more eggs, and, when the market is perfectly competitive, producers will reduce their production of eggs. Thus, there is a tendency for equilibrium to be restored between demand and supply, in the case of the two commodities mentioned and in the case of the many others that could be mentioned. In the movement toward equilibrium, the public gets the kinds and quantities of products desired, although complete equilibrium is probably never achieved, for prices are forever changing in response to changes in the desires and plans of consumers and producers. The whole problem might be likened to a dog chasing a rabbit. Equilibrium is realized when the dog catches the rabbit, but when the dog (transaction price) reaches the point at which the rabbit (equilibrium price) was when the dog started, the rabbit has hopped to a new position.

These adjustments toward equilibrium take place in markets for factors of production, as they do in consumer-goods markets. If peach pickers, rather than cow milkers, are needed, job opportunities will be more favorable in the former field. The price of peach pickers (their hourly wage) will tend to rise, while that of cow milkers will tend to fall. All other things equal, this shift in relative prices (wage rates) causes a shift of labor resources into the desired production. Or when tractor power becomes more efficient, hence, more desired than horse or mule power, farmers will shift their purchasing power toward tractors and away from horses and mules. The consequences of this action are to expand the demand for tractors and, assuming technological development to be constant for the moment, to raise tractor prices, ultimately increasing the supply of tractors. In the opposite direction, the demand for horses and mules contracts, their price falls, and eventually the supply is reduced. So the adjustment toward equilibrium goes on at all levels and for every unit in society that commands a price.

"In other words, we have a vast system of trial and error, of successive approximation to an equilibrium system of prices and production. When supply everywhere matches demand and prices match costs, our three economic problems have been simultaneously solved."[1] *For whom* goods and services are produced is determined by demand and supply, in the markets for productive services, by wage rates, land rents, interest rates, and profits, which add up to total personal incomes received. *How things* are produced is determined by the competition of different producers. The low-cost method, at any one time, based upon technical efficiency and a combination of low-priced inputs, will displace a high-cost method, because the only way a high-cost producer may maximize his profits (particularly when prices are falling) is to adopt the more efficient methods. *What*

---

[1] Paul A. Samuelson, *Economics: An Introductory Analysis* (New York: McGraw-Hill Book Company, Inc., 1948), page 37.

things will be produced is determined by the choices of consumers in decisions to purchase this product and not that. And the expenditures that consumers make, the money they pay into business establishments, ultimately provide the wages, rent, dividends, and profits that they (consumers) receive as income. The circle is complete and, in the total complex of decisions and actions that we term the operating economy, *price* (*or prices*) has provided the basis for making decisions and taking actions that fit together in an integrated whole.

Income-producing (using) role. Abstracting from the over-all, integrating role of prices presented above, we wish to analyze, in some detail, two specific functions that price performs. The first of these is the income-producing (using) function of price. This is the obvious role and, to the worker, the farmer, and the retailer, the all important role that price performs. Assuming, for the time, a full use of resources, the money income of a steel worker depends upon the hourly wage rate received by him, the cash receipts of a corn-hog farmer depend upon the price received by him for hogs, and the cash receipts of the retailer depend upon the price of the goods sold by him. This is so obvious that the man in the street and the men who represent him in local, state, and Federal governments find it hard to attach any importance to other roles. It is so obvious that the economist often forgets the importance of this role. But we must never lose sight of this obvious relationship, *where quantities are unchanged, the income of a productive agent depends upon the price it receives for its service.*

Now dissatisfaction with the income received by productive agents through the automatically operating price system has led, in many, many cases, to tampering with the price system. Productive agents, in most cases, are unwilling to accept the income verdict of an automatically operating pricing system, when that verdict is a low price for their service. We know something of the story in agriculture. Farm people have banded together and requested the Federal government to support the price of their products, hence, their gross incomes. This is not a unique or exceptional experience. Labor has combined in unions to protect and support wage rates. And business concerns have amalgamated and formed trade associations to enhance and support the prices of their products. So we find the incentive to discard the automatically operating price system and to substitute for it a system of managed prices. This incentive exists in the dissatisfaction of producer groups with the income-producing role of prices in perfectly competitive situations. An automatic pricing system in a perfectly competitive economic society *may* be best for all of us, but rarely is a particular group willing to accept the income consequences of such a system if it can avoid it. We have, therefore, metamorphosed into a mixed capitalistic system, with government *intervention* and *private price management.*

Upon this point we should be clear. The drive toward a mixed capitalistic economy has not come from government. The drive grows out of individual producer groups seeking to enhance and protect their incomes. We have corporations administering prices, unions bargaining over wage rates, and farm people invoking the power of government to support farm prices.

The income-using role of prices is the converse of the producing role. When consumer incomes are fixed, the higher the prices of consumer goods, the lower is the purchasing power of incomes, and vice versa. Very simply, if food prices rise, we have less money income to use in purchasing other goods and services; if food prices fall, we have more money to use in purchasing other goods and services.

Resource-allocation role. This is the role that intrigues economists, but to which the man in the street pays little attention. In this role, prices serve as signals. When egg prices are high, relative to the prices of products that are close substitutes, egg producers are likely to take one or more of the following actions: cull laying hens less closely, increase the care of the laying flock, buy more baby chicks to increase the size of the laying flock, and build more houses to handle a larger flock. And new producers may be attracted into egg production. In brief, the economy is allocating more resources to egg production. On the other hand, the increased price of eggs has flashed a signal to consumers too. Consumers realize that eggs are expensive and that they had better substitute other foods for eggs whenever possible.

In the other direction, should egg prices fall, relative to other farm prices, producers would first cut output by employing fewer resources in egg production, perhaps by reducing purchases of feed or by culling more severely. But in the longer run, producers would be induced to employ new methods and reduce their costs. So we see that this allocating role is a highly important one. Price changes direct consumers to use more of one product and less of another, and direct producers to use more resources here and less there, as well as new methods whenever they are cheaper. Hence, we obtain a solution to the questions: *what* commodities, and in *what* quantities, and *how* shall they be produced? In a perfectly competitive economic society and even in a mixed capitalistic economic society, *relative prices,* the price of one commodity relative to another, tell producers how to combine resources to produce the kinds and quantities of products demanded.

No wonder economists are impressed; this is no little achievement. But this process of resource allocation does not work timelessly or instantaneously. Some resources may be added to a production process quickly and effectively, whereas others take time, much time. So it is customary in economic analyses to study production changes, made in response to price changes, by time periods.

The time periods that we shall consider are as follows: The market day—a period so short that supply may not be altered; the short run—a period in which supply may be varied as such non-fixed agents as labor, feed and fertilizer are varied in productive combinations; and the long run—a period in which supplies may be varied importantly as all agents of production are varied (for example, the size of barn, number of acres, arrangement of ditches, number of producers). And in all this, we make one important assumption. We assume the state of technology is constant—unchanged. This simplifying assumption helps considerably. Later when we see where we are going we can drop it.

The market day. Let us assume that our market is New York City and that our product is dressed chicken. In the market day, the supply of dressed chicken in the New York City market is fixed. At extremely low prices, dealers might hold back some portion of the day's supply and, at extremely high prices, they might be able to divert some additional supplies into the market. But on an average market day, the total amount of chicken offered on the market is a fixed amount. The marketing channel leading into New York City is emptied in any one day, and the amount flowing in must sell at whatever price clears the market.

This situation is illustrated in Figure 14-1. The fixed supply of chicken in the market day is indicated by the vertical line *FS*. That line tells us that, regardless of the price, 750,000 pounds of dressed chicken are offered on the market. That was the amount that moved up through the marketing channel during the night, and now there is little or nothing that can be done to alter that supply. The demand in the wholesale market on this given day, derived from the demands of consumers in New York City, is indicated by the curve *DD_c*. In the very short run of the market day, the equilibrium price is determined at $.38, which is determined by the intersection of the demand curve *DD_c* and the supply curve *FS*.

But what if demand should change? The consequence of an increase in demand is illustrated in Figure 14-1. When the demand for

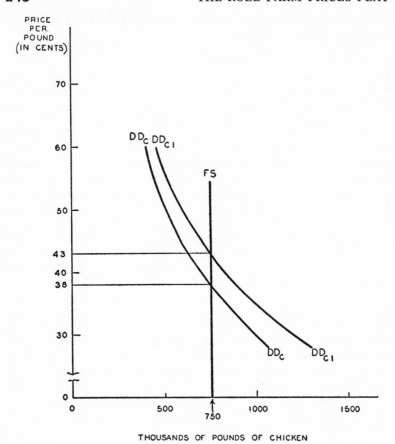

Fig. 14-1. Derivation of the price of chicken in the *market day*, wholesale level, New York City.

chicken expands from DD_c to DD_{c1} and the amount supplied is fixed at 750,000 pounds, the equilibrium price rises from $.38 to $.43. Price rises by the full amount of the expansion in demand. Or, stated differently, the full force of the expansion in demand is absorbed in the price rise. So in the market day, when the amount supplied is fixed, we say that price is determined by and varies directly with the conditions of demand.

The short run. The short-run situation grows logically out of the market day. The expansion in demand from DD_c to DD_{c1} in the very short run of the market day forced the wholesale price of chicken up to $.43. These higher prices were transmitted back through the marketing system to take the form of higher producer prices. Higher producer prices are a signal to farmers to devote more resources to the production of chickens, as a means of increasing their income. Spurred by the incentive of selling more chickens at the existing high market, producers take those actions open to them in the short run to expand their production.

Now what can producers do in the short run to expand their production and sale of chicken? They can market broilers and roasting chickens earlier, at lighter-than-optimum weights. But probably producers would attempt, through increased care and control over feeding operations, to put meat on their chickens more quickly. Or, if the short run is long enough (and the length of each of these periods is relative), producers could expand output by ordering more baby chicks and raising more broilers in their existing buildings.

In the short run, then, there are several ways a producer could expand his output of chicken. But additional output, without an improvement in technology, entails additional cost. To sell more pounds of chicken next month than he had planned, in response to the now higher market prices, the producer incurs extra costs, which cause the unit costs of the additional pounds of chicken to rise. What we are describing for the individual producer is, then, a movement along his marginal-cost curve. The summation of the marginal-cost curves, for all producers, yields the short-run supply curve SRS_1 in Figure 14-2. This curve describes how the supply offered increases as price rises. But we should appreciate that increases or decreases in supply, associated with price changes, take time; in this case they take place over the short run.

Induced by the high market price of $.43 (Figure 14-1), producers expand output as described by the curve SRS_1 (Figure 14-2). The intersection of the supply curve SRS_1 with the expanded demand curve results in the short-run equilibrium price of $.415, when 790,000 pounds of chicken are cleared through the wholesale market. In the short run, then, price falls from the *responsive* price of $.43 to the new equilibrium price of $.415. This price decline results from the production adjustment process whereby producers intensify their productive efforts. In this process, they supply a greater quantity of chicken; but the additional quantity is forthcoming only at a higher cost, $.415 per pound, to be exact.

Two points need to be made regarding this short-run equilibrium price of $.415. First, it does not grow out of an actual market situation; it is a normal concept. In any market day following these short-run developments, a fixed quantity of 790,000 pounds would be

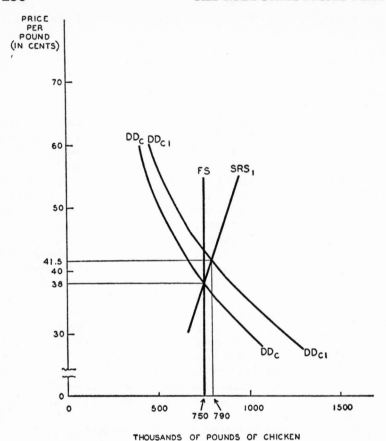

Fig. 14-2. **Derivation of the price of chicken in the** *short run,* **wholesale level, New York City.**

offered on the market, and the equilibrium price for the market day would be determined by the intersection of a vertical supply curve, at a quantity of 790,000 pounds, with the given demand curve DD_{c1}, which yields the identical price of \$.415. And, of course, actual transaction prices would cluster about the equilibrium price of \$.415. To repeat, the supply curve SRS_1 indicates the supplies forthcoming at various prices, when a short period of adjustment is permitted. But for any one market day, when transactions occur and transaction prices emerge, the supply offered is fixed in amount.

Second, we see that the explanation of price determination, in the previous chapter, was really oversimplified. The case we described was this short-run case, in which the supply curve represents the sum of the marginal-cost curves for all firms. But at that point we said nothing about time. We ignored it. Now we see that the quantity supplied may vary only as producers are able to vary the units of resources employed, *which takes time.*

The long run. We have seen that the equilibrium price of dressed chicken falls over the period of the short run (from $.43 to $.415). But the short-run equilibrium price of $.415 continues to exceed the market price of $.38, which existed prior to the expansion in demand for chicken. Hence, there remains an incentive to increase supplies, since individual producers are making good profits (marginal costs are equal to price, but average unit costs are less than price: refer to Chapter 5). In the long run, the total output of chickens may be increased in several ways not feasible or possible in the short run, for it will be remembered that the long run is a period of sufficient length to permit any type of production adjustment. Nothing is fixed in the long run. Plant capacity may be expanded or reorganized (that is, new buildings may be constructed, the layout may be re-arranged). Induced, then, by the remunerative price of $.415 (Figure 14-2), producers already in the field enlarge their plant capacity.

But high prices and high profits also attract new producers. And in the long run, there is time for new producers to enter the field of producing chickens for meat. In general terms, the favorable price signal for dressed chicken is directing (allocating) more and more resources to the production of chicken. The automatically operating pricing system is working as it is expected to work. The higher prices attract additional resources: more labor, more feed, more capital in the form of buildings and equipment. And these additional resources turn out more product, which, in the long run, causes the price of chicken to fall still further.

This situation is portrayed graphically in Figure 14-3. Over the long run, new producers have entered the industry and old producers have expanded their plant capacity. Hence, we obtain a new short run supply curve SRS_2 for dressed chicken. This curve, as previously defined, sums up the marginal-cost curves of all producers in the industry. But we now have more producers, and larger producers. Consequently, the short-run supply curve shifts to the right and takes up the new position SRS_2. The intersection of the supply curve SRS_2 with the demand curve DD_{c1} determines the long run equilibrium price of $.395, when a quantity of 850,000 pounds clears the market.

The industry producing chickens for meat in the New York market,

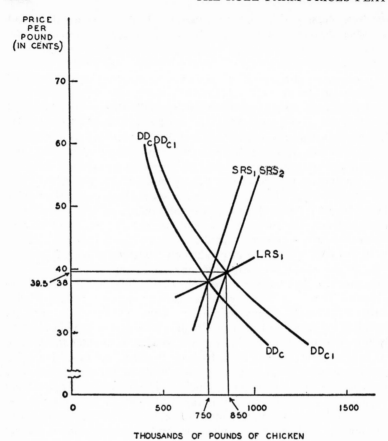

Fig. 14-3. Derivation of the price of chicken in the *long run*, wholesale level, New York City.

as described in this illustration, is one of increasing cost. The long-run curve LRS_1, in Figure 14-3, describes this condition. In response to the increase in market price, growing out of the expansion of demand, producers in this example have adjusted their chicken-raising enterprise, first, in the short run, and second, in the long run, to increase production. Output has expanded, but, after complete adjustment in the long run, supply has not increased sufficiently to bring the price of chicken back to or below the starting price of $.38. The economy has allocated additional resources to the production of chicken for the New York market, but the allocation is not sufficiently generous to bring the price back to the starting point. In the long run, the price of chicken in the New York market is rising, or so the curve LRS_1 describes.

Why should this be? In the first place, it needs to be recalled that advances in technology were ruled out of this analysis. We are analyzing price-cost relationships when the state of technological development is constant. Granted this simplifying assumption, what happened is this. New resources do not automatically flow into the chicken-raising industry, in either the short run or long run. New resources, feed, and labor, in the short run, and construction supplies and equipment, in the long run, must be bid into the industry. In this process of bidding new resources into chicken production, the prices of the productive agents involved are driven up. The prices of the productive agents involved increase as the demand for those agents increase.

In this situation, the costs of the chicken-producing enterprise must rise. At any given level of output, marginal costs and average total unit costs for the typical enterprise are higher at the end of the long-run period than they were at the beginning. The average unit costs of producing chicken for the typical enterprise are, in fact, equal to the long-run equilibrium price of $.395 per pound, because new producers continue to enter the field and old producers continue to expand operations, until price falls to the level of average unit costs of production. At this point, individual producers stop expanding, the supply curve stops drifting to the right, and the long-run normal price stabilizes at $.395. We have something of a scissors relationship here: price is falling because of increased supplies, costs are rising to produce the increased supplies, and, when they meet (as at $.395), the long-run adjustment is final and complete.

The long-run normal price, in this case $.395, is the price toward which the chicken-producing industry is *tending,* but which it never reaches. This long-run equilibrium price is not realized in the developing, changing economy for at least two main reasons: First, and most obvious, the demand for chicken is not going to hold constant in the position DD_{c1} for, say, one, two or three years. Some determinant of demand, in this illustration, caused the demand for chicken at the wholesale level to increase from DD_c to DD_{c1}. We can be certain that the determinants of demand will continue to change, and, with those changes, the demand curve shifts into new positions. Since price changes every time the demand curve shifts, producers never have the opportunity to *fully* adjust their plans to a stable price.

Before long-run production plans are executed in full, the price relationships which brought those plans into being change with changes in demand.

So the long run, and to some extent the short run, is an abstraction from the economic world that permits economists to trace the consequences of a given price change on production responses. The concept of the long-run normal price is not, then, a price that we may expect to meet in the real world.

The above conclusion is buttressed by another reason, one that helps explain why food costs, outside of wartime, do not tend to rise as total output expands. To this point we have assumed no change in the state of technology. We made this assumption to simplify the analysis. But in the dynamic economy in which we live, technological advance is rapid and widespread. Almost every day we read of some new method of processing food, controlling insects and weeds, and in enticing Mother Nature to give forth more abundantly. And when the demand for a particular product is strong and its price high, that is the time when farmer-producers adopt new methods, the time of innovation.

In our example of the chicken industry, producers would be inclined to try new methods—new feeding techniques, new breeds, new equipment—when demand is strong and the price of dressed chicken is high. During such periods, producers have the necessary bright expectations to invest in new and, for the moment, costly methods. In Figure 14-4, the process of long-run adjustment is portrayed in which technological advance takes place. As in the previous case, high chicken prices and high profits attract new producers, and old producers are induced to expand their operations. These actions have the effect of raising the prices of productive agents, hence, raising average costs of production. *But in this case there is a difference.* Producers, new and old, adopt a new production technique that, in itself, lowers costs of production.

The net effect of these opposing influences is assumed to be that of modestly reducing the average total unit costs for typical producers. In this context, the short-run supply curve of the industry shifts to the right until it reaches the position SRS_3, where the long-run equilibrium price is determined at $.37 and a quantity of 930,000 pounds clears the market. It will be observed that the supply curve SRS_3 shifts farther to the right than in the case of the supply curve SRS_2. This occurs because costs have not risen; on the contrary, they have fallen modestly, and the only way that the profit gap may be closed, when price exceeds average unit costs, is for supply to increase. And supply does increase, by the action of new producers entering the

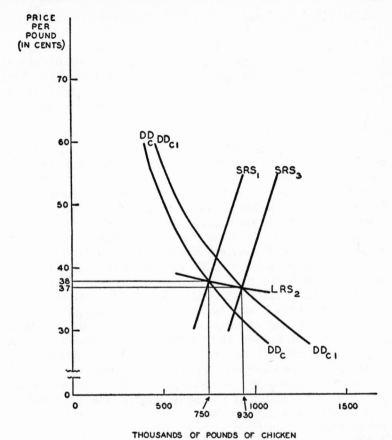

Fig. 14-4. Derivation of the price of chicken in the *long run*, when cost-reducing technologies are introduced, wholesale level, New York City.

field and old producers expanding, until we obtain the supply curve SRS_3. At the new wholesale price of $.37, prices received by producers equal average unit costs of typical producers. At this price, a long-run price equilibrium is established, for producers no longer have any incentive to expand their individual outputs, or to contract them.

In all this, our industry has metamorphosed into a "decreasing cost industry": the long-run curve LRS_2 slopes downward and to the right. This occurred because producers took advantage of new production techniques; they devised means of producing the same quantity with fewer inputs, or a larger quantity with the same inputs. They reduced the cost of producing a pound of chicken.

Some dynamic considerations. We have discussed at some length the allocative role of prices and analyzed the way in which this allocative role unfolds itself through time. Yet, perhaps, the most exciting role of prices in the allocation of resources remains to be discussed. We have in mind the role of expected, future prices. What decisions we make today depend, in large measure, on what we expect the price of our product to be next month, next year, and five years from now. This is particularly true in respect to investment decisions, decisions to make expenditures now that will influence costs and output in the future.

The decision to buy a farm, for example, is a tremendously important one, which depends, or should depend, on expected future price relationships. If the prices of farm products are expected to fall over the long run, a farmer would be ill-advised to purchase high-priced land in the current period. If, on the other hand, farm prices are expected to rise over the long-run future, high-priced land in the current period may, in fact, represent low-cost land. The decision to plant a commercial orchard is not of the same importance as a decision to buy a farm, but the problem is similar. The decision turns, or should turn, on expected price relationships over the forthcoming five to ten years. If fruit prices are expected to fall, the farmer may find it to his advantage to use his land for other purposes.

So we see that decisions to combine resources, one way or another, or to allocate resources, do not depend solely on current prices. Resources are allocated by producers, through time, in accordance with the dictates of *expected prices*. Expected prices provide the grist out of which investment decisions are ground.

The problem of entrepreneurship in the *static state* is the selection and combination of various agents to yield a maximum surplus of receipts over costs. And the selection and combination of productive agents is based upon current price relationships. This is the case we analyzed earlier in this chapter, under the allocation of resources in the market day and in both the short run and the long run. In that *static theory,* we recognized that time is required in the adjustment of productive agents to current prices. *But in all cases, the adjustment of resources was made relevant to current prices.* The problem of entrepreneurship in the *dynamic state* (one step nearer the real world) is the selection of a certain production plan, from among many alternatives, to yield a maximum surplus of receipts over costs throughout the expected life of the enterprise. The formulation and selection of the specific plan is based upon *expected price relation-*

ships. The dynamic problem is, then, the organization of resources through time in such a way as to obtain the greatest net return to the enterprise over its lifetime.

But how is a preferred production plan to be selected? In the dynamic situation, it is clear that a chicken, hog, or wheat producer is not looking at the possible surplus of receipts over costs in the current season. It is a stream of surpluses going on from season to season that occupies his attention. If two alternative streams were such that every surplus in one stream was greater than the corresponding surplus in the other stream, then there would be no question as to which was the larger and which the producer would select. But the alternatives are rarely so clear-cut.

Let us consider a rather typical example. A producer has two production plans under consideration: (1) the development of a turkey enterprise on his farm, or (2) the employment of approximately the same quantity of resources in a hog enterprise. This producer expects futures prices for these two products to be such that, in the turkey-producing enterprise, the stream of surpluses is small to begin with, but becomes larger and larger over the years; whereas for hogs, the stream of surpluses is large to begin with and becomes smaller and smaller over the years. Which will he choose? We cannot say exactly, since we have not assigned values to the alternative surplus streams. But we can suggest a basis for ascertaining the preferred stream: The choice between the alternative production plans, with their attendant surplus streams, will be made on the basis of the *present value* of the two streams. The expected surplus in each year for each stream is discounted by the current and going rate of interest to obtain the present value of each of those expected surpluses.[2] The present values of the stream of surpluses, under one plan, and the present values of the stream of surpluses, under the other, are then summed to obtain the present values of the two production plans. And whichever plan yields the greater net return, discounted to present value, is the preferred plan.

The preferred production plan can be determined easily when product and resource prices are *anticipated with some certainty*. But therein lies the rub. How can we know the future with certainty? Most of us judge the future by past experience, and the most recent past experience usually dominates our judgment. Thus, each of us, including our farmer who is trying to decide whether to equip his farm to produce turkeys or hogs, probably projects the pattern of

---

2 The present value of $100 due five years hence at 5 per cent interest, compounded annually, is, for example, equal to $78.35. If, then, the expected surplus in the fifth year is equal to $100, we know its discounted present value.

prices existing over the past year into the short-run future with little modification. We may vary the pattern modestly, as a hunch or a bit of recent information suggests, but in the main, our short-run forecast mirrors the recent past.

Long-run price forecasts by the producer and consumer alike are even less well-grounded. About all that any of us can do is guess. It is true that some of these guesses represent informed opinions. But it is equally true that expected prices are not scientifically determined values. Expected prices are vague things, ranging from crystal ball projections to elaborate statistical extrapolations. And the individual producer (and consumer), who must make decisions involving the future, probably does not *expect* in any absolute sense. More probably, he conceives of the expected price of his commodity, as of some specific date, in the form of a range of possible prices, each with some degree of probability. For example, the uncertain producer, whom we have been considering, *might* view hog prices one year from his day of decision in the following way:

(1) There is one chance in ten that the price will be $.25 per pound.

(2) There are four chances in ten that the price will be $.20 per pound.

(3) There are four chances in ten that the price will be $.15 per pound.

(4) There is one chance in ten that the price will be $.10 per pound.

The mean expected price is $\frac{1}{10} \times \$.25 + \frac{4}{10} \times \$.20 + \frac{4}{10} \times \$.15 + \frac{1}{10} \times \$.10 = \$.175$. The price of $.175, expected one year ahead, represents a weighted average of this particular producer's range of price expectation, and hence, may be interpreted as the most probable price expectation of this producer. But producers don't formulate the probabilities so precisely. In some vague way, each producer formulates the most probable price out of a range of possibilities and then acts, making production decisions on the basis of that probable expected price.

This much seems clear. The further into the future that a price forecast is made, the wider will be the range of price possibilities. This follows from the obvious: the more distant the future the more uncertain the future. The mean expected price, or the most probable expected price, becomes less reliable[3] as a basis for planning. Hence, producers plan less rigorously and formally as the planning dates recede into the future. In short, the entrepreneur cannot plan, when

---

[3] The variance of the probability distribution becomes greater and greater.

the principal elements of the problem, prices, cannot be anticipated.

In the short-run future, then, production plans are rather concrete affairs, based upon price relationships expected with a relatively high degree of probability. But as we move further into the future, these production plans merge into dreams, hopes, and, at best, flexible plans. And as production plans become more indefinite, so does the process of resource allocation, for the use of resources is determined by the production plan (or plans) and, when plans become vague, so does the allocation of resources.

In this dynamic setting, the entrepreneur comes into his own. The man who judges the future reasonably accurately and who formulates an effective production plan to exploit that future will reap the large rewards. The Johnny-come-lately's, attracted by large profits, rarely enjoys such success. But most people will agree that price expectations are rarely realized in full, and if they are, more luck than skill may be involved. The second test of an entrepreneur is, then, his ability to reformulate plans as expected prices go awry. The successful farm operator modifies his production plan as quickly as possible when his expectations of the future turn out to be wrong. But such adjustments are not easily made. In the first place, it is easier to operate by habit than by conscious adjustment. And, in the second place, investments already sunk into items such as barns, dairy equipment, and irrigation systems do not fit into a changed plan on a moment's notice. A great deal of skill is required to modify long-range production plans quickly and efficiently. But change they must, for price relationships are forever changing, and only the omniscient producer could foresee and create a plan to exploit all possible price changes over long periods of operation.

Production responses to price changes. Throughout this chapter and the previous one, we have held to the assumption that farm operators behave in a rational way, that is, they make those adjustments in production plans, in response to price changes, that maximize the profits of the farm operation. In a broad, general way, this assumption does not seem to contradict past experience. Certainly few farmers take actions aimed at lowering profits. But we must recognize that habit and custom play an important part in the determination of producer behavior. Many farmers become accustomed to feeding dairy cows a certain ration and continue to feed that ration regardless of price changes. It has long been the custom in Pennsylvania to raise winter wheat and farmers continue to produce that wheat regardless of current cost-price relationships. And many farmers in the South prefer to raise only one crop, cotton. These customary practices and many more are not undertaken to reduce the return to the farming operation. As the term "custom" implies, they were acquired over a long period of time, perhaps in a period when they represented efficient practices, and farmers continue to apply them without any conscious consideration of their consequences. *The effect of custom is, then, to slow down production adjustments in response to price changes.* The regrouping of productive agents into new and more efficient combinations, in response to price changes, takes place slowly as customs and habits are modified.

This does not mean that the price system has failed in its resource allocation role. If only 5 to 10 per cent of the farmers change their production plans in response to a change in price relationships, that is enough to keep the allocation process in motion. And studies indicate that just this happens. A small percentage of the producers affected by a price change, usually those who can most easily shift into an alternative enterprise, modify their production plans, and bring about, in most cases, but not all cases, the desired change in output. The total output of a particular product expands a little in response to a price rise, and contracts a little in response to a price decline.

If we think about this "dragging" allocative process, we will see the advantage (and the disadvantage) involved. Custom, habit, and the limitation of technical possibilities prevent farmers from moving from one extreme to another. Hence, custom and habit help protect the economy against an "explosive" type of behavior where all resources are first devoted to the output of one commodity, and then are all shifted into the production of another. Take the case of potatoes and sugar beets in the irrigated valleys of the West. If, in response to a rise in sugar-beet prices, all producers moved out of potato and into sugar-beet production, consumers would find their food supply disrupted in the extreme. But some shift from potatoes to sugar beets is called for by the rise in sugar-beet prices, and the usual modest output response is sufficient to bring the price disparity between sugar beets and potatoes back into line.

But there are times when widespread production adjustments in agriculture are called for, and, in those times, custom and habit do interfere with effective resource allocation. World War II was such a period. And in some areas custom and habit are so ingrained, so crusted over, that we get almost no output response to price changes. There, custom and habit interfere. In most cases, however, the modest total adjustment in the production plans of from 5 to 10 per cent of the farmers affected by a price change serves to allocate resources *within* agriculture, in accordance with the needs and demands of consumers.

REFERENCES

Heady, Earl O., *Economics of Agricultural Production and Resource Use*. Chapters 15, 16, and 17. Englewood Cliffs, N.J.: Prentice-Hall, Inc., 1952.

Samuelson, Paul A., *Economics: An Introductory Analysis,* 3rd ed. Chapters 2 and 3. New York: McGraw-Hill Book Company, Inc., 1955.

Schultz, T. W., *Redirecting Farm Policy*. New York: The Macmillan Co., 1943, pages 1-38.

Stigler, George J., *The Theory of Price,* rev. ed. Chapters 9 and 10. New York: The Macmillan Co., 1952.

POINTS FOR DISCUSSION

1. How does the automatically operating price system integrate the economy?
2. What do we mean by the income-producing (using) role of prices? How has dissatisfaction with this role of prices led to governmental intervention in the private economy?
3. In what sense do prices direct the use of resources? How does this direction or allocation take place?
4. What is the elasticity of supply in the market day? How is supply modified in the short run? How is supply modified in the long run? How do these changes in supply through time influence prices?
5. How does the adoption of new technologies on farms influence supply?
6. How do price expectations influence the current use of resources? What type of resources would you expect to be allocated primarily on the basis of current prices, what type of resources primarily on the basis of expected prices?
7. How do habit and custom influence producer behavior? Is the role of prices in resource allocation impaired?

CHAPTER 15

Two Farm Price Problems

A REVIEW of the behavior and structure of prices in Chapter 12 indicates that there are two different kinds of price variability in agriculture: (1) wide swings in the farm price level, and (2) year-to-year, even within-the-year, variations in commodity prices around the moving farm price level.

The complex of lines running across Figure 12-1, which looks something like a frayed rope, illustrates the two different types of price variability found in agriculture. The heavy line at the center of the frayed rope in Figure 12-1 describes movements in the farm price *level*. The differently labelled lines, or frayed rope ends, describe variations in commodity prices around the moving farm price level (for seven of the more important farm commodities).

The farm price level is unstable, moving through time in broad and dramatic sweeps (Figure 12-2). The upswings are associated with economic recovery and wars; the downswings with economic depressions, post-war periods and chronic over-production in agriculture. For example, the level of prices received by farmers fell 43 per cent between 1919 and 1921, fell another 56 per cent between 1929 and 1932, rose 185 per cent between 1940 and 1948, and then fell by 22 per cent between 1951 and 1955. And this last decline was moderated by various price-supporting actions on the part of the government. In sum, the farm price level fluctuates in the extreme, but it does not fluctuate in a regular, or rhythmic, pattern.

A different story emerges with respect to the year-to-year variations in individual commodity prices around the moving farm price level. Some commodity prices move in close harmony with the over-all level; others fluctuate wildly about it. This can be seen in Figure 12-1.

Whole milk prices, for example, tend to move closely with—parallel with—the farm price level; potato and hog prices, in contrast, fluctuate around the price level in a sharp and uncertain fashion. Measures of the year-to-year *percentage* variations in the prices of selected farm commodities around the moving farm price level for the long period 1920-55 are as follows:[1]

Whole milk	6.1
Beef cattle	9.7
Wheat	13.7
Corn	17.8
Hogs	15.3
Soybeans	19.2
Potatoes	48.7

In general, what we observe from these estimates, and other available data, is a continuum of commodity price variability around the farm price level, ranging from modestly variable for commodities such as milk and eggs, to substantially variable for cotton, corn, wheat, and hogs, to very great for potatoes. When this pattern of year-to-year commodity price variability is superimposed on to the farm price level, which does, in fact, move through time in wide and dramatic swings, we obtain a vivid picture of the jumbled, gyrating price structure confronting farmers.

Two economic problems. These two characteristic movements of farm prices give rise to two important but distinctly separate economic problems. The wide swings in the farm price level give rise to even wider swings in aggregate net farm income. *This is the price-income problem.* The fluctuations of commodity prices about the farm price level give rise to uncertainty with regard to the planning of future farm operations. *This is the resource allocation problem.*

To illustrate the price-income problem, in 1956 total farm receipts for the nation amounted to $34.4 billion, of which 65 per cent, or $22.3 billion, was used to meet farm expenses, and $12.1 billion represented realized net farm income. If, for some reason, the farm price level had fallen 10 per cent in this situation, such a fall would have reduced gross receipts to $31 billion. And with expenses unchanged, this would have represented a decline of 28 per cent in rea-

---

[1] Individual commodity prices were deflated by the index of prices received by farmers for all commodities. Estimates were derived by computing link relatives, then computing the reciprocal of the link relatives below 100, and taking the unweighted arithmetic mean of the resultant numbers, all of which are 100 or more. An index of 100 represents no variation under this computation; hence 100 is subtracted from these results to obtain the percentage estimates presented above.

lized net income of farm families. And since we have assumed that all farm prices have declined—the level has declined—the individual farm operator cannot protect himself by shifting enterprises; in one of these price-level downsweeps the income problem becomes general; the individual farmer, efficient or inefficient, can find no place to hide. Of course, the great price-level upsweeps turn out to be a pure joyride for farmers, as the efficient and inefficient, experience rising incomes whichever way they turn.

This is *the* paramount problem of food and agriculture that terrifies farmers in the downswings and sends them scurrying to government for income protection, and that terrifies consumers in the upswings and sends them scurrying to government for cost-of-living protection. The general price-income problem of food and agriculture is the problem above all others that demands an adequate explanation and ultimately an adequate solution.

But if there were no general price-income problem in agriculture (that is, if the farm price level were perfectly horizontal) there would still remain the resource-allocation problem. It arises out of the circumstance that individual commodity prices fluctuate, and often sharply as well as irregularly, around the farm price level. It arises out of the fact that, to the farmer-producer, next year's price is *uncertain.* Confronted with this kind of uncertainty the farmer plans next year's production without much information; his planned production rarely turns out to be what he would have produced if he had known the realized market prices with certainty at planning time. In short, his planned production rarely turns out to be right. In other words, an inefficient use of resources occurs among commodities and on farms when farmers fail to use their productive resources in their most advantageous enterprise alternatives. And this is a general occurrence in agriculture because before the fact of sale, which may be three months or three years hence, farmers cannot know their most advantageous enterprise alternatives.

An analysis of the resource allocation problem—the cobweb analysis. In the late 1930's Mordecai Ezekiel formulated the cobweb theorem to explain commodity price-output sequences in agriculture.[2] And we shall make use of it here to explain year-to-year commodity price gyrations. The cobweb analysis is an equilibrium type of analysis, making use of the traditional concepts of demand and supply. But, whereas the typical demand-and-supply analysis is static (see the analysis in Chapter 13), the cobweb analysis is semi-dynamic; it is concerned with price-output sequences *through time* where the rele-

---

[2] Mordecai Ezekiel, "The Cobweb Theorem," *Quarterly Journal of Economics* (February 1938), pages 255-280.

vant demand and supply relations do not shift during the span of time under consideration. This partially dynamic analysis facilitates the formulation of an explanation of price-output behavior in agriculture where a *growth period,* often a season in length but perhaps longer, separates the decisions to produce and the decisions to sell a finished product. The introduction of a growth, or production period, recurring periodically, into the analysis to correspond to such production periods in agriculture is, no doubt, the novel aspect of the cobweb framework of analysis.

Not so generally recognized, but central to the cobweb analysis, are two different but related concepts of supply. It takes two concepts of supply, related in a time sequence, to make the analysis valid. First, we have a supply relation which describes those quantities of a commodity that farmers *plan* to produce at varying prices. It is a planning curve, to which we give the name *schedule of intentions to produce.* Second, we have a supply relation which describes at the close of the growth or production period those quantities of a commodity that farmers stand ready to offer on the market at varying prices. And since it is assumed: (1) that most farm products are perishable, and (2) that farmers have poor storage facilities, it is further assumed that this second supply relation, to which we give the name *market-supply curve,* is severely or perfectly inelastic. Given these concepts of supply, let us take a trial spin around the cobweb.

Two cobweb models are presented in Figure 15-1; later we will draw certain comparisons between these models, but for the present let us concentrate on Model I. To get under way in this analysis we must arbitrarily break into the continuing price-output sequence at some point in time, and this we do at price P_o in year O. Price P_o in year O induces farmers to plan to produce quantity Q_1 in year 1. This quantity information we read off the schedule of intentions to produce curve S_1S_1, which describes those quantities of this commodity that farmers intend to produce at varying prices.

Now let us assume that the farmers' intentions to produce are just realized, and that quantity Q_1 is forthcoming in year 1. This quantity comes to market in a rush—is dumped onto the market—since it is assumed that the commodity is perishable and farmers lack adequate storage facilities. Thus, in fact, the market-supply curve in year 1 is perfectly inelastic and is described in Model I by the line Q_1S_m. The market-supply curve intersects the demand curve for the commodity at price P_1; this intersectional point provides the price solution for year 1. Farmers receive price P_1 for an output of Q_1 in year 1. Price P_1 in year 1 now induces farmers to *plan* to produce Q_2 in year 2.

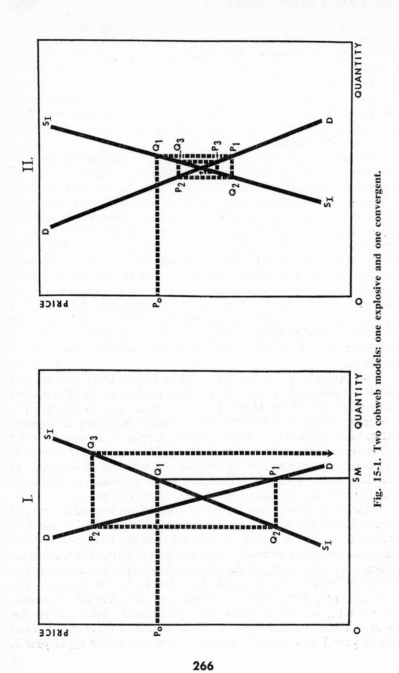

Fig. 15-1. Two cobweb models: one explosive and one convergent.

This quantity sells in turn at a price P_2 in year 2. The cobweb is forming, and will continue until something comes along to break it.

It will be observed that the price-output path of Model II differs markedly from that of Model I. Model II is convergent; Model I is explosive. Now why does the price-output path of Model II converge on its equilibrium position, and the price-output path of Model I explode? The answer is to be found in the relative slopes of the demand relation and the schedule of intentions to produce. Whenever the slope of the schedule of intentions to produce exceeds (that is, is steeper than) the slope of the demand relation, the price-output path converges. And, of course, whenever the slope of the demand relation exceeds that of the schedule of intentions to produce, the opposite is true. Finally, in that unlikely case where the slopes of the two curves are identical, the cobweb action goes on endlessly in the same track.

In the world of reality, it seems reasonable to assume that most commodity cobweb patterns are of the Model II type. This must be the case; otherwise agriculture would be flying apart. True, price variability is extreme for certain agricultural commodities, but to date agriculture has not exploded. And this would be the tendency if commodity patterns were generally of the Model I type.

If we superimpose, in our thinking, the cobweb model onto the farm price level, we have an explanation for year-to-year commodity price variations about that level. Assuming the demand- and supply-cross (that is, the equilibrium position) is at or near the price level, then the cobweb interaction can and does generate individual commodity movements about that level. Where the demand for the commodity is highly inelastic, but the schedule of intentions to produce is also inelastic, the cobweb model generates extreme year-to-year price fluctuations; this situation applies to the commodity potatoes. If the elasticity of the schedule of intentions to produce is observably less than the elasticity of demand, the year-to-year price variations dampen down rapidly as the model converges on its equilibrium position; this is clearly the case with fluid milk. In sum, the cobweb model explains how we get continuing commodity price variability around the price level, and explains further why in some cases that variability is extreme and in other cases it is mild.

But it may be observed that the cobweb models generate smooth, rhythmic patterns of price behavior, whereas commodity price variability in the real world is jagged and irregular. How then are these real world phenomena to be explained?

It is probably true that no situation can be found in the real world of food and agriculture which fits perfectly the neat cobweb pattern of either Model I or Model II of Figure 15-1. In other words, it would be difficult if not impossible to find a commodity situation in agriculture where (1) last year's price is always used as the planning price in the current year, (2) actual production never differs from planned production, (3) conditions on farms and in the market are such that the market-supply curve is always perfectly inelastic, and (4), and most important, the demand relation and the schedule of intentions to produce hold fixed, unchanging, positions for many years. For a countless number of *specific reasons* the above conditions are violated in practice, and the regular price-output path of the cobweb is broken. Demand changes with changes in consumer tastes; the schedule of intentions to produce expands with technological advance; and weather and other natural conditions bring about, in time, discrepancies between planned production and actual production in most agricultural commodities. The occurrence of any one of these developments breaks the regular price-output path around the cobweb and gives rise to a price irregularity. The changing world breaks down the classic cobweb model, yields irregular commodity price patterns, and, hence, price uncertainty to producers.

It would be wrong, however, to ignore or deprecate the cobweb framework of analysis in developing a general explanation of farm-price behavior. *The principal features of the cobweb model are inherent in the structure of most of agriculture.* The use of prices received in the past to arrive at current planning prices, the disjointed and recurring growth period in agricultural production, and the tendency for finished agricultural products to come to market in a rush following the growth period—these are all typical structural features of the agricultural economy. Thus, an analysis that purports to explain *commodity* price-output behavior in agriculture must assume some sort of cobweb form.[3]

An analysis of the general price-income problem of agriculture— the beginning. Since we have gained some experience with single-commodity analysis in the two preceding chapters, and we have just inquired into the causes of individual commodity-price variability about the price level, let us introduce this analysis of the general price-income problem in agriculture by way of a single-commodity analysis —for instance, hogs. The prices received by farmers for hogs have fluctuated extremely since 1910 (see Figure 15-2). An explanation for these wide swings in hog prices can be set forth in terms of a single-commodity supply-and-demand analysis. The prices received

---

[3] For a more complete treatment of the cobweb framework of analysis in explaining commodity price variability, see Willard W. Cochrane, *Farm Prices— Myth and Reality.* Chapter 4 (Minneapolis, Minn.: University of Minnesota Press 1958).

by farmers for hogs fell between 1919 and 1924, because the demand for hogs, relative to the supply, was weak during that period. And prices received by farmers for hogs rose between 1940 and 1948, because the demand for hogs, relative to the supply, was strong. Further, the short-run, saw-tooth price effects are explained by the workings of the cobweb. But this explanation, although correct in itself, is not very satisfying. A full explanation should provide more insights into the kind of a farm economy that is capable of generating such wide swings in hog prices.

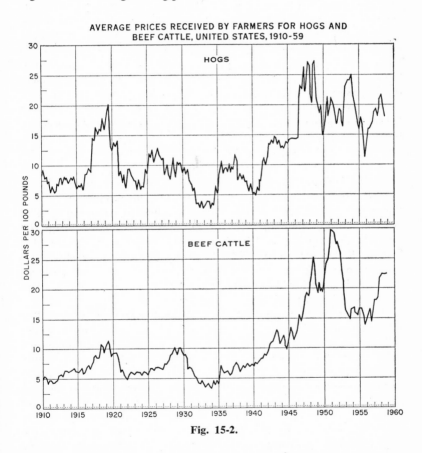

AVERAGE PRICES RECEIVED BY FARMERS FOR HOGS AND BEEF CATTLE, UNITED STATES, 1910-59

HOGS

BEEF CATTLE

DOLLARS PER 100 POUNDS

Fig. 15-2.

Let us expand the analysis by looking at the relation of hog prices to other agricultural commodity prices. We observe that the prices received by farmers for beef cattle (a close substitute for hogs on both the production and consumption sides) fluctuate in much the same pattern as hog prices (Figure 15-2). It is true that the amplitude of beef-cattle price fluctuation is not as great as in the case of hogs, but it is also true that the broad swings closely parallel one another. If, further, we compare the movement of hog prices between 1910 and 1958 with the index of prices received by farmers from all commodities (Figure 12-3) and with the various commodity groupings (Figure 12-4), we see that all farm prices, and particularly the prices of close substitutes for hogs, move up and down together in a discernible pattern.

Dairy-product prices, meat-animal prices (including hogs), poultry and egg prices, and grain and hay prices tend to parallel one another for one important reason: resource substitution. If, for example, hog prices rise, relative to the general pattern of prices for these product substitutes, producers devote more feed, more building space, more time to hog production and less to beef-cattle production, butterfat production and egg production. The result of these shifts, the substitution of resources into hog production, is that of increasing the supply of hogs and reducing the supplies of beef cattle, butterfat, and eggs. The increased supplies of hogs act to pull down hog prices, and the decreased supplies of the other commodities act to pull up their prices. The original price relationships between the product substitutes thus tend to be restored. We do not mean to imply that all the price humps shown in Figure 15-2 are ironed out, or that the short-run, saw-tooth price effects resulting from the workings of the cobweb are eliminated; we mean only that resource substitution operates to keep hog and beef prices moving in a roughly parallel fashion. Stated more generally, when resources may be freely substituted among different productive enterprises, the prices of the commodities involved will hold their relative positions in the general pattern with some precision.

An industry analysis: agriculture. Broadly speaking, we say that all commodity prices in agriculture move up and down together. But this is not quite correct. We observed (Figure 12-4) that cotton prices rose above the general contour of farm prices between 1920 and 1925, and between 1935 and 1940 cotton prices failed to rise to the extent that animal product prices did. We also find similar deviations from the general contour of farm prices for meat animals and certain of the minor crops—citrus fruit, for example. One reason, and an important reason, that we get these deviations from the average pattern of farm prices is to be found in the breakdown of the substitution process between these product enterprises and the rest of agriculture.

We noted in the last chapter the deterring influence of custom and habit on production adjustments (that is, the substitution of productive resources between enterprises). The influence of custom and habit has been particularly pronounced in the Cotton South. Tradition, coupled with a paucity of attractive alternatives, have in the past acted to hold southern producers in a single commodity. In the case of livestock, it is not easy to transfer resources into such enterprises and increase supply. It takes time to increase cattle numbers, for example, and in the early phases of the build-up, beef production declines as breeding stock are withheld from market. Thus, the length of the reproduction, hence expansion, process can force cattle prices away from the level of farm prices for extended periods.

In the case of a commercial fruit enterprise, it is obvious that the substitution of resources between enterprises is reduced to a minimum. It takes a long time to bring a grove into bearing, and growers do not pull up their trees at the first price decline. Resources devoted to fruit production are "sunk" for long periods of time. There is no easy, quick way for fruit growers to respond to price changes in the way of shifting resources from one enterprise to another. Hence, fruit prices may get out of line and stay out of line for a considerable period of time.

In these illustrations, we find a clue to the farm price problem. When the process of resource allocation among enterprises, which occurs through substitution, does not or cannot work, the price of a single commodity or the prices of a group of commodities can get out of line and stay out of line. When we say that a price gets out of line, we mean that it (or a group of prices) breaks away from the general level and goes off on a tangent, perhaps up, perhaps down. This, we suggest, is what happens between the smaller agricultural segment of the economy and the larger nonagricultural segment. Farm prices fluctuate to a greater extent than nonfarm prices, because labor and capital resources do not readily move back and forth across the rural-urban line, in response to the greater price movements in agriculture.

The aggregate output problem in agriculture. The farm segment and the nonfarm segment of the economy are sometimes compared to separate, watertight compartments, between which there is a connective valve that works poorly, in the long run and not at all in the short run, *in response to price-level changes.* Since the separate tanks contain water, movement within the tanks is easy. This analogy is meaningful when we consider the nature of the substitution process. Farmers shift readily between potatoes and sugar beets, between the cash sale of corn and the feeding of corn to hogs, and between the production of butterfat and whole milk, but not between farming and banking and farming and manufacturing. There is some degree of resource substitution between individual farm enterprises within most agricultural areas and a significant degree at the extensive margin of all areas, in response to commodity price changes, but not between farm and nonfarm enterprises.

We have not said that farm people do not migrate to the city and *vice versa*. Except for two brief periods, there has been a net migration from farms to urban areas since 1920. Since 1950 the rate of migration out of agriculture on a net basis has been very heavy— averaging nearly 1 million persons per year. But the net movement seems to be more closely associated with job opportunities in industry than with fluctuations in the farm price level, relative to the nonfarm price level. In fact, one of the two periods of net movement from the city to the farm (1932-33), coincides with extremely low prices in agriculture. Hence, we conclude that labor resources leave agriculture as population pressure builds up in agriculture and as job opportunities open up in industry and service trades, but not readily in response to low farm prices relative to nonfarm prices.

What are the consequences for aggregate farm output of this failure to get labor and other resources to shift back and forth across the rural-urban line in response to price-level movements? The consequences in the aggregate are nearly the same as for a single commodity. When resources do not, or cannot, shift in response to price changes, output does not change. The price of a commodity, or the price level for a composite of commodities, may go up or go down, but if that price movement has no effect on the number and quality of resources at work, the output of those resources will not change. And that, in broad outline, is what we have in agriculture. In the short run, aggregate output is constant, or nearly so.

The story changes when technological advance on farms is rapid and widespread. But putting aside that complication for the moment, we conclude, on the basis of the empirical analysis that follows, that the aggregate supply curve for agriculture is perfectly inelastic or nearly so. This conclusion is more extreme than that arrived at in Chapter 6 on the basis of logic. But we have no alternative but to present the results of the empirical research on the aggregate supply relation for agriculture and to caution the student that, although the true relation is probably highly inelastic, it is probably not perfectly inelastic.

In any event, the industry supply relation for agriculture is given statistical expression in Figure 15-3. In Figure 15-3, an index of aggregate food production[4] is related to an index of "responsible prices" (the prices in existence when the production decisions for the

---

[4] The food component of the *Index of Farm Marketings and Home Consumption* (Published regularly by the U.S.D.A., Agricultural Marketing Service).

forthcoming production period were made). In other words, the aggregate food output for any given year, say 1924, is related to the level and composition of prices (responsible prices) that were in existence at the time when the production decisions for 1924 were made. The points that relate the index value of responsible prices to the index value of aggregate output, for each year over the period 1912-56 fall into three obvious patterns: the AA pattern, the BB pattern, and the CC pattern. Ignoring the now somewhat historical period 1912-21, let us consider the BB pattern covering the period 1923-36. The index of responsible prices rose from 118 in 1924 to 141 in 1929, fell from 141 to 66 between 1929 and 1933, and then rose again to 100 by 1936. But these large price-level movements did not induce any significant change in aggregate food output; aggregate food output held practically constant over the period 1923-36; the index values of aggregate food production for sale hovered around 98 to 99 over the entire period.

The period 1923-36 was one in which farm technological advance was at a minimum; output per unit of input for agriculture as a whole showed no upward trend. In this context, the unresponsiveness of total farm output to farm price-level changes is illustrated beautifully. The total resources—land, labor, and capital—committed to agriculture production by farmers held almost constant, whereas the farm price level changed dramatically. Hence the total output from farms in the United States did not change. (The small variation from year to year is explained by variations in the weather.) When, therefore, we fit a line to the price-quantity points for the period 1923-36 in Figure 15-3 to derive the aggregate supply curve for food, it turns out to be perfectly inelastic—the vertical line *BB* in Figure 15-3. And the line *BB* is a legitimate supply curve, since it is derived for a period in which the index of farm efficiency, as an indicator of farm technological advance, is constant.

The dashed line running from 1937 to 1944 in Figure 15-3 brings out a new set of relationships. This was a period of rapid technological advance. Hybrid seed corn swept through the Corn Belt. A tremendous investment was made in tractor power and farm machinery. This was the time when farmers greatly increased their applications of commercial fertilizers. Hybrid seed corn increased corn yields by 20 per cent. The substitution of tractor power for animal power released millions of acres from feed production to food production. The increased use of tractor power also greatly improved the timeliness of farming operations. Considering all factors, however, none was more important in the expansion of total food output than the increased use of lime and commercial fertilizer.

What we have, then, between 1936 and 1944 is a shifting of the

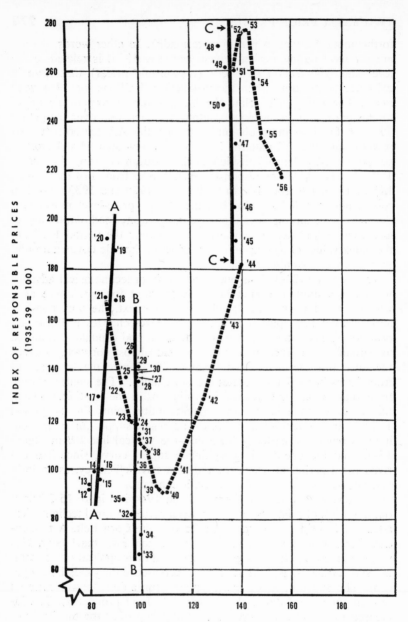

Fig. 15-3. The aggregate supply curve for food.

short-run aggregate output curve to the right as output per unit of input increased by some 40 per cent. (The action here in the aggregate is similar to movement of the commodity-supply curve for chicken in Figure 14-3). The dashed line running over the period 1937-44 is not a short-run supply curve; it is a long-run supply curve, a trend line, similar to that developed in the last chapter. It traces out the intersections of the short-run aggregate output curve with the aggregate demand curve, as the curve *BB* drifts to the right taking up successively more productive positions.

We do not get any movement along the short-run aggregate-supply curve during this period in response to price changes. Producers were not varying the variable factors of production (labor, feed) to obtain more output at higher cost from old combinations. They were innovating, combining resources in new ways, to obtain a greater output. And this action, in the aggregate as for a single commodity, resulted in an expansion in supply.

But by 1944, the post-depression, wartime spurt in farm technological advance seemed to have spent itself. Spectacular price increases between 1944 and 1948 failed to induce the adoption of more cost-reducing, output-expanding innovations. Either important new technologies were not coming along, their adoption was being held up by the war effort or some other factors were operating. In any event, worker productivity temporarily ceased increasing around 1944-45. As a result, the expansion in aggregate output, based on technological advance, came to an end.

The aggregate supply curve for food *CC* for the period 1944-50, like the similar curve *BB* for the period 1923-36, is perfectly inelastic. It indicates that all farm producers, regardless of the farm price level, kept on using the same total number of resources in the same ways to obtain the same total output. In the aggregate, sustained output was the norm for the period 1944-50. And since output per unit, too, was constant over this period, the aggregate curve does not shift to the right. This supply behavior is baffling to us. Why should farm technological advance slow down and come to a halt during these six years? We need more and better data and more powerful analyses to answer this question. But the quandary is short-lived; the aggregate supply curve *CC* began its rightward drift once again in 1951. And all during the 1950's, powered by a broad front of new knowledge and new technologies, the aggregate supply relation has expanded.

From this discussion of aggregate output, we have uncovered some interesting relationships, but we have not provided a complete explanation for the wide price swings in agriculture. The breakdown of the substitution process across the rural-urban line explains, in large measure, how the farm price level gets out of line and stays out of line. *But what starts all farm prices up or down in the first place?* Where does the initiating force come from?

A close observer of the behavior of the aggregate output curve, in Figure 15-3, might say that the expansion in supply between 1937 and 1943 could provide the unbalancing action. But an even closer inspection of Figure 15-3 indicates that there is something wrong with this explanation. It is true that the level of responsible prices fell between 1937 and 1940 with the expansion in output. But it is also true that prices rose between 1940 and 1943 with a much greater expansion in output. And we know that an increase in supply, *when demand is unchanged,* leads to a price decline.

Even more to the point, the level of responsible prices rose between 1923 and 1929, fell between 1929 and 1934, and then rose again between 1934 and 1938, when aggregate output clearly was unchanged. Changes in supply could not have initiated the price changes during this period. These price changes were initiated by changes in the aggregate demand for food. What we need, then, to complete the explanation of farm price-level changes is a description of the behavior of aggregate demand. For demand is the restless, unbalancing force in the picture.

The aggregate demand for food. The aggregate demand for food, just as in the case of a single commodity, states a relation between price and quantity. In the short run, the principal determinant of demand, the shifter of demand, is income. When consumer incomes are high or expanding, consumers allocate more dollars to the purchase of all foods and this shifts the demand curve for food to the right. In the opposite direction, when consumer incomes are low or contracting, consumers allocate fewer dollars to the purchase of all foods and the demand curve for food shifts to the left. And as we shall discover later, a small movement in demand gives rise to a large price change.

What, then, does the aggregate demand curve for food look like? One formulation is presented in Figure 15-4; the regression line *DD* relates the index of retail food prices to the index of per capita food consumption. And the relation *DD* describes the aggregate quantity of food consumed per person at different levels of retail food prices, all other influencing factors held constant. In other words, the curve *DD* is a conventional demand curve, which measures an aggregate rather than a single commodity.

It will be noted that the demand curve *DD* in Figure 15-4 (a straight line on arithmetic paper) fits the annual price-quantity points closely. In other words, this demand relation does a good job of ex-

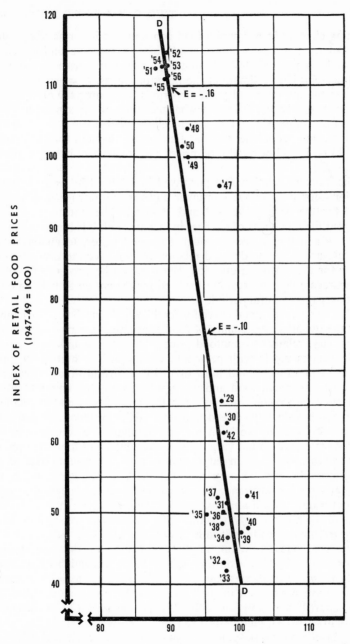

Fig. 15-4. The aggregate demand curve for food.

plaining changes in per capita food consumption in terms of changes in retail food prices, where the influences of income and time are removed from the analysis. It should be noted further, however, that the price-elasticity estimate at the point of means, $E = -0.1$, falls in between the interwar and postwar periods. Reporting the elasticity at that point on the curve is somewhat meaningless. At a price level of 110 on the index of retail prices, the elasticity estimate is $E = -0.16$. Thus, we may conclude that the elasticity of demand for all food at the 1950-55 level of retail food prices was somewhere between -0.15 and -0.20.

The demand relation DD portrayed in Figure 15-4 is an average relation—for the average consumer and for the average income and trend for the period 1929-42 and 1947-56. The statistical analysis removed the influences of changes in income, and, it is hoped, changes in tastes and preferences, through the trend factor, to enable us to estimate an aggregate demand relation for food for the *average consumer* for the period in question. But it would be wrong to visualize the aggregate demand relation for food *for the nation* as holding constant over this eventful period.

The aggregate demand curve for food is highly inelastic. Consumers vary the quantity and quality of food consumption very little as food prices vary, relative to nonfood prices. This fact should not surprise us; it squares nicely with personal experience. The human stomach is limited in capacity and most of us fill it several times every day. It requires so much food and we supply it with that amount. When food prices are rising, we may eat a few more beans and a little less red meat, a little more bread and fewer dairy products. The substitution process is at work on the consumption side too. But in the United States, we do not vary the poundage intake of food much from year to year. We keep on eating about the same amount of the same kinds of food regardless of price. When the family budget is squeezed, we may drop an insurance policy, put off buying a new car, or go without a deep freeze unit, but we keep on eating. In short, the food needs of the human body, together with food habits, conspire to make the aggregate demand for food highly inelastic.

We have one more link in the explanation of the extreme behavior of farm prices. Consumers, too, find it difficult to adjust the *total amount of food consumed or taken* in response to price changes. So, we have a situation in food and agriculture in which, excepting these spurt-like periods of technological advance, (1) the agggregate output of agriculture is fixed in quantity (sustained in flow), and (2) the aggregate amount demanded varies little with changes in prices. The first condition exists because farm operators cannot, in the aggregate, readily adjust the number of resources employed in agriculture in response to price changes. The second exists because consumers cannot adjust their intake of food in response to price changes. Consequently, when consumer incomes change, let us say decrease, and the aggregate demand for food declines, we get very little adjustment on either the production or the consumption side to act as a brake on the falling food prices.

In the single commodity analysis, a fall in the price of pork acts to reduce the output of pork and to increase the amount demanded. These adjustments act to stop the price decline. *But in the aggregate, we simply do not get these adjustments in production and consumption,* hence, we get extreme price fluctuations. In one sense, this is a fortunate occurrence. The health and working efficiency of members of society would certainly suffer if they curtailed their consumption of food every time food prices rose and if producers curtailed their output every time food prices declined. We want a continuing and certain supply of food. But we must recognize that a sustained flow of food products accentuates the farm price-level problem.

The general price-income problem in agriculture. We now have at hand the principal elements of the general price-income problem in agriculture. Most farm products move up and down together over the same tortuous road, because changes in consumers' incomes shift the demand for most foods in the same direction and because producers can and do substitute resources between enterprises, as prices and profits dictate. If prices and profits are relatively high for a particular type of enterprise, producers shift more resources (land, labor, and capital) into that enterprise. This process acts to pull the price of the product involved back into the average pattern. Hence, we are justified in using an aggregative type of analysis in which all foods are treated as one commodity to be related to the food price level.

The extreme movements in the food price level (farm price level) grow out of the peculiar relation of aggregate supply to aggregate demand. In the short run, the total resources employed in agriculture do not change readily in response to price level changes. When farm prices are high, we generally find that urban incomes are also high, growing out of a high level of employment in industry and the service trades. Hence, agriculture cannot readily attract labor and capital resources from the nonfarm segment of the economy. When farm prices are low, farm operators keep right on producing with the resources already "sunk" in farming. And in such situations, unemployment in urban areas often slows down, or cuts off, a shift of labor away from agriculture. Thus, since the total resources employed in agriculture do not change readily in response to price-level changes, aggregate output tends to hold constant.

The aggregate demand for food is similar in one respect to the aggregate supply of food; the amount demanded is unresponsive to variations in price. But it is dissimilar in another respect. Aggregate demand varies directly and continuously with variation in personal, disposable incomes. Shifts in aggregate demand usually are not great, for consumers try to maintain the consumption of food when their incomes fall. And increases in aggregate demand represent, for the most part, attempts to shift from cheap, energy producing foods to more expensive protein foods, not attempts to eat more of all foods. *But a shift in aggregate demand does not have to be great to initiate an important price change. That is the principal point of this aggregative analysis.* Since farmers cannot shift out of farming and consumers cannot consume more total pounds of food in response to a decline in food prices, *any small contraction in aggregate demand* leads to a large price decline. An expansion in aggregate consumption and a contraction in aggregate output do not come into play, in response to a decline in the farm price level, to place a brake on that decline.

In Figure 15-5, four basic models portray different historical phases of the fluctuating farm price level. A panorama of farm price-level behavior over the period 1929-59 emerges in Figure 15-5. In each of these models an inelastic supply curve *SS* is related to a highly inelastic demand curve *DD*—a demand curve with an elasticity approximating -0.2 at the base point, price $= 100$, quantity $= 100$. The supply curve *SS* is given some slope because the logic of farm firm behavior suggests that the aggregate supply curve does have some slope (see Chapter 6). In these highly simplified models, the marketing system is assumed not to exist as the farm level supply curve is related directly to the consumer demand curve. This is a heroic assumption, but it does not invalidate the analysis and it permits us to avoid a maze of statistical manipulations. In any event, the empirically based, although not derived, models of Figure 15-5 illustrate the basic concepts developed in this chapter, and place them in an historical setting.

In the 1929-33 model, demand contracts, and the supply curve is positionally fixed and severely inelastic. In this context, the food price level falls precipitously, from 100 to 48 on the index. But the quantity adjustment is small, from 100 to 96. This is the case that farm people dread: the situation in which the individual producer is helpless. Hence, farm people have requested and obtained from government price floors, below which the price of some farm commodities may not fall.

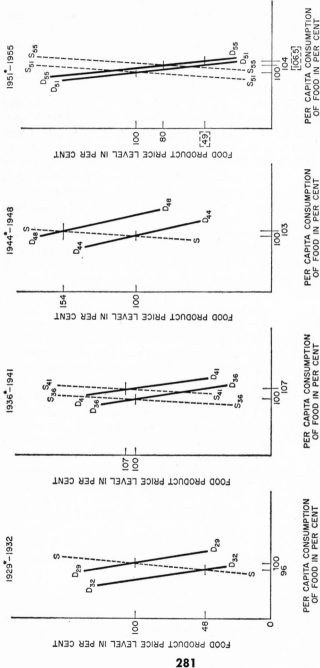

* THE PRICE-QUANTITY DATA FOR 1929, 1936, 1944, AND 1951 RESPECTIVELY EQUAL 100

Fig. 15-5. Farm price fluctuations, basic models.

281

In the 1936-41 model, demand expands modestly, but, in this case, *the supply curve shifts to the right, along with the demand curve.* Thus, the price level holds fairly constant as output expands. This is the happy case. The nation needs more food, as the expansion in demand indicates, and farmers are able to satisfy that need through the adoption of new methods and new practices.

In the 1944-49 model, demand expands, and the supply curve again is fixed and inelastic. The price level rises to an extremely high level, from 100 to 154 on the index. But the quantity adjustment is small, from 100 to 103. This is the wartime case that urban consumers dread: a "food shortage," when housewives queue up before grocery stores and low-income people tighten their belts. Hence, urban consumers have requested and obtained from government the legal right to establish ceilings, above which the price of food may not go.

In the 1951-55 model, demand expands modestly, but the supply curve out-races demand. The technological revolution in agriculture production pushes the aggregate supply curve out ahead of the modestly expanding demand curve and holds it there. This is the case of chronic overproduction in agriculture in an advanced economy. The price level falls from 100 to 80 on the index, and at that level is supported by governmental action. Without governmental support the farm price level would fall to 49 on the index. In this case rapid and widespread farm technological advance has converted the problem of price-level instability into one of chronic overproduction and a persistent downward pressure on farm prices.

Two final and summary points need to be made with respect to the models in Figure 15-5. First, the steep slopes (that is, the extreme inelasticity) of the aggregate curves are such that any small shift in one curve relative to the other gives rise to a relatively small response along the quantity axis and a relatively large response along the price axis; and the nature of the curves is such that this leads to wide price-level fluctuations. Second, in no case does the aggregate supply curve shift to the left; it holds constant and it expands, but it does not contract. This is the law of agricultural production in the United States.

A final note. A theoretical explanation of farm-price behavior has been formulated in this chapter. It builds on a conventional demand-and-supply type of analysis; it is sufficiently general to have widespread application; and it meets the test of historical fact. Further, it provides a framework of analysis for considering future developments. *But as a predicting device, it is no better than the judgments and expectations that may be interjected into it.*

Whether the farm-price level will fall in the future, or rise, depends on a host of considerations: the rate of technological advance, personal disposable incomes, rate of population growth, peace, limited mobilization or war, and so on. On certain of these items, it is possible to hold informed opinions; on others we can only guess. But even if we cannot predict with certainty, we can understand, hence, contribute to a solution of current problems. The latter has been the objective of this chapter.

REFERENCES

Cochrane, W. W., *Farm Prices—Myth and Reality*. Chapters 1-4. Minneapolis, Minn.: University of Minnesota Press, 1958.

———, "Farm Price Gyrations—An Aggregative Hypothesis," *Journal of Farm Economics* (May 1947).

Schultz, T. W., *Agriculture in an Unstable Economy*. Chapters 2 and 3. New York: McGraw-Hill Book Company, Inc., 1945.

———, *The Economic Organization of Agriculture*. Chapters V, XI, XII, XIII, and XIV. New York: McGraw-Hill Book Company, Inc. 1953.

POINTS FOR DISCUSSION

1. What kinds of price instability do we find in agriculture? What kinds of economic problems result from price instability?
2. What is the cobweb theorem? How is it used to analyze price behavior in this analysis?
3. Why is the aggregate output curve so very inelastic when such is not the case for single commodities?
4. What causes the aggregate output curve to shift to the right, to expand? Does it ever shift to the left, contract? If not, why not?
5. What is the configuration of the aggregate demand curve for food? What explanation do you have for this configuration?
6. Relating the aggregate supply curve to the aggregate demand curve, how is the level of farm prices affected by any small change in either curve?
7. What type of force generally initiates a price rise? What type of force generally initiates a price decline? What types of information must the analyst have at his command to use these tools of analysis as predictive devices?

PART FOUR

Farmers in the National and World Economies

CHAPTER 16

Business Fluctuations
and Agriculture

GOOD BUSINESS conditions may exist in one industry or area like an island in a sea of depressed economic activity (or conversely). But usually the more dynamic conditions, good or bad, spread throughout the national economy to assume the *general condition* of either prosperity or depression. Thus, business fluctuations tend to be general in scope, encompassing the entire economy. The impact of business fluctuations on different segments of the economy is, of course, different. And it is the primary objective of this chapter to describe and analyze the ways in which changes in over-all business conditions affect farmers and their farm businesses.

First, however, let us take a look at the most disrupting influence, hence, the most critical problem of modern economics, the business fluctuation.[1] With broad sweeps of the brush, we will describe the ups and downs of business conditions since 1920, point out the symptoms and forces involved, and set forth a method for analyzing such fluctuations. Once the nature and magnitude of business fluctuations have been established, we shall turn to a study of their consequences on agriculture in terms of (1) the structure of the industry itself, (2) investment in agriculture, (3) labor mobility, and (4) the operation of the farm firm. The impact of business fluctuations on farmers can be appraised rather completely under these four headings.

Prosperity and depression in the United States, 1920-60. A pano-

---

[1] A term more often used here is *business cycle*. We avoid the use of that term wherever possible in discussing the ups and downs of the total economy, since we do not find a regularity or periodicity in these phenomena that the word cycle connotes.

rama of business conditions and business fluctuations over the 1920-60 period may be seen in Figure 16-1. The top line, describing the size of the gross national product, we take as a measure of the performance of the national economy. The gross national product series, which measures the total output of goods and services from productive activity in the United States, is the best indicator of national economic activity that we have. In Figure 16-1, we see two things: (1) business-level fluctuations, some severe and some minor, with peaks coming in 1920, 1929, 1937, 1945, 1948, 1953, and 1957 and troughs hitting in 1921, 1933, 1938, 1946, 1949, 1954, and 1958, and (2) the great secular growth of the national economy beginning about 1940.

The outlook was bright in 1920. Business had picked up after the slump following the Armistice of 1918. Investment in physical plants and equipment by manufacturing firms was running at an annual rate of $3 billion (a higher dollar value than that realized in 1929). And investment in inventories was estimated at almost $5 billion, the highest in our history prior to 1946. But such a rate of inventory accumulation could not continue. Investment in inventories fell from almost $5 billion in 1920 to $100 million in 1921. The contraction in inventory investment was not offset by an expansion elsewhere, aggregate expenditures declined, and a contraction in total activity and output was the direct result. GNP (gross national product) declined from an annual rate of $90 billion in the first half of 1920 to $64 billion in the last half of 1921. The 1921 crash is a clear-cut example of an inventory recession.

Inventory accumulation and diminution induced some mild fluctuations between 1922 and 1929. (See the modest waves in the GNP series, Figure 16-1.) But the accumulation of inventories does not explain the great prosperity in the United States of the late 1920's, unique in the world during that period. It rests on a more substantial underpinning. First, investment in housing over the period 1923-27 reached new high levels. Second, local, state, and Federal governments were making substantial investments in roads, buildings, and public facilities. Third, in the final year of that period, private business was investing heavily in new plants and equipment.

But the prosperity of the late 1920's came to an end. The gross national product fell from $104 billion in 1929 to $56 billion in 1933. Leading this fall in over-all economic activity was the precipitous decline in private investment, from $16.2 billion in 1929 to $.9 billion in 1932. (Fluctuations in private investment do not stand out in Figure 16-1 because of the compressed vertical scale.) Private businessmen almost stopped purchasing the materials, machines, and equipment out of which to produce consumer goods. And there was no expansion in expenditures by the government to offset the contraction in private investment expenditures. In fact, expenditures of all units of government fell off somewhat.

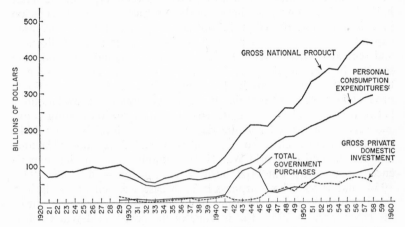

Fig. 16-1. Gross national product and expenditure, United States, 1920-58.

By 1933, unemployment had risen to alarming proportions, to between 13 and 15 million. Prices generally, and farm prices particularly, had fallen to very low levels. Social unrest was widespread and pleas for relief poured into the Federal government from laborers, farmers, and businessmen alike. In this chaotic situation, businessmen were unwilling to invest in new plants and equipment. Hence, plants and equipment simply wore out without being replaced. Investments by manufacturing firms fell short of depreciation charges by approximately $2 billion over the period 1930-32.

But growing out of this latter circumstance and in conjunction with increased Federal expenditures, revival at long last got underway in 1933-34. If the economy and the society were to survive, that is, meet the essential needs for food, clothing, and shelter, the productive capacity of the national economy could not be allowed to drop further. Inspired, then, with the efforts of government in 1933-34 and backed by the knowledge that new machines and equipment were sorely needed, businessmen began to take hope and risk investment in producer goods. But the recovery from 1933 to 1937 differed from that of 1922-29 in two important respects. First, it was never full or complete. Unemployment in the peak year of this upswing, 1937, is estimated at between 8 and 9 million.

Second, inventory accumulation and governmental expenditures dominated the investment scene in this period, whereas housing and plant construction played the more dominant roles in 1922-29.

Inventory accumulation, which was taking place at a rapid rate in 1936 and the first half of 1937, dropped off sharply in the latter half of 1937. Hence, we have another inventory-induced recession in 1937. But this recession did not last long; it could not. Increased expenditures by government, first in re-armament and mobilization and second in World War II, created a total demand for goods and services beyond anything we had ever before experienced. Expenditures by the government in 1944 approximated the gross national product of 1929. (Note the bulge in governmental expenditures between 1940 and 1946, Figure 16-1.) The expansion in total goods and services produced and the rise in the price level between 1940 and 1946 were such as to make all previous efforts look picayune.

Since the end of World War II, the national economy has experienced some sharp but brief business contractions—in 1946, 1949, 1954, and 1958. The sharpness in each case was felt primarily in a rise in unemployment—with unemployment rising to 6.8 per cent of the labor force in 1958. But in none of the post-World-War-II business contractions has the GNP fallen by more than a few percentage points, and in none have personal consumption expenditures declined. The flow of incomes and expenditures has leveled off in these business recessions, but it has not declined substantially. These interruptions in the growth of the economy, for that is what they have been, have been brief and moderate, coinciding with slack periods in business investment in plant and equipment and inventories.

The big picture that comes to the fore in Figure 16-1 is that of the great growth of the American economy from 1940 to 1958. There is some price inflation in the GNP measure of the growth of the total product over the period 1940-58 (the GNP is measured in current dollars), but the total output of *real* goods and services increased importantly between 1940 and 1948. In real terms (in constant 1958 dollars), the Gross National Product increased about 93 per cent between 1940 and 1958—or the total real product of the economy nearly doubled. And per capita GNP in real terms increased by over 50 per cent during this period. Thus, the over-all picture for the period 1940-48 is one of great growth and great prosperity, marred by several minor business recessions.

A generalized view of business fluctuations. It is clear from the 1920-60 experience that no single cycle, from peak to peak or trough to trough, is similar in all details to any other. Each has some peculiar characteristic of its own, for example, first point of weakness, segment of the economy most affected, length of time elapsing from peak to peak, and so on. (See the similarities and differences in business cycle patterns in the post-World-War-II period as portrayed in Figure 16-2.) Yet it is important to have a picture of the forces at work on, as well as the overt symptoms of, the various phases of the business fluctuation. And that is what we want to provide here.

Let us begin this description at the bottom of the trough, in the pit of the depression. At such a time, business firms (farm and nonfarm) have reduced their orders for equipment, land, buildings, and other producer goods to the minimum, possibly below the replacement rate. Business firms are delaying decisions to invest as long as possible, because they fear the future. Businessmen do not feel certain that the bottom has been reached, and they do not want to sink their scarce funds in heavy equipment if conditions are going to get worse. Foreign demand for goods is usually low in such a period. Government purchases may be greater than usual, but not large enough to offset the decline in investment by private firms. Inventories of retail, wholesale, and manufacturing firms are being depleted, perhaps at a rapid rate. Interest rates are likely to be low; prices may or may not be falling (there is an increasing tendency for nonfarm prices to be sticky—to not fall); and unemployment in urban areas is large and perhaps still mounting.

Expectations of businessmen are likely to be pessimistic in the type of situation that we have been describing. But there are some favorable elements in the situation: (1) inventories cannot be depleted indefinitely if businesses are to live, (2) the cost of new capital goods is likely to be low, relatively at least, and (3) in time, individuals with funds to lend become venturesome, credit becomes available on easier terms. Thus conditions eventually become favorable to entrepreneurs with a production plan and an investment program.

When the decline in retail sales comes to an end (or even slows down), profit expectations are raised and orders are increased all along the line to maintain or, perhaps, increase inventories. Next, orders for producer goods must go up, first, to keep machinery and equipment from going into further disrepair and, second, to undertake new production plans growing out of rising profit expectations and anticipations. This expansion in investment brings about an increase in consumer purchases; consumer purchases increase with expanding payrolls. So all this makes the situation look even more hopeful. Further expansion in investment now becomes profitable and the process becomes cumulative. New investment creates new

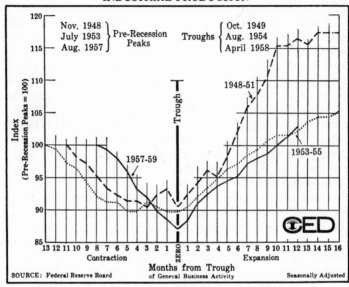

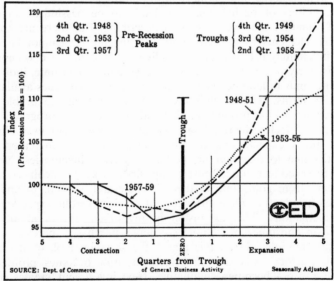

Fig. 16-2. Indicators of prosperity and depression, selected periods, 1948-59.

EMPLOYMENT
Of Wage and Salary Workers in Non-Agricultural Establishments

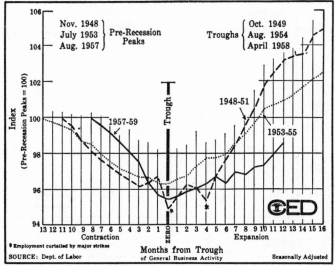

PERSONAL INCOME FROM PRODUCTION [1]

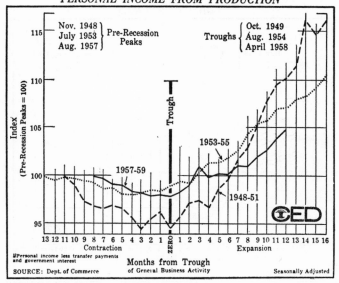

Fig. 16-2 (Cont.).

REAL RETAIL SALES[1/]

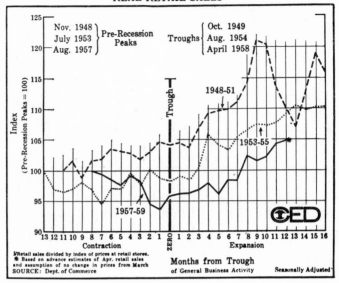

CONSUMER PRICES

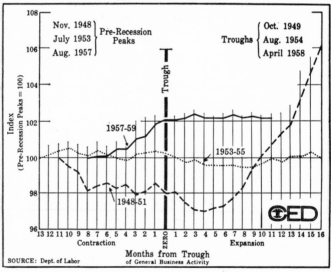

Fig. 16-2 (Cont.).

activity, new jobs, greater product, and higher prices. Out of this combination of circumstances the purchasing power of consumers expands, and so the spiral grows.

It is difficult to see why or how this joyful cumulative process ever comes to an end. But there are some disquieting elements in the picture, too. Interest rates probably will be rising (or, if interest rates are pegged by the government, sources of credit will be drying up). Prices, hence costs, of producer goods will also be rising. But most important, the investment in new, additional producer goods is building up *the stock* of new machines, equipment, and buildings. This growing stock acts as a brake to further investments in capital goods. The increasing cost of investment, taken in conjunction with the saturation of investment opportunities and the tendency for consumers to save increasing proportions of their rising incomes, causes entrepreneurs to become cautious and less optimistic about the future. At this point in time, the total economy ceases to expand and begins to contract.

The turning point comes when it no longer *appears* profitable to add to stocks of inventories and producer goods—when the rate of investment falls off. With this decline in investment, unemployment in producer-goods industries increases and aggregate consumption falls off. And this decline in consumption accelerates the contraction in investment. Thus, the bubble of prosperity is pricked and optimistic profit expectations give way to pessimistic expectations. This shift in the state of expectations may lead to panic selling, a break in the stock market, and a loss of confidence on the part of banks and other lenders. Credit is restricted, sales fall, unemployment rises, and the gloom deepens. Now the cumulative process is driving the economy into a depression.

The income-expenditure approach to business fluctuations. We cannot enter into a full and detailed account of business fluctuations here. We are primarily concerned with the economics of agriculture; we are concerned with changes in over-all business activity only as it affects agriculture. But that effect can be great, and although the income-expenditure approach does not in itself provide answers as to what caused a downturn here and upturn there, it provides a useful framework for considering the various factors at work. So let us spend a short time constructing a framework for analyzing business fluctuations, which we call the income-expenditure approach or sometimes macro-theory.

In this approach, we use the same categories that we have been using to describe business fluctuations: income, consumption, saving, and investment. But we had best define these categories in a precise manner. By income we mean the funds received by all individuals in the form of wages and salaries, rents, interest and dividends, and profits for productive services rendered. Consumption is defined as that portion of income allocated to and expended for goods and services used in everyday living. Saving is equal to income minus consumption. Investment is defined as expenditures made in the acquisition of producer goods, goods used to produce consumer goods and services. This investment category, however, is not as clear-cut as we might wish. Housing, for example, is classed as an investment good because the purchase is large and it occurs over a long period of time; it acts like an investment good. And governmental expenditures are usually placed under the investment heading, although only deficitly financed governmental expenditures act like private investments.

In this approach, total economic activity (production times price) varies directly with aggregate demand. When total expenditures (consumption plus investment) are increasing, production must increase or prices rise, or some combination of the two. All this we call an upswing in business activity. But when total expenditures are decreasing, production must decline or prices fall, or more probably some combination of the two. This is the familiar downswing in the business fluctuation.

The question is immediately posed: What causes aggregate expenditures to rise and fall? Without developing specific causes, we can see how this unbalancing takes place through the income-expenditure approach. If all income received by individuals were immediately paid out in the acquisition of consumer goods, no problem would arise.[2] All the income earned by individuals in the production of all goods and services is paid out in the current period to purchase those goods and services for everyday living. Perfect stability is achieved; all goods and services produced in each production period are sold at the price expected at the time of production.

But consumers do not spend all the income they receive in the current period on consumer goods. A part of the income received is saved. Now the act of saving, as far as the circular flow of income is concerned, represents a destruction of purchasing power. Funds that are saved are sucked out of the circular flow of income; they are not immediately and directly available for expenditure. The story does not end at this point, however. We have an offsetting action to saving. The act of investment represents the injection of purchasing power

---

[2] Two implicit assumptions are made here: (1) the state of the arts is constant, there is no technological advance, and (2) depreciation of plant and equipment is included as a cost of production in the price of consumer goods.

into the circular flow of income. Investments, made out of past savings or bank loans, add to the total flow of expenditures and, for the period in question, act as an offset to saving. (Rarely are the funds saved in one period reinvested in the same period.)

In the circular flow of income, then, we have a sucking action in the form of saving, which has the effect of reducing total expenditure, and an injecting action in the form of investment, which has the effect of enhancing total expenditures. When the sucking action exceeds the injecting action, total expenditures contract and a downswing is initiated, and vice versa. Now we see why the great emphasis was laid on investment in the review of business fluctuations in the United States between 1920 and 1960. When the flow of investment expenditures is great and exceeds the drain of savings, the circular flow widens into a prosperity condition.

We cannot overlook the role of consumption on business fluctuations. It has the nature of a passive role, yet it has important implications. It has been observed that, when incomes of individuals are increasing so that total national income is increasing, individuals step up their consumption, but not as rapidly as the increase in income. Neither do consumers reduce expenditures for everyday living at a rate proportionate to decreases in income. We can see this relationship in Figure 16-1. The gap between GNP and consumption expenditures narrows between 1929 and 1932, widens between 1932 and 1937 and widens again over the period 1948-58. We have a situation in which the gap between income and consumption widens, and the flow of savings increases as personal incomes rise. Hence, the sucking action in the circular flow of income increases in magnitude at high levels of income and decreases at low levels of income. This means that, as the national income rises, the investment expenditure must constantly increase to offset (or more than offset) the widening drain of savings. Finally, a point is reached at which the capital market is saturated · and investment expenditures cease expanding; at this point, the sucking action becomes greater than the injecting action, and a downturn is initiated.

The unfavorable passive action of consumption in the upswing turns out to be the salvation of the economy in the downswing. As total income declines, the savings gap is narrowed, because consumers do not reduce their level of living as rapidly as the decline in income. And a point is reached, as it was reached in 1932-33, at which almost the total income received was paid out in consumer expenditures. Here the downswing was halted and a bottom placed under the economy. The amplitude of business fluctuations is thus delimited, on the lower side, by a level at which consumption equals income and, on the upper side, by a level at which the savings gap widens beyond the flow of investment expenditures.

In this simplified version of the income-expenditure approach, no mention has been made of the role of government, a role which is becoming increasingly important. Further, many refinements of the approach are omitted. But we do see how an unbalancing can occur in a free enterprise economy. Or more properly stated, we see why economic stability at or approaching full employment of labor resources is not *automatically* achieved. The decisions to save are made by all income receivers for one set of reasons; the decisions to invest are made by relatively few businessmen for altogether different reasons. Hence, there is no reason why the sum of saving decisions should equal the sum of investment decisions; an equality at full employment would be purely accidental. The private economy is forever expanding and contracting in response to changes in the relative strengths of the sucking (saving) action and the injecting (investment) action; we have, therefore, fluctuations in business activity.

The agricultural industry and business fluctuations. The agricultural segment of the economy does not behave in a fashion similar to the nonfarm segment in the various phases of business fluctuations. A quick look at Figure 12-6 establishes that fact. During the years of the Great Depression, total production in agriculture was almost constant in contrast with the sharp decline in total output of industry. During the period of World War II, agricultural production increased in a persistent fashion, but not in the spectacular fashion observable for nonfarm industry. In response to the needs of war and a modest price rise, the total output of manufacturing rose nearly 130 per cent between 1939 and 1944, in comparison to an increase in agricultural output of 21 per cent for the same period. The output of industry oscillates in the extreme, from very low levels in the trough of a depression to very high levels at the peak of prosperity. The total output of agriculture contracts little if at all in depressed periods and it expands, in a relentless fashion, in periods of prosperity.

The price response in the two segments of the economy is just the converse of the production response. In agriculture, prices fall precipitously in a downswing in economic activity, whereas industrial prices hold fairly constant. On the other hand, prices of farm products shoot skyward in periods of great prosperity, whereas nonfarm prices move upward less dramatically.

The point we wish to underscore is the following: *when aggregate expenditures increase something must give, must expand, in both the farm and the nonfarm segments.* In the farm segment, prices customarily break loose as production advances slowly, whereas in industry the greater response comes in output as prices advance slowly. An upswing in business activity brings increased incomes in manufacturing and the service trades, by reason of increased employment, and, in agriculture, by reason of rising prices. In the downswing, just the opposite occurs. Something must give, as total expenditures decline, and, in agriculture, it is price that declines, whereas in industry it is production and employment.

Professor Dale Hathaway has investigated in detail the effects of business fluctuations on agriculture. Let us look first at his findings with respect to the income structure of agriculture.

In examining the effects of business cycles upon the agricultural sector of the economy, it was assumed that changes in level of nonfarm business activity were to be considered as the causal or determining factor. Therefore, in Table 1 [Table 16-1], the time periods are divided into two groups. The first group contains years of expansion in nonfarm business activity; the second group contains years of contraction. These periods are arrayed in terms of the magnitude of change in gross national product from the trough year to the peak year for expansions and the peak year to the trough year in contractions rather than in time sequence. The other columns of Table 1 [Table 16-1] show the percentage changes in various measures of the well-being of farmers during the same period.

In columns 4 and 6 of Table 1 [Table 16-1] the relationships between the business cycle and gross and net farm income appear. Gross farm income increased during each of the 10 periods of business expansion from 1910 to 1956. Net farm income, perhaps the most commonly used measure of agriculture's well-being, increased during 9 of the 10 periods of business expansion, the exception being in 1954-56. It should be noted, however, that only during periods of vigorous business expansion (as measured by increases in gross national product) has there been consistent relationship between the magnitude of increase in either gross or net farm income and general business activity.

The columns relating to prices paid by farmers and farm production expenses are also worth noting. Prices paid by farmers (col. 3) have remained stable or increased during every business cycle expansion. Farm production expenses (col. 5) also increased during every period of expansion except 1924-26.

Gross farm income has declined in 7 of the 10 business contractions, and has declined in every severe contraction. On the other hand, farm production expenses have declined in only 4 out of the 10 periods of business decline, and in every case the percentage reduction in farm expenses was less than the reduction in gross farm income during the same period. As a result, net farm income (excluding Government payments)

TABLE 16-1

Percentage Changes in Gross National Product, and in Measures of Farmers' Income During Periods of Business Expansion and Contraction, 1910-1956

Periods of Business	Gross National Product (1)	Prices Received by Farmers (2)	Prices Paid by Farmers (3)	Gross Farm Income* (4)	Farm Production Expenses (5)	Net Farm Income* (6)	Average Per Capita Net Income from Farming (7)	Number of Farm Workers (8)	Average Annual Farm Income Per Worker (9)
Expansion:									
1911-13	8.7	8.5	2.0	10.2	10.9	9.6	9.1	0.2	8.7
1927-29	11.7	5.7	0.0	4.5	2.6	7.0	7.0	1.0	4.8
1924-26	14.3	1.4	0.0	4.1	1.1	11.3	20.9	-.4	11.0
1954-56	14.3	-5.6	2.1	1.1	3.4	-3.2	-10.9	-6.9	4.9
1921-23	19.9	14.5	1.2	15.2	6.2	30.5	45.0	-1.8	27.3
1946-48	23.0	21.6	30.2	20.2	30.7	9.8	17.7	-13.9	16.9
1949-53	41.2	3.2	13.9	11.2	18.6	1.4	24.3	.7	10.8
1932-37	55.2	87.7	6.5	72.5	36.0	156.7	158.8	-6.5	141.9
1914-19	100.3	114.9	94.1	131.0	106.8	157.4	122.1	-2.5	131.7
1938-44	148.1	103.1	33.3	144.8	110.2	195.9	224.8	-12.1	222.5
Contraction:									
1910-11	.3	9.6	4.2	-3.9	1.4	-8.7	-17.7	-.1	-7.2
1948-49	0.0	-12.9	-2.4	-8.5	-3.9	-14.0	-25.8	-3.9	-9.1
1953-54	-.6	-3.5	1.1	-4.2	1.3	-12.6	-1.1	-1.5	-10.7
1944-46	-1.0	19.8	14.3	20.8	17.6	24.1	21.7	.7	22.0
1923-24	-1.1	.7	0.0	5.1	5.5	4.5	-2.7	-1.0	5.6
1926-27	-1.9	-3.4	-1.2	.3	1.2	-.8	-2.3	-2.6	1.6
1913-14	-3.8	-1.0	0.0	-2.5	1.4	-6.5	9.8	.1	-5.4
1937-38	-6.2	-20.5	-4.5	-12.2	-4.7	-21.3	-26.1	-3.0	-15.7
1920-21	-18.4	-41.2	-18.3	-33.9	-24.9	-45.0	-54.3	.3	-42.9
1929-32	-44.0	-56.1	-24.8	-54.1	-41.8	-69.2	-65.2	.4	-65.8

* Excluding Government payments.

has declined in 8 of 10 periods of business slackening. One of the exceptions was the period 1944-46, when an unusual postwar foreign demand existed for food and fiber.

Although the observations are limited there are some indications that some changes of importance have taken place in the post-World-War-II period. In each of these recent expansions, the rate of increase in prices paid and production expenses exceeded that for prices received and gross income, whereas prior to World War II the opposite held for every expansion. Non-farm-produced items make up an increasing proportion of production expenses in recent years, and their prices rise during periods of expansion. As a result of this greater dependence of farmers upon such non-farm-produced items, in the future relatively moderate periods of business expansion may inflate farmers' cost more rapidly than either farm prices or income.

There are other measures of farmers' well-being which should not be ignored and which appear highly associated with the expansion of general business activity. First, during 7 of the 10 periods of expansion the number of farmworkers has declined. As a result of the decline in numbers and the coincident increase in income, the income per farmworker has increased during every expansion in business activity. The magnitude of the increase appears quite directly related to the magnitude of the increase in gross national product. In many ways income per worker seems the most significant statistic with which to measure the well-being of agriculture, since presumably we are more interested in the well-being of the people engaged in agriculture than of the industry as such.[3]

Investment in agriculture. Farm businessmen, like other businessmen, invest heavily in machines, equipment, plants, and buildings when prices are high, receipts large, and expectations bright. In other words, the investment decisions of farmers contribute to, and coincide with, upturns in over-all business activity. But like other businessmen, farmers curtail their investments in producer goods, in the downswing, hence, contribute to an intensification of the decline in business activity. This is made clear in Figure 16-3.

Over the period 1910-48, purchases of farm machinery and motor vehicles averaged about 7 per cent of the total receipts from farming. But nowhere is a more meaningless average to be found. In 1932, these purchases were equal to only 4 per cent of cash receipts and in 1948 these purchases equaled 11 per cent of cash receipts. If, further, we compare investment fluctuations in Figure 16-3 with the gross national product in Figure 16-1, we see that the dips in the purchase of farm machinery and motor vehicles coincide with the dips in the GNP. In the depression years of 1921-22 and 1930-34,

[3] "Agriculture and the Business Cycle," *Policy for Commercial Agriculture,* Joint Committee Print, 85th Congress, 1st session (November 22, 1957), pages 53-55.

farmers did not purchase sufficient machinery and equipment to cover the depreciation on their old stock. The productive capacity of farm firms was running downhill.

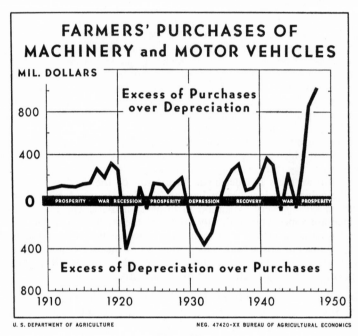

U. S. DEPARTMENT OF AGRICULTURE   NEG. 47420-XX BUREAU OF AGRICULTURAL ECONOMICS

Fig. 16-3.

But in periods of prosperity, machinery and equipment purchases bulge above the break-even line. These bulges also coincide exactly with the peaks in gross national product. This tendency toward investment, in good times, and restriction, in bad times, may be illustrated by the number of tractors purchased each year by farmers in the United States from 1929 to 1948:

Year	Tractors Purchased	Year	Tractors Purchased
1929	137,000	1939	161,000
1930	116,000	1940	219,000
1931	58,000	1941	297,000
1932	25,000	1942	218,000
1933	25,000	1943	85,000
1934	65,000	1944	215,000
1935	122,000	1945	200,000
1936	165,000	1946	257,000
1937	221,000	1947	416,000
1938	151,000	1948	501,000

The effect of business fluctuations on investment in agriculture in the 1950's is less clear. It is either nonobservable, or the opposite of what one might expect. To illustrate, total domestic shipments of wheel type tractors (primarily for farm use) have run as follows in the 1950's:

1950—424,815
1951—472,821
1952—360,366
1953—387,422
1954—210,567
1955—284,690
1956—170,421
1957—179,134
1958—188,100

These data indicate that tractor purchases by farmers declined over the whole period 1950-58, a period of great growth and prosperity in the general economy; and tractor purchases reached a low point in 1956, a year in which the crest of the business cycle occurred. The data presented by Hathaway on farm production expenditures suggest this same inverse relationship (see below).

Recessions and recoveries in the general economy have not played their usual roles in the farm economy in 1950's for several reasons. First and foremost, the farm economy has been plagued by overproduction and low prices and incomes throughout the 1950's. Hence farmers have responded in their investment decisions to the unique, but chronically adverse, conditions in agriculture, that have not paralleled conditions in the general economy. Second, governmental price and income support has protected agriculture from drastic price and income declines. Hence, farmers' investment decisions have been buoyed up to some degree by this supporting action. Thus, farm production expenditures and investments have tended to follow the depressed, but nonetheless stabilized, conditions of agriculture in the 1950's rather than the historic response to changes in general business conditions.

The Hathaway analysis with respect to farm production expenditures during the cycle is illuminating:

To examine the changes in expenditures of farmers the same periods of general business expansion and contraction have been used as in the earlier sections. However, in this case the order was determined by the order of magnitude of change in farm income. Changes in both current and constant dollar expenditures are presented, where possible, the latter as a rough measure of the change in physical quantity of inputs. In some cases the physical quantity purchased may have more effects on levels of employment than do the dollar expenditures, which are partially determined by prices. One note of qualification should be added regarding these data. Many are official estimates of the Department of Agriculture and other agencies, some are not. In certain cases these estimates undoubtedly contain a substantial margin of error. All of the sources used are shown, and where more than one estimate is available, all are shown.

Let us first examine the record of farmers' purchases of variable inputs used in farm production, shown in Table 2 [Table 16-2]. Farmers' current expenditures on purchased feed rose during every period in which farm income was rising but one—the period 1924-26. However, physical quantity purchased rose in only 8 of the 11 periods that farm income rose. Both the quantity purchased and expenditures rose significantly during periods of substantial increase in farm income.

During the 10 periods of business contraction since 1910, farm income has declined in 8. It also declined in one period of business expansion, 1954-56. Farmers' expenditures on purchased feed were reduced in 5 of the 9 periods of decline in net farm income, including substantial declines during the 4 periods when farm income was most sharply reduced. The quantity purchased was reduced in 6 of the 9 periods when farm income declined, the most notable exception being the period 1920-21, when feed prices apparently fell more rapidly than expenditures.

Turning to the series on fertilizer and lime, it appears that farmers' expenditures for these items have increased during every period of expansion in farm income. The index of tonnage applied tells much the same story for fertilizer, except for the period 1914-19, which was presumably a period of shortage. The tonnage of lime applied declined in 2 periods that farm income was increasing.

Expenditures on fertilizers and lime contracted in 5 of the 9 periods that farm income was contracting, with the largest reductions in the periods of greatest decline in farm income. However, the tonnage of lime applied declined in only 2 of the periods of contraction, 1 of which was the 1929-32 period.

In summary, it appears that variations in farmers' expenditures for current operating expenses have been partially obscured by the strong secular rise in such expenditures. However, it appears that in periods of very sharp reductions in farm income, such as those experienced in 1920-21 and 1929-32, farmers do reduce both expenditures and physical inputs of these items. As the upward trend in these expenditures tend to level off when their economic usage approaches the maximum point of profitability for most farms, it seems reasonable to expect the usage will become more sensitive to changes in farm income.[4]

Population in agriculture. The pull of the city has been strong in the twentieth century. There has been a net movement of people out of agriculture in almost every year since 1920; and this net migration

---

[4] *Ibid.,* pages 62-64.

TABLE 16-2

Percentage Changes in Farmers' Expenditures and in Physical Quantities Used of Nonfarm-Produced Items Used in Current Production During Periods of Business Expansion and Contraction, 1910-56

Periods of Business	Net Income of Farm Operators from Farming* (1)	EXPENDITURES					EXPENDITURES		
		Purchased Feed		Fertilizer and Lime:	Fertilizer (tons used)	Lime (tons used)	Petroleum, Fuel and Oil		Other Motor Vehicle Operation:
		Current dollars (2)	Constant dollars (3)	Current dollars (4)	(5)	(6)	Current dollars (7)	Constant dollars (8)	Current dollars (9)
Expansion:									
1954-56	-1.0	0.3	10.1	-2.1	1.6	15.0	5.4	-0.5	16.4
1949-53	1.5	24.2	12.7	39.2	44.5	-25.9	19.9	8.2	32.0
1927-29	7.0	3.0	-3.6	12.4	20.3	2.9	23.6	19.2	-1.0
1911-13	9.6	16.0	19.7	4.2	5.3	30.4	57.1	—	142.9
1946-48	6.3	32.2	5.8	20.9	10.8	-12.8	56.9	20.9	35.8
1924-26	11.3	-20.2	-9.1	12.9	11.0	3.5	45.6	47.1	39.4
1921-23	30.5	15.4	-10.2	.6	33.8	10.1	6.8	35.0†	-8.0
1914-19	157.4	165.0	29.8	83.6	-15.0	52.3	447.8	170.9	481.8
1932-37	171.4	131.3	19.3	136.4	98.3	297.5	42.7	24.2	32.9
1938-44	185.9	335.7	134.2	123.3	76.8	212.6	54.7	26.2	130.0
Contraction:									
1944-46	22.8	24.5	7.7	18.6	22.2	19.9	26.3	19.1	11.0
1923-24	4.5	36.3	32.3	.4	7.8	4.6	8.9	7.7	11.8
1926-27	-.8	.1	-4.0	-10.4	-3.9	14.0	-1.2	-3.4	2.0
1913-14	-6.5	2.0	-3.1	11.4	12.9	11.7	4.5	60.0	29.4
1910-11	-8.7	-17.8	-19.5	10.5	9.6	18.0	27.3	—	75.0
1953-54	-12.2	4.0	4.5	2.2	7.4	-8.5	.4	0.0	-5.2
1948-49	-14.2	-24.3	-8.1	8.4	6.0	8.6	12.4	2.0	2.5
1937-38	-18.3	-30.8	-7.7	-7.5	-6.2	9.2	1.5	-4.5	4.0
1920-21	-45.0	-43.4	12.1	-36.2	-30.9	5.3	19.2	41.9	-2.1
1929-32	-69.2	-62.1	-19.5	-60.7	-44.1	-53.6	-25.3	-21.5	-24.0

* Including Government payments.
† Deflated, using wholesale price of petroleum products.

out has been great enough to more than compensate for the natural population increase in agriculture. Hence, the population in agriculture has declined persistently (see Table 16-3). But in concentrating on the net flow, we should not ignore the two-way movement. During the period 1950-59, when people literally poured out of agriculture on a *net basis* (at an average rate of 800,000 per year) the movement to farms averaged 540,000 persons per year and from farms 1,340,000 persons per year. A lot of people were moving to and from agriculture, as well as leaving on a net basis.

The net movement of people off farms, which has taken place in most years since 1920, accelerates in each period of business revival or general prosperity (see Table 16-3). And in periods of very great economic activity, such as 1939-44, when the economy was operating under a forced draft of war mobilization, farm people were literally sucked off farms. On the other hand, the only periods of net movement from city to farm over the years 1920-59 occurred in the depressions, or recessions, of 1932-33 and 1945-46.

The period 1950-59 is most interesting with respect to the migration of people off farms. In the first place, as already noted, it is a period of very heavy movement out of agriculture. In the second place, the influence of business fluctuations—of job opportunities in the nonfarm sector—on migration from the farm sector shows up most clearly. In the year 1956, over 1 million people moved out of agriculture, on a net basis.[5] But, as the national economy dipped into a recession in 1957, the net flow of people out of agriculture dropped sharply. In 1957, only 576,000 people left agriculture. In 1958, the net flow of people out of agriculture continued at a low level. It did not return to the 1956 level because recovery in 1958 was not complete.

These shifts in the direction of net movement make good sense. Young people leave the farms for the city in great numbers when job opportunities are more attractive in the city (when, in fact, there are job openings in the city), and that is generally the case in periods of high-level economic activity. In periods of business depression, however, unemployment rises in urban areas and two things happen: (1) many young men and women, who would have migrated if business conditions were bright, remain on the farm and (2) unemployed workers in urban areas return to the farm and live with the "old folks."

It would appear that this movement across the rural-urban line invalidates orthodox economic analysis, for what often happened in

[5] The year runs from April, 1956 to April, 1957.

TABLE 16-3

Farm Population and Migration, 1929-58

Farm Population
(April 1) *

Period	Number (thousands)	As Per Cent of Total Population†	Net Migration to and from Farms (thousands)‡
1929	30,580	25.1	−477
1930	30,529	24.8	−61
1931	30,845	24.8	156
1932	31,388	25.1	607
1933	32,393	25.8	−463
1934	32,305	25.5	−527
1935	32,161	25.3	−799
1936	31,737	24.8	−834
1937	31,266	24.2	−661
1938	30,980	23.8	−545
1939	30,840	23.5	−703
1940	30,547	23.1	−633
1941	30,273	22.7	−1,424
1942	29,234	21.7	−2,975
1943	26,681	19.5	−1,563
1944	25,495	18.4	−564
1945	25,295	18.1	864
1946	26,483	18.7	151
1947	27,124	18.8	−1,686
1948	25,903	17.7	−371
1949	25,954	17.4	−1,314
1950	25,058	16.5	−1,302
1951	24,160	15.7	−271
1952	24,283	15.5	−1,996
1953	22,679	14.2	−962
1954	22,099	13.7	−25
1955	22,438	13.6	−435
1956	22,362	13.3	−1,134
1957	21,606	12.7	−576
1958	21,388	12.3	−548
1959§	21,172	12.0	not available

* Farm population as defined by Department of Agriculture and Department of Commerce, is the civilian population living on farms, both urban and rural, regardless of occupation.

† Total population as of July 1 including armed forces overseas.

‡ Net change for year beginning in April, estimated by Department of Agriculture. For 1940 and subsequent years, includes inductions and enlistments into the armed forces, and persons returning from the armed forces. For all years, includes persons who have not moved but who are in and out of the farm population because agricultural operations have begun or have ceased on the place where they are living.

§ Preliminary.

Sources: Department of Agriculture and Department of Commerce.

the past is the following: In periods of prosperity, farm prices rise relative to nonfarm prices and workers migrate on a net basis toward the area of lower product prices, to the city. In depressed periods, farm prices fall relative to nonfarm prices and the rate of off-farm migration slows down or reverses itself. The movement of workers is inversely related to relative price changes.

These shifts in product prices, farm relative to nonfarm, do not dominate the net flow of people out of agriculture for at least one reason. Even when farm product prices rise relative to nonfarm prices, the resulting incomes in agriculture on the average remain low relative to nonfarm incomes. Thus, the income incentive to shift out of agriculture and into nonfarm employment remains strong whether farm prices are relatively high or low. Hence, the net flow has been in the direction of the city for many decades. And what really governs this flow is the number of nonfarm employment opportunities together with information and access to them, not relative price movements.

The farm firm. It is often said that success or failure in farming depends on when a man is born. If he reaches maturity during a peak of prosperity and buys a farm during that period, the large and fixed payments for land in the following depressed period may force him into bankruptcy. But if a man is lucky enough to buy his farm in the trough of a depression, he can ride the crest of general business prosperity to success and perhaps riches. This view oversimplifies the problem of entrepreneurship. But it does symbolize an important problem in the business of farming: the problem of high overhead costs.

Many, if not most, of the resource inputs of the farm to which we attach a cost are in the nature of overhead costs. By this we mean that the inputs cannot be varied in accordance with price, or with any other independent variable that we might select. Resource inputs such as land, buildings, labor, breeding stock, machinery, and equipment are tied to the farm and their costs go along whether they are employed or not. These resources, acquired in a previous period, to be used over a long period of time, carry fixed charges, which must be met periodically if the farm is to be operated on a commercial basis.

What then does the farm operator do when faced with a downswing in business activity, which means lower prices to him? He perhaps reduces his applications of fertilizer, and he may skimp on his feeding rations. At least the Hathaway analysis suggests that this is what happens. But our main point is this: the farmer continues to employ all of his land, all of the family labor, and the stock of machinery and equipment on hand. Further, the producer must undertake certain out-of-pocket costs, such as spraying and fumigating in the case of fruit and vegetables, and irrigating, if he lives in the arid West, if he is to harvest a crop at all. So in the face of declining farm prices, growing out of a downswing in business activity, the individual producer continues to turn out about the same total product. The total output of the farm may decline modestly, and the composition of the total may change modestly. But the change is not great, and often there is no noticeable change.

This action, on the part of farm producers, intensifies the depression. Constant total output on individual farms means constant aggregate output for the industry. In more precise language, the aggregate output curve is highly inelastic (we meet an old friend again). In this situation, the full force of a decline in aggregate demand, resulting from the contraction in over-all business activity, shoots into a price decline. A significant reduction in total output does not come about to arrest or check the price decline. In sum, *the economics of overhead costs forces the individual producer, and producers in the aggregate, to employ their productive resources as fully as possible.*

The behavior of farm firms in the upswing of business activity does not follow the pattern just described. Producers can and, to some extent, do increase their inputs of such variables as fertilizer and feed. But for the most part their actions are not limited to such a narrow field. Rising prices bring about rising incomes, which, in turn, create happy price and income expectations for the future. In this setting, farmers, as we have already noted, invest heavily in land, buildings, machinery and equipment. But the area of innovation and investment is wider than construction and mechanization. Spurred into action by rising incomes and the expectation of even greater incomes, farmers adopt new methods and practices whenever possible. They are willing to incur the additional costs that are involved in trying out a new practice. For example, a farmer may worm his pigs for the first time. He may experiment with a new pasture grass. He may try out a new and heavier feeding scheme. He may purchase the equipment to spray potatoes in a new, improved way. In short, this is the period in which technical practices on the farms undergo a great change, for this is the time when farmers can afford to try and possibly fail.

But the net result of these periods of intense technological advance on farms is not failure. The average commercial farmer, in the present day, is too good a technician and too much research stands back of almost every technological development to permit wholesale failure. On the contrary, the acceptance and adoption of new technical methods, in combination with investments in heavy producer goods, almost always has the effect of expanding the total output of individual farms and of shifting the aggregate output curve to the right.

Do producers give up these new production techniques once prosperity gives way to depression? The answer is no. In most cases, the new practices are continued. In most cases, it would have been profitable for the farmer to have adopted the improved technologies in question at lower price levels. In most cases they are cost-reducing, not cost-enhancing, when considered from the point of view of costs per unit of output.

One proof of this argument exists in the behavior of the aggregate output curve (Figure 15-3). This curve did not drift to the left (contract) in the period 1929-33. Even taking into consideration the droughts of 1934 and 1936 and attempts at control during those years, the aggregate output of food did not contract. Farmers continued producing about the same amounts of the same kinds of products in the face of the worst depression in the history of the United States. And there has been no tendency for the aggregate output of agriculture to contract in any of the brief recessions experienced in the post-World-War-II period.

Some conclusions. From his study of the effects of business fluctuations, Hathaway draws the following *firm* conclusions:

1. Vigorous expansions and contractions in the nonfarm economy affect the well-being of agriculture and farm people. Regardless of the measure used, the income of farmers has moved in the same direction as the income in the nonfarm economy during major business cycles.
2. During periods of mild expansion and contraction in the nonfarm economy the income of farmers is likely to be subject to other influences which override the effects of changes in nonfarm business activity. However, even mild expansions tend to provide employment opportunities for underemployed farmworkers so that the income per worker has usually increased.
3. During periods of sharp reductions in income, farmers reduce their expenditures on and physical inputs of production items purchased from nonfarm sources.
4. Farmers' expenditures upon consumers' durables, automobiles, and other items for consumption tend to vary with their income.[6]

The above conclusions are valid and to the point, as with much of the discussion of the previous section dealing with the impact on

---

[6] *Op. cit.,* pages 75-76.

the firm, *where the general business fluctuation breaks through and has an important impact on agriculture.* The devastating downturn in the early 1930's, the recession of 1937-38 and the spectacular upsurge of business activity in the period 1938-44 are cases in point. These business fluctuations had a direct and important impact on agriculture, and the consequences for, and the behavior of, agriculture were as Hathaway concludes, and as our discussion of the farm firm suggests.

But the 1950's have been different. Since 1952 agriculture has experienced chronic overproduction and depressed prices and incomes. However, farm prices and incomes have not fallen disastrously in this context; they have not because they have been riding on a massive price-supporting, loan-purchase, storage-disposal governmental program. Agriculture has been stabilized in a semi-depressed state at the level of price and income support afforded by the government. In this context, agriculture has not felt to any important degree the impact of prosperity and depression in the general sector of the economy. Business fluctuations in the general economy have, so to speak, swept over the head of agriculture without touching it. Agriculture has responded to its semi-depressed, but nonetheless stabilized, condition, as well as to certain indigenous developments, rather than the broad sweeps of general business conditions. Thus, for example, we have the curious phenomenon of agricultural incomes rising in 1958—a recession year for the general economy—and falling in 1959, a year of sharp recovery for the general economy. Price supporting action, payments under the Soil-Bank program, a widespread crop-crippling winter freeze, and the build up phase of the beef and hog cycles all met in a happy coincidence to push up farm prices and incomes in 1958, when past experience with business fluctuations would indicate that farm prices should have fallen.

In one respect the response of agriculture to general business fluctuations in the 1950's has been traditional. The movement of people in and out of agriculture has followed the traditional pattern: in periods of business recovery and high-level employment, farm people have moved out of agriculture at a rapid rate, but in periods of business recession and heavy unemployment, the flow of people out of agriculture has slowed down and been reduced to a trickle. Even here, however, the pattern of response to business fluctuations differs in the 1950's, from earlier peacetime periods. The migration response in agriculture to changes in general business conditions is much accentuated in the 1950's.

But in other respects agriculture in the 1950's has reacted as if general business fluctuations did not exist. The aggregate output of agriculture has increased persistently throughout the 1950's without regard to changes in general business conditions and in spite of relatively low prices and incomes. This it has achieved through the widespread adoption of new and improved production techniques and the increased investment in such capital items as fertilizer, tractors, farm machinery and electric power. The incentive of reducing unit costs and the expectation of continued price and income support have induced farmers generally to make these adoptions and investments. And this farmers have been able to do because their asset positions, their financial positions, generally have not been seriously impaired during the 1950's. Price and income support has kept the representative commercial farmer solvent, hence in a position to finance the adoption of new and improved techniques and the investment in additional capital items.

In sum, the traditional response of agriculture to prosperity and depression has gone off the track in the 1950's. Agriculture, by individual farms and in the aggregate, is adjusting, and responding, to a unique condition of chronic overproduction and depressed but stabilized incomes rather than the ups and downs of general business conditions. And so long as the above set of conditions continue to dominate, yes plague, agriculture this 1950's type of unresponsiveness to prosperity and depression in the general economy will characterize agriculture.

REFERENCES

Hathaway, Dale E., "Agriculture and the Business Cycle," *Policy for Commercial Agriculture,* Joint Committee Print, 85th Congress, 1st session, November 22, 1957.

Polanyi, Michael, *Full Employment and Free Trade.* London: Cambridge University Press, 1945, pages 1-64.

Samuelson, Paul A., *Economics: An Introductory Analysis,* 3rd ed. Chapters 11 and 12. New York: McGraw-Hill Book Company, Inc., 1955.

Schultz, T. W., *Agriculture in an Unstable Economy,* Chapter VI. New York: McGraw-Hill Book Company, Inc., 1945.

Tarshis, Lorie, "National Income and Employment," Part IV, *The Elements of Economics.* Boston: Houghton Mifflin Company, 1947.

POINTS FOR DISCUSSION

1. Describe the pattern of business fluctuations in the United States since 1920. What role did investment play in these fluctuations?

2. What do we mean by the income-expenditure approach to business fluctuations? What causes aggregate demand (aggregate expenditures) to expand and contract? How does the relation of saving to investment, in the circular flow of income, influence aggregate demand? What is the influence of consumption on aggregate demand?

3. Why does not the total economy stabilize automatically at full employment?

4. In what respects does the agricultural segment of the national economy behave differently from the nonagricultural segment in business fluctuations?

5. How is investment in agriculture associated with business fluctuations? How is investment in agriculture associated with expansions in output?

6. How do farmers' expenditures for production items vary over periods of business contraction and expansion?

7. In what periods do we find the rate of migration from farm to city accelerating and in what periods decelerating? What is the explanation for changes in the rate of farm to city migration?

8. What are the factors that operate to maintain farm output in periods of falling prices?

9. How has agriculture responded differently to business fluctuations in the 1950's, than it did in earlier times?

CHAPTER 17

Agriculture in a Dynamic, Developed Economy[1]

IN THIS CHAPTER we want to explore the growth problems of agriculture in a dynamic, developed economy—the economy of the United States. The rapidly growing and highly prosperous economy of the United States in the 1950's has not produced a healthy and prosperous agriculture. In general, agriculture has lagged in the sharing of the riches and affluence of the great and growing national economy of the United States. Because the reasons for this, until recently, have been poorly understood, we need to inquire into them here.

The long-run race between aggregate demand and aggregate supply. As we already know, the farm price level fluctuates in response to a shift in aggregate demand relative to supply, or a shift in aggregate supply relative to demand. But it is not correct to visualize these aggregate relations shifting back and forth in a static, no-growth context. Over the long run, both of these aggregate relations have been expanding; what we have had is a race between aggregate demand and aggregate supply. And changes in the farm price level that have occurred, growing out of shifts in the *relative* positions of the aggregate demand and supply relations, have most often resulted from unequal rates of expansion in these aggregate relations. The race has rarely been equal, and at times it has been very unequal, with extreme income consequences.[2]

---

[1] Adapted from Willard W. Cochrane, "The Agricultural Treadmill," *Farm Prices—Myth and Reality* (Minneapolis: University of Minnesota Press, Copyright 1958 by the University of Minnesota).

[2] For a good discussion of the unequal rates of growth between aggregate demand and aggregate supply, see T. W. Schultz, *Agriculture in an Unstable Economy.* Chapter III. (New York: McGraw-Hill Book Company, Inc., 1945).

Demand shifters. During the nineteenth and early twentieth centuries both rising real incomes and population growth operated to expand the aggregate demand for food. Rising real incomes enabled the average consumer to move away from a plain diet heavily weighted with potatoes and cereals to a varied and more expensive diet—varied in terms of more animal products, more fruits and vegetables in and out of season, and more delicacies (cheeses, sea food, baked goods); and expensive in terms of greater dollar cost as well as the more farm resources required to produce it. And population growth contributed more mouths to feed.

It is generally believed that the population elasticity for food approximates 1.0—meaning that a 1 per cent increase in population growth results in a 1 per cent increase in food consumption. This population elasticity estimate will vary as the means of population growth (from immigration and natural increase) varies; but it is probably a useful rule of thumb. And since the total population of the United States increased by about 2,000 per cent between 1800 and 1920, it follows that the aggregate demand for food increased by roughly the same amount as the result of population growth. During this long period, the market for farm food products widened, first, because there were many more mouths to feed and, second, because each mouth demanded a more varied and expensive diet.

Now let us take a more careful look at the causes of shifts in demand that have been at work in the first half of the twentieth century. And let us look first at the demand shifter, change in income. Sometime in our national history, the income elasticity for food fell, and fell drastically—a development that probably occurred during the decades preceding and following 1900. In other words, it is posited here that real income increases for the average consumer were so great during this period (about 100 per cent between 1880 and 1920) that the average consumer broke through, to an important degree, that real income range where rising incomes shoot into the purchases of more food and more expensive food, and moved into that income range where changes in income have little effect on total food consumption. In any event, the income elasticity for *farm food products* is now in the neighborhood of 0.2—meaning that the consumption of farm food products by the average consumer increases 2 per cent with a 10 per cent increase in his income. Consumers in the 1950's prefer to use additional income to purchase automobiles, durable goods, sporting goods, vacations, and services with their food, rather than more food.

In this instance we are *not* talking about the income elasticity of food items purchased by consumers in retail stores; the income elasticity of food items purchased by consumers at retail runs about 0.6 to 0.7, and it is this high because the income elasticity for nonfarm food services associated with, or built into, those food items (that is, storing, transporting, packaging, processing, and merchandising) is much higher—running between 1.0 and 1.3. In less technical language, consumers are ready and eager to buy more conveniences and gadgets (TV dinners, for example) associated with farm food products, as their incomes rise. But they are not so willing—in fact they are reluctant—to buy more farm food products as their incomes rise.

The income elasticity of farm food products is not likely to approach zero in the late 1950's or early 1960's, but it may approach zero by 1975, and if not by 1975 then certainly by the year 2000. The income elasticity for farm food products cannot fall immediately because there were some 60 million consumers in the United States in 1955, living in families and as single individuals, with incomes of less than $3500. These are the consumers that currently increase their consumption of animal products and fresh fruits and vegetables importantly as their incomes rise. This is the group that has pulled the income elasticity for farm food products for the average consumer up to as high as 0.2 in the 1950's.

But if per capita real incomes increase by as much from 1955 to 1975 as they did from 1935 to 1955, the poorest family in 1975 will, relatively speaking, be living in luxury in that not too-distant year. That is, barring a major economic depression, we can look forward to a time, perhaps by 1975 and certainly by 2000, when the basic wants of all families in the United States will have been satisfied with respect to farm food products—when the income elasticity of those products will have fallen to zero. This is the first great damaging circumstance to agriculture of an affluent society. This, however, is not to say that the income elasticity for *nonfarm* food services will have fallen to zero. On the contrary, this latter elasticity may remain above 1.0 as more and more wives escape from the kitchen and experience the joys of dining out.

The key point to keep in mind in all this is that consumers purchase two very different categories of resources in what is commonly called food: (1) farm resources embodied in farm food products and (2) nonfarm resources converted into services associated with and built into farm food products. The consumption of the second category of resources increases at least proportionately with increases in income, but the consumption of the first category of resources increases only modestly with increases in income, and may in the foreseeable future cease to increase at all.

Now we turn to the second demand shifter, population growth. Fortunately for the agricultural sector, developments with respect to population growth as a demand shifter have not paralleled those of rising real incomes. For a while it was feared that population growth as a shifter of demand was losing its power too; in the 1930's most predictions of population growth had the population of the United States leveling off and declining in the 1960's. But for some totally unexplainable reason, the people of the United States decided during and following World War II to wreck the prewar population projections of demographers by going on a child-producing spree. The rate of population increase in the United States in the 1950's is among the highest of the nations of the world—15 per thousand as compared with 4.5 for the United Kingdom, 13 for India, and 20 for China.

In comparative terms, perhaps more relevant for this discussion, the total population of the United States increased nearly 9 per cent in the decade ending in 1935, 9 per cent in the decade ending in 1945, and 16 per cent in the decade ending 1955. And if the 1954-55 rate of increase is maintained, total population in the United States will increase by some 16 per cent in the decade ending in 1965, to reach a figure of 193 million; and by 37 per cent in the two decades from 1956 to 1975 to reach a figure of 228 million. Even if the 1954-55 rate of population increase moderates slightly, as some experts believe that it will, there are still going to be many more people around in 1975 to be fed—certainly no fewer than 210 million.

The picture that emerges with respect to further expansions in the demand for food looks like this: The United States is approaching that state of opulence where further increases in real personal incomes will not act to expand the demand for food. Expansions in the aggregate demand for food are becoming dependent upon population growth alone. But during the period 1955-75, population growth is going to be a powerful force acting to increase the demand for farm food products.

One more idea should be incorporated into this discussion of the aggregate demand for food. As this aggregate demand relation expands through time, driven by population growth, it will, in all probability, become even more inelastic than it is now. Further decreases in the price elasticity of the aggregate demand for food will result from further increases in real personal incomes. Rising real incomes historically have had the effect of reducing the price elasticity of the aggregate demand for food, and there is every reason to believe that this tendency will continue until food, like safety pins now, has a zero price elasticity. When this happens—and the time is not too far off—if the rapid rate of economic development of the 1946-56 period is maintained, the aggregate demand for food will expand in a perfectly inelastic manner, powered by population growth alone.

Supply shifters. During the nineteenth century, total farm output in the United States increased as the result of two basic forces: (1) farm technological advance and (2) an increase in the size of the total fixed plant—an increase in the number of acres incorporated into going farm units. The former was a minor cause and the latter the major cause. Regardless of the level of farm prices, or the pattern of commodity prices, settlers pushed back the frontier year after year and added land and farmsteads to the total fixed plant. Land settlement was part of the great westering movement in America over three centuries, and although it may have grown out of certain economic dislocation and adjustments in the Old World, it was in no way related to the pricing system, except insofar as hard times in the cities forced more people to the frontier.

With the turn of the century, this means of expanding total farm output began to disappear—the country was almost completely settled. And by 1920, except for some irrigation developments in the arid West, the total agricultural plant stopped growing. *Total farm output did not, however.* Total farm output increased about 100 per cent between 1910 and 1958. This great increase resulted almost exclusively from technological advance on existing farms—a process that gained momentum in the latter part of the nineteenth century, in the form of farm mechanization particularly, and became an all-inclusive, ever-present force by the end of World War I. The minor force behind output expansion in the 1800's became the major force in the 1900's.

The development and adoption of many new technologies have contributed to the expansion of the total marketable output of farm commodities since 1920, but none has been so important as the tractor. The substitution of tractor power for animal power has released some 70 million acres, or one-fifth of our crop land, for the production of marketable crops. And the myriad of hookups that have been developed to go with the tractor have released several million workers for nonfarm employment (a development that is sometimes considered a mixed blessing). Certainly the gasoline engine in its many forms and uses dominated farm technological advance between 1920 and 1950.

Now there are some who say, because they see evolving no single technology comparable in importance with the tractor, that farm technological advance is losing its steam, too, as a shifter of the aggregate supply relation. Although Bressler is no alarmist, he is of the opinion that agriculture will be hard pressed to meet the food needs of the American population in, say, 1975. Writing in 1957 he argues:

> . . . These projections indicate an increase in net agricultural production during the next 20 years approximately equal to the record breaking increases of the past 20 years. Because of nonrepetitive factors such as the replacement of horses by tractors, the production job ahead is perhaps 40 per cent greater than the achievements of the past 20 years . . .[3]

Then stating his case more generally he argues:

> If our analysis of future requirements is correct, agriculture is faced with a production and productivity problem for the next 20 years that far exceeds any accomplishments of the past. That this challenge can be met is not denied, but to suppose that such impressive advances can be accomplished and sustained—not only in the next two decades but to an increasing extent in the years beyond 1975—without continuing and substantial contributions in agricultural research and extension activities seems entirely unwarranted.

Bressler is correct; a large task confronts technicians and farmers in the years ahead if agriculture is to feed and clothe adequately the rapidly growing population; the new production techniques necessary to this achievement must be developed, extended and adopted. But to fear that this will not be done is another matter. Few people appreciate the extent to which the development and application of new knowledge and new technologies now blanket and permeate the agricultural scene. True, no single developing technology dominates the scene in the 1950's to the extent that the tractor did in the previous three decades. But one dominant technology is not a requirement of rapid technological advance, and hence of a rapid rate of output expansion. Total farm output is expanding rapidly in the 1950's as the result of technological development and adoption on many fronts: plant and animal breeding; plant and animal disease control; feeds and feeding practices; water control and usage; and soil, crop and animal handling equipment. Advances on all of these technological fronts, together with a more skilled working force, contribute to a situation in which the typical farmer adopts one or several new practices each year, becoming thereby a more productive farmer.

In this connection we should recognize, too, that the development

---

[3] R. G. Bressler, Jr., "Farm Technology and the Race with Population," *Journal of Farm Economics* (November 1957), pages 862-863.

of new technologies and their adoption on farms is no longer left to chance. The outpouring of new production practices and techniques that occurred between 1920 and 1955 did not result from a few lonesome inventors working in attics or old barns; rather it resulted from organized and well-financed research at several levels: pure research on natural phenomena, applied research on agriculture problems, and commercial research on specific products and techniques.

Private and public agencies currently spend up to $200 million, and perhaps more, each year on the development of new technologies for *farm production*.[4] And all the efforts directed toward carrying these new technologies to farmers must run into sums much larger than the $200 million. Consider all the agencies, private and public, involved: the federal-state extension service; the vocational agricultural teaching program in high schools; the soil conservation service; the service work of farm cooperatives; and, finally and probably now most important, the selling and service work of private feed firms, machinery and equipment firms, processing firms, and producer associations.

The adoption of new production techniques has become as much a part of farming as getting up in the morning; the farmer is "expected" to adopt new practices and technologies which reduce his costs and expand his output in the same way that he is "expected" to care for his livestock, send his children to school, and honor his wife; the farmer is the last link in an endless chain of events, called technological advance, which almost everyone considers good.

Those folks looking for (or trying to hide from) a second revolutionary development to follow the tractor may find it before the turn of the next century. If and when artificial photosynthesis breaks out of the laboratory, where it is now an established fact, that institution-shaking technology will have arrived. When we can produce carbohydrates directly from the sun's rays, without the work of plants, then the production of foodstuffs can be transferred from farms to factories and the greatest of all agricultural revolutions will rage across the land. And the process of artificial photosynthesis is certainly further advanced in the 1950's than was the unleashing of the atom in 1900.

So we conclude that farm technological advance, development and farm adoption, gives every evidence of remaining a powerful force in agriculture, driving the aggregate supply relation before it in an expanding action. And truly revolutionary developments which could turn present-day agriculture upside down are in the offing.

---

[4] This amount does not include funds used to finance research on the handling, processing, and distribution of products after they leave the farm.

The Brewster historical analysis. The key developments in American agriculture from 1870 to 1960, together with the inter-relations and implications of those developments emerge in the Brewster analysis presented in Table 17-1.[5]

Prior to the decade 1910-20 agriculture was an expanding industry employment-wise. Employment in agriculture, to illustrate, increased 26 per cent over the decade 1870-80, but agriculture had so changed by 1950-60 *that employment decreased 25 per cent in that ten-year period.* Coincidental with the great change in agriculture as an employer, worker productivity—output per worker—increased importantly: from an increase of 3 per cent for the decade 1900-10 to an increase of 65 per cent for the decade 1950-60. Output per worker increased so rapidly from 1930 to 1960 that total farm output pushed ahead of total population growth in spite of the declining labor force. World war and world famine saved agriculture during the decade 1940-50, but the pressure of food supplies on population growth depressed farm prices and incomes in the 1950's, just as it did in the decades of the 1870's, 1890's and 1930's.

The propelling force in Table 17-1 prior to 1900 was territorial expansion—bringing new lands into cultivation. But since 1920 the propelling forces have been capital formation and technological advance. These forces acting and interacting have first forced a release of labor from agriculture of almost unbelievable proportions and second increased the productivity of labor remaining in agriculture in equally unbelievable proportions. The result has been a persistent pressure of total food and fiber supplies on total population growth since the 1930's. And without the numerous, although somewhat ineffectual production controls employed in agriculture during the 1950's, that pressure could have been substantially stronger.

The race, 1955 to 1975. The long-run race between aggregate demand and aggregate supply, thus, for all practical purposes, turns out to be a race between population growth and farm technological advance. Since, however, nobody is omniscient, it is impossible to demonstrate that population growth will outrun technological advance between 1955 and 1975, or the converse. If an observer is more impressed with the capacity of Americans to reproduce themselves than with their ability to create new ways of producing goods and services, then he will probably conclude that population growth will win the race. But if, on the other hand, he is more impressed with their in-

---

[5] First presented by John M. Brewster, "Farm Technological Advance and Total Population Growth," *Journal of Farm Economics* (August 1945) and brought up-to-date in the note by the same title, *Journal of Farm Economics* (February 1955).

TABLE 17-1

Changes in Farm Employment, Production, Output per Worker and Total Population, 1870-1950 with Projections for 1960 (1870 = 100 for all indexes)

Year	Farm Employment			Farm Output		Output per Worker		Total Population		
	Number* (Million)	Index	Per Cent Change	Index†	Per Cent Change	Index	Per Cent Change	Number‡ (Million)	Index	Per Cent Change
1870	8.0	100	—	100	—	100	—	39.9	100	—
1880	10.1	126	26	152	52	122	22	50.3	126	26
1890	11.7	146	16	187	23	128	5	63.1	158	25
1900	12.8	159	9	243	30	153	20	76.1	191	21
1910	13.6	169	6	267	10	158	3	92.4	232	21
1920	13.4	166	-1	289	8	174	10	106.5	267	15
1930	12.5	158	-7	328	13	208	20	123.1	308	16
1940	11.0	137	-12	363	11	265	27	132.1	331	7
1950	9.3	117	-15	443	22	379	43	151.7	380	15
1960	7.0	88	-25	550	24	625	65	179.8	451	19

* 1870 to 1900 based on data from U.S. Bureau of the Census, Population Series P-9, No. 11. From 1910 to 1950 the figures are from *Average Annual Farm Employment*, U.S.D.A. Agricultural Marketing Services. Projection for 1960 based on trends in later part of 1950-60 decade.

† Three-year averages centered on the year indicated except for the 1960 projection. Estimates for 1870-1900 made by the Agricultural Adjustment Research Branch, Farm Economics Research Division, U.S.D.A. Agricultural Research Service. From 1910-1950 figures are from *Changes in Farm Production and Efficiency*. Projection for 1960 based on trends in later part of 1950-60 decade with allowance for unusually good weather in 1958.

‡ Population July 1, Bureau of Census *Population Reports 1870-1950*. Projection for 1960, Bureau of Census "Current Population Estimates," November 10, 1958, P-25, No. 187. "Illustrative projections of the population of the United States by age and sex, 1960-1980." The projected figure in this table is taken from the III Series of source cited.

ventive genius and ability to adopt new technologies, then he will probably put his money on technological advance.

Which wins is terribly important to American farmers. If population growth outraces technological advance, other things being equal, aggregate demand will press against supply and push the level of farm prices upward, as did occur between 1895 and 1915. But if technological advance outraces population growth, other things being equal, aggregate supply will press against demand and drive farm prices downward, as has been the tendency since 1948.

Some evidence can, however, be adduced about the outcome of the race between aggregate demand and aggregate supply over the period 1955-75, where conclusive proof is impossible. First, there are the Brewster projected data for the decade 1950-60, already considered. Second, during the period 1950-58, total population in the United States increased by exactly 14 per cent. At the same time the total output of marketable farm products increased by 19 per cent. Clearly, the total output of farm products in the 1950's is outracing population growth.

James T. Bonnen, looking forward to 1965 in a major study which assesses the output expanding potential of all "known and almost known technology," suggests that the trends of the early 1950's will not be reversed.[6] Assuming that the farm price level is maintained at the 1955 level, which relatively speaking is low, Bonnen estimates that the annual rate of farm surplus, which stood at 8 per cent of total supply in 1955, would be enlarged to 12 per cent as of 1965. In other words, this study, taking a comprehensive look to 1965, concludes that output expansion will increase its lead over demand expansion in the years ahead.

If labor would flow out of agriculture at a faster rate than it has, and if some important blocks of lands would drop out of production, these actions would offset the inflow of improved technologies and new capital, and hence act to slow down the rate of aggregate output expansion. But we are already aware that labor has been shifting out of agriculture at a furious pace—25 per cent of the agricultural laboring force in one decade—and it is difficult to speed up this already rapid rate of out-migration without creating grave social problems on the land, along main street, and in urban receiving areas.

---

[6] From a paper entitled, "Adjusting the Structure of Agriculture to Economic Growth," presented before the North Central Farm Management Research Committee, Chicago, March 18-20, 1957, and published in part as an essay, Bonnen and Cromarty, "The Structure of Agriculture," *Agricultural Adjustment Problems in a Growing Economy* (Ames, Iowa: Iowa State College Press, 1958).

Further, sunk capital (for example, fences, specialized machinery) and farm land have few good economic alternatives; hence they are slow to go out of agricultural production. In short, it is terribly difficult to shrink the agricultural plant: capital substitutes readily for labor and land, and sunk capital items have "no place to go." Land and labor resource adjustments have not been able, and give little evidence of being able, to offset the inflow of improved technologies and new capital and thus dampen down the rate of output expansion.

It is the judgment of the authors that the rate of aggregate output expansion can easily exceed the rate of aggregate demand expansion over the period 1955-75. And what can easily occur may occur. In this event, one of two things must happen: (1) the annual accumulation of surplus stocks by government must increase, or (2) the farm price level must fall. In other words, the authors believe that the capacity to expand farm output beyond the needs of the population is there, and, *unless counteracted in some effective way,* this capacity will further intensify the general income problem in agriculture.

All that has been said to this point with regard to the race between the aggregate demand for, and the aggregate supply of, food over the period 1955-75 has assumed an expanding, total economy with full, or nearly full, employment. In other words, implicit in the discussion up to now has been the assumption of continued prosperity. This appears reasonable, but it is only an assumption. A slowing down in the rate of total economic growth is a distinct possibility, and a major and prolonged economic depression is at least a possibility during the period.

The principal short-run effects on agriculture of a business depression are: (1) a slowing down—and possibly even a contraction—of the rate of aggregate demand expansion, by reason of a decline in real personal incomes and (2) a drying up of job opportunities for surplus agriculture workers in the nonfarm sector. Both of these effects work in the direction of pushing down the farm price level. The longer run effects on agriculture of a general economic depression might be (1) a slowing down of the rate of population growth and (2) a slowing down of the rate of farm technological advance. These effects would tend to cancel each other out, but to what extent it is impossible to say.

Market organization and technological advance. Why in the face of falling farm prices and declining gross incomes do farmers persist in adopting new technologies, and thus expanding output? Why, in the 1950's, have farmers pushed aggregate output ahead of demand through widespread technological advance, and thus driven down the prices of their own products? And why are they likely to keep right on behaving in this seemingly irrational manner? In the main, the answer is to be found in the market organization of agriculture. But given this market organization, some other factors need to be considered: the role of society acting through government and the financial position of farmers. So let us inquire into the manner in which farmers adopt new technologies to see how and where they are led astray.

Market organization and the adoption process. To this point farm technological advance has been considered in terms of the total agricultural industry—in terms of its shifting effects on the aggregate supply relation, hence upon the farm price level. In this view, we see the effects on the industry of a particular technology or production practice after it has been *widely adopted throughout the industry.* If, however, we take as a unit of analysis not the industry but rather different firms in the dynamic process of adoption, the story changes. And this is what we shall do now: consider the effects of farm technological advance on firms that adopt the technique early, then on the more typical followers, and finally on the laggards.

It should be recognized, first, that farmers typically operate in a special sort of a market—one that satisfies the key conditions of a perfectly competitive market: namely, a market in which no one farmer can have, or does have, any perceptible influence on the price of his product (or his factors of production). The farmer is a price-taker; he takes the price offered him because he is such a small part of the total market that he can have no perceptible influence on the market or on the market price.

Second, it will be recalled that a technological advance has the effect of lowering the *per unit costs of production* of the farm firm (typically, per unit costs of production are reduced as the total value product on the farm in question increases by more than the increase in total costs; it is extremely difficult to think of a new technology that does not increase output). This being the case, farm producers who adopt a new technology (for example, growing hybrid seed corn) early in the game realize increased net returns from undertaking that enterprising act. The new technique reduces costs of production for the enterprising few, but they are such a small part of the market that total output is not increased noticeably and price does not come down. Net incomes of the few who adopt the new technology are increased and a powerful incentive is created for other farmers to adopt the technique.

In this explanation we find the basis of continuing and widespread farm technological advance. The operators who first adopt a new technology reap the income benefits (the difference between the old price and the new, lower unit costs). Then other farmers in the community see the income advantage accruing to Mr. Early Bird; also the Extension Service and other educational units spread the information around. Thereupon Mr. Average Farmer decides he will adopt this cost-reducing technique, and this includes most farmers in the community. *But the widespread adoption of this new technology changes the entire situation. Total output is now increased, and this increase in the supply of the commodity lowers the price of that commodity.* And where the price elasticity of demand at the farm level is less than 1.0 (that is, demand is inelastic), as is commonly the case in agriculture, gross returns to all producers must fall.

As the dynamic process of technological adoption unfolds, we see two things happening: (1) in those cases in which the output of the commodity is increased, the price of the commodity falls relative to commodity substitutes; and (2) unit costs of production rise after their initial decline, as the gains from the new practice, or technique, are capitalized into the value of the fixed asset involved. So in the long run, by the time most farmers have adopted the technology, the income benefits that the first farmers realized have vanished. Mr. Average Farmer is right back where he started, as far as his income position is concerned. Once again, average unit costs of production are equal to price and no economic surplus remains.

If this is the typical result, why do farmers generally adopt new methods? It is easy to see why the first farmers undertake a new method or practice. They benefit directly. And we can understand why neighbors of the enterprising first farmers adopt the technology; they see the income advantage and make up their minds to give it a try. But, as more and more farmers adopt the new technology, output is affected and the price of the commodity declines. This price decline acts as a burr under the saddle of the followers, the average farmers; the price of their product is declining, but their unit costs of production are unchanged. *To stay even with the world these average farmers are forced to adopt the new technology.* The average farmer is on a treadmill with respect to technological advance.

The position of the laggard, who will not or cannot adopt the new technologies, is a tragic one. The farmer who belongs to a religious sect that does not permit technological advance, the aged or beginning farmer who cannot afford the initial cost of the technology or production practice, or the lazy fellow who prefers to go fishing, finds himself in an income squeeze. The relative price of the commodity falls as one technique after another is adopted throughout the industry, but his unit costs of production do not come down. Thus, the farmer who does not adopt new technologies and practices is squeezed and squeezed. Farm technological advance for him is a nightmare.

In the preceding analysis, we reached the conclusion that any economic surplus growing out of the introduction of a new technology is squeezed to the zero point or below in the long run. But this does not mean that the labor income to operators and hired labor *must* fall, even when the price level is falling. We have yet to take up another dynamic consideration: the substitution of machinery and equipment for labor. Increased farm mechanization most often takes the form of substituting a machine process for a hand process. If in these situations gross returns are unaffected and total costs of the unit under consideration (the firm, or total agriculture) decline, then the labor income of those workers remaining *must* be increased.

In the more typical case in which output expands, demand is inelastic and gross revenue declines. If the impact of the new technology (the general purpose tractor and the variety of hookups, for instance) is such as to reduce the number of workers required in the industry, as well as to reduce total costs of production, the average labor income of those remaining *may not* decrease; or, if it does, it will not decrease as much as would otherwise be the case. In this situation, the average labor income of those remaining in agriculture develops into a three-sided struggle between declining total revenue, declining total costs, and declining number of workers. Again, no firm generalization can be made with respect to the outcome of this race in the 1960's and 70's, but the low labor returns on representative farms in the late 1950's—typically falling well below $1.00 per hour[7]—suggest that labor is losing the race in the 1950's. Workers are not, and probably cannot, move out of agriculture rapidly enough to hold up and increase their rates of return, given the present and prospective technological revolution in agriculture. The technological revolution in agriculture requires a rate of out-migration (if labor incomes are to be maintained and enhanced) that is incompatible with the aspirations of farm people, nonfarm job opportunities and a stable social structure. Hence, returns to farm workers continue to lag.

Social action and the adoption process. The typical small family farmer, of course, is not and has not been in a position to undertake the costly, time-consuming work of developing new technological practices for his farm operation. But the many small farmers who make up the agricultural industry have rarely organized to promote

---

[7] "Farm Costs and Returns," *Agricultural Information Bulletin 176* (U.S.D.A., June 1958), pages 46-76.

and finance research and development through their own private agencies. In fact—and even though farmers are notorious tinkerers— farm people have often displayed an antagonistic attitude toward scientific inquiry and development. In recent years they have come to accept and even rely on a continuing change in the state of the arts in agriculture, but in most instances they have not initiated those changes. Thus, we conclude that if the availability of new production practices and techniques for farm adoption were dependent upon farmers' initiative, such practices and techniques would have been in short supply for many years.

But new production practices and techniques for agriculture have not been in short supply; to the contrary, there has been a continuous outpouring of these new technologies in the twentieth century. And the most important reason why there has been this generous supply since the turn of the century is that the *total society* decided to take collective action to assure this ample supply of new technologies.

The nation established "agricultural and mechanical arts" colleges in the mid-nineteenth century to service the technological needs of agriculture. Society, acting through the federal government and the various state governments, has generously financed the research and development work in those colleges and in governmental research agencies ever since. This is not to say that every important technological development in agriculture has been the direct result of work in the land-grant colleges and governmental research agencies. Far from it: private agencies have contributed many new technologies for use in agriculture, and appear to be providing an increasing proportion. But it is to say that *society has covered the overhead costs of training scientists and carrying on the basic research which lies behind every applied technique.*

The point is that society has underwritten technological advance in agriculture by guaranteeing a continuous outpouring of new production techniques for adoption on farms. If farm technological advance does not outrace population growth in the period 1955-75, it won't be because the new techniques are not there to be adopted. By generously financing research and development in agricultural production, society has made as certain as possible that an ample outpouring of new techniques will continue.

This willingness of society to finance research and development in agricultural production is in many ways a strange phenomenon. Perhaps in some collective and intuitive sense society feels that a rapid rate of technological advance in agriculture is basic to rising levels of living for its members—as indeed it is. By underwriting a rapid rate of technological advance, society assures itself of a bountiful food supply at relatively low prices. But the strange aspect of all this is that this generous financing of research and development is done in the name of helping farmers, and it is *so* accepted by most farmers and their leaders.

Now in the short-run monopoly sense (that is, the highwayman sense), nothing could be farther from the truth. The monopolist always seeks a position where his product is relatively scarce and the products of all other groups are plentiful; from this position of market power the monopolist trades scarce, dear items for cheap, plentiful items. But a rapid rate of technological advance—a rate of technological advance that drives aggregate supply ahead of aggregate demand—places the farmer in just the opposite position; places him in the weak market position of producing bountiful supplies at low prices.

Farmer asset positions and the adoption process. In a free market at least, aggregate supply cannot outrace aggregate demand indefinitely. At some point in time, its pace must slow down and become equal to, or perhaps even lag behind, the rate of demand expansion. In other words, the expansion rates of these two relations are related; the connection is somewhat indirect, but it is there. The aggregate demand and the aggregate supply relations are related through the nexus of the *asset positions* of farmers.

Most new technologies adopted on farms are capital using—that is, their adoption requires an additional cash outlay, or some kind of additional financial commitment. But since the adoption of a new technology reduces unit costs, farmers are willing to make the additional investments as long as they can. And they can, as long as their liquid and capital asset positions are strong and unimpaired.

But these asset positions deteriorate under a falling farm price level with the attendant declines in gross and net incomes. The liquid asset position typically goes first; but with the passage of time capital assets become encumbered in order to cope with losses resulting from declining incomes. In a free market situation, then, farm technological advance sows the seeds of its own slowdown. If aggregate output outraces aggregate demand long enough and far enough, and the farm price level falls far enough and stays down long enough, the asset position of farmers generally will become weak, and the process of farm adoption of new technologies must be choked off. In this way the rate of output expansion is slowed down and brought into equality with the rate of demand expansion.

This, of course, is a painful process, as farmers in a limited way have discovered in the 1950's. Furthermore, it is no simple process. The slowdown in farm technological advance will not be uniform. It will first strike the inefficient farmers and the beginners: the vulnerable asset positions of these farmers deteriorate rapidly when the farm price level declines. The average farmer will hold out longer, and the very efficient farmer succumbs to the slowdown only in extreme situations. The efficient farmer, the early adopter of new techniques, who reaps the income rewards accruing to him as such, and who successfully increases his labor income by substituting machinery and equipment for labor, can withstand and even thrive in a major price decline *to a point*.

It should be emphasized here, however, that the rate of output expansion, powered by farm technological advance, does not slow down immediately when it encounters a price level decline. Witness the rapid rate of output expansion in the 1950's in the face of a falling farm price level. Farmers generally came out of the World War II period with strong asset positions and for this reason generally have been able to maintain a rapid rate of technological advance in the face of a falling price level. The rate of output expansion in the 1950's and 1960's will not slow down until the asset positions of these many average, or representative, farmers are impaired— until the average farmer is hurting badly. But in a free market situation the slowdown in the rate of aggregate output expansion must ultimately come, as the slowdown in the adoption of new technologies engulfs more and more farmers.

The consequences of farm technological advance. The spotlight in this section will be on the period 1920-55, the period in which total inputs employed in agriculture remained constant, and when increases in total output must therefore have resulted from new configurations in the use of productive resources made possible by technological advance. It will be recalled that total farm output increased throughout the nineteenth century and during the first two decades of the twentieth as the result of: (1) an expansion in the size of the fixed plant of agriculture and (2) technological advance, with the former decreasing in importance and the latter increasing over the long period. Hence, it is difficult, if not impossible, to know what part of the increase in total output is attributable to technological advance and what part to an increase in the size of the fixed plant during that long period. But from 1920 to 1955 all, or practically all, of the increase in total marketable output must be attributed to technological advance (in the inclusive sense discussed in Chapter 6). There is nothing else to which it can be attributed.[8]

---

[8] It is sometimes argued that increases in total output between 1920 and 1955 may be attributed to farm firms' becoming more efficient (that is, that farmers were successful in locating and moving toward the minimum point of

Food supply. The technological developments that occurred during the period 1920-55, and which were adopted on commercial farms during that period, enabled farmers to produce with the same total volume of resources a more than adequate food supply for the growing population. Thus, the first and most necessary goal of this and every society was achieved: an adequate food supply. Never before had it happened that an adequate food supply for an expanding population was provided without the employment of more total resources in agriculture. John M. Brewster sums up the consequences of farm technological advance for the food supply in these words:

> For the first time in history, gain in labor productivity appreciably outraced the rate of population increase during the 20's and became four times faster during the 30's. For every 100 workers needed in agriculture in 1930, only 79 were needed in 1940. The pressure of population upon the food supply had done an about face.[9]

First, through the beneficence of plentiful and fertile land resources and second, because of technological advance, consumers in the United States enjoy a rich, varied, and, if they so choose, nutritious diet. This is a blessing that few people in the past have enjoyed, and that relatively few people in the world enjoy even today.

Release of human resources. Farm technological advance not only assures Americans of an adequate food supply in the 1950's, but over the years it has released millions of farm-reared people to work in manufacturing, in the distributive system, and in the arts, sciences, and professions. This, of course, is the mark of economic progress: first, the release of workers from agriculture to go into manufacturing, and then the release of workers from both of these categories to enter the service trades (and to enjoy increased leisure time) *as the real incomes of all continue to rise.*

The process by which these people have been released from agriculture has not always been a kindly one, but it has taken place. It has happened as workers in agriculture have become increasingly

---

of their long-run planning curves) over this long period. But this argument flies in the face of facts and logic. The state of the arts was changing over the entire period, sometimes slowly, sometimes rapidly. Farmers were continuously adjusting to new levels and patterns of technology over the entire period. By what logic, then, can one argue that farmers were more nearly at the minimum point of their long-run static cost curves in 1955, than farmers were in 1920? None, except by assertion. The facts are that farmers were adjusting to new technologies over the entire period, not seeking minimum points on *static* planning curves.

[9] "Farm Technological Advance and Total Population Growth," *Journal of Farm Economics* (August 1945), page 515.

productive—as one worker, armed with new production techniques, has been able to produce enough food and fiber to meet the wants of more and more nonfarm people. To illustrate: in 1820 one worker in agriculture could support 4.1 persons including himself and by 1920 one worker could support 8.3 persons; but by 1955 one worker in agriculture could support 19.7 persons and by 1958 he could support 23.6 persons (see Figure 17-1). Since 1940 the capacity of the average farm worker to produce has literally shot skyward.

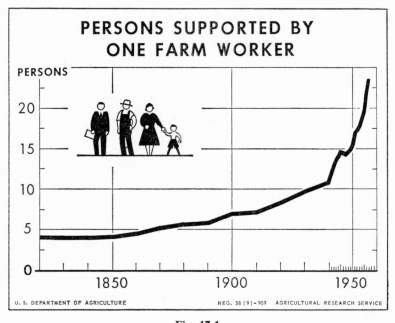

PERSONS SUPPORTED BY ONE FARM WORKER

U. S. DEPARTMENT OF AGRICULTURE   NEG. 58 (9)-909   AGRICULTURAL RESEARCH SERVICE

Fig. 17-1.

The proportion of the total labor force of the United States employed in agriculture has declined steadily over the long-run past: from 72 per cent in 1820 to 18 per cent in 1920 to almost 8 per cent in 1958. This is common knowledge. But not so generally known is the fact that total employment in agriculture reached a peak of 13.6 million workers in 1910 and has been declining ever since. Further, the movement of labor resources out of agriculture has been rapid in recent years: the total number of workers in agriculture fell from 11 million persons in 1940 to 9.9 million in 1950 and to 7.5 million in 1958. This is no small decline.

Since 1920 the substitution of machines for men in agriculture has been rapid indeed. Where this process of substitution will end no one knows, but it is reworking the face of agriculture in the 1950's, increasing the average size of farms (in acres), greatly increasing the capital investment on farms, and commercializing the farm operation.

Farmers' incentive incomes. Incentive income is a concept developed by J. R. Bellerby[10] to describe the return to human effort and enterprise. In farming this is the return to the farmer as a manager, laborer, and technician. It does not include any return to property or capital. The income incentive ratio relates the incentive income of farmers on a per-man unit basis to the incentive income of persons engaged in nonfarm enterprises on a per-man unit basis. The incentive income ratio, thus, compares the average, or per unit, return to human effort and enterprise on the two sides of the farm-nonfarm fence. By five-year intervals, the farm-nonfarm incentive income ratio for the interwar period is as follows:[11]

1920	46
1925	38
1930	32
1935	43
1940	32

During the interwar period the incentive income of farmers was consistently less than 50 per cent of nonfarm incentive incomes. In other words, when only the returns to human effort and enterprise are considered (when the returns to capital are excluded), the returns to farmers as compared with nonfarm workers are extremely low.

It is interesting to note that Bellerby computed these incentive income ratios for many countries for the interwar period, and that the United States falls near the bottom of the list. The incentive income ratio is higher for all the following countries than for the United States: Australia, New Zealand, France, United Kingdom, Denmark, Sweden, and Canada. The incentive income ratio of the United States exceeds that of only a few underdeveloped countries—Egypt, Mexico, and Thailand, for example.[12]

As we have observed, widespread technological advance on farms in the United States since 1920 has assured the growing population of the United States of an adequate food supply and gives promise of underwriting an adequate food supply in the foreseeable future.

---

[10] *Agriculture and Industry Relative Income* (New York: The Macmillan Company, 1956), page 16.

[11] *Ibid.,* page 187.

[12] *Ibid.,* page 270.

Widespread farm technological advance has also released several million agricultural workers for nonfarm employment, and gives promise of releasing many more in the foreseeable future. But widespread farm technological advance during the interwar period did not result in high incentive incomes for farmers relative to nonfarm workers. It contributed to low incentive incomes for farmers, as farm technological advance first expanded aggregate output, and then sustained aggregate output in the face of a contraction in aggregate demand during the Great Depression. In the United States, then, where farm technological advance was the most rapid in the world during the interwar period, the incentive income ratio was among the lowest in the world.

Immediately following World War II, when the United States made an effort to feed the hungry, famine-ridden peoples of Europe and the Far East, the income incentive ratio rose to the 50 per cent level. But with the falling gross and net farm incomes in the 1950's resulting from the falling farm price level which resulted, in turn, from aggregate output marching ahead of aggregate demand again, the incentive income ratio fell back to the levels of the depressed 1930's. The incentive income ratio is given below for selected years:

1947	50
1950	44
1955	30

Truly, the American farmer is on a treadmill. On it he is running faster and faster in the quest for higher incomes growing out of the adoption of new and more productive techniques, but he is not gaining incomewise. *He is losing.*

The general theory of agriculture in a dynamic, developed economy. The capacity of American farmers to command good and stable prices and incomes in the market is weak; the power position of farmers in the market is weak. The farmer *takes* the prices that the market offers him, and very often these are low prices.

The farmer's weak position in the market (that is, his inability to reject the low prices which are offered to him and command higher ones) grows out of four related circumstances: *first,* the high value that American society generally places on technological development and application; *second,* the market organization within which farmers operate; *third,* the extreme inelasticity of the aggregate demand for food; and *fourth,* the inability of resources previously committed to agricultural production to be shifted readily and effortlessly out of agriculture. These are the essential components of a general theory of agriculture in a dynamic, developed economy such as the economy of the United States in the 1960's.

The American people have not singled out agriculture to carry the burden of technological advance; Americans prize technological advance highly, expect it, and demand it in all segments of the economy. As Bushrod W. Allin stated in the 1957 Lecture Series of the Graduate School of the United States Department of Agriculture, belief in technology is a part of the American creed:[13] The "dynamics in American culture I shall call the American creed—a blend that is peculiarly American. The three principal dynamics of this creed are:

> (1) Belief in enterprise
> (2) Belief in democracy
> (3) Belief in technology."

Americans are willing to back this belief in technology with dollars—in fact with 7 billion of them for research in 1956.[14] With few exceptions, businessmen believe that it is good business to develop new and better products, and to this end they spend vast sums in research and development. In fact, competition in the nonfarm sector commonly takes the form of product competition; in this common situation firms do not compete through price; they compete through product differentiation—by means of an improved product, or a different product. As we have already noted, society has been generous in the financing of research and development in agriculture. Our society expects a rapid rate of technological development, and it has experienced a rapid rate of technological advance in most lines of endeavor, including agriculture.

The farmer operates in a sea of competitive behavior; each farmer is a tiny speck on this sea and the output of each farmer is a tiny drop in this sea. With rare exceptions, the single farmer operates in a market so large, that he can have no perceptive influence on it. In this situation, the farmer must take as given to him the prices generated in the market.

Confronted with this situation, he reasons "I can't influence price, but I can influence my own costs. I can get my costs down." So the

---

[13] "Rural Influences on the American Politico-Economic System," lecture before the U. S. Department of Agriculture Graduate School (April 1957).

[14] "Report to Congress," *Senate Document No. 45,* Commission on Increased Industrial Uses of Agricultural Products, 85th Congress, 1st session (June 1957).

typical farmer is always searching for some way to get his costs down. By definition a new technology is cost-reducing; it increases output per unit of input. Thus, the farmer is always on the lookout for new, cost-reducing technologies which usually increase the total output of his farm. Built into the market organization of agriculture, then, is a powerful incentive for adopting new technologies and expanding output—the incentive of reducing costs on the individual farm.

If the demand for food were highly elastic, all would be sweetness and light in agriculture. If the aggregate demand for food were *elastic,* the bountiful and expanding supplies of food that farmers want to produce would sell in the market at only slightly reduced prices; gross incomes to farmers, in the aggregate and individually, would increase. But the aggregate demand for food is not elastic; it is inelastic and extremely so. For this reason, a little too much in the way of total output drives down the farm price level in a dramatic fashion, and reduces the gross incomes of farmers in a similar fashion.

Finally, the persistent pressure on each farmer to adopt new technologies and thereby reduce unit costs has the effect of continuously putting a little too much in the way of supplies on the market where there is not an offsetting outflow of resources from agriculture. And it is not easy to achieve the necessary rate of resource movement out of agriculture where technological advance is rapid and widespread, and becoming more so. Land and sunk capital cannot be moved. And labor does not move into new jobs easily for many reasons: the value of agriculture as a way of life, monopolistic restrictions in nonfarm labor markets, insufficient financial base, lack of nonfarm skills, and so on. Resource adjustment, particularly human resource adjustment, takes time, but the technological revolution in agriculture sweeps forward. Hence, we find a general tendency, in peacetime, for aggregate supply to outrace aggregate demand and thus keep farm prices relatively low.

A general theory of agriculture in a dynamic, developed economy, has been sketched. The high value that society places on technological advance guarantees a continuous outpouring of new technologies. The incentive to reduce costs on the many small farms across the country results in a rapid and widespread adoption of the new technologies. Rapid and widespread farm technological advance drives the aggregate supply relation ahead of the expanding aggregate demand relation in peacetime; and, given the highly inelastic demand for food, together with the inability of resources previously committed to farm production to be shifted readily and effortlessly out of agriculture, farm prices fall to low levels and stay there for long periods.

REFERENCES

Black, John D. and James T. Bonnen, "A Balanced United States Agriculture in 1965," *National Planning Association Special Report No. 42* (April 1956).

Bonnen, James T., "How Large is the Surplus of Farm Products?," reprinted from the *Quarterly Bulletin,* Vol. 40, No. 4. East Lansing: Michigan Agricultural Experiment Station (May 1958), pages 920-931.

Bressler, R. G., Jr. "Farm Technology and the Race With Population," *Journal of Farm Economics,* (November 1957).

Brewster, John M., "Farm Technological Advance and Total Population Growth," *Journal of Farm Economics,* (August 1945).

Schultz, T. W., *Agriculture in an Unstable Economy.* Chapter III. New York: McGraw-Hill Book Company, Inc., 1945.

POINTS FOR DISCUSSION

1. What have been the long-run shifters of the aggregate demand for food in the United States? Indicate their role and relative importance.
2. What have been the long-run shifters of aggregate supply in the United States? Indicate their role and relative importance.
3. What is the outlook in the race between aggregate demand and aggregate supply in the 1960's?
4. Who gets the benefits of farm technological advance—farmers or consumers? By what line of reasoning do you reach your conclusion?
5. Why do we have widespread and rapid farm technological advance in the United States?
6. What is the nexus between movements in long-run supply and long-run demand in a free market?
7. What have been the consequences of the rapid and widespread farm technological advance in the United States—food supplies, workers in agriculture, and workers' incomes?
8. What do we mean by incentive income? Is it a good measure for comparing farm incomes with nonfarm incomes?
9. What is the general theory of agriculture in an advanced economy such as the United States?

Foreign Markets, Surplus Disposal and Agriculture

SINCE Colonial times farmers have been interested in the export market. This interest became particularly keen in the first half of the nineteenth century, with the settlement and development of the fertile Mississippi Valley. The tariff question commanded the principal attention of those giants of the United States Senate, Calhoun, Clay, and Webster and their followers, for four decades, but they could not evolve a satisfactory solution to it. The Civil War itself grew in large measure out of the struggle over trade policy: the agrarians versus the industrialists. The war split the agrarians into two camps and dissipated their demands for an expanded foreign market. Further, the tremendous growth in domestic population in the latter decades of the nineteenth century dulled the previous acute need for an expanding export market. The agrarians mellowed with the widening of the domestic market.

World Wars I and II, however, reawakened farm groups to the potentialities of the export market. After each of these world conflicts, farmers and their organizations sought a solution to the problem of chronic peacetime surpluses through export. There runs a feeling, a deep feeling, that in some way the needs of the world and the productive capacity of American farmers could and should be harnessed together. Thus, we must analyze the foreign trade problem and the farmer's position in it to complete the picture of the total market for farm products and its relation to supply.

What is international trade? Private commercial international trade is a two-way proposition. Any private trading transaction is, but this fact is sometimes overlooked in domestic transactions. We exchange money for goods at home, why not abroad? It happens, however, that producers of wheat and cotton for export do not want to be paid in English sterling in London, French francs in Paris, or Dutch guilders in Amsterdam. They want to be paid in United States dollars in their home town. In order for this perfectly natural desire to be realized, commercial imports and exports must come close to balancing. Imports into the United States earn dollars for traders in foreign countries that they may then use to buy wheat and cotton, trucks and turbines produced in the United States. Imports provide the *dollars* with which exports are paid for; in reality, goods are traded for goods.

Imports and exports rarely balance exactly; the difference is made up by shipments of gold (a universally accepted product), or the extension of credit. A country whose exports exceed its imports must extend credit to the foreign buyers involved, or accept gold shipments as payment from those buyers. But either of these means of balancing the payments between one country and others cannot go on indefinitely. Sooner or later exports must fall to the level of imports. If trade is conducted on a commercial basis (as against Marshall Plans and the like), the exports of a country must be balanced by imports in the long run.

We should not get the impression, however, that the trade between any two countries must balance (that is, that the exports of country A to country B must equal the exports of country B to country A). When such a bilateral condition exists, trade between the two countries is limited to the volume of the lesser country in the trading relationship. The main arteries of world trade prior to World War II ran as follows: the tropics exported more to the United States than they bought in return; the United States exported more to the British Dominions and temperate Latin America than it bought; the British Dominions and temperate Latin America exported more to continental Europe than they bought, continental Europe exported more to Britain than it bought. The circle of trade and payments was closed by Britain exporting more to the tropics than she bought from them. This is the multilateral system of trade, so sought after by countries interested in expanding free commercial world trade. Each of these trading areas had a deficit with one area, but each deficit was balanced by a surplus with another area. Thus, imports and exports for the system as a whole were in balance, since imports and exports for each trading area were in balance, and payment balances between pairs of countries were effected through the purchase and sale of foreign exchange (another country's currency), in organized markets dealing in foreign exchange. *The key to the private commercial trade problem exists in each country's importing as much as it seeks to export.*

What does the farmer gain from international trade? To the cotton farmer of the South, the wheat farmer of the Great Plains, and the fruit grower on the Pacific Coast, international trade is advantageous because the export market provides an additional market for their products. The export market for these and other commodities supplements the domestic market; it increases demand and buoys up prices. Hence, the incomes of these farmers are directly affected by the volume of international trade carried on in their commodities. Here we find the first tangible gains from trade, as well as the source of the most vigorous arguments for expanding international trade.

But as was pointed out above, private trade is a two-way proposition: to export we must import. If we are to export cotton, wheat, and dried fruit, we must import something. Therefore, we conclude that the market for *all goods and services* produced in the United States is not widened by international trade; we sell certain goods and services and in return buy others. It does not follow, however, that trade is not advantageous. On the contrary, all groups in the United States, including farmers, gain from international trade. The material level of living of the average American is enhanced by the production and export of commodities that we produce efficiently, when they are exchanged for items that we cannot produce, or for the production of which we are not adapted. We all gain from the production and export of cotton and wheat, automobiles and tractors, motors and machine tools in exchange for bananas, sugar and coffee, tin and copper, and travel.[1] What we have here is the old principle of comparative advantage, first encountered in Chapter 2, but now operating on a world-wide basis. The basic argument for international trade rests on the principle of comparative advantage. The real income of all people is increased by (1) their specializing in those lines in which they have the greatest advantage (or the least disadvantage) and (2) trading back and forth between specialized producing areas. It is what we do in the free-trade area of the United States, and that principle has world-wide application.

One more gain from international trade needs to be mentioned: if it is fairly developed and honestly conducted, world trade con-

---

[1] Travel is an important invisible import. We cannot bring Buckingham Palace to the United States, but we can go to see it. And in so doing, we provide the British with dollars to buy dried fruit and steel plate in the United States.

tributes to world peace. Access to raw materials and markets through international trade tends to minimize frictions between nations and to facilitate the settlement of commercial disputes. Of course, trading policies and practices of nations can, and have, contributed to war. But economic causes of war most often grow out of a lack of resources or a lack of markets, and expanded international trade helps ease either situation. Thus, the farmer, along with everyone else, may benefit from an expansion in world trade when it has the effect of lessening tensions and frictions between nations around the world.

What trade cannot do. Private commercial international trade cannot provide an important market for farm products when the volume of imports is, for one reason or another, seriously restricted. As was pointed out above, the ability to export is limited by the willingness to import; when imports are restricted, exports are reduced. In such a situation, which has been typical in the United States, the export of farm products suffers doubly. First, a contraction in total exports has the obvious adverse effect on farm commodities. But second, and more important, the rest of the world has become increasingly dependent on the United States for heavy producer goods. Hence, a dollar shortage, growing out of protectionist trade policy, forces foreign customers (private or public) to use their scarce dollars for the things they need most: machines, tools, and heavy equipment. They can purchase food products elsewhere, from the Argentine, Australia, and other surplus areas, which they do. The result, then, of a reduction in total exports, relative or absolute, is a disproportional contraction in farm products. The export market for farm products cannot expand and, in the past, has been hard hit by national policies aimed at restricting imports.

International trade cannot provide an important market for farm products when domestic prices for the commodities involved are held above the structure of world prices. Foreign buyers of wheat and cotton are not going to purchase those products in the United States if they can go elsewhere and obtain those supplies at lower prices. And domestic price policies have had the general effect of lifting prices of farm products at home above the structure of world prices.

A way out of this problem is sometimes suggested and sometimes acted upon; it calls for selling domestic supplies at the domestically supported price and selling the remainder in the world market for what it will bring. That part sold in the world market is excluded from resale in the higher home market by tariffs and import quotas. This trade tactic is called "export dumping," and these are the kinds of trading actions that make competing countries angry. Competing nations argue, and not without good reason, that domestic policies aimed at supporting the prices of such commodities as cotton and wheat cause farmers to overexpand in those commodities. Then, if the "surplus" is "dumped" on the world market, it unfairly and unduly depresses the world price. Certainly, unilateral dumping is no way to win friends among trading nations.[2]

Last, but not least, two-way trade does not and cannot contribute directly to the achievement of full employment. It can and will contribute to a more efficient use of resources, and it may contribute indirectly to a greater use of resources by influencing profit expectations. But of itself, two-way trade does not touch the employment problem. We say two-way trade, because in the past some countries have found it expedient to "export" unemployment, that is, reduce unemployment at home by subsidizing the export of goods and services. In such instances, exports were maintained in excess of imports by the device of the national government's extending credit to foreign purchasers. Needless to say, such actions by one national government in a period of world depression, when most governments are wrestling with unemployment and low prices, adds to the fear, uncertainty, and tensions of such a period.

In the opposite direction, if the only purpose of economic policy were the creation of jobs, one way to achieve that purpose would be to withdraw entirely from international trade. Bananas and coffee could be grown in the United States in greenhouses. The various nonferrous metals that we import could perhaps be produced at home from low-grade ores, or from scrap. Of course, we would have smaller quantities of these products, probably of poorer quality, which would make them and associated products more expensive. But to build and operate the facilities involved would require more labor than it now takes to produce the things that are traded for these commodities. In this way, jobs would be created. But it is extremely doubtful that we would want to solve future unemployment problems by this method.

The long-run past, 1866-1940. The composition of foreign trade has shifted steadily since the Civil War (see Figure 18-1). Two trends stand out in the export chart of Figure 18-1. First, we see the decline in the relative importance of raw material exports. In the period 1866-70, those exports constituted two-thirds of the total, and the big item in this component was raw cotton. This pro-

---

[2] The term "unilateral" refers to actions or decisions taken by one nation independent of their consequences to other trading nations. "Bilateral" refers to actions or decisions reached by two nations without consideration of or consultation with other countries. "Multilateral" refers to actions or decisions taken in full consideration of the consequences to *all* other trading nations.

PERCENTAGE OF TOTAL EXPORTS AND IMPORTS REPRESENTED BY
FINISHED MANUFACTURED GOODS AND CRUDE MATERIALS (INCLUDING
FOOD STUFFS), UNITED STATES, FIVE YEAR PERIODS, 1866-1940

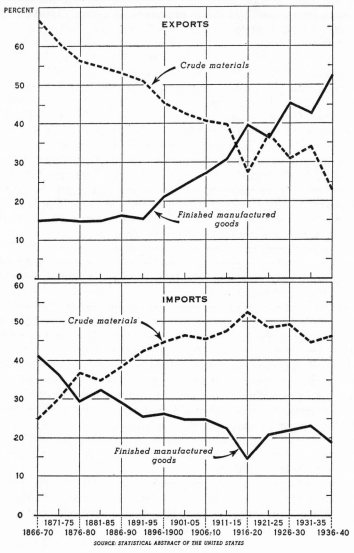

SOURCE: STATISTICAL ABSTRACT OF THE UNITED STATES

U. S. DEPARTMENT OF AGRICULTURE   NEG. 45317   BUREAU OF AGRICULTURAL ECONOMICS

Fig. 18-1.

portion declined over the years, until in the period 1936-40, crude materials accounted for less than one-fifth of total exports. Second, we see that, as raw materials lost ground, finished manufactured goods began a sustained rise to pre-eminence among exports. From a modest 15 per cent in the decade following the Civil War, finished manufactured goods forged ahead until, just before World War II, they accounted for more than one-half of total exports. This latter development becomes even more impressive when considered in conjunction with a parallel rise in the export of semi-manufactured goods.

The statistical trends on the import side are the reverse of those described for the export trade (Figure 18-1). Imports of finished manufactured goods declined from two-fifths to one-fifth of the total import trade over the seventy-five-year period under consideration. And imports of crude raw materials rose from one-fourth to about one-half of the total import trade. A listing of the more significant imports that have increased in volume over the years should be of interest. The more important food imports are mostly products that cannot be grown in the United States, except at prohibitive costs: coffee, tea, cocoa, tropical fruits, nuts, cane sugar, and edible vegetable oils. The more important imports of raw materials, in either a raw or partially processed state, include: rubber, wood pulp, hides, furs, wool, silk, vegetable oils, jute, copper, tin, nickel, petroleum, and a variety of steel alloys.

As pointed out on several occasions, the net result of all economic and political forces operating between World Wars I and II was to decrease, both absolutely and relatively, the volume of foreign trade of the United States. This shrinkage is well illustrated in Table 18-1. The level of foreign trade declined gradually, but persistently, relative to the national income (or capacity to trade) in the interwar period. Exports of agricultural commodities declined more sharply, relative to our capacity to trade, than did total exports over the same period. And as might be expected, the United States' share of total world trade was declining during this period. In sum, the world trade picture and the United States' part in it was bleak indeed in the period between the two world wars.

The volume of all the principal agricultural exports from the United States declined during the interwar period, and decreased substantially for cotton, wheat, lard, and other pork products. Exports of cotton from the United States declined from something over 8 million bales per year in the early 1920's to 3.6 million in 1938, 6.5 million in 1939 and 1.2 million in 1940. The contraction of wheat exports was of the same magnitude; wheat exports from the United States declined from the approximate level of 200 million

TABLE 18-1

National Income and the Value of Foreign Trade, Total and Agricultural, United States, 1920-40
(Billions of Dollars)

Year	National Income	Total Trade			Agricultural Trade		
		Imports	Exports	Exports as a Percentage of National Income	Imports	Exports	Exports as a Percentage of National Income
1920	69.2	5.3	8.2	11.8	3.2	3.4	4.9
1921	51.9	2.5	4.5	8.7	1.3	2.1	4.0
1922	59.7	3.1	3.8	6.4	1.6	1.9	3.2
1923	69.5	3.8	4.2	6.0	2.0	1.8	2.6
1924	69.2	3.6	4.6	6.6	1.9	2.1	3.0
1925	73.6	4.2	4.9	6.7	2.3	2.1	2.9
1926	76.6	4.4	4.8	6.3	2.4	1.8	2.3
1927	76.1	4.2	4.9	6.4	2.2	1.9	2.5
1928*	78.8	4.1	5.1	6.5	2.1	1.9	2.4
1929*	87.4	4.4	5.2	5.9	2.2	1.7	1.9
1930	75.0	3.1	3.8	5.1	1.5	1.2	1.6
1931	58.9	2.1	2.4	4.1	1.0	.8	1.4
1932	41.7	1.3	1.6	3.8	.7	.7	1.7
1933	39.6	1.5	1.7	4.3	.7	.7	1.8
1934	48.6	1.7	2.1	4.3	.8	.7	1.4
1935	56.8	2.0	2.3	4.0	1.1	.7	1.2
1936	64.7	2.4	2.5	3.9	1.2	.7	1.1
1937	73.6	3.1	3.3	4.5	1.6	.8	1.1
1938	67.4	2.0	3.1	4.6	1.0	.8	1.2
1939	72.5	2.3	3.2	4.4	1.1	.7	1.0
1940	81.3	2.6	4.0	4.9	1.3	.5	0.6

* The increase in national income between 1928 and 1929 is exaggerated here, because of the introduction of a revised national income series beginning in 1929.

Source: Adapted from *Miscellaneous Publication 582* (U.S.D.A.), Table 1.

bushels per year in the early 1920's to as low as 8 million bushels in 1935 and stood at 37 million bushels in 1940. This kind of contraction, commodity by commodity, is, of course, consistent with the over-all trends shown in Table 18-1.

Post-World-War-II trade developments. The trend in agricultural exports from the United States did an about-face during and immediately following World War II. Exports of agricultural products expanded beyond any reasonable expectation in the years immediately following World War II. A chronic food crisis in both Europe and the Far East, which continued into 1949, created a great need for the surplus food products of the United States. The Federal government contributed importantly to a solution of the financing problem by making loans and gifts to needy nations. Thus, the dollar value of agricultural exports increased from $748 million for the period 1935-39 to $3.6 billion in 1947, although the percentage of agricultural exports in total United States exports increased from only 26.4 per cent in 1935-39 to 27.6 per cent in 1945-49. In short, we increased our exports in all lines. Some of this increase in the export of agricultural commodities is to be explained by a rising price level, but there can be no denying the fact that volumes increased greatly. And the high level realized in 1947 was maintained into 1949, when total agricultural exports amounted to $3.8 billion.

The great post-World-War-II expansion in agricultural exports from the United States had, however, run its course by 1949 (see Figure 18-2). In the trade year, 1949-50, the dollar value of agricultural exports fell sharply. Actually, the structure of agricultural exports was reverting toward the pattern of the 1930's when hostilities broke out in Korea in 1950. The Korean "police action" pushed agricultural exports upward once again in 1951 and 1952 (see Figure 18-2). But the $4 billion export level of 1951-52 could not be maintained. The dollar value of agricultural exports from the United States dropped below $3 billion in 1952-53 with the shift from a hot to a cold war. And it seemed for a year or two that agricultural exports from the United States were going to level off at about $3 billion. But they did not. Agricultural exports from the United States were expanded greatly over the period 1954-58 as the result of special governmental export programs—barter sales, sales for foreign currency, grants under mutual security arrangements, and for charity. Foreign surplus disposal became a major part of domestic price-income policy for agriculture during the period 1954-58 and gave agricultural exports from the United States a strong push.

Foreign trade developments in agricultural commodities since the end of World War II with respect to the United States cannot be understood and appreciated without an understanding of the important role of government in that trade. Special governmental export programs have dominated the export trade in agricultural commodities from the United States since 1946. Prior to World War II, almost all agricultural exports were commercial in the sense that transactions were initiated and negotiated by private firms. But during and following World War II, substantial quantities of agricultural products have been exported by government, or with the aid of some kind of governmental program. Hence, agricultural exports are now regularly reported under two headings—"total under special programs" and "sales outside government programs" (that is, commercial exports for dollars). Sales outside government programs, or so-called "dollar sales," include such transactions as those conducted under the International Wheat Agreement and certain Commodity Credit Corporation sales abroad. Thus, there is some overstatement of private, commercial exports in the latter category.

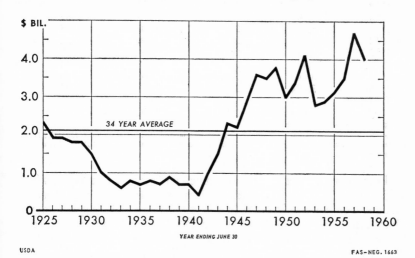

USDA   FAS–NEG. 1663

Fig. 18-2. United States agricultural exports, 1925-58.

Commercial exports of agricultural products have fluctuated from year to year since 1951, *but there has been no noticeable upward trend in sales outside governmental programs* (see Table 18-2). The great increases in agricultural exports from the United States following World War II and again in the late 1950's are accounted for almost entirely by special governmental programs. Further, the contraction in total agricultural exports which began in 1953 is to be explained by a contraction in special governmental export programs (see Figure 18-2 and Table 18-2). And it may well be the case that a high volume of agricultural exports from the United States in the future will be dependent upon strong and well-conceived governmental programs.

TABLE 18-2

Agricultural Exports, Total, Commercial and Under Special Programs, Percentage Comparison, United States, 1946-1958

Agricultural Exports*

Year	Total	Commercial Sales for Dollars	Under Special Programs	Per Cent under Special Programs
		(Millions of Dollars)		
1946	2,857	875	1,982	69
1947	3,610	1,540	2,070	57
1948	3,505	1,606	1,899	54
1949	3,830	1,486	2,344	61
1950	2,986	981	2,005	67
1951	3,411	2,201	1,210	35
1952	4,053	3,157	896	22
1953	2,819	2,273	546	19
1954	2,936	2,225	711	24
1955	3,143	2,213	930	30
1956	3,494	2,061	1,433	41
1957	4,727	2,742	1,985	42
1958	4,008	2,508	1,500	37

* Fiscal year ending June 30.
Source: "Foreign Agricultural Trade, Statistical Handbook," *Statistical Bulletin 179* (U.S.D.A., Foreign Agricultural Service, August 1946 through 1955); and relevant issues of *Demand and Price Situation* thereafter.

Looking more closely at the commercial category of exports, when agricultural exports in current dollars are translated into constant dollars, commercial exports in the 1950's are only slightly larger than total exports in the 1920's and 1930's—a relevant comparison. Thus, there does not appear to be any significant upward trend in the real value of commercial exports from the agricultural sector during the past several decades even though the national economy has grown enormously; the real volume of agricultural exports handled by private firms has held almost constant in peacetime since the end of World War I.

This last observation is reflected in one further set of trade statistics. Agricultural exports moving in commercial channels (that is, sales outside of government programs), as a percentage of total merchandise exports of the United States, have declined steadily since the turn of the century—falling from nearly 60 per cent in the period

1902-06 to between 12 and 14 per cent in the latter part of the 1950's. In other words, commercial exports of agricultural commodities in the 1950's continue the long downward trend as a percentage of total United States exports.

Why a peacetime stagnation of commercial exports? An important part of the explanation to this question is to be found in the commercial policy of the United States. The United States has long been a high-tariff country. The highwater mark of this protectionist policy, designed to limit and restrict imports, came in 1930 with the passage of the Smoot-Hawley Tariff. This act was passed to make the tariff really effective, to plug all gaps and to keep foreign products out. The hundred years of protectionism culminating in the Smoot-Hawley Tariff had the effect that was intended, namely, reduced imports. It also had the effect of reducing the number of dollars earned by foreign traders. Hence, it had the further effect of restricting exports. And agriculture, which has always depended on the export market, suffered. At the turn of the twentieth century, tariff restrictions did not hurt too much; the domestic market was growing at a rapid pace. But in the last few decades, as in the early nineteenth century, American farmers have needed the export market as an additional market in which to dispose of their surpluses. The tariff wall, however, has had the effect of sealing off that market.

Since 1934, tariff rates have been reduced steadily. Through the Reciprocal Trade Agreements Program, tariff rates were reduced about 50 per cent between 1934 and 1949.[3] These important rate reductions must have an expansive effect on the foreign trade of the United States, hence, on the agricultural component. Unfortunately, quantitative trade controls and the necessity of reconstructing war-devastated areas have prevented the full effects of these rate reductions from being realized. Still, it is a hopeful sign and cannot help but contribute to an expansion of world trade in a period of peace.

The failure of the United States to develop a policy aimed at the expansion of international trade (by increasing imports) no doubt goes back to a more basic consideration: the lack of a need to import. The United States is as nearly self-sufficient as any other country in the world, and more so than most. Most of the resources needed to build a rich and highly productive economy were to be found within the borders of the United States and in relative abundance. In the nineteenth century, the United States had need of few things in world trade except an export market for surplus agricul-

---

[3] See the study by Lawrence W. Witt, "Agriculture, Trade and Reciprocal Trade Agreements," *Michigan State College, Tech. Bul. No. 220* (June 1950).

tural products. Blessed with a rich and fertile land, many people felt that a policy of tariff protection would best serve the needs of the nation: tariff protection to permit the development of those abundant resources without too much outside competition. And that is the course which was followed.

The restricted role of merchandise imports, as a source of dollar exchange, in the 1950's is portrayed in Figure 18-3. In 1957, foreign traders earned less than one-half of the total dollars available for purchasing American goods and services from the shipment of merchandise—commodities—into the United States. Over one-half of the dollar exchange available to foreign traders resulted from government loans and grants, private investments abroad and tourism. The commercial policy of the United States is highly restrictive with respect to foreign merchandise; hence, to export we must rely more and more on loans to foreign countries, which, more and more, means governmental loans and grants.

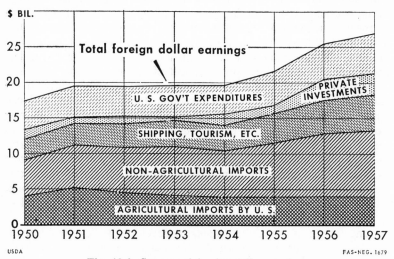

Fig. 18-3. Sources of foreign dollar earnings.

But the peacetime stagnation of commercial exports from the United States does not stem entirely from a restrictive commercial policy. The volume of private, commercial agricultural exports from the United States has declined, and seems destined to continue to decline as the result of the growing tendency for nations to engage in economic planning to achieve some goal (such as capital formation, high levels of employment, human welfare objectives). The economically underdeveloped countries are using government controls, some effectively, some not so effectively, to form capital and to develop economically; such advanced economies as the United States are using the power of government to maintain high levels of employment and to redress inequities (to support farm prices and incomes); and older, advanced economies such as Britain are driving toward a welfare state.

The point is: When a country plans internally it must plan externally. A nation cannot engage in economic planning (the purposive, collective direction of the use of resources to achieve some goal) within its national boundaries and let its foreign trade be directed solely by profit motives; Sweden and Thailand, for example, tried this after World War II, and it did not work. Foreign trade patterns that develop in reasonably free world markets at best fail to fit, fail to mesh, with the internal plans of a particular country, and in the more probable case violate, or render ineffective, the domestic plan. A country engaged in internal economic planning to achieve some goal (for example, a five-year plan of industrialization, or the maintenance of full employment) must use quantitative controls[4] to guide and direct its external trade, and will probably engage to some degree in state trading. In this institutional climate private commercial trading cannot flourish.

Looking into the future, it seems clear that, barring an international holocaust, the worldwide forces of population growth and rising real per capita incomes will have important implications for world trade, although it is easy to overstate the income force outside

---

[4] Quantitative Controls are defined in the pamphlet *Quantitative Trade Controls: Their Causes and Nature* (League of Nations, June 1943), pages 7-9, as follows:

Quantitative controls are measures which limit the quantities—or in exceptional cases the value—of goods that may be exported or imported. These limits are fixed by the authorities of a country either by autonomous action or in agreement with other countries ("autonomous" or "unilateral" as against "contractual" or "bilateral" restrictions).

Normally such measures are restrictive—in other words, the quantities permitted are less than what would be exported or imported if there were no controls. . . .

Quota and licensing systems are the principal forms of direct quantitative trade controls. . . .

Quantitative restriction is also exercised indirectly by means of foreign exchange control—that is, the regulation of the flow of money and payments which involves the regulation of the flow of goods. . . .

Under the heading of non-quantitative controls fall export and import duties, fees and taxes of all kinds, differential transportation charges, veterinary and packing regulations, mixing and milling regulations, premia and subsidies, as well as currency appreciation or depreciation. . . .

the western world. And almost certainly the working of the worldwide forces of population growth and rising incomes means that the volume of world trade will increase, as well as the United States' part in that trade. But does this mean that private, commercial exports of farm products from the United States will increase? It may; but we are inclined to doubt it.

We doubt it on these grounds. First, the United States is not likely to drop its equity goals for agriculture, that is, a substantial amount of price and income support for agriculture. Second, countries striving to form capital and develop internally will use their limited dollar exchange, insofar as they are able, to purchase specialized machinery and equipment from the United States and go to less developed countries for additional food and fiber supplies. Third, and perhaps most important, the build-up of technical knowledge and production "know-how" around the world acts to reduce the advantage in agriculture associated with land and climate, and will slowly equalize cost advantages in agriculture production as well as reduce trade in bulky, high-moisture food products. In other words, foreign trade seems destined to become more and more associated with the finished products of complex human skills and less and less with heavy raw materials.

In summary, it seems probable that the total foreign trade of the United States will increase along with the total trade of the world, but *private commercial* exports of agricultural commodities as a percentage of total exports from the United States may continue to decline. *And such agricultural exports may decline absolutely.* But what happens to the *total* level of agricultural exports for dollars will depend upon the number of intergovernmental arrangements negotiated and entered into, such as the International Wheat Agreement, in which the farm commodity is sold for dollars but under governmental controls. Trading under governmental agreements of this kind might lead to an expansion of agricultural exports for dollars. But this is hardly private commercial trading in the conventional sense. It is trading for dollars, but not on private account. This kind of intergovernmental trading *together with noncompetitive subsidized exports is probably the way that total agricultural exports from the United States will be maintained, or expanded, in the next two decades*—if it is expanded.

The foreign surplus disposal market. In the early post-World-War-II years, farm commodities moving under governmental export programs accounted for 60 to 70 per cent of total agricultural exports. This percentage fell to 19 per cent in 1952-53, but under a battery of programs including sales for foreign currencies, grants, loans, and barter, the percentage climbed to 42 per cent in 1956-57 and stood at 37 per cent in 1957-58 (see Table 18-2 and Figure 18-4).

In dollar terms, this means some $2 billion worth of agricultural commodities were exported under the direction and with the aid of government in 1956-57, and some $1.5 billion in 1957-58. And these magnitudes *do not* include exports under the International Wheat Agreement. Now the question to be answered is this—Can foreign surplus disposal operations of this size be maintained and expanded? The answer to this question must, of course, remain conditional, but if the United States acts wisely, there is a good chance that it can.

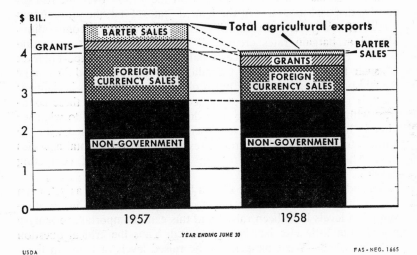

Fig. 18-4. **Agricultural exports under government and nongovernment auspices, 1957 and 1958.**

All is not bad with respect to special export programs for agricultural commodities. They were too small, but invaluable, during the famine years immediately following World War II; they made a great contribution to European recovery under the Marshall Plan; some real wealth in the form of food and fiber products was transferred to impoverished peoples badly in need of such wealth in the 1950's; and the sale of food for foreign "soft" currencies is a commendable institutional innovation which merits special mention. Such sales are conducted under Title I of Public Law 480, and in the late 1950's constituted the principal avenue of foreign surplus disposal for agricultural commodities (see Figure 18-4). Under this program surplus food and fiber products in the United States, typically wheat, cotton, dairy products, and fats and oils are sold to underdeveloped countries for their currencies—currencies which are left in those countries (there is no easy way to convert such currencies into dollars, hence, the name "soft" currency); such currencies are used in turn to pay for whatever expenses the United States may have incurred in those countries (for example, the maintenance of the Embassy) or to lend to the foreign governments in question to further their development plans. The more important beneficiaries of such sales in the 1950's have been India, Spain, Yugoslavia, Pakistan, and Turkey.

Some serious difficulties developed in the 1950's over the foreign surplus disposal programs of the United States. First, the promotional tactics of this government in selling surplus agricultural commodities abroad at bargain rates created ill will among friendly competing nations. How much these concessional sales cut into the export market of such friendly nations as Canada, New Zealand, and Denmark we will probably never know, but probably not as much as is claimed; there is probably more fear expressed in the protests of these countries with respect to what we may do, than with respect to what we already have done. Further, as experience has been gained with the various foreign disposal programs, responsible governmental agencies have acted to protect the foreign market interests of competing nations.

Second, although everyone likes a bargain, there have, as yet, been few lasting benefits to the recipient countries involved. Current consumption levels have been raised and this can be important to hungry people, but little else has been achieved. Thus the critical question is fairly asked—What happens to the raised levels of living in these countries, if and when our disposal operations come to an end? In short, the agricultural disposal programs of the United States have been expedient, temporary, disposal programs.[5] Further, in some cases our disposal programs may have harmed the recipient countries, first by depressing prices for the domestic agricultural producers involved and second, by reducing the incentive to develop and thereby increase the productivity of the recipient countries' agriculture.

Third, and most important, our foreign surplus disposal programs have created great uncertainty. Neither we ourselves, our competitors, nor the recipients know how long we will place primary emphasis on this type of adjustment, what forms the programs will take, the extent of the price concessions and the nature of the conditions attached to such sales. In this context, rational action is impossible;

[5] The experience in Japan may turn out to be an exception.

plans involving economic development and adjustment in foreign nations, as they relate to agricultural exports from the United States, must be made in a state of uncertainty, hence often are not made. This is the irresponsible aspect of our recent foreign surplus disposal policies.

A new look at surplus disposal. Experience and reason suggest that if the United States wishes to dispose of its agricultural surpluses on a sustained basis in poor, underdeveloped countries, it must be prepared to follow a course of action with lasting benefits to all— the United States, competing countries, and recipient countries. In such a course of action the United States must be prepared to make some policy commitments of long duration with respect to the objectives of programs, eligible recipients, means of financing, and so on. The general content of these policy commitments might be as follows: except in famine situations, surplus food and fiber products from the United States will be used only to finance, to support, economic development. Economic development here is given a broad interpretation to include human resource development and broad development plans as well as physical capital formation. Foreign surplus disposal is here conceived of as a humanitarian program in which the agricultural bounty of the United States is made available to peoples living in poverty, but who are willing to work and build. Hence the emphasis of the programs cannot be on the disposal of physical surpluses, or on bargaining over concessional prices; the emphasis must be placed on the *contribution* that agricultural surpluses of the United States can make toward economic development in the recipient countries.

In other words, if foreign surplus disposal of agricultural commodities is to be placed on a sustained basis, it must lose the expedient, disposal qualities that characterized it in the 1950's and must become a vehicle for developing the recipient countries. This can be done if the disposal program is put on a permanent basis, and the disposal of food and fiber products abroad is tied to, is geared into, specific plans and projects of development. In this context, the program ceases to be a disposal program for getting rid of United States surpluses and becomes a developmental program with lasting benefits for all.[6]

There are shortcomings to this developmental approach. First, it would cost more than the present program for comparable quantities. Second, many governments in underdeveloped countries are not suf-

---

[6] For a full discussion of this approach, see the article by Willard W. Cochrane, "Farm Technology, Foreign Surplus Disposal and Domestic Supply Control," *Journal of Farm Economics, Proceedings Issue* (December 1959).

ficiently strong, or sufficiently responsible, to effectively administer the development plans and projects envisaged. Third, the substitution of "development supplies" for regular imports will not be stopped in every case, and the demonstration that "development supplies" are not being substituted for regular imports will never be completely satisfactory to all parties concerned. But, there are problems to be encountered and surmounted whatever trade policy is adopted with regard to agricultural commodities.

Perhaps a brief look at two development examples will illustrate how food and fiber may be used to finance, in part, economic development. Let us look first at the simple road-building, canal-digging, or land-clearing project in a very poor country. The country involved would plan the project and mobilize the workers involved, together with their families, into construction camps. The United States would agree to provide the food and clothing needed by the workers and their families for the duration of the project. The U. S. would grant the country a loan to permit them to acquire the hard goods required on the project—picks and shovels and some heavy equipment, but not the ultimate in modern earth-moving equipment. The food and clothing costs of the project would probably run to 60 to 70 per cent of the project, which the United States would defray. The foreign country involved would pay the workers a small cash wage in its own currency.

Let us now turn to a more complex example in which food supplies are used to underwrite, in part, a national plan of economic development. Assume that a country such as India comes to the United States with a ten-year plan involving the transfer of thousands, possibly millions, of workers first from low production jobs in agriculture into some kind of training, and then into manufacturing and construction jobs. In the early phases of such a plan total output of food would probably decline somewhat. In later phases, the demand for food resulting from the increased productivity of the workers involved would probably increase more rapidly than agricultural production. To execute such a plan, without causing serious price inflation, the country would need to increase its imports of food supplies for five or ten years. But it is already using its scarce foreign exchange to import the hardware central to the execution of the plan. Here the United States could step in and offer to provide those food supplies at such prices and under such loan conditions that would not impair the financial structure of the developing country. This is approximately what the United States was doing in India in the late 1950's, but we should formalize the procedure and suggest its use in other underdeveloped countries with responsible governments (such as Brazil, Turkey, and perhaps Egypt and Pakistan). In both of these examples surplus food and fiber products from the United States are used to finance, to generate, increased productive capacity. In these illustrative cases, foreign surplus disposal goes somewhere!

A general conclusion. In the larger international arena, once we direct our gaze away from private commercial trade, the opportunities to increase exports of food and fiber products from the United States to underdeveloped national economies become great, as do the chances of failure. Further, the stakes in this policy game are breathtaking. If we can formulate and pursue effectively a course of action that uses surplus food and fiber products from the United States to finance economic development in the impoverished areas of the world, we can make a great contribution toward improving levels of living throughout the world. In this context, our farm surpluses do not seem to be nearly so burdensome; they even appear to be a blessing. But we will not formulate and pursue effectively such a policy by hawking our products around the world like a nation of soap salesmen; that policy will come, if it comes, out of the tradition of a wise and enlightened self-interest—the tradition that gave us Lend-Lease, the Marshall Plan, and the institutional device of making sales for foreign currencies.

REFERENCES

Davis, John H., "Surplus Disposal as a Tool for World Development," *Journal of Farm Economics, Proceedings Issue,* (December 1958).

"Eighth Semiannual Report of Activities Under Public Law 480, 83rd Congress, as Amended," *House of Representatives Document No. 431,* 85th Congress, 2nd Session, August 5, 1958, and more recent reports.

Foreign Agricultural Trade Outlook: Charts, U.S.D.A., Foreign Agricultural Service (November 1958); and current annual issues.

Johnston, Bruce F., "Farm Surpluses and Foreign Policy," *World Politics* (October 1957).

Johnson, D. Gale, *Trade and Agriculture: A Study of Inconsistent Policies,* Chapters 1-4. New York: John Wiley & Sons, Inc., 1950.

The Network of World Trade. League of Nations, 1942.

Witt, Lawrence W., "Agriculture, Trade and Reciprocal Trade Agreements," *Michigan State College, Technical Bulletin 220* (June 1950).

1. In what sense is international trade a two-way proposition? How does an international trading transaction differ from a domestic transaction?

2. What were the main arteries of multilateral world trade prior to World War II? In this network of trade, did exports and imports balance between each pair of trading countries? If not, how were payments made between pairs of countries?

3. What does the farmer stand to gain from an expansion in the foreign trade of farm products?

4. What do we mean by dumping? Why do countries sometimes engage in this practice? What are some of the consequences that stem from this practice?

5. Can employment in a given country be expanded through foreign trade? If so, how? And with what consequences?

6. What has been the trend in food and fiber exports from the United States over the past century? Can you give some reasons for this trend?

7. What happened to agricultural exports during and immediately following World War II? Why do we distinguish between commercial exports and exports under governmental programs in the post-World-War-II period?

8. What is the probable development of private commercial agricultural exports from the United States during the 1960's and 1970's? Be able to defend your conclusion.

9. What means did the United States employ in the late 1950's to dispose of agricultural surplus abroad? Indicate strong and weak points of such programs.

10. Give your appraisal of the set of ideas presented in the text for improving, and placing on a sustained basis, the foreign disposal programs of the United States.

PART FIVE

*Human Resource
and Land Policy Problems*

CHAPTER 19

The Poverty Problem

IN THE LATE 1950's approximately 22 per cent of all farm families had money incomes from all sources, including non-farm employment, of less than $1,000. Or, to put it in other words, after farm production expenses had been paid, over a million out of a total of 4.8 million farm families received money incomes from both farm and non-farm sources of less than $1,000. In contrast only 3 per cent of the 19.7 million urban families, or about 600,000, received incomes of less than $1,000 in the late 1950's.

The contrast is equally marked if one compares numbers of families with money incomes of less than $1,500. The Bureau of the Census estimates indicated that approximately one-third of the farm families in the late 1950's had incomes of less than $1,500 in contrast to only 6 per cent of the urban families.

The Bureau of the Census maintains a threefold classification of families on the basis of place of residence, urban, rural nonfarm and rural farm. In the late 1950's approximately 20 million families lived in urban areas, 11 million were classified as rural nonfarm and approximately 4.8 million were classified as farm families. About 11 per cent of the rural non-farm families also had incomes of less than $1,500.

These data indicate quite clearly that the poverty problem in the United States is predominantly a rural problem. In the late 1950's there were roughly 2.7 million families in rural areas with incomes of less than $1,500 in contrast to 1.0 million families with similarly low incomes in urban areas. If an allowance is made for the higher living costs in urban areas one still finds the poverty problem concentrated in rural communities.

The major low income areas. Rural families with low incomes are found in all parts of the country. But farm families with low incomes are most numerous in areas of dense rural settlement with high birth rates, where there are few outside jobs, and where topography or other obstacles hinder the use of modern machinery. In such areas the land is overcrowded and the abundance of hand labor and scarcity of capital have tended to perpetuate farming practices which, in the more productive and progressive farming areas, would be considered obsolete. The major low income and low level of living areas are shown in Figure 19-1.[1]

These areas were set up on the basis of three criteria: (1) net income of full-time farmers, (2) level of living, and (3) size of operation. Thus, areas with incomes under $1,000 and/or having a level of living in the lowest fifth of the nation, and/or having 50 per cent or more of the commercial farms classed as low production, were delineated. The darkest-colored areas on the map are those where all three of these criteria applied, and are the areas where the problem is most serious.

These problem areas, so-called, strikingly contrast with the rest of the United States. Within these areas in 1950 there were 1 million full-time farmers of working age who sold less than $2,500 worth of products. Out of this gross sum they had to pay expenses and rent, as well as family living. They represented about 40 per cent of all the farms in these areas. Another 40 per cent also sold less than $2,500 of products but were primarily nonfarmers or were more than 65 years old. Less than one-fifth of the farms in these areas produced and sold $2,500 worth of products.

Education among farmers in the low-income areas is below average. In the problem areas they average only 7 years of school completed, and only 1 out of 10 is a high school graduate. By contrast, other farmers in the nation average 8.5 years of school and 1 out of every 4 is a high school graduate.

The farmers in the problem areas average somewhat older than outside—although 85 per cent of them are under 65 years of age. They also differ from other regions in racial composition, one-fourth being nonwhite. Elsewhere the nonwhite farm population is only one-seventeenth of the total.

In the problem areas the investment in land and buildings is only about one-third that elsewhere. Cropland averages only 40 acres, compared with 120 acres outside these areas. Studies indicate that net incomes are less than half those in the rest of the country.

[1] From a report prepared for the Secretary of Agriculture entitled *Development of Agriculture's Human Resources* (U.S.D.A., April 1955).

LOW-INCOME AND LEVEL-OF-LIVING AREAS IN AGRICULTURE

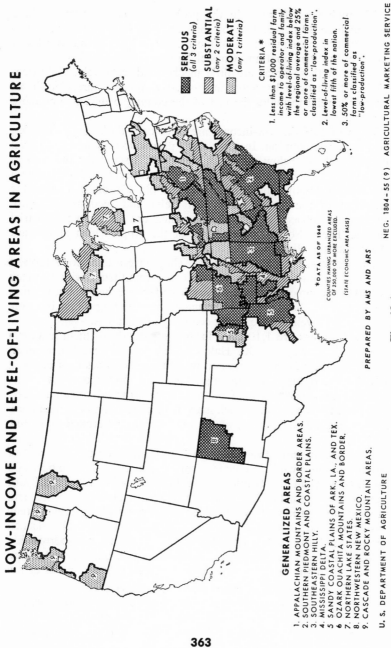

SERIOUS (all 3 criteria)

SUBSTANTIAL (any 2 criteria)

MODERATE (any 1 criteria)

CRITERIA *

1. Less than $1,000 residual farm income to operator and family with level-of-living index below the regional average and 25% or more of commercial farms classified as "low-production".

2. Level-of-living index in lowest fifth of the nation.

3. 50% or more of commercial farms classified as "low-production".

GENERALIZED AREAS

1. APPALACHIAN MOUNTAINS AND BORDER AREAS.
2. SOUTHERN PIEDMONT AND COASTAL PLAINS.
3. SOUTHEASTERN HILLY.
4. MISSISSIPPI DELTA.
5. SANDY COASTAL PLAINS OF ARK., LA., AND TEX.
6. OZARK OUACHITA MOUNTAINS AND BORDER.
7. NORTHERN LAKE STATES.
8. NORTHWESTERN NEW MEXICO.
9. CASCADE AND ROCKY MOUNTAIN AREAS.

*DATA AS OF 1949

COUNTIES HAVING URBANIZED AREAS OF 250,000 OR MORE EXCLUDED.

(STATE ECONOMIC AREA BASIS)

PREPARED BY AMS AND ARS

U. S. DEPARTMENT OF AGRICULTURE   NEG. 1804–55 (9)   AGRICULTURAL MARKETING SERVICE

Fig. 19-1.

Although most farmers in the problem areas are owners, these areas include 80 per cent of the sharecroppers in the country. Share-croppers are most numerous in the Mississippi Delta and to a lesser extent in the Piedmont and Coastal Plains.

Farms in these areas are little mechanized, relatively. Only one-third of them owned tractors in 1949. By contrast, three-fourths of the commercial farms in the rest of the country owned one or more tractors.

The worst of the low-income areas, colored darkest on the map, merit separate mention. In these areas production, income, and level of living all fall below minimum standards. Except for the area in northwestern New Mexico, these areas lie entirely within the South and Border South. They encompass the old Cotton Belt, with the exception of the fertile Mississippi Delta and sections that have switched to tobacco or peanuts or which are near large industrial centers. They also encompass most of the Appalachian and Ozark Mountains and Plateaus.

The worst areas are mainly rural. They have a total population of 13.5 million but there is not a single city within them having as many as 150,000 people. Movement away from farms is heavy, but families are large and the number of young people coming along is larger than can live well in the present economy of the areas.

In these areas are 1,100,000 farms. Nine-tenths of them had farm sales of less than $2,500. Half of these farmers were dependent largely on their farm income and were under 65 years of age.

The value of land and buildings is less than $5,000, on the average. In 1950 only one-fourth of all the farmers owned tractors. Many farms are too small to use such machinery effectively. Although there are some good soils, much of the land is hilly or eroded or of low fertility.

Low income farm families in the South. Seventy-one per cent of all farm families with cash income from all sources of less than $1,000 in 1949 were in the South.[2] These families consisted primarily of complete operator families whose heads were male, able-bodied, and in their more productive years. They are poor primarily because they have produced little. They have produced little because they lacked enough land and capital and also lacked off-farm job opportunities.

Why has this heavy concentration of low-income farm families developed in the South? Early settlement in the hillier areas of the

[2] The discussion in this section is based on an excellent report, *Rural Low-Income and Rural Development Programs in the South* (National Planning Association, 1959).

upper South led to the development of a pattern of pioneer, small-subsistence farming. The favorable markets for their small offerings of crops and livestock products were soon lost in competition with the producers on the more productive lands of the Midwest. These early families failed to find alternative sources of income. Farms in the upper South became even smaller and the region soon became overpopulated and capital-poor.

In the other parts of the South, the highly profitable combination of cotton and slavery in the early nineteenth century channeled most available capital into specialized cotton-producing, slave-holding plantations. The social organization of the rural communities was dominated by a planter class opposed to broadening the suffrage, establishing free universal education, and the taxing of property for community welfare programs. Prior to the Civil War, the importation of slaves created, for the South, a large penniless class of people, the forebears of one of the region's most disadvantaged classes of farm people. This slave labor helped reduce the earnings of all labor, free and slave alike, to the subsistence level.

Thus, even before the disastrous effects of the Civil War and Reconstruction were felt, the Cotton South had already developed social, political, and economic institutions which discouraged broadly based economic progress. War and Reconstruction not only impoverished the South, they also brought a system of crop-share wages for Negro labor and costly merchant credit for planters, saddling the region with a low-productivity organization of its agriculture.

The bitterness which Reconstruction aroused was slow to die. Cultural isolation and a backward-looking political and social system were continued during the crucial years when the rest of the nation was undergoing one of its most rapid periods of economic development. Thus, poverty in the rural South tended to become community-wide and self-perpetuating as a consequence of its peculiar social and political history.

Poverty areas outside the South. Why have low-income rural areas developed and persisted outside the South, such as in northwest New Mexico, in the southern parts of Missouri, Illinois, Indiana, southeast Ohio, central Pennsylvania, and in the northern part of the Great Lake States? In a sense, these low-income areas can be explained only in terms of the failure of the economic system to function effectively in channeling labor resources into the more productive lines of employment. When farming was largely a matter of hand labor and ox power, differences between areas in levels of income per farm were not great. But as industry developed and farming outside the South became mechanized, differences between areas widened. The farms increased in size in the more level and more productive areas, and machinery was used to replace human labor wherever possible. The excess farm population migrated to industrial and other nonfarm employment.

But in the less-productive areas located some distance from expanding industries, where the land was too hilly for the use of power machinery, farm population continued to increase and hand-labor methods prevailed. However, when the less-productive areas, not adapted to power machinery, were located near expanding industries, as in the East and Northeast, farm people took up nonfarm employment, returning their farm lands to nonfarm uses. Northwest New Mexico is somewhat of an exception to this general rule. The land in this section of New Mexico is little different from other parts of the Southwest but the majority of the farm families are of Mexican or Indian origin. A majority speak Spanish and many are illiterate. Families are large and health conditions poor in this area.

Community-wide poverty, as found in the problem areas outlined in Figure 19-1, without exception is the result of differential economic development. The key factors responsible for the lack of economic development in these areas, while the rest of the economy enjoyed unprecedented progress, are both cultural and economic. There is the saying that poverty breeds poverty. Lack of family income prevents parents from giving their children medical attention, education, and cultural advantages that fit them for a variety of job opportunities. Families living in poverty lack the reserves to cover the cost of moving to a new location in search of higher-paying jobs. This circle, of poverty breeding poverty, apparently explains the much higher man-land ratio and lower level of farm family income in the areas outlined in Figure 19-1, as compared with the Corn Belt, the Great Plains, and the dairy areas of the United States.

The continuing problem of poverty in agriculture. Both because of the undesirable social consequences of families living and raising their children in poverty and the loss in potential labor output, the continued existence of large numbers of low-income, underemployed families on small-scale farming units is one of our most serious economic and social problems. Continued high-level business activity, with job opportunities available to all seeking employment, is essential for a solution to this problem. In addition, programs that focus directly on it are needed.

We noted in Chapter 17 that those who first introduced innovations gained the benefits, often at the expense of those who continued using the old production techniques. Farmers on these small-scale units are notably backward in the adoption of improved farming methods. Lacking adequate income, capital reserves, and education, they continue to use outmoded production techniques long after they have been discarded by the more progressive farmers. Migration to non-farm jobs is prevented by lack of family savings, lack of knowledge of nonfarm jobs available, and lack of education and required skills.

Proposals for long-run programs for the solution of this problem call for increased educational facilities in these communities, increased health and medical facilities and vocational guidance services. Students of the poverty problem in agriculture are in general agreement that although communication and transportation facilities have increased greatly in recent years, the migration of people out of these areas is not proceeding at a sufficiently high rate to raise the relatively low level of incomes. Also, although industrialization is spreading through many rural areas in the South and the increase in nonfarm jobs in recent years is most encouraging—still, available evidence indicates little progress has been made in improving poverty conditions in the areas outlined.

Many handicapped families in low income areas. The more recent studies indicate that possibly one-half or more of the farm families in major low-income areas with money incomes of less than $1,000 have family heads for whom, because of advanced age and other physical handicaps, income-improvement potentialities in either farm or non-farm employment are limited.[3]

In most low-income areas, not more than about 25 per cent of the family heads with money incomes under $1,000 are both relatively young (under 45 years of age) and free from handicaps. Yet it is only these families which are most likely to be able to improve their productivity and incomes, either by improving and enlarging their farming operation or by shifting to nonfarm jobs.

Low incomes of those with limited employment opportunities pose serious welfare problems, especially in view of the limited health and welfare programs in the low-income rural areas. The older rural people are now assisted through the Social Security's Old Age and Survivors' Insurance program which was extended to self-employed farm people in the mid-1950's. Unfortunately the younger low-income farmers with severe physical handicaps which limit employ-

---

[3] The discussion in the paragraphs immediately following is based largely on, William E. Hendrix, "Problems of Low-Income Farmers," *Farm Policy Forum* (Summer 1958).

ment opportunities are among the nation's most neglected and most needy people.

National economic policies required. The low-income farm families without physical handicaps tend to be underemployed because they have far too little land and capital to employ their labor effectively. Improvement opportunities within agriculture are limited by the relatively inelastic demand for farm products and by the limited supply of land in the low-income areas. Where opportunities do exist, however, local credit institutions and the Farmers Home Administration may provide supervised credit for farm improvement and farm enlargement.

When all is done that can be done within agriculture, however, a large part of the solution to the underemployment of labor in these areas will have to be found in nonfarm employment. Few low-income farm areas have the resource bases needed to attract industries that can appreciably raise their levels of employment and income.

Thus, the poverty problem in agriculture is not one which individual low-income farm families or local areas can solve by themselves. *The poverty problem in rural areas, in terms of both causes and possibilities for solution, is part of the nation's general employment and income problem as well as a part of the income problem of agriculture.*

Since the end of World War II the nation's economy has grown at an unprecedented peacetime rate. But this rate of growth has little more than kept pace with the growth in the working-age population. The growth has been far from sufficient to create new jobs for those released by technological progress in industry and on the farms and to permit absorption of the underemployment in the low-income rural areas.

In view of this inadequate growth trend, it is evident that the poverty problem is not one that can be solved by individual rural families or local areas through their own efforts. Nor is it primarily a farm problem.

It is true that individual families and single communities can do some of the things needed to solve their poverty problem. But some of the very important things needed for the problem's solution can only be done through appropriate national policies. In a modern exchange economy there is no family, no community, and no region whose income and well-being are not affected by what is being done or not done in other parts of the economy.

By far the most important national requirement for the solution of the poverty problem in rural areas is a rapid rate of economic growth—a growth rate sufficient to absorb: (1) the natural additions to the labor force through population growth, (2) workers released by technological advance in agriculture and industry, and (3) a large number of underemployed workers from rural areas where poverty is general.

Yet, in spite of the need for a solution to the poverty problem in rural areas, the nonfarm labor markets appear to have become less competitive in recent years. Wages in some industries are increased by collective bargaining even though there is substantial unemployment in the industry or in other closely related parts of the economy. Wage rates in industries are often maintained and the hiring of additional workers limited even though there is a surplus of labor in relation to employment opportunities in the community. Wage rates have tended to become institutionalized in this way, limiting the ability of nonfarm labor markets to absorb the underemployment from rural areas. Is it not possible that even with fairly rapid economic growth in the nation as a whole, with declining competition in the nonfarm-labor market, that underemployment will continue to grow in agriculture?

Given less than full employment conditions in the nation's economy, agriculture in general, and its lower income areas in particular, will continue to bear an unduly large part of the nation's underemployment. Given full employment, in view of developments to date, if the community-wide rural poverty problem is to be solved, there will be required a four-pronged attack: (1) improvement of educational and health facilities in these areas, (2) encouragement of industrial development in these areas, (3) policies to facilitate migration, and (4) policies to encourage farm improvement and enlargement for those families continuing in agriculture.

Poverty problem a dilemma for farm leaders. Underlying the lack of progress and the absence of widespread concern about the rural poverty problem are two sets of conditions. First, the low-income areas in Figure 19-1, and especially the lower income families living in these areas, have few spokesmen in group meetings and in the legislative halls. The low-income rural people have little political power. Second, there is a widespread belief that our educational facilities and private enterprise system gives all people, including all rural families, equal opportunities in the economy. There is a widespread belief that the Coxes and the Johnsons have no one but themselves to blame if they continue to live on small run-down farms and get little reward for long hours of work.

Farm leaders are faced with a dilemma in this regard. Since low-income farm families are in a minority in general farm organizations and in most organized rural groups, how much time and effort should be devoted to a solution of their problems? The dilemma is even greater than this. An ample number of small tenants, sharecroppers and small farm owners in a community assures the larger landowners in the community that they will have an ample supply of local labor for seasonal hire at "reasonable" rates. Programs and policies which drain off the underemployed workers in these rural communities increase the larger farmers' problems.

There also is the consideration that solutions to problems which are peculiar to low-income families and poverty areas, that is, increased school facilities and improved and expanded educational programs, usually require financial assistance from the rest of society. These conflicts of interest create a serious dilemma for farm leadership in seeking solutions to the poverty problem in agriculture. Is it surprising that farm leaders have devoted most of their time and energy to finding solutions for the problems of commercial farmers? Is it also not likely that the rural poverty problem will continue to be one of our most serious economic and social problems for *at least* the next decade?

REFERENCES

"The Rural Development Program," *Farm Policy Forum*. Ames, Iowa: Iowa State College Press, Summer 1958.

Schultz, T. W., *Agriculture in an Unstable Economy*, Chapters 3 and 4. New York: McGraw-Hill Book Company, Inc., 1945.

Wilcox, Walter W., *Social Responsibility in Farm Leadership*, Chapter 6. New York: Harper & Brothers, 1956.

Development of Agriculture's Human Resources, U.S.D.A. (April 1955).

POINTS FOR DISCUSSION

1. How many families in rural and urban areas had incomes of less than $1,000 last year?

2. To what extent is the poverty problem in the United States located in rural areas?

3. What cultural factors tended to create community-wide poverty in the South?
4. What factors tended to create farm areas of low income in other parts of the United States?
5. In what way is the rural poverty problem a part of the nation's general employment and income problem?

Income Improvement Prospects in Low-Income Areas

Synopsis of paper by William E. Hendrix,
Journal of Farm Economics, Proceedings issue
December 1959.

DESPITE current programs, there are reasons to fear that relatively low incomes will continue to persist on an extensive scale in much of American agriculture for a long time to come. This is so, not because the problem is insoluble but because it is much more complex than most of the proposed solutions imply.

Most economists ascribe the excess labor and associated under-employment in agriculture to impediments that are indigenous to farm people, or to conditions that affect them as a supply of labor for nonfarm-labor markets rather than to nonfarm-labor market imperfections which restrict the nonfarm-labor demand.

Limited knowledge by farm workers of nonfarm job opportunities and their lack of capital with which to move into nonfarm employment are the impediments most frequently mentioned as posing economic problems. In this view, the requirements for correcting the underemployment in agriculture are simple. Normally, all that would be needed would be to provide farm people better labor-market information and credit funds for moving. If the problem were as simple as this, probably improvements in economic education that would clarify the nature of the farm-income problem would soon lead to such a policy, except for local self interests.

In support of this simple thesis, it can be proved without difficulty that many farm people have very little capital and very limited knowledge of nonfarm jobs. But at their worst, are these limitations any more than the results or the symptoms of much more deeply rooted impediments to labor transfers? More pertinent is the question,

How can one explain chronic underemployment and low income associated with it as general economic phenomena—whether in farm or nonfarm areas or whether small or large in extent? Having explained underemployment as a general economic phenomenon, Why is agriculture, particularly that in the lower income areas, more subject to its incidence than are other parts of the economy? Answers to these questions are basic to understanding the causes of low incomes in agriculture, and to appraising alternative solutions and the prospects of early elimination of widespread low incomes in the nation's poorer farm areas.

Underemployment and the competitive model. Can chronic underemployment persist in a perfectly competitive economy—one in which: (1) there are no externally imposed restrictions to the movement of factors of production in search of the most remunerative employment, and (2) there is no decision-making unit that by its own actions can affect the price of what it buys and sells? If underemployment cannot persist in such an economy, then we must look to deviations from this competitive model rather than to the knowledge and capital limitations of farm people for its explanation.

If the economy were perfectly competitive, farm underemployment would mean that nonfarm employers pay more for labor than comparable labor from farms would cost if they were to recruit this labor, equating marginal costs and returns from such recruitment as for other operations. In other words, in a competitive economy, underemployment in agriculture is impossible without occurrence at the same time of underemployment of the management and capital resources of nonfarm employers. Under competition, such a condition would correct itself. Nonfarm employers would need to engage in labor-recruitment activities as a condition of both income maximization and competitive survival. Through these recruitment activities and competitive bidding, they would extend to underemployed workers in agriculture (as well as to those elsewhere in the economy) the knowledge they need in choosing their most remunerative employment. In these recruitment activities, it would be to the interest of nonfarm employers also to finance to the extent needed, the movement by farm workers into nonfarm employment, equating the marginal costs and returns for this activity as they do for other operations. No other possible result is consistent with a perfectly competitive economy.

Hence, the survival of nonfarm-employing firms without the continual seeking out of cheaper labor services depends on the fact that: (1) a position of static equilibrium has been achieved; or (2) nonfarm employers cannot or will not take advantage of a cheaper supply of labor than they now employ because of deviations from the characteristics of a fully competitive economy. The first of these possibilities is precluded by the dynamic character of the economy, as well as by the fact of underemployment in agriculture or of involuntary unemployment in the nonfarm economy. Therefore, the underemployment and the related low income in agriculture must result from market characteristics that limit competition.

Underemployment under deviations from perfect competition. Administrative pricing in product markets may lead to a lower general level of employment and labor earnings than would otherwise prevail. But with perfect labor mobility, or competition among employers for labor, imperfections in product markets cannot in themselves account for differences in labor earnings among workers of comparable ability and tastes. Underemployment and the low income resulting from it can persist only if there are first imperfections in the labor market that impede the movement of workers from lower to higher income occupations. Given such imperfections in the labor market, then imperfections in product markets can accentuate underemployment in the economy by restricting production and employment in the higher wage industries and forcing more of the nation's workers into lower wage occupations or into the ranks of the unemployed. *Hence, given labor-market imperfections, both wage and price policies in monopolistic and oligopolistic sectors of the economy can increase the number of workers and press down per capita earnings in competitive industries like agriculture.*

Furthermore, as competitive sectors of the economy shrink in relative importance, workers remaining therein can be subjected to increasing underemployment even when underemployment is decreasing in the nation as a whole.

In the literature of the labor-transfer problem, two major classes of impediments are commonly named: (1) externally imposed or institutional barriers, such as long apprenticeship requirements, high trade-union membership fees, and discrimination by employers or trade unions against workers of given geographic or ethnic origins or against those of particular ages, educational levels, or physical characteristics; (2) wage policies resulting in wages that cannot be maintained without restrictions on the number of persons employed. Of these, wage policies appear to occupy the *primary* role with other impediments related to wage policies as means or results. For example, wage policies—by permitting a supply of labor that is larger than the demand—enable employers to discriminate in the selection of workers beyond normal job requirements. In the meantime, they provide employed workers with incentives to support measures that restrict freedom of entry into their respective occupations. Therefore, while wage policies are *primarily* responsible for underemployment in the economy, *other impediments help to determine which workers and which parts of the economy bear most heavily the resulting underemployment.* Wages which permit the supply of labor to exceed the demand may persist, not only because of employee policies, but also because of the wage policies of employers and those ascribable to the standards of society at large.

However, underemployment is impossible without labor policies that permit the supply of labor in the higher wage industries to exceed the demand. It is this resulting excess in the supply of labor over the demand that is the definitive characteristic of underemployment wherever it occurs and whatever its extent.

Conditions that make agriculture vulnerable to unemployment. Given the conditions that permit underemployment, the question remains, Why is agriculture, and especially that in low-income farm areas, more subject to bearing its incidence than are other major parts of the economy? There are at least three main reasons.

The most important reason is that in its labor market agriculture is a highly competitive occupation within a larger general economy that is characterized by significant deviations from the competitive model. Its laborers consist of two main classes: (1) self-employed workers and members of their families; and (2) workers employed on a wage basis. Restrictions have seldom, if ever, been placed on the entry of qualified wage workers into agricultural employment. The only restrictions upon entry into agricultural production as self-employed workers is that imposed through capital markets. In much of agriculture, very little equity capital is needed to become a low-income farmer.

With its competitive features, agriculture, although declining in relative importance, is rapidly being left as the nation's only major industry with characteristics that permit rapid absorption of large amounts of underemployment. Thus, like the lower end of a lake whose upper part is being filled in, agriculture may be subject to a rising groundswell of underemployment, even if underemployment should decrease in the nation as a whole.

The second major reason why agriculture is highly subject to bearing the incidence of the economy's underemployment lies in the selectivity processes through which underemployment is distributed. Notwithstanding the competitive character of farm labor markets, if this were the only disadvantage of farm workers, they could compete for new job openings in nonfarm industry on equal terms with workers of nonfarm origins. Thereby, they could distribute underemployment more equally between themselves and workers of nonfarm origins. But a supply of labor that exceeds the nonfarm demand: (1) permits increased selectivity, or discrimination, in the hiring of workers on the basis of their age, education, physical condition, ethnic and geographic origins, heterogeneity considerations, and other factors; and (2) yields a large advantage in obtaining jobs to workers who are the most readily available and accessible to them.

The greater distances of farm people from urban and industrial centers, which are sometimes associated with large cultural differences, make farm workers less readily available for newly-opening nonfarm jobs, than their nonfarm competitors. In a fully competitive labor market, farm workers could always obtain nonfarm jobs merely by offering to work for wages not exceeding the value productivity of their labor. But when the supply of labor exceeds the nonfarm demand, differences in the distance at which workers live from newly-opening jobs helps to determine which ones obtain such jobs and which remain under-employed.

Finally, agriculture, especially in low-income farm areas, is highly vulnerable to underemployment because of: (1) its large natural labor increases and (2) its declining labor needs as a result of farm technological advances and market limitations. But it should be noted that large natural labor increases, rapid farm technological progress, and a low elasticity of demand for agricultural products are not alone sufficient to explain the underemployment and low per capita income in agriculture. These conditions make it necessary that each year a large number of farm workers move into nonfarm employment to achieve and maintain a farm-nonfarm income equilibrium. But except for labor-transfer impediments, no one nor any combination of these conditions could lead to excess capacity and to a low per capita income in agriculture. Rather, a low farm income can result from technological advances and limited farm-product markets only because agriculture is a highly competitive industry in a world dominated by monopolistic and oligopolistic market structures.

Summary. As thus depicted, the income and employment problems of agriculture—both of agriculture as a whole and of the lowest income farm areas—cannot be solved by intrafarm adjustment and labor-transfer programs alone. These measures have their place. But our farm income problems are so closely related to the problems of economic growth, full employment, and wage and price stability in the whole economy that low-income farm policy, as well as the income policy of agriculture as a whole, must be developed increasingly as an integral part of the nation's general economic policy.

CHAPTER 20

Farm Tenancy,
Farm Transfers, and Credit

Social status of farm tenancy. Americans look upon tenancy as distinctly inferior to land ownership; in fact, they regard it as a social disease.[1] As early as the days of Thomas Jefferson, small farm owners were considered "the most precious part of a state." As late as 1948, a church-sponsored conference stated somewhat the same view: "It is . . . the mature judgment and sincere belief of the commission that ownership of family farms is essential to the preservation of the democratic way of life in rural America."[2]

The wide acceptance of this point of view throughout the past 250 years has resulted in the passage of a number of acts designed to promote family farm ownership. Among these are the Homestead Act of 1862, the Reclamation Act of 1902, the Federal Farm Loan Act of 1916, and the Bankhead-Jones Farm Tenant Act of 1937. The problems of farm tenancy continue to be important in local, state, and national affairs.

The growth of farm tenancy. National leaders in the United States, holding the favorable views toward family farm ownership stated

---

[1] R. R. Renne, *Land Economics* (New York: Harper & Brothers, 1958), page 387.

[2] *A Protestant Program for the Family Farm* (Evanston, Illinois: Garrett Bible Institute, March 1948), the proceedings of a conference held on that subject.

For a study that objectively analyzes the role of family farming in the maintenance of democracy see A. Whitney Griswold, *Farming and Democracy* (New York: Harcourt, Brace and Co., 1948). In this study, Mr. Griswold shows that democracy has enjoyed its greatest development in countries where urbanization and industrialization, rather than farming, dominated the economy.

above, insisted on disposing of the public domain at low prices and on easy terms. Later, outright gifts in 160-acre units were provided under the homestead laws. In view of these land sale and settlement policies it was a shock to learn that, in 1880 when the question was first asked by census takers, 26 per cent of the farms in the United States were operated by tenants. At that time, as now, farm tenancy was highest in the southern states. As pointed out in Chapter 1, between one-fourth and one-half of the tenants in the South are sharecroppers, who are comparable to hired laborers in many ways. But the South would still lead in percentage of tenancy and hired labor, even though regular hired workers were included with the tenants in other sections of the country. The percentage of farms operated by tenants by geographic areas from 1880 to 1954 is shown in Table 20-1.

TABLE 20-1

Percentage of Farms Operated by Tenants, by Geographic Areas, 1880-1954

Geographic Subdivision	1954	Census Year 1950	1940	1930	1920	1910	1900	1880
United States	24	27	39	42	38	37	35	26
The North	20	21	31	30	28	26	26	19
New England	3	4	7	6	7	8	9	8
Middle Atlantic	7	8	15	15	21	22	25	19
E. North Central	19	20	28	27	28	27	26	20
W. North Central	27	28	42	40	34	31	30	20
The South	30	34	48	55	50	50	47	36
South Atlantic	29	32	42	48	47	46	44	36
E. South Central	32	37	50	56	50	51	48	37
W. South Central	29	34	53	62	53	53	49	35
The West	12	13	21	21	18	14	17	14
Mountain	15	16	25	24	15	11	12	7
Pacific	10	11	18	18	20	17	20	17

Source: U.S. Census.

Tenancy has remained high throughout the entire period in the West North Central States as well as in the South. In contrast, tenancy was low in New England in 1880 and has declined still further since then. Obviously, differences in the land resources, the kind of farming followed, and the ratio of people to the land affects the percentage of tenancy in each area. Tenancy tends to be highest in the areas of highest land values and in commercial agricultural areas where the ratio of population to the land is high. In contrast, farm ownership is highest in the self-sufficing farming areas and in the less productive parts of the commercial-farming areas. An over-all trend toward more rented farms was in process from 1880 to 1935.

Since 1935, the trend has been downward again. A number of factors contributed to the decline in tenancy after 1935. Farm real estate values had declined until they were again in a favorable ratio to current farm incomes. Mechanization and the Federal farm programs caused a considerable reduction in the number of sharecroppers in the South, offset, in part, by increased numbers of wage hands. The sharp decline in farms operated by tenants after 1940 has been due largely to the favorable war and postwar level of income earned by farmers. The strong demand for industrial workers after 1940 encouraged high rates of migration out of agriculture, thus reducing the number of farm tenants. Numbers of full owners, part owners, and tenants, with the percentage of farms operated by tenants from 1900 to 1954 are shown in Figure 20-1. Between 1940 and 1954, the percentage of tenancy dropped from 39 to 24 per cent, and it is now lower than it was in 1880.

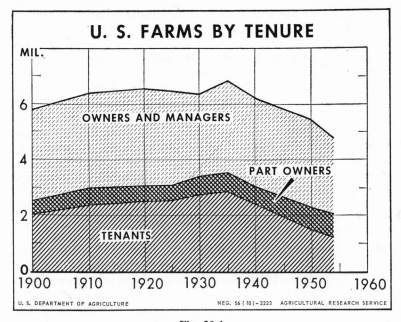

Fig. 20-1.

Functions of tenancy. Tenancy performs a very useful role in a capitalistic society in which individuals purchase and sell land on almost the same terms as other commodities. The advantage of young people's renting farm land, rather than buying it largely on credit, is primarily a reduction in economic uncertainty. But the advantage is even greater for families with few assets. Under the conditions for granting credit, outlined later, a family, unless it already has substantial assets, cannot obtain sufficient credit to purchase a productive farm. Tenancy, the practice of renting farm real estate, permits families with limited assets to obtain the use of productive farms that they would be unable to acquire by purchase. Conversely, it permits the land owner to obtain an income from the farm without working the farm himself, or without hiring the necessary labor to do the farm work. *Without tenancy a larger proportion of our farm population would be hired workers and a larger proportion of our farm owners would be heavily in debt.* Farm owners might let their farms remain idle or operate them at only part capacity in the later years of their life if they could not rent them to others.

A common practice in many communities is for the owners of small farms to rent additional land to give them an efficient operating unit. Often this additional land is rented from an older neighbor who wishes to discontinue his active farm work, but to continue living on the farm. This practice gives a community considerable flexibility in getting its land into the hands of those farmers most capable of operating it. In 1954, there were 857,000 part owners or about 20 per cent of all farms enumerated in the United States. This part-owner group is classified with the full owners, when computing the percentage of farms operated by owners and tenants.

The rental of farm real estate is far more flexible than is farm ownership. Families that take up farming in a strange community, or urban people with limited farm experience, find it advisable to acquire experience on rented farms before buying a farm, even though they have sufficient assets to buy a farm of their own.

With these desirable functions of tenancy in mind, some students have reached the conclusion that approximately 30 per cent of the farms might well be rented at any one time.[3] New England, the Middle Atlantic, and the Pacific States all have had a much lower percentage of tenancy for years than is suggested as desirable, and they have a slightly higher debt load, as compared with other sections of the United States.

Undesirable aspects of tenancy. The undesirable aspects of farm tenancy largely grow out of the peculiar conditions under which tenancy has been practiced in the United States. In all sections farming practices have been of an exploitive character as a result of our virgin soil resources. In the South, they have been greatly

---

[3] H. C. Taylor, "What Should Be Done About Farm Tenancy?" *Journal of Farm Economics* (February 1938).

influenced by the high ratio of people to the farm land and the low level of education generally achieved. The high mobility of American people is another influence giving American tenancy some undesirable features.

Keeping in mind these underlying influences, we may examine the undesirable aspects of tenancy from the standpoint of the landlord's relations to the land, the tenant's farming practices, and the effect of tenancy on community development. The landlord is usually a retired farmer, a widow, or a business or professional man. These individuals may live in the community where the farm is located or they may live long distances away. Regardless of where they are living, they seldom have as much interest in maintaining the land and in making improvements as owner-operators who live on their farms. Since many of the landlords are older people, they are less receptive to new ideas, such as soil conservation practices and improvements in buildings, than the younger owner-operators.

Absentee owners who do not see their farms frequently often lack interest in making capital investments needed to permit tenants to develop efficient farming programs. Lack of capital and income is another difficulty that arises, particularly when land is owned by widows. Forty-five per cent of the owners who rented out land in 1946 were dependent on that land as their principal source of income.[4] Such landlords often encourage their tenants to exploit the land to obtain a high current income and skimp on the maintenance investments. It is a common saying that a rented farm must support two families, and an owner-operated farm supports only one. The difference may not be great, however, if the owner-operator is heavily in debt.

Farming communities adjacent to large urban centers have many exceptions to the generalization noted above. Business and professional men who buy farms as a hobby often invest large sums from their other businesses and their farms are "show places" in the community. In spite of these exceptions, the generalization holds that many landlords find their personal needs for the rental income so great that they cannot maintain the improvements on the farm.

Tenants' farming practices are greatly influenced by their rental arrangements and by their expectations as to the length of time they will remain on the farm. Farm account records in the better farming areas of the Corn Belt show that tenants usually operate larger farms than owners in these areas; often the rented farms are the better, more highly productive farms in the community. After adjusting for differences in personal capital invested, tenants often earn

[4] *Miscellaneous Publication 699* (U.S.D.A., 1949), page 43.

higher incomes than owners in the same community, largely because they are farming the larger, more productive farms.

But if one takes into account the poorer farms that are rented and the poorer tenants, as well as the better tenants, in the typical farming community of the United States, one concludes that tenants' farming practices are not as efficient as those of owner-operators. They usually do not follow as satisfactory rotations including legumes and grasses, their livestock herds are not as well bred as owners' livestock herds, and their crops and livestock are not as well cared for. There are many individual exceptions to this generalization. Good tenant farmers, renting from up-to-date landlords or from landowners who have a commercial farm management company managing the property for them, may excel most of the owner-operators in the community in both their cropping practices and their livestock program.

Yet there are two basic reasons why, on the average, we may expect inferior farming practices on most rented farms. Most important is the tenant's expectation as to occupancy. He may stay on the same farm twenty years, but, if he expects that each year may be his last one, he fails to seed legumes, cut the weeds, and do many other jobs that he would do if he were sure of staying on the farm long enough to get the full benefits. His livestock program is also under a cloud of uncertainty. He may have to move any year and the buildings on the next farm may be inadequate for a good herd of livestock. Tenants do not have the same incentives as owners for building up highly productive livestock herds.

A second reason for the poorer farming practices of tenants, taken as a group, as compared with owners, is the superior management qualifications of the owners. Tenancy is but a step toward ownership for many farm families. Tenant families are typically either young and relatively inexperienced or, if older, they are often below average in ability.

Community institutions suffer in areas where there is a high percentage of tenancy, primarily because the tenant families move so frequently that they have little interest in building up local community services. Farm owners who do not live in the community often have more interest in keeping their taxes low than in improving such community services as the schools.

Need for more landlord management. Many, but not all, of the present evils of tenancy in the United States could be eliminated by "good management" on the part of the landlords. Tenants cannot be expected to take a long-run interest in the farms when they operate them under relatively short leases. But the landlords, in their own economic interests, should place restrictions in the leases requiring tenants to follow good rotations and approved soil conservation practices. Similarly, it is in the landowners' long-time economic interest to keep the buildings in a good state of repair and to make additions to the buildings as necessary to house the livestock and machinery required for profitable farming.

Commercial farm management services. Many of the landowners are too far distant to manage their farms, lack the technical knowledge needed for up-to-date landlord management, or are too busy with other activities to give their farm property the attention required. An increasing number of such landowners are hiring managers on a fee basis to supervise their farms. This practice is growing most rapidly in the Midwest. A large number of individuals and firms in that section specialize in managing farm properties for absentee owners. The services provided by these management companies include selection of tenants, drawing up a desirable lease, planning the farming program, advising on repairs and improvements on the property, and collection of the rent.

Management companies specializing in this field keep up-to-date on the newer farm practices and advise the tenants on improving theirs. (Most of the farm properties managed by commercial farm managers are rented on the crop- or livestock-share basis.) Commercial farm managers charge fees based on the services they render. A rather standard practice is to charge 10 per cent of the gross rental income for managing a farm leased to a tenant on a share rental basis, with extra fees charged for supervising the construction of new buildings or for other extra responsibilities. The landowner finds it profitable to hire a farm management company for it usually is able to find superior tenants and, by working with the tenants, it gets a superior job of farming done. The farm itself gets more attention from a company than the landowner has time to give it. Many of the evils of tenancy that are due to the landlord are corrected under the supervision of a good farm management company.

Improvements in leases needed. Many, if not most, renters lease their farms on a verbal basis, without benefit of a written contract. If misunderstandings arise and the issues are taken to court, they are settled on the basis of the existing state laws, or, if there are no state laws covering the issue, on the basis of common law. Verbal leases often do give rise to misunderstandings. But even more important, they result in a minimum of interest on the parts of tenant and landlord in the long-term productivity of the farm.

Both landlords and tenants, to an increasing extent, are adopting the practice of signing a written rental agreement. The written lease is a memorandum of agreement in which the landlord agrees to perform certain functions and agrees that the tenant shall have certain rights in the use of the farm for a specified length of time. Among the requirements on the part of the tenant the following are the most common:

That he will not sublet any portion of the farm without the landlord's permission.

That he will not damage the farm or commit waste.

That he will yield possession of the farm at the end of the tenancy.

That he will operate the farm in a good workmanlike manner.

That he will cut noxious weeds as required by state law.

That he will use the buildings in conformity with specifications of fire insurance companies (for example, not keep gasoline or a tractor in hay barn).

In addition to these minimum essentials, which are included in almost all written leases, a number of provisions are desirable. They should assure the practice of improved soil management and provide for arbitration of disagreements and for a reasonable notification period if the tenant is not to have the farm for the following year. A short-time lease is preferred by many landlords and tenants because of the greater flexibility it gives them as compared with longer-term leases. An excellent compromise, one finding increasing favor, is the use of an automatic renewal clause in the one-year lease. Under a lease including such provision, the agreement remains in effect from year to year, unless notice of termination is given four to six months before the end of the lease year. This provision assures the tenant that he can continue leasing the farm as long as both parties are satisfied and that, unless notice is given before the specified time, he is expected to and can legally stay for the following year.

Leases between the more progressive landlords and tenants often include provisions for compensating the tenants for unexhausted improvements made during occupancy. Few improvements are made by tenants because they have no assurance that they will be permitted to stay on the farm long enough to gain their full benefit. Landlords customarily add the new improvements to a farm. But many of the smaller improvements would be undertaken by the tenant if he had assurance of compensation for their unexhausted value at the end of the tenancy. Examples of land improvements for which the tenant should receive compensation for their unexhausted value when he leaves are:

1. Recently seeded alfalfa or other legumes, or pastures on which the tenant has paid for labor, limestone, fertilizer, or seeds.

2. Application of limestone, phosphate, or other fertilizer, bought and applied by the tenant, resulting in residual benefit to the land.
3. Certain specified erosion-control devices, such as check dams and terraces constructed at the tenant's expense.
4. Clearing land.
5. Leveling land for irrigation.
6. Improving pastures.[5]

Fair rental rates. People interested in farm tenancy have, from time to time, attempted to determine what are "fair rental rates." It is assumed that, if the rental agreement is "fair," the landlord earns 4 to 5 per cent interest on his investment, plus depreciation on the buildings, and the tenant gets interest and depreciation on his machinery and equipment, plus going wages for the unpaid labor. But this approach fails to recognize the essential nature of the rental rate.

The rent paid for the use of real estate is a price, comparable, in most respects, to prices paid for other resources. If we ask the fair price of a dairy cow or a used tractor, we are told immediately that it depends on supply and demand. In the case of farms for rent, the supply of farms for rent varies with the economic advantage of owning farms for rental. Thus, if rental rates are high, relative to real estate prices, landowners rent their farms, rather than sell them and vice versa. Demand varies both with the profitableness of farming and with the number of tenants wanting to rent farms. When farm prices are high and many families are in the market to rent farms, rents are bid up. But if farm prices are high, but nonfarm job opportunities are attracting many of the rural people into the cities, rental rates may not rise in the same proportion as the prices of farm products. Similarly, even though farm prices and farm incomes are relatively low, if there is unemployment in industrial centers the competition for farms to rent may cause prospective tenants to pay disproportionately high rents, in order to get farms to operate until other job opportunities become available.

Share-rental rates change far more slowly than cash-rental rates. Within any community, the rental share of the crops or livestock products tends to be the same, regardless of the productivity of the farm. And this share continues on the same basis from year to year, with very little change due to changes in the demand for farms to rent. Under these circumstances, how does a tenant bargain for a farm, or a landlord for a renter?

What we find in the share rental market is competition among

---

[5] *Farmers Bulletin No. 1969* (U.S.D.A., 1946), page 21.

tenants for the best farm at the established share rental rate. Conversely, landlords compete with each other for tenants at the going rental rates. The owner of a better-than-average farm can attract a better-than-average tenant. He is a poor business man if he is satisfied with less. And the tenant with good equipment and a reputation as a good farmer can have his pick of several of the best farms available for rent. In addition to this competition of tenants and landlords, each attempting to get the best farm or the best tenant available at prevailing share-rental rates, there may be some bargaining on the cash-rental charges for pasture, hay land, and buildings and the sharing of expenses for fertilizer, combining, and so forth. This is especially true when farms are rented for a share of the main crops, such as corn, small grain, and soybeans, and when a cash-rental charge is made for the hay land, pasture, and buildings. Competition takes the form of bidding higher or lower on the cash rentals associated with the fixed share of the crops.

It is only when demand gets badly out of adjustment with the supply that changes are made in prevailing rental shares. As pointed out earlier, there is a tendency for rental rates to lag on both the upswing and the downturn of economic activity. But if one views rental rates as the competitive price for the use of these resources, he will avoid the futility of trying to determine "fair rates" in an ever-changing market.

FARM TRANSFERS

Elements of the family farm transfer problem. In recent years, more and more attention is being directed toward facilitating the transfer of the family farm to one of the children. Families run into difficulties from several sources. In the first place, the young people are ready to go into farming for themselves before their parents are ready to retire. A farm couple with children born when they are between the ages of 22 and 36 will have children ready to start farming for themselves when the parents are 44 to 58 years of age. Assuming that the son or son-in-law is married at 23 and is willing to work with the father on a partnership basis for five years, the young couple will be ready for a farm of their own when the father is 50 to 54. Yet it is estimated that only 12 per cent of the farm owners retire before the age of 55. Although there has been some tendency toward earlier retirement in industry, a trend toward later retirement has been observed among farmers (Table 20-2).

TABLE 20-2

Percentage of Owners, by Age at Retirement, Specified Periods, United States

	Age at Retirement (Years)		
Period of Retirement	*Under 55* (per cent)	*55-64* (per cent)	*65 and over* (per cent)
1917-20	22	40	38
1921-24	23	40	37
1925-28	27	32	41
1929-32	14	34	52
1933-36	7	30	63
1937-39	10	26	64
1940-41	8	28	64
1942-43	9	31	60
1944-45	12	27	61

Source: Miscellaneous Publication 600 (U.S.D.A.), Table 51. Data are corrected for deaths by Ralph E. Botts, Bureau of Agricultural Economics, on the basis of the 1937 Standard Annuitants Mortality Table.

Among the reasons for the later retirement of farm owners in recent years are the rising living standards that require more cash expenditures, the longer life span of individuals, and use of modern machinery, which lightens the hard physical labor of farming and permits farmers to operate their farms at older ages. Modern machinery mounted on rubber tires also permits more flexibility in farm operation within communities than was possible when horses were used for power. Older farm operators now often rent out a part of their land or hire field work done on a custom basis without actually retiring and turning the farm over to another operator. Older families often are forced to do this because of the loss of income they would suffer should they fully retire. Most of our farms are not large enough to furnish a living at modern standards for both the retired family and the young family, which would like to acquire the farm. By the time the older family is ready or is forced to retire, the children are established on some other farm, or in some other business, and prefer not to move.

The declining number of full-time, commercial family farms further complicates the problem. Not only do the young people in the family desire a farm of their own before their parents are ready to give up theirs, but many of the farms are not large enough for an economic family unit if modern machinery is used. For every 3 farms vacated by older people in many communities, only 1 or 2 young families can obtain economic farming units.

Adequate size of farm essential. Many of the conditions that have led to the relatively small number of farm transfers within the family are conditions associated with economic progress.[6] We can expect these same dynamic conditions to continue to limit the number of farm transfers within families in the years ahead. Yet the improvements in living and working conditions on farms, relative to the improvements in urban centers in the last twenty years, have greatly increased the incentive for the children reared on the larger, more productive farms to continue in farming. On these farms, plans can be adopted, without hardship to either family, which will permit an early transfer of farming operations and of a part interest in the farm itself to the younger family. Unless a farm is large enough to furnish productive employment for approximately two men, income difficulties will be serious.

A review of the family cycle and its relation to size of farm needed for economic utilization of labor during the transfer process is of interest. We can assume a son is ready to work full time at home at the age of 20, when the father is 45. During the next ten years, the father-son partnership can operate approximately a full two-man farm. As the father gets older and his labor contribution declines, the son's children reach working age and take over a part of their grandfather's duties. It may be necessary to hire extra labor for a few years if the family cycle does not fully match the labor needs of the farm. There is more likelihood, however, of an excess of family labor on this two-man farm at certain stages in the family cycle than of the need for hired labor. A normal farm family, with one to three sons, has a peak labor supply when the operator is 35 to 45 years of age and his boys are 13 to 23 years of age.

If family plans for keeping the farm in the family are successful, they must include provision for other children, as well as for the one that will take over the farm. From the standpoint of age, unless the children were born after the parents were past 35, the youngest, rather than the oldest, son is more likely to be ready to take over the farm when the parents are ready to retire. Thus, parents might well make plans for their older children to take over other farms or go into other occupations.

Written contracts for farm transfer desirable. As pointed out earlier, the really difficult economic problems in transferring the farm within the family involve making a modest income from an average farm cover the needs of both a young growing family and the older retiring family. If the farm is sufficiently large and productive to give the son's family a good income (with opportunities for savings) on

---

[6] Seventy-four per cent of the active farmers in the United States who own farm land acquired it without the assistance of gifts or inheritance. *Miscellaneous Publication 699* (U.S.D.A., 1949).

a full rental basis, and if the rental income is sufficient for the living needs of the parents, early contractual arrangements for transfer of the farm are unnecessary. No sacrifice of current income is involved for the son's family and, at the time of the parents' death, they may buy out the other heirs if they wish. It is indeed a happy family situation when these conditions exist, but, even under these conditions, it is usually preferable for the parents to arrange in their will for the farm to go to the son (or son-in-law) who has been operating it. The other children can be provided for in the will by having the one who inherits the farm pay them some share of its fair appraised value. If the son or son-in-law on the farm has increased the farm's value during the time it was under his management, this should be recognized appropriately in the will.

The son or son-in-law who expects favored treatment by the parents in the disposal of their property is often disappointed. Parents often change their minds regarding verbal promises, or merely forget to put them in their will. Other members of the family do not recognize the special services that the family on the home farm have rendered to their parents or to the farm. They insist on an equal division of the inheritance under the prevailing laws of the state. If the members of a family on the home farm had expected compensation for past services out of the estate, without a written contract they are likely to be disappointed.

Parents maintenance contracts. Most of the farms in the United States are too small to provide productive employment for two men throughout the entire year. They produce too small an income to support both the young growing family and the retiring family, without some sacrifices from each during certain periods. Yet family and social interests combine to point to the need for more formal arrangements for transferring the farm within the family. During periods of high-level business activity, either the father or the son may be able to supplement his farm earnings by off-farm work. When possible, this is an excellent method of meeting the economic problem.

But thousands of farm families remember periods when it was difficult to find work off the farm and almost as difficult to make the farm income cover the essential needs of two families. One of the most satisfactory ways of meeting such emergencies is for the operating son or son-in-law to enter into an agreement with the parents for their support during old age in return for the farm.[7]

Continuing farm ownership problems. Data in the appendix to this chapter (Table 20-4) indicate that, in 1946, 54 per cent of the

---

[7] "Keeping the Farm in the Family," *Wisconsin Research Bulletin 157* (1945), pages 6-7.

farm land in the United States was held by 7 per cent of the owners. In the Northeast and North Central States relatively little of the land was held in farms in excess of 500 acres. But in the South, 8 per cent of the owners had farms in excess of 500 acres and these holdings accounted for 59 per cent of the farm land in that section. In the West, an even higher proportion of the farm land is held in large holdings. Six per cent of the owners held units in excess of 1,500 acres, and this 6 per cent owned 57 per cent of the farm land.

The growth in large-scale holdings, either as operating or ownership units, but especially as ownership units, has been viewed with concern by a number of individuals and groups. It is a trend away from the family farm. At the other extreme, farm leaders are becoming increasingly aware of the problem of too small farm units.

One of the leading farm organizations that has been concerned with these problems for several years declared in its annual resolutions:

The land belongs to all the people of the nation. It should be used and tended for the greatest good of the greatest number both of those living and of those unborn. He who works the land today stands guard over it not alone for his own children but for the children of all Americans.

·   ·   ·   ·   ·   ·   ·   ·   ·   ·   ·   ·

. . . The government should develop into a large-scale program the present obscure provisions of law authorizing farm enlargement loans and it should establish a new program for the purchase of large farms as they come onto the market and the subdivision of those farms. The objective in each of these programs would be the establishment of as many economic family farming units as possible in as short a period as possible.

As a practical and realistic tool to discourage excessive land holdings and to encourage family type farm ownership, we urge a graduated land tax.[8]

Other organized groups of farmers annually pass resolutions that favor strengthening the position of the family farm. Most farm leaders support government credit programs for family farms and object to measures that would put the family farm at a disadvantage. But those in favor of either a graduated land tax to discourage ownership of large units or the purchase and subdivision of large farming units are a small minority.

For the most part, farm leaders study all new data relating to trends in size of ownership and of operating units in farming with

[8] From Farmers Union Program for 1950-51, adopted by delegates to biennial convention, Farmers Educational Cooperative Union of America, March 8, 1950.

great interest—and in some cases with concern. Thus far, however, government action, directly affecting the size of farm operated, has been limited to credit to small farmers for enlargement purposes.

Many of the large-scale farms would not make satisfactory family farming units if subdivided. In the future as in the past, ownership problems probably will be primarily concerned with achieving a large enough unit for efficient production and satisfactory living standards.

FARM CREDIT

The function of credit in farming. The availability and use of credit in farming permit individuals to acquire ownership of physical assets for use in production in advance of their having saved the necessary funds to make the purchase. It is only one, but still a very important, method by which a young farmer may expand his business more rapidly than he accumulates savings.

In a sense, credit performs the role of a catalyst, permitting farmers to acquire and utilize resources in production on the basis of their ability to realize profits, rather than making them entirely dependent on their own capital (assets) accumulated out of savings or inheritance.

TABLE 20-3

The Farm Balance Sheet, January 1, 1940, 1950, and 1959

(in Billions of Dollars)

Assets	1940	1950	1959
Real estate	$33.6	75.3	125.1
Other physical	15.2	39.6	59.0
Financial	4.2	15.9	19.0
Total	53.0	130.8	203.1
Claims			
Real estate	6.6	5.6	11.3
Other debt	3.4	6.9	12.0
Owners' equities	43.0	118.3	179.8
Total	53.0	130.8	203.1

Source: "The Balance Sheet of Agriculture," *Agricultural Information Bulletin 201* (U.S.D.A., 1958). Also, *Federal Reserve Bulletin* (July 1959).

Production versus consumption credit. At this point, we should distinguish between production and consumption credit. In many American families, children are taught the virtues of thrift and the dangers of going into debt. Yet credit used for productive purposes and debts assumed in the organization of a profitable business has an entirely different standing than credit used and debts acquired for consumption purposes.

Credit is said to be used for production purposes when the loan is used to purchase assets, land, livestock, machinery, fertilizer, seeds, and so forth, which are employed with the expectation of increasing the net income sufficiently to repay the loan and interest. Credit of this type, or debts incurred in such transactions, if the business investments are sound, will increase the family's income in the future, rather than decrease it. The successful business venture based on credit produces a surplus over and above the funds necessary to repay the loan with interest.

In contrast, consumption credit (which has increased greatly in recent decades) consists of loans that permit individuals and families to purchase durable or non-durable consumer goods in larger quantities than they have cash to pay for at any particular time. By far, most of the consumption credit today is used for residential housing loans and installment credit on automobiles, household equipment, and furniture. Some families also find it necessary to borrow from their local banks, local credit unions, or personal finance companies to meet doctor bills, extra expenses associated with weddings or deaths in the family, and for other purposes. Considerable consumption credit is in the form of book credit extended by the merchants, doctors, and undertakers who sell the family the merchandise or perform the services for them. Merchants who make a practice of extending book credit must charge higher prices than those who do business on a cash basis. This type of consumption credit is largely limited to department and clothing stores.

Consumption credit, consistently used over a period of years, reduces, rather than increases, the size of the income stream that can go for personal goods and services. At the time the credit is extended, the family obtains the use of more consumer goods than could be purchased out of current income. But the future purchases of consumer goods must be reduced sufficiently to repay both the loan and the interest charges.

It is only in the case of credit for residential housing and similar investments that families find the criteria governing the economic use of consumption credit similar to those governing the use of production credit. Thus, under certain circumstances, a family may be able to obtain the use of a given amount of housing cheaper by purchase through the use of credit than on a rental basis. Under such circumstances, the appropriate consideration is the cost of hiring or renting the comparable consumer goods as against purchase through the use of credit.

Criteria for use of production credit. From the standpoint of efficiency, credit should play a neutral role in entrepreneurs' decisions. Plans for business expansion or contraction should be based upon the expected returns over costs from the particular activity. The entrepreneur should earn a return on his own funds comparable with the interest he pays for borrowed funds. Whether or not he has to borrow funds for the venture should be a matter of indifference. Actually, of course, it is never a matter of indifference. Many business decisions turn on whether or not credit must be used. *And, in many cases, entrepreneurs are prevented from making and carrying out plans because lending institutions will not grant them the credit requested.*

One way of looking at the use of credit is to think of it as the hiring of liquid capital. When a farmer borrows $1,000 at the bank for a year, he has hired the use of that capital for twelve months for a wage of $60 if the interest rate is 6 per cent. From this point of view, employing credit is similar to renting land, hiring labor, or hiring machine work done at fixed rates. The farmer uses marginal analysis to determine how much of any factor of production to hire in each production operation. Thus, a farmer finds it highly profitable to borrow $600 to buy two cows to fill his dairy barn and utilize extra feed available, but he could not house more cows and hence could not use more credit for such a purpose.

Commercial and government farm real estate mortgage credit agencies. As early as 1913, dissatisfaction with the farm mortgage credit facilities led Congress to appoint a special commission to study European experience and development in the farm real estate mortgage field. Following the report of this commission, a Federal Farm Loan Act was passed in 1916. This Act provided for the establishment of twelve Federal Land Banks.[9] Although the banks were set up by this Act subject to supervision by a Federal Farm Loan Board, they were planned as cooperatives. Farmers interested in borrowing funds organized into local National Farm Loan Associations. Five per cent of each loan was used to buy stock in the Federal Land Bank. Thus, the borrowing members of the local associations gradually acquired ownership of the capital stock of the Federal Land Banks, which was first subscribed by the United States Treasury. Funds for the loans to individual borrowers were obtained by pooling the mortgages as security for Federal Land Bank Bonds, which were sold in the investment fund market to financial institutions and individuals.

---

[9] This Act also provided for the establishment of a national system of Joint Stock Land Banks, which were later liquidated.

Before the passage of the Federal Farm Loan Act, the two chief complaints of farmers were the high interest rates charged for farm loans and the unavailability of longer-term loans, especially in the higher risk areas of the United States. Most insurance company loans on real estate mortgages at moderate interest rates were located in the Corn Belt. The availability of funds through the Federal Land Banks caused a sharp drop in interest rates in the high interest sections of the country. The land banks met the demand for longer-term loans by introducing the thirty-three-year, amortized loan for farm borrowers. Under the terms of these loans, a borrower liquidated his debt in thirty-three years by making annual or semi-annual payments on the principal, when paying the interest. This longer-amortized loan was an important innovation that has now been adopted, in modified form, by many private lending agencies.

In addition to the loans available through the Federal Land Banks which are now fully owned and operated by farmers, a few farm families may obtain long-time real estate mortgage loans from the Farmers Home Administration, or similar loans from private agencies insured by the FHA. This government agency is authorized to loan a few million dollars each year to outstanding tenants for 100 per cent of the purchase price of family-type farms, and to owners of inadequate, unimproved low-production farms for farm improvement and enlargement purposes.

Commercial and government non-real estate mortgage credit agencies. As was pointed out earlier, merchants, dealers, and finance companies, with a financial interest in selling supplies, furnish a large part of the short-time, non-mortgage credit to farmers. Machinery and equipment companies have organized affiliated finance companies, which arrange for installment credit to cover the purchase of their products.

Commercial banks have long been the primary source of short-term loans. Farmers have found their local bank a relatively satisfactory source of short-time credit, except during depression periods. The amount of funds available for loans by banks depends on their volume of demand deposits. As demand deposits grow, the bank may expand its loans. But the reverse is also true: banks must reduce their loans as demand deposits shrink.

If a farmer does not wish to use installment or bank credit, in most sections of the United States he can go to a local Production Credit Association and borrow funds for the purchase of livestock, equipment, and supplies used in farm production. These local co-operative associations of borrowers are sponsored by the Farm Credit Administration, under legislation passed in 1933. As in the case of the Federal Land Banks, the government provided the original capital required in setting them up. The loan funds are obtained by discounting the notes given by farmers with government-owned Federal intermediate credit banks (set up in 1923). These Federal intermediate credit banks get their funds by selling debenture bonds to banks and other investors in the money market.

Although the Production Credit Associations furnished less than 10 per cent of the total short-time credit used by farmers in recent years, government-sponsored, cooperative credit is an essential part of the short-term credit system. It was brought into existence in the depression years when banks were unable and unwilling to make many of the short-time loans needed by farmers. Since their loan funds are not dependent on bank deposits, Production Credit Associations are believed to be a much more stable source of funds than commercial banks.

Farm families, without sufficient assets to borrow from these commercial lending agencies, in some cases may borrow directly from the government. In 1935, a program of granting supervised rural rehabilitation loans for periods of five years was undertaken as an alternative to continued relief payments to destitute rural families. Legislation in 1946 established the Farmers Home Administration, as a successor to the Farm Security Administration, with authority to continue making operating loans, as well as the real estate loans described earlier.

Since 1935, loans of this type, totaling several billion dollars, have been made. Families, to be eligible for such loans, must: (1) be unable to get the loan from regular credit agencies, (2) develop a farm and home plan indicating that they can maintain their family and repay the loan out of increased income, and (3) accept the supervision of the local officer of the Farmers Home Administration, who will advise the family on improved farm management practices.

Economic instability, economic progress, and farm credit. Business fluctuations, which lead to fluctuations in demand deposits, affect commercial banks' ability to make loans. Fluctuations in the value of farm assets that are used as collateral in obtaining loans also have forced lending agencies to adopt a relatively conservative policy with respect to the size of the loan in relation to the value of the assets of the farmer. On the borrower's side, uncertainty with respect to production, but especially with respect to prices, forces him to limit his borrowing in the interest of security, regardless of his technical competence to manage a larger business.

Economic fluctuations are an inherent part of a growing, expanding economy. We must expect them to continue, but there is general agreement that they have been unnecessarily severe in past years. One of the substantial gains resulting from a reduction in economic fluctuations would be increased effectiveness of credit in permitting and assisting resources to combine more efficiently in farm production.

Farm credit and technological advance. Between 1940 and 1959, farmers' investment in machinery, equipment, livestock, crops, and inventories of supplies increased almost four times (Table 20-3). On a per-farm basis, the increase is even larger, for the number of farms declined during the period. Somewhat over one-half of this increased investment in equipment and production supplies is the result of rising prices. Technological advance in farming is increasing capital investment requirements in equipment at a rapid rate, however, and is giving rise to more or less acute problems in obtaining adequate intermediate credit on terms adapted to farmers' needs. The land banks and other mortgage-lending institutions provide an adequate source of long-term real estate credit needed by farmers. The local banks and the production credit associations supply the short term or seasonal credit needed.

An increasing number of farmers, however, find themselves in need of three- to seven-year loans to finance investments required for technological advance, yet most commercial banks are unable to grant credit for periods in excess of twelve months. In recent years production credit associations and a limited number of other financial agencies have begun to make intermediate term loans. Great expansion will be required in this field as technological advance requires larger and larger capital investment in both real estate and equipment for an optimum operating unit.

If farm prices and income continue to fluctuate sharply, as they have in the past 50 years, it may be impossible for the typical farm operator in the early part of his productive life to borrow sufficient funds on a loan basis to achieve an economic producing unit involving an investment of $100,000 to $200,000 or more. Recent trends toward increased farm ownership may be reversed, with more farmers renting their farms and utilizing their capital accumulations and credit for investments in equipment and other operating capital. Another possible development may be increased incorporation of farming units and the use of equity capital to finance capital expansion on the larger farms requiring investments of several $100 thousand.

REFERENCES

Ackerman, Joseph, and Marshall Harris, editors, *Family Farm Policy*. Chicago: University of Chicago Press, 1947.

Annual Reports of the Governor of the Farm Credit Administration and
the Administrator of the Farmers Home Administration.

Parsons, K. H., and E. O. Waples, "Keeping the Farm in the Family,"
Wisconsin Research Bulletin 157 (1945).

Renne, R. R., "Agricultural Land Tenure and Tenancy," Chapter 17,
Land Economics, rev. ed. New York: Harper & Brothers, 1958.

POINTS FOR DISCUSSION

1. Why has farm ownership been the goal of most farm families?
2. What is needed to cure the "evils" of tenancy in your community?
3. Do tenants have lower incomes and lower living standards than farm
   owners in your community?
4. Why are so few farms kept within the family over a period of two or
   three generations?
5. Outline a desirable procedure for parents to use in transferring their
   farm to a son or son-in-law.
6. Do farmers use too much or too little credit?

APPENDIX

The first comprehensive study of farm ownership in the United
States was published in 1949.[10] This study, based on a sample of
47,197 replies to a series of questions concerning landownership,
gives a clear picture of the ownership pattern of farm land. As
expected, the study found that most of our farm lands are owned
by individuals: 85 per cent of the total farm land, according to this
study. This individual ownership is widely dispersed, for there were
approximately 5,025,000 different owners of farms in the United
States in 1946, which compares with 5,859,000 operators enumerated
in the 1945 agricultural census. The relative importance of various
types of ownership in each major area in the country is shown in
Figure 20-2.

In addition to land owned by individuals, 9 per cent of the land
in farms (excluding Federal land grazed under permits) is owned
and administered by government agencies, including the Indian
Service, which holds the Indian lands in trust for them. Most of these
publicly-owned farm lands are located in the West and are unappro-
priated Federal lands and school and tax-reverted state and county
lands.

---

[10] "Farm Land Ownership in the United States," *Miscellaneous Publication
699* (U.S.D.A., 1949).

Corporate holdings accounted for another 6 per cent of farm lands, located mostly in the West and in the South. Railroads, industrial corporations, and financial institutions, as well as farming corporations, reported ownership of farm land.

PRIVATELY AND PUBLICLY OWNED FARM LAND, 1954

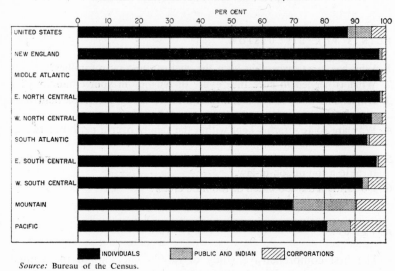

Source: Bureau of the Census.

Fig. 20-2.

Occupation of individual farm owners. In all sections of the United States, approximately three-fourths of the owners were farmers or retired farmers. The percentage of owners in each occupation group is shown in Table 20-4. Farmers and retired farmers owned somewhat larger and more valuable farms than owners in the other occupations, hence they held 79 per cent of the acreage of land and 76 per cent of the value of land owned by individuals. Information on residence of owners is also of interest (see Table 20-5).

TABLE 20-4

Percentage of Landowners in Each Occupation, 1946

Occupation	Per Cent
Farmer	65
Retired farmer	8
Housewife	3
Business-professional	10
Clerical-laborer	14
Total	100

Source: Miscellaneous Publication 699 (U.S.D.A. 1949), Table 3.

TABLE 20-5

Percentage of Owners Living on Farms, by Occupation of Owner

Occupation	Per Cent
Farmer	94
Retired farmer	74
Housewife	53
Business-professional	42
Clerical-laborer	68

Source: Miscellaneous Publication 699 (U.S.D.A.), Table 5.

Experience of farm owners. The process of becoming a farm owner has been called climbing the agricultural ladder to ownership. The first round on the ladder starts with the young man working on the home farm, or as a hired man. The second round is the period when he operates a farm as a tenant, gradually accumulating sufficient funds to become a landowner. The third round is the period of ownership, with a debt, on the farm, followed by a fourth round, the top of the ladder, debt-free ownership. This farm ownership study indicates that farm ownership is attained on the basis of a variety of experience and that less than one farm owner in six had climbed the agricultural ladder by way of becoming a tenant. Perhaps even more surprising, almost two-thirds of these owners had worked at nonfarm occupations for a part of their lives. On the other hand, 97 per cent of the owners had been farm operators before acquiring the property they owned in 1946.

Size of holdings. The farm ownership units parallel the farm-operating units rather closely in size. For the United States as a whole, 38 per cent of the farmers owned units of 69 acres or less. In the South, this percentage was 43, in the West 48, and in the Northeast 51. Only 7 per cent of the farmers had units in excess of 500 acres in the United States as a whole, with 8 per cent of the owners in this class in the South and 17 per cent in the West.

TABLE 20-6

Percentage of Farm Owners and Percentage of Farm Acreage Owned, by Size of Holdings, 1946

Size of Holdings (Acres)	Per Cent of Owners	Per Cent of Acreage Owned
Under 30	19	1
30-69	19	4
70-139	26	11
140-219	16	11
220-499	13	19
500 and over	7	54

Source: Miscellaneous Publication 699 (U.S.D.A.), Tables 9 and 10.

Five per cent of the farm land is in ownership units of less than 70 acres and over one-half the farm land held by individuals is in holdings of 500 acres or larger. Seven per cent of the owners hold 54 per cent of the farm land in the United States and, in the South, 3 per cent of the owners hold 46 per cent of the land (Table 20-6).

Extent of family assistance. Sixty-eight per cent of these owners acquired their land entirely through purchase (Figure 20-3).

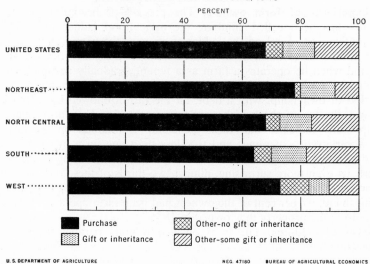

PERCENTAGE OF OWNERS BY METHOD OF ACQUISITION, UNITED STATES AND REGIONS, 1946

Fig. 20-3.

The importance of gifts and inheritance varies with the occupation of the owners. More than 78 per cent of the clerical-laborer group bought all of their holdings, compared with 70 per cent of the business-professional men, 69 per cent of the active farmers, 61 per cent of the retired farmers and 38 per cent of the housewives.

Age at time of becoming owners. Most farm owners acquire their first land between the ages of 25 and 34 years. For the United States as a whole, 20 per cent of the farm owners acquired land before they reached 25 years of age (often by gift or inheritance), 42 per cent between the ages of 25 and 34 years, 25 per cent between the ages of 35 and 44, 10 per cent between the ages of 45 and 54, and 3 per cent after they had reached the age of 55 years.

CHAPTER 21

Hired Labor
in Agriculture

IN THIS CHAPTER, we will examine the economic problems presented by the use of hired labor and the social and economic problems of the hired workers and their families.

Three groups of hired workers. Around 3.5 million hired workers are employed on farms during a part or all of the year.[1] This total may be divided into three groups: (1) those regularly employed on one farm for most of the year, about 1.0 to 1.5 million people; (2) those employed seasonally in the community of their residence, about 1.5 to 2.0 million; and (3) migratory workers employed seasonally to care for and harvest the different crops, about 800,000 people. Special surveys indicate that about one-half of those in the migratory group are domestic workers and the other half are foreign nationals

TABLE 21-1

**Per Cent of Male Hired Farm Workers
In Specified Age Groups, 1958**

Age Group	Per Cent of Total
14-17	18
18-34	39
35-64	39
65 and over	4
Total	100

Source: *The Hired Farm Working Force* (Agricultural Marketing Service, 1958).

[1] This statement and several of the succeeding ones are based on *Technical Bulletin 895* (U.S.D.A.), pages 17-20; *The Labor Market and Employment Security* (1959); and Special Reports of the Agricultural Marketing Service, *The Hired Farm Working Force* (1956, 1957, and 1958).

admitted into this country to do farm work. About one-half of the farm workers are unmarried. In 1958, some 2.3 million wage earners, two-thirds of whom were white, worked twenty-five days or more on farms.

Hired farm workers are predominantly younger men. After working as hired laborers for a few years, they either start farming for themselves as tenants or owners, or migrate to urban occupations. Only 43 per cent of the male workers were over 35 years of age in 1958. (Table 21-1.)

Seasonal variation in hired labor. December, January, and February are the low months for farm employment. During these months, about 1 million hired workers are employed on farms. Employment increases throughout the spring and summer, reaching a peak in September, and then drops rapidly in October and November. (Figure 21-1).

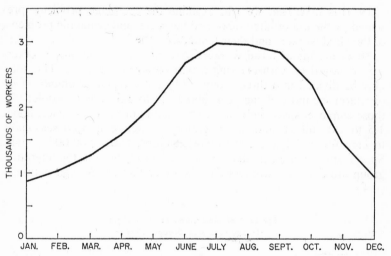

Fig. 21-1. Number of hired farm workers employed on farms by months, 1957-58.

This wide seasonal fluctuation in employment of hired workers on farms is matched by a similar fluctuation in the employment of family workers. In December and January of 1958 and 1959, 4.4 million family workers were employed fifteen hours or more per week on farms. In September of 1958, 6.5 million family workers were employed on the same farms. The total number of people working on farms in September was double the number who reported similar work in December and January. Family workers do as much of the extra seasonal work as possible on most farms. Hired workers are employed to do the work that cannot be handled by the family workers.

Number of workers hired per farm. Less than 5 per cent of the farms in the United States employed 3 or more workers in the week of the Census enumeration in the fall of 1954. The number of farms employing specified numbers of workers during a week in late September or October 1954 is shown in Table 21-2.

TABLE 21-2

Commercial Farms Employing Specified Numbers of Workers, 1954

Number Regular and Seasonal Workers Employed	Number of Farms	Per Cent of All Commercial Farms	Per Cent of All Farms with Sales of $10,000 or More
1	347,392	7.9	22.9
2	132,318	3.0	10.0
3 or 4	94,956	2.1	6.9
5 to 9	68,684	1.5	4.7
10 or more	54,522	1.2	5.6
All farms hiring workers....	697,572	15.7	50.1

Source: U.S. Agricultural Census, 1955.

Only 323,444, or 9.7 per cent, of all commercial farms hired *regular* workers in the specified week in September or October 1954 and only 1.5 per cent of the commercial farms hired 3 or more regular workers at that time. It is evident from these data that only a small percentage of the farms in the United States employ any hired workers at all in late September or October. *Even a smaller percentage employ regular hired laborers.*

Trends in the use of hired labor. Data on the average number of hired workers employed on farms (average of the twelve monthly reports) are available from 1910 to date. They indicate relatively little change in the average number of hired workers employed on farms from 1910 to 1942, except for a brief decline during the depression years 1931 to 1936. The number of hired workers on farms dropped sharply during the war and has remained below prewar levels since that time. (Figure 21-2.)

On a percentage basis, the decline in hired workers was slightly less than the decline in family workers. Hired workers made up 24 per cent of the farm working force in 1910-11, and 26 per cent in 1957-58. These percentages are in terms of numbers of people included in the monthly reports. Hired workers work fewer days per year than family workers. They must perform about 20 per cent of the farm work in the United States.[2] In view of the extensive mechanization that has taken place in agriculture since 1910, it is surprising that the use of hired farm labor has not dropped even further. Although data are not readily available, it seems probable that the decline in the use of hired labor on the family farms is greater than the national average, with some increase in the use of hired labor in growing the larger acreages of vegetable, fruit, and truck crops on large-scale farms.

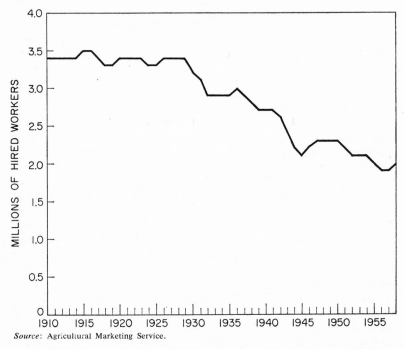

Source: Agricultural Marketing Service.

Fig. 21-2. Average number of hired workers employed on farms, 1910-58.

Wages of hired farm workers. Throughout most of the period, 1910 to date, cash-farm wage rates have averaged less than $.25 an hour; they exceeded $.50 an hour for the first time in 1946.

---

[2] Farm employment statistics, compiled by the Agricultural Marketing Service, are based on monthly surveys made by mail. The reporting farmers are asked to report each member of the family who worked fifteen hours or more during the last week in the month. They also are asked to report each person hired for one or more hours on the farm during that week.

Wages of hired farm workers have been relatively low in past years because of the large number of farm boys seeking employment and their difficulty in finding nonfarm jobs. Each year fully twice as many farm boys reach working age on the farms as there are farm jobs released by the retirement and death of older farm men. Typically farm boys work for a short time on a farm in their home community and then either rent a farm of their own, take over the home farm, or find nonfarm employment and are replaced by the younger boys who are growing up. In this kind of labor market, wages are always depressed, as compared with markets in which laborers must be attracted in increasing numbers and in which the wages must be attractive to mature men throughout their lives.

During the depression years, 1932 to 1936, average cash farm wage rates dropped as low as $.11 to $.15 an hour, and as late as 1940 the lack of nonfarm jobs kept average cash-farm wages down to $.17 an hour. As labor shortages developed during the war, farm wage rates rose rapidly, reaching $.58 an hour in 1948, more than three times the 1940 level. As would be expected, in view of the nature of the farm-labor market, farm-wage rates have fluctuated much more than the hourly earnings of workers in manufacturing industries. Throughout most of the period 1914 to date, for which comparable data are available, the hourly earnings of workers in manufacturing industries have been a little more than double the average or composite cash-farm wage rates (Table 21-3). Hourly earnings of workers in manufacturing have been almost three times the composite cash-wage rates of farm workers since World War II.

Direct comparisons of farm and nonfarm wage rates are not possible, because of differences in the cost of living and in the perquisites furnished the worker in addition to cash wages. Real wage differentials are not as great as is suggested by the cash wage differentials in Table 21-3. The difference in wage rates, nevertheless, plus the attraction of shorter hours of work and the social functions in the urban community, causes young people to leave farm employment rapidly when jobs are available in the city.

Migrant farm labor. Thus far, we have been discussing farm labor as though it were a uniform commodity. Hired farm workers naturally divide themselves into two groups: (1) residents of the community and (2) migrant workers.

Employment of migratory workers is primarily a feature of the pattern of production of that part of American agriculture characterized by relatively large-scale specialized production, often referred to as industrialized farms. Migratory workers make possible the cultivation and harvesting of large acreages in fruits, vegetables, and such field crops as cotton, sugar beets, and hops.

Several factors enter into the employment on these farms of migratory rather than local seasonal workers. The number of workers required for hand labor in cultivating or harvesting operations may be so large and the periods of employment so short that the recruitment of the necessary numbers of workers from the local labor supply is difficult or impossible. Moreover, the arduousness of the work together with the wage and living conditions that accompany it, are often of such a nature that the locally resident population of working age would not accept.[3]

TABLE 21-3

Composite Hourly Cash Wage Rates of Hired Farm Workers and Hourly Earnings of Production Workers in Manufacturing, 1910-1958

Year	Farm Laborers	Production Workers, Manufacturing
1910	$ .13	
1911	.13	
1912	.13	
1913	.14	
1914	.13	
1915	.14	
1916	.15	
1917	.19	
1918	.24	
1919	.28	
1920	.32	
1921	.21	
1922	.20	
1923	.23	$ .52
1924	.23	.55
1925	.23	.55
1926	.24	.55
1927	.24	.55
1928	.24	.56
1929	.24	.57
1930	.22	.55
1931	.17	.52
1932	.13	.45
1933	.11	.44
1934	.13	.53
1935	.14	.55
1936	.15	.56
1937	.17	.62
1938	.17	.63
1939	.16	.63
1940	.17	.66
1941	.21	.73
1942	.27	.85

[3] Louis J. Ducoff, *Socio-Economic Backgrounds of the Migratory Labor Situation* (Mimeo.) (Bureau of Agricultural Economics, September 1949).

TABLE 21-3 (*Continued*)

Year	Farm Laborers	Production Workers, Manufacturing
1943	.35	.96
1944	.42	1.02
1945	.47	1.02
1946	.50	1.09
1947	.54	1.24
1948	.58	1.35
1949	.56	1.40
1950	.56	1.46
1951	.62	1.59
1952	.66	1.67
1953	.67	1.77
1954	.66	1.81
1955	.68	1.88
1956	.71	1.98
1957	.73	2.07
1958	.76	2.13

Source: Agricultural Marketing Service and Bureau of Labor Statistics.

Migratory farm workers have numbered 800,000 to 900,000 in recent years, about half of whom entered the United States from other countries especially to engage in migratory farm work. One-half of these workers find employment in the South, one-fourth in the northern states and one-fourth in the western states.

Mexicans, people of Mexican descent, Filipinos, and other Orientals have been the most important groups of migrant farm workers in the Pacific Coast states. Mexican families have done most of the hand labor in the sugar-beet fields in the intermountain states and in the Midwest. Southern Negroes are most important in the South and follow the harvests of the special crops up the Atlantic Coast. These special groups are joined by native whites from small farms, rural residences, and from small towns, particularly in southern states. Male migratory workers in 1957 earned approximately $1,045 from both their farm and nonfarm work.

Hired labor on the family farm. We have already noted that, in terms of numbers, about 25 per cent of the hired farm working force has been made up of migrant workers in recent years. In general, these people are not employed on family farms. Not all of the resident hired farm workers are employed on family farms, but by far most of them are so employed. What are the forces which determine the quantity of labor hired on the family farm?

Assuming that all of the migrant farm workers are employed on large-scale farms, we estimate that the number of hired farm workers employed on family farms varies from somewhat less than 1 million in midwinter to somewhat more than 2 million in September. Most of the farms employing hired labor in midwinter are dairy or live-stock farms, on which hired workers are employed on a monthly basis throughout the year. The size of farm operated in such cases usually requires the labor of two men throughout the year, with some extra help provided by other members of the family during the cropping season. These are often called two-man farms in contrast to the typical one-man farms, on which the operator has only the help of his family, none of whom are the equivalent of a full-time worker.

The question may well be raised as to why we have a substantial number of two-man farms utilizing a hired worker throughout the year, although one-man farms continue to be the most numerous. Without question, in normal or prosperous years, the two-man farms are the most profitable. The operator and his family, on these larger farms, usually have higher net incomes after paying the hired labor than the families on the smaller one-man farms, for which only a small amount of seasonal labor is hired. Immediately after World War II, farm wage rates remained so high while farm prices were falling that some farmers reduced their operations, believing that hired labor cost more than the value it added to farm production. Usually, however, a decision regarding the scale of oper-ations and whether to employ one more hired worker turns on other factors fully as much as on the wage rates.

An important consideration limiting two-man farms is the diffi-culty many families have in acquiring sufficient land, either by rental or ownership, and sufficient operating equipment and livestock to utilize profitably the labor of two full-time men. Shortage of family capital and unwillingness to use credit, or the unwillingness of credit institutions to extend credit on satisfactory terms, is the key factor in many situations. Again, as explained earlier, competition for small farms, for homes, and for self-sufficient farming activities often keep rental rates and purchase prices of small farms at levels that make it unprofitable for one-man farms to expand their farming operations, particularly in the less-productive farming communities.

In recent years, an important consideration regarding hiring farm labor on a monthly basis has been the difficulty of obtaining steady workers. Rather than run the risks of being without hired help when they are needed, many farmers prefer to adjust their size of business to the amount they can handle with their own labor and that of other members of the family.

Still another consideration in hiring farm labor is the housing problem. Many farms have only one housing unit, and living quarters and board with the farm family must be provided for the hired laborers. Farm women increasingly object to opening their homes to hired farm workers. This results from the desire of farm women to lighten their household work and have more time for community activities. It is also a reaction against taking into their homes the type of individuals who are willing to accept wage work on farms today. As compared with earlier years, migration from rural communities is more rapid than formerly. Years ago, the young man looking for wage work in a community was often a son of one of the larger, respected, families in the community. Today such boys often migrate to nonfarm jobs and those willing to accept wage work on the farm are individuals who are misfits in industrial jobs or members of some of the poorest families in the neighborhood.

Seasonal hired labor on family farms. Farming has peak labor requirements that grow out of the crop seasons. These requirements cannot be leveled out, either by the use of machinery or by adding supplementary enterprises. Crop farms, such as cotton, potato, wheat and other cash-grain farms, have sharp labor requirement peaks spaced between relatively long periods when little labor is required. Livestock added to a crop farm provides profitable employment at times when labor would otherwise have no profitable employment. Cattle fattening in the winter on Corn Belt farms is one of the best examples of a supplementary livestock enterprise that levels out labor requirements throughout the year. The cattle are often purchased in the fall after the crops have been harvested and are sold in the spring before field work starts.

Dairy farming has relatively uniform labor requirements throughout the year. For the dairy herd these are highest in the winter months when cows must be housed and fed in the barns. In the spring, summer, and fall, when farm labor is needed in the fields, the cows spend most of their time in the pastures. Yet even in dairy farming, peak seasonal labor requirements for the total farm operation occur in the spring and fall. In other types of farming, the seasonal peaks are even greater. These seasonal peaks in labor requirements are met by the operator's working longer hours, by the help of other members of the family, by the employment of hired workers for short seasons, and by the use of special, labor-saving machinery.

Most of the seasonal hired labor on family farms is made up of school youths, older men who normally are not employed, nonfarm workers who take on extra work in addition to their regular jobs or who may be temporarily laid off, and others. Seasonal labor has been especially difficult to obtain in recent years with increased use being made of women and young people who normally are not part of the labor force. Labor-saving machinery also is being used to an increasing extent as a means of meeting the peak labor loads on the farm.

The practice of hiring the owner of a machine, such as a hay baler, combine, corn picker, or cotton picker, to do the harvesting on a piece rate or "custom" basis is a common substitute for hiring seasonal harvest labor. Machine-picking of corn has almost completely replaced hand-picking in the Corn Belt and has eliminated the need for large numbers of seasonal workers. Farmers who do not have large enough acreages of crops to justify the purchase of a special harvesting machine either buy one jointly with their neighbors, or hire their work done on a custom basis. Seasonal peak labor requirements have been reduced enormously by these labor-saving machines and even further reductions are in prospect.

The individual farmer has two alternatives to consider when deciding how much seasonal labor to hire and the price he can afford to pay. On the one hand, he must either estimate the cost of hiring the owner of a machine to work on a custom basis, or the annual cost of owning and operating the labor-saving machine himself. When owning and operating the machinery himself is cheaper than hiring seasonal labor, the shift is made to mechanical harvesting. On the other hand, a farmer must consider how much he can profitably change his farm enterprises to reduce the peak labor load. Since the operator and family labor is available throughout the year, many farmers can profitably change their combination of crops and livestock to give themselves and their families fuller employment during the slack seasons of the year and to reduce the seasonal peak labor requirements.

In a general way, farmers make both of the above types of calculations. Their seasonal labor employment is limited to those jobs that cannot be done cheaper by labor-saving machinery and to those peak loads that cannot be avoided without lowering the net farm income during the year.

Under practical farm-operating conditions, farmers often purchase labor-saving machinery, even though it raises their production costs in comparison with hiring seasonal labor or hiring a custom machine operator. They justify such purchases on the basis of reducing uncertainty, which is inherent in depending on seasonal hired or custom labor. Crop-harvesting must be done within a few days after the crop has reached the harvest stage. If at that time the operator is unable to hire the necessary extra labor, or if the custom machine operator fails to come on schedule, heavy losses are incurred. Much of the apparent overinvestment in machinery on family farms has occurred because of the operator's desire to remove the uncertainty associated with hiring labor or machines when needed.

Hired farm workers and mechanization. Some writers view further mechanization of farming with apprehension, from the standpoint of the economic problems it will create for farm workers. This is particularly true in the South, where mechanization of cotton production and harvesting has been going on rapidly for a number of years. Mechanization of sugar-beet growing has made great strides in recent years, sharply reducing the amount of migrant labor employed in producing this crop. Most of the migratory labor associated with the small-grain harvest before the general adoption of the combine has already been eliminated. There is little doubt that further progress in mechanization will eliminate much of the seasonal manual labor now required in crop production. The average number of persons employed on farms has already dropped from 12 million in 1910-14 to around 7.7 million in 1958 and we can expect a further decline, even though farm production continues to increase.

The hired farm-labor market has been a low-wage market. Hired farm workers have had low annual incomes, as pointed out earlier, primarily because fully twice as many young men are born and reared on farms as are needed to replace the older men. Mechanization, which further reduces the number of jobs on farms, increases the number who must migrate to nonfarm jobs. There is considerable evidence to indicate that mechanization in recent years primarily replaced labor that had already left the rural community for nonfarm jobs, rather than that new machinery took jobs away from local workers. *Whether or not the continued mechanization of agriculture in the future will lead to rural unemployment depends more on the availability of nonfarm jobs and on the ease or difficulty of shifting to these jobs than on the rate of mechanization.* The first eleven years following World War II were years of ample nonfarm job opportunities, and farm operators were forced to introduce labor-saving machinery at a record rate in order to replace the labor which had left for urban jobs. Farm wage rates rose rapidly in response to the competition with urban industries for workers.

If the general adoption of labor-saving machinery for cotton and other high labor-using crops should be accompanied by substantial unemployment in industry, rural social problems will be great indeed. But if a high level of business activity prevails and nonfarm job opportunities continue to be available, displaced farm workers will find employment in nonfarm jobs, increasing both their own incomes and the total national product.

Social and economic problems of hired workers' families. Many farm families accept lower incomes than they could earn as hired farm workers. Studies of farm family earnings in typical farming communities in different sections of the United States indicate that families on the smaller and less productive farms have lower incomes than the wages of year-round hired workers on the large, more productive farms in the community. A number of factors contribute to this situation. In some cases, they prefer the lower income to working as regularly as is required when employed by others. Other families keep no records and do not know that they could earn a higher income as hired farm workers.

Probably the most important reason for renting or buying a small farm of low productivity, rather than working as a hired man for another operator, is the greater independence, the higher social status, and the greater security a family enjoys as a renter or owner, as compared with being a hired worker. Except in the South, non-migratory, married, hired-farm workers typically are young couples who are just getting started. They seldom stay on the same farm for more than a year or two. They seldom continue as hired farm workers more than a few years. Unless their parents were already well established in the community, these hired workers are relative strangers and have an inferior social position in the community. The housing provided for them by the farm owner is often inadequate and of inferior quality. The relations between farm operator and the hired man involve close, personal, day-to-day association and are subject to the usual difficulties of compatibility. Hired farm workers are often discharged or quit of their own volition as a result of personal disagreements with the farm operators. (A hired worker, however, can legally require the owner to furnish him employment for the duration of his contractual arrangements.)

In more recent years, a number of farm operators have greatly improved the housing for their married hired workers as a means of attracting and keeping competent help. The tenant houses on many farms today are equipped with electricity, running water, and central heating and are far more attractive than the living quarters of many workers' families in industry. Working hours have been shortened, too, as a means of making working conditions more attractive on the farm.

Until 1951, hired farm workers were not covered by Social Security legislation and were not eligible for old-age pensions. They still do not have the benefit of unemployment compensation, group health, and recreation programs available to workers in the large industrial plants. Only a few hired farm workers are members of labor unions and labor organizers have been conspicuously unsuccessful in attempting to organize farm workers. One of the reasons for this is the difficulty of getting a large number of farm workers to attend a central meeting place. Farm workers are so scattered throughout a community and so few in numbers in most communities that it is not feasible for them to get together often. Only in gangs of migrant labor have labor unions been even moderately successful.

Special social problems of migrant labor. Most of the social and economic problems of hired farm workers' families outlined in the preceding paragraphs apply to migrant as well as to resident workers. In addition, migrant families have a number of other problems. Adequate housing is perhaps their most serious problem. Moving from community to community as they do, these families are almost wholly at the mercy of their employers and often live in congested camps, with inadequate space and health facilities. Since the families will stay in the community for only a few weeks during the year, the employer and the community hardly feel justified in going to considerable expense for housing for migrant workers. As a result, the families move from community to community throughout the season, often living wretchedly, yet hoping for better accommodations in the next community.

Often migrant workers find themselves in strange communities at times of the year when their children should be in school. The children may be kept at work to help increase the family earnings, thus breaking the local school regulations. But to attempt to send these children to school for a few weeks in a strange community places a great burden on the schools. There appears to be no really satisfactory solution to the school training problem of children in migrant farm-worker families.

Since many of the migrant farm-worker families are other than native whites, they often encounter racial barriers in the communities where they go to work. They are looked upon as an inferior group and are segregated from the regular residents. Local residents sometimes object to having migrant workers' families brought into the community. Special problems are created if families become relief cases because of the illness of workers.

Large fruit and vegetable growers and others who must depend on a large number of seasonal workers to cultivate and harvest their crops in a few weeks of the year want to assure themselves of a labor supply when needed, *but want to be free from any social or economic obligations to the workers* as soon as their short period of employment on the farm has been completed. In many areas this has led to the development of the labor contractor or crew leader who organizes a crew of migrant domestic workers or foreign nationals or a mixed group and contracts with producers to do the work they desire to have done. The contractor or crew leader may be able to arrange six months of employment for a group of workers whereas any single producer may have only six weeks work.

Often the crew leaders, especially those with crews of alien workers, act as interpreters, make all arrangements for the workers in the community, act as arbitrators in disputes among the workers or between the workers and the farm employer, in short "wet nurse" the workers and their families. In some cases the crew leader acts as a bona fide contractor paying the workers hourly wages out of the fees charged the farmer. In other cases the farmer pays the workers directly, giving the crew leader a commission for his services.

Migrant worker families are in the weakest bargaining position of any group of workers in our economy. They leave their home communities because of lack of employment possibilities. In strange communities without savings, they must accept the wages, working conditions, and housing offered them.

In 1959, Secretary of Labor Mitchell reported that the number of migratory farm workers in the United States had not decreased in the preceding ten years and that their economic status was getting progressively worse. He cited their average earnings in 1957 as only $892, lower than in any previous year since 1951. He pointed out that these workers not only do not have the benefit of a minimum wage, but also are deprived of the benefits of a free labor market by legislation which permits the importation of foreign labor to work at the prevailing wages whenever there is a shortage of domestic labor at prevailing wages, at the time and place needed.

Secretary Mitchell acknowledged that there clearly were situations where supplemental foreign labor is required to meet seasonal needs. But, he said, "unfortunately foreign labor programs often permit employers to evade the necessity to pay the wages and to do the many other things needed to attract and retain domestic workers."[4]

Legislation affecting farm labor. Farm workers were specifically omitted from Social Security benefits in the early years, primarily because of the administrative difficulties in collecting the payroll taxes and because of the large numbers of casual workers in agriculture who work only a short time during the rush seasons of the year. Hired farm workers are specifically exempted from coverage in the mini-

---

[4] Speech before the National Conference of Farm Labor Services, Los Angeles, California (February 23, 1959).

mum wage legislation although in 1959, Secretary of Labor Mitchell indicated he favored the extension of minimum wage legislation to farm workers. States that have legislation setting up working condition standards and that require the employer to carry workers' compensation insurance in case of accident usually exempt farm employers when only a limited number of workers are employed.

In fact, very little labor legislation is applicable to hired farm workers. Soon after the Farm Security Administration was created in 1937, it developed a program for migratory farm workers. An important part of its farm labor program was the construction and operation of migratory farm labor camps. Migratory farm workers were housed in these government-owned camps under much better conditions regarding the minimum essentials for comfort and health than had been provided by the employers of migratory labor. During the war these camps continued to be operated by the government as a part of its labor supply program. When the wartime farm labor supply program was discontinued, however, the Farmers Home Administration, successor to the Farm Security Administration, was directed by Congress to sell these labor camps to public or semi-public non-profit associations of farmers in the communities where they were located. Later legislation permitted the government to maintain ownership of these camps.

More legislation affecting hired farm workers is contained in the Sugar Acts, dating from 1937. Basically, the Sugar Acts, as amended, provide for government participation in setting production quotas and prices for domestically produced sugar cane and sugar beets. One of the provisions of this legislation is that, to be eligible for government benefits, the producers of sugar cane and sugar beets must meet certain minimum standards regarding working conditions and rates of pay for their hired workers.

A number of states are improving the housing, health, transportation, educational, and community-welfare facilities for migrant farm workers and their families. President Eisenhower in 1954 appointed a cabinet committee on migratory labor to assume national leadership in improving the social and economic welfare of domestic migratory farm workers. In the late 1950's some 20 states had committees developing recommendations for improved administration of existing legislation and for making recommendations with respect to legislation needed to improve the welfare of migrant workers' families. Pennsylvania, New Jersey, and New York were considered the leading states at that time in adopting legislation for the improvement of migrant workers' living conditions.

As pointed out in the earlier paragraphs, many of the hired workers' families, especially those employed on the family farms producing crops and livestock, have better living conditions and higher incomes than the owner-operator families on the smaller, less-productive farms in the same communities. Many of the farmers of larger farms also provide fully adequate housing and pay their hired workers good wages.

We should not conclude that all communities and all employers take advantage of the weak bargaining position of the migrant workers. It might be well, however, to close this chapter with the following thought-provoking observations:

Reform is more frequently a problem of power than of knowledge. The unpleasant and even shocking facts of disease and malnutrition, the brutalizing effects of poverty, are well enough known to lie heavily on the conscience of large sections of the American public. One of the curious characteristics of [the migratory worker] problem is that the facts are rediscovered every few years. It is testimony to the drama and eloquence of the facts that we have not yet become altogether accustomed to them and they still have power to awaken conscience and even guilt.[5]

REFERENCES

Fisher, Lloyd H., *The Harvest Labor Market in California.* Cambridge: The Harvard University Press, 1953.

Migratory Labor in American Agriculture, President's Commission on Migratory Labor. Washington, D.C.: U.S. Government Printing Office, 1951.

"The Hired Farm Working Force," *Annual Reports,* U.S.D.A., Agricultural Marketing Service.

"Farm Labor," *Monthly Reports,* U.S.D.A., Agricultural Marketing Service.

POINTS FOR DISCUSSION

1. Why are so few of the workers in agriculture hired (as compared with other industries)?
2. To what extent do farmers use economic analysis in determining the amount of labor hired?
3. Could the average farmer in your community afford to pay current wage rates and increase his business by hiring a full-time worker?

---

[5] Lloyd H. Fisher, *The Harvest Labor Market in California* (Cambridge: The Harvard University Press, 1953), page 140.

4. Why have farm workers been excluded from most social welfare legislation for urban workers?
5. Do the farmers in your state employ migratory workers? If so, what, if any, state legislation do you have for the protection of their health and welfare?

CHAPTER **22**_____

Economics of
Soil Conservation

FROM A national point of view, conservation of our soil resources, the basis of our continuing food supply, is second in importance only to the maintenance of the health and the education of our people. Living in a relatively new country, we underestimate the rate at which we have been using up our accumulated store of productive topsoil and soil fertility.

Yet the great growth and development of our country, our schools, hospitals, churches, and our great educational system has been made possible by the transfer of assets from virgin soil fertility into these other forms. We could not have maintained the virgin soil fertility of this continent except to continue a seminomadic type of agriculture such as the Indians practiced.

The economic problems associated with the use and maintenance of our soil resources are of several kinds. One centers on the level of current use that is most economic, from an individual farmer's standpoint. Another centers on the appropriate sharing of costs of conservation measures between the individual owner and the public. Conservation measures such as check dams, tree planting on badly eroded slopes, and permanent shifts to less intensive land use, that is, from wheat to range in the western states, involve high costs for the private land owner and substantial public benefits. A third type of problem is found in our less productive soil areas. Here, public ownership of certain lands appears to be needed, in the interests of their conservation and development, for the extensive uses to which they are adapted. The critical question is the determination of the conditions that make public ownership more desirable than private ownership.

Influence of available new land. Without question, the availability of additional new land had a great influence on the land-use and soil-management practices followed by the early farmers. But probably even more important, the large store of fertility in the virgin soils permitted farmers to continue exploitive cropping practices for many years before important declines in yields took place. Improvements in seed strains and cultural implements permitted the farmers to maintain, or even increase, crop yields, without employing good soil-management practices. When the cropland, after years of use, failed to respond to the usual cultural practices, farmers were at a loss to know what changes were needed. They had developed practices suitable to the exploitation of a new continent and had forgotten the farming practices of the older stabilized farming areas. For example, during the first fifty to seventy-five years of farming on the prairie and hardwood timbered soils of the humid sections of the United States, there was sufficient calcium in the topsoil to obtain good stands of legumes. Later, when clover seedings failed year after year, farmers did not know what measures were needed to correct the difficulties. It is only in the last fifty years that the general need of agricultural limestone was recognized.

Influence of private ownership. One of the important advantages attributed to private property is the ownership interest that results in better care than public property would receive. It was partly with this interest in mind that the decision was made to vest all the ownership rights in land in individuals. Our government not only followed the policy of selling the publicly owned land to individuals at low prices as rapidly as possible, it failed to reserve to the government any control concerning its use. One-hundred years later, when the public became concerned about excessive soil erosion losses, the farm land was in private ownership and the Federal government had no authority to restrict even the worst abuses of the land.

Comparisons between public and private ownership indicate many advantages for private ownership in line with our American ideals. Yet the fact that the farm land of the United States is owned by nearly five million different families adds to the difficulty in making rapid progress with public soil conservation programs. Further interesting background information on the nature of the conservation problem is that, under our constitution, the police power, with reference to regulating land uses, remains with the states rather than residing in the Federal government. The Federal government may encourage soil conservation by making payments for specific conserving practices as it has done since 1936 under the agricultural adjustment programs. It may furnish technical assistance in helping farmers make soil and water conservation plans and in applying those plans. It may carry on educational programs through the Federal-state extension service. Yet any particular farmer or group of farmers may ignore all of these programs if they wish. If they continue to abuse their lands, the Federal government is powerless to take more positive action.

All states, Puerto Rico, and the Virgin Islands in recent years have adopted legislation permitting farmers to organize new legal units of government, soil conservation districts, for group action on soil conservation problems. In 33 states this enabling legislation delegates to the newly formed soil conservation districts the authority to establish and enforce land use regulations. Before adopting such regulations, a favorable majority vote by all land owners or users or both is required. Except for a few isolated examples, land use regulations have not been invoked. Public activities in the field of soil conservation have been limited to research, education, technical assistance and payments for applying practices, changing land use, and providing some equipment and materials such as seeds, seedlings and fertilizers.

Conservation versus production. Soil conservation, in the minds of many people, is the prevention of soil erosion losses. When we go beyond this very general statement to a more precise definition, we have difficulty. There are four major ways of preventing excessive soil erosion on farm land. The most spectacular one, engineering practices, involves terracing sloping fields, planting crops on the contour, strip cropping (alternating strips of sod and intertilled crops planted on the contour), planting of wide grassed waterways and diversion check dams to slow down the water runoff.

A second method of reducing soil erosion losses involves the use of crop rotations with more years of sod-forming grass and legume crops and fewer years of intertilled crops. Soil losses are at a minimum when the soil is held together by heavily rooted, sod-forming grass and legumes and are at a maximum when the land is planted to an intertilled crop, such as corn or cotton. The third method of reducing soil losses is to build up the organic matter in the soil. It is the organic matter in the soil that absorbs and holds the moisture while acting as a stabilizer of the mineral particles. Soils high in organic matter permit a greater infiltration and reduce the runoff as compared with soils of the same slope and texture, but low in organic matter. Reduced runoff means reduced soil losses. The fourth method is to change the use of land from cultivation to permanent grass or trees.

Conservation has been defined as the use and treatment of land to maintain its capacity to produce on a sustained basis. Other definitions differ in detail, but agree that the central objective of conservation is the saving of a resource for future production in contrast to present use or waste. Thus, we think of conservation activities as those directed toward maintaining resources for future use, in contrast to production activities that are directed toward the transformation of resources into products wanted by consumers.

When one attempts to classify activities relating to land use and treatment into these two categories, conservation and current production, he finds that often they are not competing objectives. Terraces, contour strip-cropping, and contour cultivation not only retard and reduce water run-off and soil erosion, saving more of our soil for future generations, but, at the same time, increase the amount of moisture held for the current crop and, thus, increase production. Terracing, where practiced in the southern states in the early history of this country, was primarily a practice to increase crop yields currently, rather than a means of saving soil resources for future generations.

Other practices, such as rotations including more grass and legumes, not only reduce soil losses, but also increase total production as compared with prevailing crop rotations in most of the northern, humid sections of the United States.

The use of agricultural limestone, phosphates, and potash increases legume growth, improves the organic matter content of the soil, and thus reduces erosion losses. But here again, soils high in organic matter and in plant nutrients (resulting from the legumes) produce much higher crop yields than similar soils low in organic matter and nutrients. Farmers usually do not decide whether to include more grass and legumes in their rotations or to use soil amendments and fertilizers entirely on the basis of their interest in soil conservation. They adopt these practices to increase or maintain production as well as to conserve the soil. Additional inputs of materials and labor, or rotations including more grass and legumes that reduce soil erosion losses, usually increase crop yields immediately, or within the near future. (Grassed waterways may be an exception.) In most agricultural areas, the conflict between soil conservation objectives and current production objectives is not serious when farmers are following accepted good farm management practices. In almost any community of the United States where soil erosion losses are large enough to be considered serious, most changes in cropping and fertilizer practices that conserve the soil also increase current crop production. Thus, we conclude, much of the problem of soil conservation is solved by better farm management, including land use, crop rotations, and fertilization practices which are profitable production practices.

Conservation in low rainfall areas. The humid sections of the United States are fortunate in having sufficient rainfall to permit a rotation of crops, including grasses and legumes, such as timothy, clover, and alfalfa. Beginning in the western part of the Corn Belt and extending westward to the mountains are vast areas where annual rainfall is insufficient to permit a regular rotation of crops, yet heavy enough to cause serious erosion losses. In the western Corn Belt, corn and small grains are rotated with legumes and grasses, but less successfully than farther east. The new seedings often fail, and legumes and grasses have a lower economic value in the rotation than they have farther east where the rainfall is more ample.

Wheat and grain sorghums are the predominant crops in the inadequate rainfall areas. Land broken out of the native range grasses and planted to wheat can be seeded back to grass only with great difficulty. Farmers may summer-fallow a part of their land to conserve moisture and increase crop yields; they may use mechanical practices to reduce the wind and water erosion losses; but rotations with sod-forming grasses and legumes are not feasible. Permanent grass for both conservation and livestock production is an economic alternative on the less productive lands now in wheat production in the Great Plains States, but even "long" rotations, including both wheat and grass, are not feasible because of moisture conditions.

Conservation in the South. In those sections of the Southwest where rainfall is less than 25 to 30 inches annually, farmers have even more acute problems in maintaining the organic matter in their soils and in developing a rotation with sod-forming crops. Farmers in the humid sections of the South also have a more difficult soil conservation problem than in the North for two reasons: (1) Their land is open to the weather the entire year; it is not frozen several months as is the case farther north and in some sections it is made "floury" by intermittent freezing and thawing. (2) Intertilled crops, such as cotton, peanuts, and tobacco, have a great comparative advantage over grass and legume crops (in part, because high yielding perennial grasses and legumes adapted to the South are only now in the process of development).

Good farm management practices, such as the use of terraces, winter cover crops, and the plowing down of green manure crops, both increase production and conserve soil resources as compared with the indifferent farming practices followed on many farms. Yet with cotton so much more valuable than most other crops, a conflict between the objective of conserving the soil and maximum current production is reached more quickly in the South than it is in the North.

Economic formulation of the conservation problem. Obviously to the extent that increased soil conservation results from the adoption of improved (more economic) land use and production practices, there is no conflict between conservation and production objectives. There is no economic problem in the adoption of these soil conservation practices. Farmers who fail to adopt them are failing to take full advantage of their economic opportunities.

But there are conservation practices which reduce current production and income. A farmer in the northern Corn Belt, with a rotation that keeps one-third of his cropland in intertilled crops, one-third in small grains, and one-third in sod crops, might increase his total production and reduce his soil erosion losses by increasing his grass and legume acreage to 50 per cent of his cropland and reducing his intertilled crops and small grain to 25 per cent each. He could reduce erosion losses further by keeping even more of his cropland in grasses and legumes. But if he does, his feed production and income is lower than when only 50 per cent of the cropland is in sod crops. Here we find the conservation objective in conflict with the current use objective. This conflict is common on wheat farms where rotations are virtually impossible and the land must either be continually cropped to wheat or reseeded to range grasses. Under these conditions, what level of conservation is economic for the individual farmer?

Conservation of particular soils may actually involve improvement from current low productivity levels, or it may only reduce the rate of loss. In either case, we fall back on marginal analysis to determine the most profitable level of conservation. In Chapter 4, we found it profitable to increase production per acre by the addition of labor and fertilizer up to the point where marginal cost was equal to marginal revenue. The economic level of conservation is arrived at in a similar manner. Exploitation of the natural fertility of the soil continues to be economic as long as the marginal returns from the exploitive practices exceed the value of the resource used up. Investment in conservation practices or giving up current income (current production) should be carried to the point where the marginal costs equal the marginal loss prevented or marginal value added to the land.

In production, marginal costs are balanced against the marginal value of the output. *In conservation, marginal costs are balanced against the marginal losses prevented or marginal value added to the resource conserved. The primary difference is that conservation costs*

*include the value of current production given up in the interests of
conserving the soil, as well as direct labor and capital investments
in conservation practices.* These are related to the value of the soil
saved for future use. A farm management decision, commonly, has
to be made whether or not to reduce the acreage of an intertilled
crop, such as corn or cotton, and increase the acreage of sod crops.
A reduction of the intertilled crops results in some reduction in
current income. This must be balanced against the value of having
the land conserved and, hence, made more productive at a future
time. The increased future productivity of the land, as a result of
growing sod crops, rather than intertilled crops in any particular
year, must enter into the farmer's calculations and be balanced against
the current reduction in income.

The same relationships might be illustrated by the use of additional investments in fertilizer and labor to build up the future
productivity of the land. Additional inputs are profitable for the
land owner up to the point where the cost of the unit of resource
conserved just equals its value.

It should be re-emphasized that conservation costs must be balanced against changes in asset values, land values in this case, and
not against the value of the current output of the land.

Society's value of conservation expressed in price system. Writers
from time to time have stated that the public's interest in conservation of natural resources is greater than the individual owner's
interest. Urban people with no ownership rights in farm lands have
a vital interest in the continued productivity of those lands. They
are concerned about having an adequate supply of food, fiber, and
shelter for themselves and their children at a reasonable cost in the
years to come. It is often said that society's interest in land productivity is timeless, while the individual's interest is limited to his
lifetime, or at most, to his lifetime and the early years of his children's
farming activities.

In one sense, society does have a longer-run interest in land and
other natural resources than do individual private owners. A nation
expects to have an indefinitely long life and must have productive
resources to support its people throughout the life of the nation.
What few writers seem to realize is that society, the aggregate of
individuals in a nation, expresses its economic interest in conservation, in the maintenance of the productive capacity of a natural
resource, primarily through the price system.

In Chapters 13 and 14, the functioning of the price system in the
United States, which reflects consumers' wants and preferences back

to producers, was described in some detail. It is desirable to illustrate how the price system guides the conservation activities of private land owners. Let us turn back to the fundamentals of economic value. Agricultural land has economic value because it is scarce and because, in combination with other factors, it produces goods wanted by consumers. We have just seen how the individual owner of land finds it financially profitable to make conservation inputs or investments up to the point where the marginal cost of the last unit of resource conserved is just equal to its economic value. The economic value of a unit of resource (land or soil productivity) at any one time is determined by people's evaluation of the relative scarcity and the need for future uses of these resources.

When fathers could give each of their children an undeveloped farm, when the supply of land in this country was so abundant that it could be had at a nominal price, society placed little economic value on soil conservation. The individual owner could not afford to incur costs for conservation, because the value of the unit of resource conserved was almost nothing. Now that additional productive farm land can be brought into cultivation only at considerable cost, and productive cropland is relatively scarce, both operating farmers and investors in farm land pay premiums for land in a high state of productivity. A farm in a productive farming community that has been allowed to "run down" sells at a discount as compared with neighboring farms. The price differential between well-maintained farm land and seriously eroded and depleted land is an indication of society's economic interest in conservation. The market price differential (or its equivalent) between the eroded and depleted lands and similar highly productive lands determines the profitable level of conservation for the individual resource owner.

Other social interests in conservation. Society under certain circumstances has a greater interest in conservation of specific soil resources than is reflected in the value of the resource conserved. A recent *Yearbook of Agriculture* reports:

> It has been estimated that approximately three billion tons of soil are washed annually from the overgrazed pastures and cultivated or barren fields of the country. This soil is poured into streams, harbors, reservoirs, lakes, and oceans, or deposited on bottom lands and flood plains. Probably two-thirds of it becomes, at least temporarily, sedimentary deposits in stream channels, harbors, and reservoirs, or is stranded elsewhere on its interrupted journey to the sea. . . .

Lake Taneycomo on White River in Missouri is one of the largest channel-type reservoirs in the country. It provides both hydroelectric power and some measure of protection against floods, but in a little less than 22½ years silt has reduced the original storage capacity . . . by more than 46 per cent, an average annual loss of more than 2 per cent.[1]

Accelerated water run-off, resulting from cutting off timber and from plowing up grass lands, increases flood damage to highways, dam installations, and other public improvements. These social costs, arising out of damage done to other public and private property by soil and water movement, cannot be assessed back to the individual property owners where the movement originated. To this extent, the public has an interest in soil conservation and the reduction of water run-off, which cannot be reflected in the pricing of resources.

Public conservation programs supplement the price system. Public ownership of the national forests and Federal and state regulations limiting hunting and fishing are other means used by society to conserve natural resources. In the case of agricultural land, however, as pointed out earlier, society does not exercise positive controls over the individual owner in the interests of conservation. Economic incentives, operating through the price system and government programs of education, technical assistance, and payments covering a part of the cost of specific practices are the inducements motivating land owners and land users at the present time to conserve their soil. To these outside motivations should be added the cultural values, "love of the land," which vary greatly from community to community and from farmer to farmer within each community.

Contrary to the opinion held by many people, government conservation programs for farm land are not programs to get farmers to undertake unprofitable, but socially desirable, conservation practices. They are programs to speed up farmers' adoption of profitable production or conservation practices. We pointed out earlier that improved practices that conserved soil resources usually increased production over a very short period of years. Government programs of education, technical assistance, and practice payments put most of their emphasis on the adoption of practices that both increase production and conserve the soil.

In the northern states, most of the government payments for soil conservation practices have been used for applications of agricultural limestone, and phosphate and potash fertilizers used on legumes. In the South, most of the conservation practice payments have been used for winter cover crops, agricultural limestone, phos-

---

[1] "Soils and Men," *Yearbook of Agriculture* (U.S.D.A., 1938), pages 108-109.

phate and potash fertilizers, and terrace construction. Local committeemen who supervised these programs in 1947, when interviewed by the authors, were unanimous in declaring that it would have been profitable for the farmers to pay the full cost of these practices themselves, if necessary, rather than farm without them. The government payments for conservation practices have usually been designed to pay about half the farmer's cost of performing the practice. Obviously these payments, which have been effective in increasing the use of improved production-conservation practices, should be looked upon as incentive payments.

An analysis of the uses made of the technical assistance furnished by the Soil Conservation Service leads to similar conclusions. Although conservation farm plans, which technicians of the Soil Conservation Service help farmers prepare, sometimes involve shifts from cropland to permanent pasture or forestry, perhaps reducing production and income for a period, most plans help farmers increase their production, as well as conserve the soil. Economic motivation is readily apparent when one analyzes farmer practices in relation to complete conservation plans worked out for the farm. If the farm plan contains a number of new practices, the farmer often adopts those that will both increase his income and conserve his soil, but fails to adopt those that conserve his soil if, at the same time, they decrease his income in the immediate future. Thus, recommendations to keep unusually high proportions of the cropland in grass and legumes are often ignored, while recommendations for increased use of soil amendments and fertilizer are adopted promptly. The Soil Conservation Service has found that farmers will adopt most rapidly those conservation practices that maintain or increase their income within a relatively short period. They have increasingly concentrated their assistance on those practices that economic incentives lead farmers to adopt readily.

Educational programs, in the interests of soil conservation, depend almost completely on economic motivation, and this is generally recognized by all concerned. Educational programs, however, should also lead to a better understanding of the broader, long-term values of conservation.

Divergence between practice and economic optimum. The discussion, thus far, has run in terms of landowners' maximizing their long-term economic interests and of the large area of agreement between these interests and society's interest in conservation of land resources. But much of the best agricultural land of the United States is operated by tenants under short-term lease arrangements. Tenants with short leases are primarily interested in high levels of current production. Owner-operators who are in debt usually give debt repayment first priority whenever a decision must be made between debt reduction and long-run conservation investments. Still another conflict of economic interests exists. If the debt-free owners do not have sufficient current income both to make conservation investments and to maintain customary family living expenditures, conservation practices are often omitted.

The reasons for the divergence between farming practices and the optimum economic input, or investment, in soil conservation may be summarized as follows:

(1) Lack of knowledge regarding the short-term production effects of conservation practices and the cultural lag in adoption of improved technology are by far the most important.

(2) The use of short-term rental contracts on much of our best agricultural land, with insufficient consideration for conservation of the land assets in the contract, is perhaps second in importance. The tenant's interest in the productivity of a particular farm is usually limited to the current year. If he has a common year-to-year lease, which may be terminated by either party, the uncertainty regarding staying on the farm from year to year prevents him from making long-term investments in soil conservation, either in the form of labor or expenditures for materials.

The tenant may actually remain on the same farm for twenty years but each year he is uncertain as to whether or not his lease will be continued for the following year. Under such circumstances, he fails to follow the rotations, apply the soil amendments and fertilizers, and adopt the gully control practices that would have maximized his income over the twenty-year period.

(3) Credit restrictions (credit rationing), either voluntary or involuntary, exert strong pressure on both owner-operators and landlords. In order to meet repayment schedules current income may be required for debt reduction, rather than asset maintenance. Again, credit institutions often are unwilling to lend, or individuals are unwilling to borrow, funds for conservation investments, which would be made if adequate current income was at the owner's disposal. Uncertainty regarding both future prices and production prevent credit institutions from extending credit on as liberal a basis, and prevents individuals from using it on as extensive a basis, as would be most profitable under conditions of stable prices and production.

The continuing conservation problems. Public concern regarding the lack of adequate conservation of our soil resources is greater today than at any time in our history. But the public interest in conservation of resources is as old as our nation. As more and more of our national resources are used up, increased importance is attached to conserving those remaining. Unless technological progress should proceed so rapidly that food and fiber produced by our soil can be replaced from less scarce substitutes, public interest in its conservation will continue to increase.

Much of the past transformation of virgin soil resources into other forms of capital (farm buildings, education of the family, rural churches, and manufacturing plants for the production of supplies that economize land and labor in farm production) was economic. This was one of the ways this country made progress. But even in the early years, and, to an increasing extent, in more recent years, much of the exploitation of natural resources has been uneconomic or wasteful in the economic sense.

Today, the great public problem in the field of soil conservation is that of making the price system function more effectively in this field. We have found that the primary factors preventing the price system from functioning more effectively are ignorance, cultural lag, institutional barriers, such as land tenure practices, and uncertainty. Rapid progress is being made in several of these fields and there are great opportunities for further improvement in all of them. Add to these an aggressive program of research and assistance in the adoption of new technologies to lower the cost of conservation practices and one has a broad field of work for both public and private agencies interested in conservation of our soil resources.

REFERENCES

Bennett, H. H., *Soil Conservation*. New York: McGraw-Hill Book Co., 1943.

Bunce, A. C., *Economics of Soil Conservation*. Ames, Iowa: Iowa State College Press, 1942.

Gray, L. C., "Our Major Land Use Problems and Suggested Lines of Action," *Yearbook of Agriculture,* U.S.D.A. (1940), pages 398-415.

Hammar, Conrad H., "Economic Aspects of Conservation," *Journal of Land and Public Utility Economics,* Vol. 7, pages 282-290.

POINTS FOR DISCUSSION

1. List the more important soil conservation practices in your neighborhood. Which of these reduce current production?

2. Formulate a working definition of soil conservation.
3. Is the price system likely to be more or less effective in encouraging soil conservation in the future? Why?
4. What is the nature of the conflict between the individual landowner's and society's interest in soil conservation?
5. What types of government soil conservation programs are desirable?

CHAPTER 23

Taxation and Social Control
of Land Use

TAXATION IN RELATION TO AGRICULTURE

FARMERS IN 1958 paid around $3 billion in direct taxes, which could be allocated to them with considerable accuracy. In addition, their production costs were raised by other excise taxes, such as a tax of 5 to 7 per cent of the manufacturer's or importer's price on automobiles and accessories; $.05 to .09 a pound on tires and tubes; 3.5 per cent of the sale price of electrical energy and special taxes on telephone and telegraph messages. Estimates of direct taxes paid by farmers are shown in Table 23-1.

TABLE 23-1

Estimates of Direct Taxes Paid by United States Farmers, 1958

Tax	1,000 Dollars
Federal income tax	1,000,000
Farm real estate	1,044,000
Farm personal property	233,000
Licenses and permits, autos and trucks	167,000
Motor fuel, state	202,000
Motor fuel, Federal	120,000

Source: Agricultural Finance Review (U.S.D.A., Agricultural Marketing Service, April 1958). These data are preliminary; the last 3 items are taxes paid in 1957.

Shifting and incidence of taxes in relation to agriculture. Farmers have a special interest in taxes because of the effects of particular kinds of taxes on the demand and supply of farm products, land use, and land tenure. We will first review the general principles governing the shifting and incidence of taxes and then examine the general property tax in some detail, as it affects farmers.

Taxes levied on products or services do not fall wholly on either the consumers or the producers of those products. As an illustration, if a special transportation tax is levied, as it was during World War II, it is not borne entirely by the transportation companies. The tax may be added directly to the regular transportation charges or, if paid in the first instance by the transportation companies, it may cause companies to raise their rates. But a rise in transportation costs growing out of the new taxes is not fully passed on to the consumers. If consumer prices of lumber, for example, are raised by the higher transportation charges, home builders who had been considering local brick or masonry construction rather than lumber are likely to use more of these local building materials and less of the shipped-in lumber. Lumber companies, faced with higher transportation charges, find they must either lower their prices at the sawmill or accept a smaller volume of sales.

Under the pressure of these economic forces, consumers probably pay somewhat higher prices for lumber and use a somewhat smaller quantity of shipped-in lumber, thus reducing the profits of both the lumber companies and the transportation companies (since less lumber is transported). This tendency of taxes to be distributed between consumers, producers, and other business groups transporting, processing, or distributing the product is referred to as the shifting of taxes. The incidence of the tax refers to its final resting place. The extent to which a tax will be shifted and the location of its final incidence depend primarily on the elasticity of the supply and demand for the particular products the prices or costs of which are affected by the new tax levy.

The tax burden is shifted by changing the amount of a particular product produced and consumed. We put special taxes on luxuries during war times as this is one way of both raising revenue and discouraging the production of these unnecessary products. A tax system that interferes as little as possible with normal business operations is preferred by most people. Taxes on special products or services are undesirable, unless there are reasons for discouraging their production and use. It is on this basis that we justify our high current taxes on liquor and tobacco products.

The great merit of personal and corporate income taxes is that they cannot be shifted. The tax falls directly on the individuals or corporations from whom the tax is collected and, under ordinary circumstances, does not affect their business decisions or practices. Congress, in specifying the tax rates for individuals and corporations in different income groups, decides how much of the relative burden to place on each. Farmers are subject to the personal income taxes as are other citizens, but this tax creates no special problem for them. They are affected as are all producing and consuming groups by most other special taxes on products and services mentioned in the opening paragraphs and listed in Table 23-1. But farmers have a special interest in the general property tax, both because it is the largest or second largest tax paid by them and because it has a number of undesirable effects on their farming operations. The property tax on farm real estate averaged 8 per cent of net farm income in the United States in 1957 and was as much as 18 per cent of net farm income in Massachusetts (Figure 23-1).

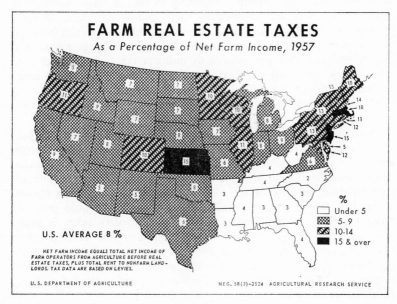

FARM REAL ESTATE TAXES
As a Percentage of Net Farm Income, 1957

U.S. AVERAGE 8 %

%
☐ Under 5
▨ 5- 9
▧ 10-14
■ 15 & over

NET FARM INCOME EQUALS TOTAL NET INCOME OF
FARM OPERATORS FROM AGRICULTURE BEFORE REAL
ESTATE TAXES, PLUS TOTAL RENT TO NONFARM LAND-
LORDS. TAX DATA ARE BASED ON LEVIES.

U. S. DEPARTMENT OF AGRICULTURE   NEG. 58(7)-2524 AGRICULTURAL RESEARCH SERVICE

Fig. 23-1.

Characteristics of general property tax. The property tax is one of the oldest forms of taxation. In the early days of its use, the ownership of property was roughly indicative of a man's income and ability to contribute to the expenses of government. When farming was the primary source of income in a community, as in colonial times, taxes based on the amount and value of property were roughly equivalent to taxes based on the incomes of the individuals in the community. As compared with income, sales, and excise taxes (taxes on products), property taxes have the advantage of being a stable source of income year after year, evasion of property taxes on land being at a minimum.

General weaknesses of the property tax. In the early days, land taxes were largely at a uniform rate per acre, with little or no adjustments for differences in value or income-producing ability.[1] Today, however, farm lands are periodically "appraised" by the tax assessor and are taxed at a uniform rate on their appraised value. The assessor, in most states, is instructed to appraise farm lands on the basis of their sale value, or on some percentage of sale value. Under this appraisal procedure, different farms should be taxed in relation to their income-producing ability. Actually, however, great inequities exist. The primary difficulty is that a large number of different assessors are required in each county and state. In spite of appraisal review procedures, substantial differences exist between values placed on equally productive lands in different parts of a county or state that are subject to uniform tax rates. Studies also have shown repeatedly that tax assessors tend to value all farm lands in their administrative unit close to an average figure. The best farm lands are systematically undervalued and the poorest farm lands overvalued relative to their income-producing ability.

Most states provide that their property taxes shall apply to personal, as well as real or landed, property. Experience with the property taxes on intangibles, such as money in bank accounts, stocks, bonds, mortgages, and jewelry, indicates they are especially difficult to administer because of the ease of concealment. For this reason, a number of states have specifically exempted intangible property from taxation. Administration of personal property taxes is probably even more inequitable than the administration of real estate taxes, because of the failure of different assessors to be equally successful in placing all taxable personal property on the tax rolls and because of differences in appraisal values assigned to similar property by different assessors.

A further weakness in the general property tax is its rigidity from year to year, regardless of the income earned by the farm family. While their stable yield to governmental units is one of the outstanding advantages of property taxes, they often cause severe hardship to farm families during extended periods of drought or low prices.

Trend in property taxes on farm real estate. Records of tax levies

---

[1] For a history of the property tax, especially in relation to land, see R. R. Renne, *Land Economics,* rev. ed. Chapter 14. (New York: Harper & Brothers, 1958).

on farm real estate exist dating from 1890. At that time they averaged $.13 an acre in the United States. After 1900, there was a gradual rise in tax rates, which continued more or less regularly until they hit a peak of $.58 an acre in 1928 and 1929. Following this peak, there was a general decline with property tax levies on farm real estate, reaching a low of $.37 in 1943. Since that time, they have increased until they reached $.97 per acre in 1957. Tax levies per acre and per $100 value are shown in Table 23-2.

TABLE 23-2

Tax Levies on Farm Real Estate, United States Average, 1890-1957

Year	Tax per Acre	Tax per $100 Value
1890	$.13	—
1900	.13	—
1910	.19	$ .47
1920	.51	.79
1930	.57	1.31
1940	.39	1.18
1950	.69	.86
1957	.97	.91

Source: *Agricultural Finance Review* (December 1958), Table 23.

As the cost of local and state governments continued to rise through the years, increasing pressure was exerted on legislatures to find other sources of tax revenue. The growth of manufacturing and business provided other sources of income that were not reached by the property tax, except to a minor extent. With the increase in numbers of automobiles, a new source of revenue was imperative to provide the necessary road building funds. This led to the general adoption of state excise taxes on gasoline. Some states segregate all their income from gasoline taxes for road building. Others use a part of it for other purposes.

During the 1930's when farm incomes were extremely low, there was a strong demand from property owners in most states for shifting a part of their tax burden to other forms of taxation, which corresponded more nearly to ability to pay. In some states, this resulted in the passage of state income taxes; others added general sales taxes and almost all states added a few excise taxes, such as those on liquor and cigarettes, to supplement their property taxes. To an increasing extent, states have been adopting aid programs that allocate a part of these state funds, derived from other than property taxes, to local units of government. This has permitted the lowering of local property tax levies, or the improvement of government services, without a corresponding increase in local tax rates.

The proportion of total state and local revenue raised by property and other taxes in several states in 1957 is shown in Table 23-3.

TABLE 23-3

State and Local Revenue Raised by Property and Other Taxes,
Selected States, 1957

	Source of Taxes			
	Property	Other	Property	Other
State	Per Cent		$ per Capita	
Illinois	52	48	93	86
Iowa	49	51	86	90
Minnesota	51	49	93	87
Nebraska	70	30	99	42
New York	47	53	109	121
Georgia	29	71	35	89
Texas	46	54	63	74
Oregon	42	58	85	115

Source: U.S. Bureau of the Census, February 1959.

Influence of property tax on land use. Taxes on land affect its use under several different conditions. In the northern counties of the Lake States and, to a lesser extent, in other natural forested areas, lands that are marginal or almost marginal for crop production have been cleared and farmed. Local governmental services have been developed to meet the needs of the population resulting in tax rates that are high, relative to the income-producing ability of the land. Farmers, who might reforest substantial acreages of these marginal lands, cannot continue to pay the taxes year after year while waiting for an income from their forest crop. Faced with the necessity of paying taxes on the land annually and with the need for income for family living, they continue to grow poor crops, always hoping that next year will be better. Absentee owners of woodlands, which are marginal for crop production, find it more economical to cut off all salable timber and let the land become tax delinquent, rather than maintain sustained yield timber cutting programs when annual taxes are relatively high.

In the Great Plains states, under the incentive of high postwar prices, thousands of acres of range land that were marginal for crop production were plowed up for wheat production. Although the long-time income-producing ability of these lands is greater in grass than in wheat, reseeding takes place very slowly. When property taxes represent a substantial annual charge, the landowner either keeps the land in wheat or allows it to become tax delinquent. He cannot afford the reseeding costs, the annual taxes, and the other

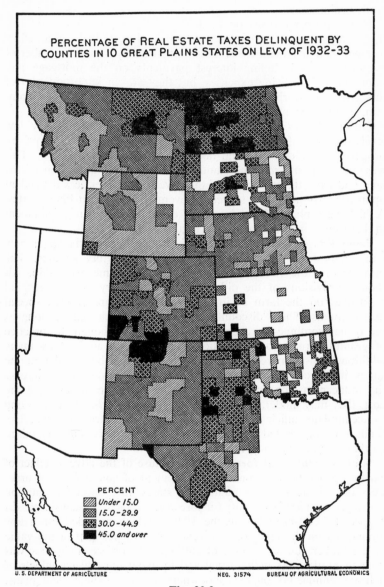

PERCENTAGE OF REAL ESTATE TAXES DELINQUENT BY
COUNTIES IN 10 GREAT PLAINS STATES ON LEVY OF 1932-33

PERCENT
Under 15.0
15.0 - 29.9
30.0 - 44.9
45.0 and over

U. S. DEPARTMENT OF AGRICULTURE   NEG. 31574   BUREAU OF AGRICULTURAL ECONOMICS

Fig. 23-2.

costs that must be incurred while waiting for income from grass lands again.

Heavy property taxes on land, especially during periods of low prices, often cause farmers to crop their land excessively, in an effort to meet their overhead costs. Taxes may be only one of a number of overhead costs including interest payments on the mortgage and minimum family living expenses, but they are an important part of this group of overhead expenses that cause a farmer to fully maintain, or even expand, his cropping operations when prices fall.

During the 1930's when farm incomes were at extremely low levels, because of both unfavorable weather and unfavorable prices, property tax delinquency and tax foreclosure were widespread. This was most serious from the standpoint of effective utilization of the land and from the standpoint of the governmental services dependent upon property taxes as a source of revenue in the Great Plains states. A high percentage of the farm real estate taxes became delinquent in these states in 1932 and 1933 (Figure 23-2).

Exemption of homesteads. Probably one-fourth of the states now have homestead exemption provisions in their tax statutes. The purpose of these exemptions is to encourage home ownership. Although provisions of the different state laws vary, owner-occupied residences on the farm or in the town or city are granted special tax discounts. These discounts are continued each year as long as the owner continues to occupy the residence. Although the practice of granting homestead exemptions has not been adopted by many additional states in recent years, it continues to be popular in the states in which it is in force. Although the lower taxes increase the inducement for home ownership, in the sense of lowering the cost, they may hinder, rather than assist, tenants who are attempting to accumulate sufficient capital to buy their own farm or home. Tax funds not contributed by the current home owners must be raised by those who do not own their homes.

Special taxation of forest lands. Because of the adverse effect of existing property taxes on the development of sound forestry practices on private lands, a number of states have special exemption privileges for lands used only for forestry purposes. Wisconsin passed a special forest-crop law in the 1930's, which provided for a low annual tax on the land for fifty years, plus 10 per cent of the value of the timber cut, at the time of cutting.[2] The object of this law was both to prevent tax delinquency and to avoid the adverse effects of a heavy annual tax on the landowners' forestry management plans.

---

[2] See *The Wisconsin Forest Crop and Woodland Tax Laws* (Madison, Wisconsin: Wisconsin Conservation Department, 1938).

An important part of this legislation is the provision for state re-imbursement of counties for revenues lost by shifting to this plan of taxation. Revenues from the cutting-yield tax are prorated to the counties according to a formula.

Incidence of the property tax. The property tax on land, like the income tax, is believed to be superior to other taxes because it cannot be shifted. A landowner cannot pass on a higher tax levied on his farm land. Since the tax does not affect the supply of land and affects the use of land only under marginal farming conditions, a farm owner's production plans are seldom affected by an increase in the tax levied on his land.

Since taxes on land are a first charge against any income that may be derived from it, they are taken into consideration in determining its value. Two farms with equal income-producing ability may have different market values because of differences in prevailing tax rates.

Using the capitalization formula: $\text{Value} = \dfrac{\text{Annual income}}{\text{Capitalization rate}}$

if the capitalization rate is 5 per cent, a \$.50 increase in taxes per acre, expected to continue indefinitely, lowers the market value of a farm by \$10 an acre: $V = \dfrac{\$.50}{.05} = \$10.$

Increases in land values, associated with the growth of population or general increases in price levels, are "unearned," in the sense that they accrue to the owner merely because he is an owner. They are not the result of any capital investments. Hence, the owner is still as well off as other members of society, even though these in-creases in value are absorbed by rising property taxes. Australia and New Zealand, in particular, have tax systems incorporating this principle. In the United States, however, difficulties in applying the principle have prevented more than a modest use of it. To the extent that property taxes are based on the appraised value of land, rather than at a flat rate per acre, land that has increased most in value over a period of years pays the highest taxes. But a forthright attempt to follow the principle of taxing away unearned increases in land values would result in such an adjustment in tax rates that no increases in value would occur, except those added by capital investment.

In principle, a prospective buyer of a farm should take into ac-count the prevailing tax levies and adjust his price offer accordingly. In this sense, the buyer of land, after a tax has been levied, buys it tax free. On the other hand, if taxes are increased after the farm has been purchased, they are an unexpected burden. Since only 3 to 4 per cent of the farms change hands each year, it would take twenty-five to thirty-five years for changes in tax rates to be capitalized into the land values: approximately the productive life of a farmer.

Another disadvantage of relatively heavy taxes on farm land is the financial distress caused in depressions. Even though the purchaser of a farm took into account the prevailing taxes when he bought the farm, heavy property taxes may contribute to his insolvency during a period of low farm prices. It is for these reasons that most students of public finance believe that, in a modern industrial society, property taxes should play a decreasing role in raising the necessary public revenues. With this brief consideration of the tax problems of most concern to farmers, we will turn to the second topic to be considered in this chapter, the social control of land use.

SOCIAL CONTROL OF LAND USE

The basis of social controls over land use. Our national government has limited powers and does not have the constitutional authority to enforce land-use legislation. If there is to be legislation at all, it must be legislation by the several state governments.

State land use legislation may provide for at least three types of governmental activity by the State and local governments:

(1) Direct administration of lands by a government agency. Instances—State or community forests and parks.

(2) Public regulation of private land use. Instances—rural zoning ordinances; conservation ordinances adopted by soil conservation districts; statutory requirements applicable to farm leases.

(3) Payment of subsidies by a governmental agency on the condition that particular land use adjustments are made. . . .[3]

Even though states have engaged in the first two activities for some time, they seldom have used subsidies to achieve land use adjustments on privately owned land. In contrast, the Federal government uses subsidies extensively to influence the use of privately owned land. Since use of the police power is reserved to the states, the activities of the Federal government in controlling land use on privately owned land are limited to education, provision of free

---

[3] "State Legislation for Better Land Use," *Interbureau Committee Report* (U.S.D.A., April 1941), pages XII-XV.

technical services in connection with soil conservation and forestry management problems, and payments for the performance of soil conservation practices. In addition to these activities relating to the use of privately owned land, the Federal government has repurchased limited acreages of low productivity lands in order to control their use more effectively.

Federal and state ownership. Some 456 million acres of land were in Federal ownership in 1950. Most of these lands (408 million acres) were public domain lands, which had never been in private ownership. These lands are either too arid, stony, or otherwise low in productivity to have value for farming purposes. Almost all remaining public domain lands require irrigation for crop production.

In 1934, with the passage of the Taylor Grazing Act, the Federal government assumed active management of the remaining publicly owned lands used for grazing purposes. Prior to that time, grazing had been allowed on these public lands with no consideration for their conservation, or for good range management practices. Under this legislation, 59 grazing districts, including about 265 million acres, have been organized. They are now supervised by the Bureau of Land Management, Department of Interior. The objectives of the grazing district include: (1) stabilization of the use rights on the Federal range, thus increasing the efficiency and security of the livestock industry using it, and (2) controlling the total amount and seasonal distribution of grazing, thus conserving the range itself.

The Forest Service is the second largest agency from the standpoint of land administration. In 1950, it was administering some 161 million acres. The Federal government owns and administers 28 per cent of all forested lands, including 19 per cent of the commercial forest area.

The reasons for public ownership and administration of these forest lands are well stated in the following quotation from a government report on government land ownership.

Even before the country was fully settled it was recognized that the forests were not inexhaustible but were, in fact, being liquidated rapidly. Depleted forest communities found here and there over large areas were in distress. This brought attention to some of the problems and difficulties of private owners in the practice of forestry and forest land management. The desirability of sustained timber management and the insuring of a future supply large enough for the needs of the Nation led to a general acceptance of the necessity of public action and cooperation.

. . . public acquisition is aimed toward lands that are unsuitable for private ownership or where private owners are not able to develop sustained-yield forestry. Such land would include that unsuitable for private ownership for reasons of inaccessibility, inherent low productivity, liquidated timber values, need for reforestation or because of inherent public values for watershed protection. . . .[4]

Other Federal agencies that own land primarily to control its use in the public interest, with the total acreage acquired by each agency, are as follows:[5]

National Park Service	13,965,000
Bureau of Reclamation	9,928,000
Soil Conservation Service	7,415,000
Fish and Wildlife Service	4,129,000
Bureau of Indian Affairs	57,280,000

In addition a number of other agencies have small acreages of land required for their activities. These include the War and Navy Departments, the Agricultural Research Administration, and others.

During the period of agricultural distress in the 1930's, considerable acreages were acquired by the Federal agencies as a part of an aggressive policy of improving land use. During that period, around 10 million acres of land, believed to be submarginal for general farming purposes, were acquired from private owners. Some of this land was added to the wildlife areas, some to the recreational areas, some to the national forests, and a million acres were transferred for administration to state agencies under agreements with the Department of Agriculture. The bulk of these submarginal lands, however, is now administered by the Soil Conservation Service, with grazing as their primary use.

Since 1943, very small acreages of submarginal land have been acquired by the government. Little, if any, public support now exists for a submarginal land purchase program and further additions to the land in Federal ownership are limited to donations and strategic purchases to round out parks, wildlife areas and national forests.

In addition to these Federal lands, the states have acquired about 20 million acres of state forests, parks and wildlife areas to control the use of these lands in the public interest. Although most of the forested lands not in private ownership are in either state or national

---

[4] *Federal Rural Lands* (Bureau of Agricultural Economics, processed June 1947), page 20.

[5] Data on Federal land ownership were taken from Clawson and Held, *The Federal Lands* (Baltimore: Johns Hopkins Press, 1957), Append. Table 1.

forests, county units of government have established forestry units on lands that have been taken over for tax delinquency in several states.

Rural zoning. Rural zoning is the division of the community, by means of local laws called zoning ordinances, into suitable kinds of districts or zones for agriculture, residences, business, forestry, and so on. Local laws are then applied in each kind of district to regulate: (1) the use of land, buildings, and structures; (2) the size and coverage of building lots or tracts; (3) the height and size of buildings and structures; and (4) the density of population.

Zoning ordinances are an exercise by local units of government of the police powers granted by the State—that is, the power to safeguard and promote public health, safety, morals, or the general welfare. The general constitutional requirements to which each zoning regulation must conform if it is to be valid are:

(1) The objectives of the regulation must promote general welfare.
(2) The methods used must have a substantial relation to the ends or objectives sought.
(3) The regulation must not be arbitrary, unreasonable, nor oppressive.[6]

One of the important objectives of rural zoning has been the promotion of local governmental efficiency through the prevention of scattered settlement in nonagricultural areas. Zoning ordinances adopted by local governmental units describe the districts zoned, the regulations applied to each, and the means of enforcing them. These districts are usually located on maps. Under most zoning ordinances, existing forbidden or "nonconforming uses," such as year-round residence and farming in an area zoned against such use, may be continued. But if and when such use has been voluntarily discontinued for a specified period, it cannot be started again.

Zoning, as a method of social control of land use, was first tried in rural areas of Wisconsin in 1929. Almost all states now have adopted legislation, enabling them to zone rural areas. The success of zoning regulations in controlling land use in the counties having land that is marginal for agriculture led to the adoption of zoning ordinances in some agricultural-industrial counties. These ordinances are designed to prevent the construction of undesirable buildings, and of undesirable suburban developments and so on, especially near the lakes and streams in the country. Rural zoning ordinances have been

---

[6] *State Legislation for Better Land Use, loc. cit.*

tested in the courts, and it seems probable that this method of re-stricting a limited number of undesirable uses of privately owned land will be extended.

Land use regulations. As mentioned in Chapter 22, 33 states, through the legislation establishing their soil conservation districts, authorize the supervisors of these districts to establish and enforce land-use regulations. The procedures require a favorable majority vote by all landowners or users, or a majority of both groups before land-use regulations may be imposed. Except in a few isolated in-stances, the local soil conservation districts have preferred to rely on education and technical assistance, rather than to adopt land-use regulations and attempt to use the police power in enforcing desirable land use in the interest of soil and water conservation. Although rural communities are aware of the need for adopting soil conservation measures and will support educational programs for this purpose, it seems unlikely that in the near future they will favor land use regu-lations.

Use of economic incentives. The use of economic incentives to control land use was undertaken on a grand scale in 1933 with the adoption of the agricultural adjustment program. In the early years, the government entered into contracts with farmers to reduce the acreage of specified crops on the basis of an announced scale of payments. These early contracts were designed to reduce the pro-duction of these crops; other effects were secondary. When the Supreme Court declared these individual contracts and the purpose for which they were made unconstitutional in 1936 the program was changed somewhat.

The new program adopted in 1936 provided for payments at an-nounced levels if the farmer kept certain crop acreages within speci-fied limits and for small additional payments if he performed certain soil conservation practices. Payments for these conservation practices were continued through the war years, even though acreage adjust-ments and payments were dropped. In 1958, these payments for conservation practices totaled about $250 million. The effectiveness of the use of these funds in increasing conservation practices is limited by the political desirability of making the conditions for earn-ing payment sufficiently general to permit most farms to qualify. As a result, a substantial proportion of the funds is used to pay farmers for practices that are recognized by most as good farming practices and that would be followed even though no payments were made. In spite of the limitations, these payments appear to have been effective in increasing the use of agricultural limestone, phosphate and potash fertilizers on legumes, the construction of terraces and grassed waterways, and related conservation practices.

Continuing problems of taxation and land-use control. Improvement in the administration of the property tax is a continuing problem. Serious inequities exist in the appraisal of farm property for taxation purposes in every state and county. The appraisal and tax assessment problem is particularly acute on the marginal and low-productivity lands, where excessive taxes force the land out of private ownership or encourage destructive land use.

Counties with sparse populations and large areas of low-productivity lands often have governmental costs that are excessive in relation to the income produced in the county. When this situation prevails, improvement in property appraisal helps but little. The only effective action is the consolidation of counties and the reduction of local government expenses to a minimum.

Rural zoning has been adopted in relatively few of the states and counties where it would be useful to limit the major uses of rural land by local governmental action. Studies are needed of both the effectiveness of existing rural zoning ordinances in meeting current needs and of the conditions in counties where zoning ordinances are believed to have a useful role to perform.

Educational programs to promote better land use can be improved as additional studies are made to indicate more clearly the best land-use practices for the different areas and communities. Economic incentives may have a larger role to play in supplementing educational programs to improve land use, especially if the government continues economic aid programs for farmers. One of the most important areas for study is the ways and means by which improved land use practices might be made a requirement for obtaining benefits from the price support or other economic aid programs.

REFERENCES

Clawson, Marion, and Burnell Held, *The Federal Lands.* Baltimore: Johns Hopkins Press, 1957.

Renne, R. R., *Land Economics,* rev. ed. New York: Harper & Brothers, 1958.

Solberg, Erling D., "The Why and How of Rural Zoning," *Agricultural Information Bulletin 196* (1958).

Timmons, J. F., and W. G. Murray, *Land Problems and Policies.* Ames, Iowa: Iowa State College Press, 1950.

1. Review the major advantages and disadvantages of the property tax.
2. To what extent do farmers buy land "tax free"?
3. Are farmers favored or discriminated against under our current system of taxes?
4. How and to what extent is the use of land controlled in the public interest in your community?
5. What land-use problems could be solved by rural zoning?
6. What land-use problems could be solved by land-use regulations of local soil conservation districts?

CHAPTER 24

Western Land Use
Problems

OVER HALF of the land in the eleven western states is in Federal and state ownership. These eleven states contain 85 per cent of the irrigated land in the United States, which, in turn, accounts for 70 to 75 per cent of the cash farm income from crops sold. Thirty to 35 per cent of the income from livestock products also comes from irrigated lands in these states.[1] The Great Plains states, just to the east of these eleven western states, have a climate neither consistently humid nor consistently arid. Uncertainty of the climate from year to year is the dominant factor in farming in the Plains states. These three facts—large acreages of public land, large acreages of irrigated land, and an uncertain climate—provide the setting for most of the western land-use problems. This chapter examines the conservation, land management, and other land-use problems, which grow out of the setting described above, in the western states.

As one writer puts it:

In the arid western part of the United States we face a test of wisdom and leadership—a test that is going to prove decisive during the coming ten or twenty years. This test will determine whether we can learn to use the resources of arid lands without destroying them, or whether we shall fall victim to the errors that have overtaken the peoples of arid lands, without exception, in the older countries of the world. . . .

---

[1] The eleven western states are California, Oregon, Washington, Arizona, New Mexico, Utah, Idaho, Montana, Wyoming, Colorado and Nevada. Data on importance of irrigated land from H. E. Selby, "The Importance of Irrigation in the Economy of the West." *Journal of Farm Economics,* Vol. 31, pages 955-964.

To a degree seldom fully realized, the western parts of the United States are yet a frontier in many aspects of land and water use. We have yet to find the key to best uses and stability for much of the land and water resources of the arid West.[2]

Problems growing out of public ownership. In the previous chapter, we saw that most of the land remaining in public ownership in these western states has been withdrawn from private entry and small amounts have been repurchased from private owners to control its use in the public's interest. The location of these lands is shown in Figure 24-1.

Most of these public lands are grazed by privately owned cattle and sheep, but they have other uses. Many of these lands have strategic watershed protection values. The high-elevation mountain lands of the West, comprising only 20 per cent of the watershed area, yield 80 per cent of the water.[3] When properly managed, these lands, largely in national forests, perform a vital function in stabilizing the flow of water for irrigation and urban uses on the lower lands.

Many of the lands in the national forests are open range, others are used for grazing interspersed with timber production. Obviously, forestry is the primary use of much of the national forest lands, with grazing and watershed protection as other important uses. In any particular area, however, any one of these uses may be most important, with the other two uses of secondary importance. But there is still a fourth use of much of this land in public ownership. Americans place a high value on recreation, on camping, hunting, and fishing. Land grazed too closely by cattle and sheep may cause deer and other wild animals to starve. The recreational and wildlife use of many of these lands must be integrated with the other three uses mentioned earlier.

The administrative agency (the U. S. Forest Service, in the case of national forest lands, and the Bureau of Land Management, in the case of most other public lands) makes the decisions when conflicts of interests among these various uses occur. People concerned with each of these uses organize into interest groups to present the claims that are often set forth in the public press and before Congressional committees. Administrative agencies and committees of Congress are responsive to these interest groups, yet government officials attempt to adjudicate the various uses in the public interest on the basis of the best scientific information available. Thus, land

---

[2] Mont H. Saunderson, *Western Land and Water Use* (Norman, Oklahoma: University of Oklahoma Press, 1950), pages 43 and 202.

[3] *Ibid.,* page 57.

use on over half the land in the western states is determined not by the pricing process, which directs land use on privately owned land, but by bureaucratic decisions based on scientific information, as modified by political pressures.

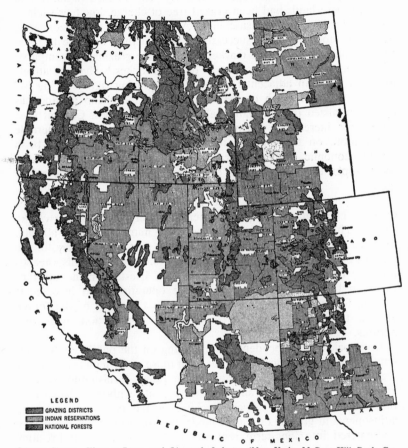

Source: Clawon, *Western Range and Livestock Industry* (New York: McGraw-Hill Book Co., Inc., 1950), Fig. 23, p. 99.

Fig. 24-1. Major areas of Federally owned or administered land in the West.

Government as a landlord. In the early days, these western public lands were grazed by ranchers free of charge. With the organization of the national forests and, later, with the organization of grazing districts under the Taylor Grazing Act, the government began to charge fees for the use of this grazing land. Forest Service grazing fees before the war averaged about $.15 a month per head, for cattle, and $.05 per head, for sheep. Public lands in the grazing districts were grazed for a fee of $.05 a month per head, for cattle, and $.01 per head, for sheep, in the early years of their organization.

Since these lands had been grazed free of charge, low fees such as these seemed high to the stockmen. Although there have been some increases, stockmen have successfully resisted their increase to more than perhaps one-half the market value of the grazing, as compared with forage on adjacent privately owned ranches.[4] These relatively low fees result in adjacent ranches' (with grazing rights) being bid up in price until much of the advantage of the cheap grazing has been capitalized into the land values of such ranches. Current proposals for increasing grazing fees are resisted, with considerable justification, on the grounds that an increase in fees would be a severe economic burden for ranchers who had recently purchased their properties on the basis of the current grazing fees on the public lands.

The continued low fees have another normal economic consequence. The demand for grazing permits is always in excess of the supply. The Forest Service has reduced the number of stock allowed to graze on the national forest lands in the past twenty years, in the interest of conservation of the native grasses. Range specialists recognize the necessity of these reductions, but livestock men object to them on the grounds that they reduce operations and income. If grazing fees were more nearly in line with the value of the forage grazed, there would be less resistance to a reduction in grazing permits.

Livestock men, dependent upon grazing on the public lands, have tenure problems distinctly different from those of farm owners in other sections of the United States. Many of the ranges furnish only seasonal grazing and a livestock ranch cannot operate without a balance of the different seasonal ranges. Because of the need for continued adjustments in grazing on public lands, the government agencies have not entered into long-term rental contracts with adjacent livestock raisers. When conditions are well stabilized, they grant permits on a ten-year basis. Yet these ranchers must have some assurance with respect to continuity of grazing permits when ranches are bought and sold.

As a means of meeting the need for stability from year to year, the Forest Service has developed a set of rules and regulations guid-

[4] *Ibid.*, pages 132-135.

ing its range management practices that are published in *The Use Book*. The Bureau of Land Management has developed a "Federal Range Code" that covers its rules and regulations worked out in consultation with its advisory boards.[5] In the early years of management of public lands by these two agencies, priority of use was given much weight in allocating grazing permits. The guiding principle, in more recent years, has been the individual rancher's need for special types of range to supplement the grazing available on his adjacent, privately owned ranch, thus permitting it to become a well balanced operating unit. As adjustments are effected in the use of public lands, there is an attempt to make these areas complement the privately owned grazing lands and water rights as fully as possible. The Forest Service, in particular, places maximum limits on permits granted to individual ranchers, in order to grant permits to as many ranchers as possible and to ease the pressure on the smaller ranchers when reductions are required to preserve the productivity of the range.

Irrigation in the western states. Contrary to much popular opinion, 90 per cent of the 33 million acres of irrigated lands in the western states in 1957 was largely the result of private enterprise. Yet public irrigation projects have been increasing in importance at an accelerated rate, in recent years. The Bureau of Reclamation now has projects under, or authorized for, construction totaling an additional 5.5 million acres. Longer-range plans look forward to a maximum of more than 40 million acres of irrigated land in the western states. Irrigation projects in recent years and those projected for the near future are usually associated with the development of hydroelectric power.

The Federal government's active participation in irrigation development began with the passage of the Reclamation Act of 1902. It was intended that these projects be self-liquidating and that they give first preference to settlers who had abandoned dry-land farms and to other families in need. A maximum limit of 160 acres was placed on the size of farm one settler could purchase in a Federal irrigation district. During the 1930's, emphasis was placed on accommodating as many families as possible on irrigation projects, yet giving them an opportunity to earn a satisfactory minimum income. Administrative procedures effectively restricted the size of farms on many reclamation projects below the limit set by Congress. On the other hand, in a few cases, Congress has set aside the 160-acre

[5] Marion Clawson, *Western Range Livestock Industry* (New York: McGraw-Hill Book Company, Inc., 1950), pages 114-117.

limitation. With the general trend toward larger farms and the increase in reclamation projects, there has been increasing pressure in recent years to remove the 160-acre limitation adopted in 1902. Thus far, however, the demand for smaller units has been so great that the advocates of removing the size limitation have been unsuccessful.

Issues in new reclamation projects. Proposals for rapidly increasing the acreage of irrigated land in the West by government reclamation projects should receive careful review in normal peacetime periods both because they add to total production and lower farm prices and because the projects are seldom self-liquidating, thus increasing government taxes. And though much of the present irrigated acreage in the West is devoted to vegetables, fruits, and cash crops, such as sugar beets, dry beans, and potatoes, most of the additional acreages proposed to be brought under irrigation will be used primarily to produce feed crops for livestock, in direct competition with feed and livestock production in other sections of the country. The question has been raised: "Should the government invest large sums to bring additional lands under irrigation when farmers, under government programs, are attempting to limit the production of the basic crops?" This question is less important when the additional irrigated land is largely a by-product of hydroelectric power development and when world tension creates a demand for all the food that can be produced.

One of the more effective arguments for bringing other irrigated land into production, under normal peacetime conditions, is that these new areas may permit lower-cost production than existing operations on some of the dry-land farms. The normal economic adjustment is for the higher cost dry-land farms to shift into grass or timber production as more low-cost irrigated farming lands come into use. From a general welfare point of view, there are net long-term gains if new irrigated lands can be brought into production at costs that are amortized by the users while selling their products at competitive market prices. All too frequently in the past, however, a public reclamation project or a private irrigation undertaking had to go into a financial reorganization, writing off most of the construction costs as a loss. Many, if not most, of the large irrigation projects in the West have gone through one or more reorganizations before attaining a solvent financial operating basis.

Property rights in water. In these western states, water is the limiting resource and is more valuable than land. As a result, a new body of "water law" has been developed and continues to be modified as new conflicts of interest in water rights develop and are adjudicated. One writer comments that, although the conflict over land in the western states has practically ended, the conflict over water and water rights has just begun.[6]

The legal basis for the use of water was developed under state laws, with priority of appropriation the primary basis of legal rights to the water in flowing streams. More recently, underground water supplies have been depleted by pumping operations of industrial and irrigation users. A body of law dealing with these newer claims is in the process of development.

Purchasers of land in western states, who expect to irrigate their crops, should carefully investigate the adequacy of the supply of the water for irrigation. It is fully as important to establish the legal right to the use of a certain volume of water as it is to make sure that the title to the land is unencumbered.

Irrigated farming requires economy in the use of water. The annual allotment of water must be allocated among the various crops in such a manner as to maximize the value of the total output of the farm. Since the allotment of water for the year or for certain seasons in the year is often fixed, the managerial decision is concerned with the most economic use of a fixed supply, rather than with the determination of the most profitable total amount to use.

Farmers, with fixed allotments of irrigation water at specific times during the year, plan their rotations and plant their crops at certain times, with a view to maximizing the value of crops produced with this fixed supply of water. In contrast to the situation in the humid sections of the United States, where farming operations are planned around a relatively fixed supply of land and family labor, irrigated farming operations are planned almost entirely in reference to a fixed supply of water.

The problems of the Plains states. During the drought years of the 1930's, a high proportion of the farmers in the Great Plains states were forced to go on public relief programs. Thousands with relatives in the more humid sections of the country also, moved in with them. During the period from 1933 to 1938, drought conditions were rather general in most of the Great Plains states each year, and the people in the area can be said to have existed on the public and private philanthropy of those sections of the United States enjoying more favorable weather.

Fortunately, during the war years the weather was highly favorable. Large wheat and small-grain crops were obtained each year

---

[6] W. P. Webb, *The Great Plains* (New York: Ginn and Co., 1931), page 452.

from 1941 through 1950. High levels of wheat, feed-grain, and live-stock production attained during World War II and in the years immediately following were, in large measure, due to the series of years of favorable weather in the Plains states. Farmers who survived the drought and low prices of the 1930's became moderately wealthy in the 1940's.

Drought conditions were serious and special drought programs again were organized in most of the Great Plains states from 1951 through 1956. Although in some areas the drought was even more severe than in the 1930's, the effects on farm families and local institutions were not as serious as twenty years earlier.

Both the farmers living in these states and the professional people working on the agricultural problems in this area are attempting to work out systems of farming and plans for financing farms that will more nearly meet the variations in weather to which they are subject. Elmer Starch, a recognized specialist in problems of the Great Plains states, writes:

On the one hand the Plains people as a community and the farm oper-ators as individuals are trying to evolve principles leading toward stabil-ization, and yet . . . flexibility is the keystone for every farm operation and every contract, as well as for the economic structure of the whole Plains. It is a case of being flexible in order to achieve stability.

Management principles for the Great Plains farmer must be such that he can shift quickly and roll with the punch. He can have a central core around which to swing his day-to-day management but he may have to shift plans rapidly. He must have speed to do jobs when the weather is right. He must . . . build up reserves when the situation is favorable. For instance, he may be planning to cultivate 200 acres of summer fallow. The rules say that he is to complete the first operation by May 15 for best results. However, when a particular spring season is dry until June 1, he must change his operating schedule so that with the first rain he will be ready to do his first summer fallow operation. He will be wasting $200 if he does that first operation according to a fixed schedule and furthermore, he would be exposing his land to wind erosion. Flexibility is the essence of management of other reserves, also, especially livestock feed. A rancher can have a stock pile of three winters' hay supply, but if a drought begins in May and persists on through July, it will be the better part of wisdom to reduce his herd.

The whole economy of the Plains must be able to expand and contract in accordance with the dictates of demand for certain crops. The cropping history of the Plains has a somewhat similar history to that of the cut-over forest lands, where a tremendously big crop is taken off once in two or three generations. In the interim periods, however, there seems to be no satisfactory or systematic set of management principles. In the Great Plains a series of big crops may be taken off the land frequently and therefore the periods of restoring lands and protecting them from deterioration come more frequently, but they are just as hard to handle as are those same tasks in a forest area.[7]

The severe economic distress of the Plains states in the 1930's resulted from a combination of unfavorable weather, low prices, and the attempt to use farming and community methods patterned after those used in more humid sections of the United States. It is doubtful that economic collapse could have been prevented in the face of the continued droughts and low prices, even though the best production and financial planning had been used. But the failures of those drought years stimulated the search for farming methods and community patterns better adapted to the natural resources in this area.

Farmers have developed a low-cost stubble mulch that reduces wind erosion, increases the absorption of water into the soil, and reduces the labor and power requirements in summer fallowing land. Water, rather than grass, was the factor limiting the survival of the cattle in some areas in the 1930's. A program of building stock ponds has been completed, which makes water facilities available now within 1.5 miles of practically all grazing. The reserve water supply is expected to last as long as the supply of grass under drought conditions.

During the late 1930's and early 1940's, an aggressive program of reseeding the less productive lands most subject to wind erosion resulted in some 10 million acres of plowed land being returned to permanent cover. Small, individual, farm irrigation systems, using both surface and well water, have added to the stability of crop production on thousands of farms. The size of farms has been increased sharply to permit economic use of modern, large-scale machinery. As the population in these states shrank during the drought and war years, local people came to realize that their entire system of public and private services must be adapted to a less dense population than had been originally planned for.

Many of these gains were offset by widespread plowing of marginal wheat lands during the period of urgent world food needs following World War II. The acreage of land seeded to wheat increased over 50 per cent, or almost 30 million acres, between 1943 and 1949. Much of this increased acreage came from summer fallow lands and from plowing range lands in the Plains states. Farmers who seeded these new range lands to wheat were fortunate with respect both to weather and prices received. Probably the wheat grown on these

---

[7] "The Future of the Great Plains Reappraised." *Journal of Farm Economics,* Vol. 31 (1949), pages 919-920.

marginal lands had produced sufficient income to cover the cost of reseeding them when they were no longer needed for wheat production. But the shift from range land to wheat is a simple, low-cost adjustment as compared with shifting wheat land to permanent grass. It can be done, as it was on 10 million acres before the war, but it is doubtful if the individuals who received the income from growing the wheat on these lands will bear the cost of returning them to grass cover. In 1950, the Great Plains Council recommended that 12 million acres of wheat land be reseeded to grass.[8] After several years of discussion, a fifteen-year Great Plains Conservation Program, Public Law 86-1021, was adopted in 1956. This legislation authorizes three- to ten-year conservation practice, cost-sharing contracts with farmers and ranchers in the 10 Great Plains States.

Further adjustments needed in the Plains economy. When all the gains have been recounted and the losses, such as the plowing of additional range land acreages for wheat, have been set off against them, there is little doubt that great progress in adapting the agriculture and the institutions of the Plains to the inherent instability of the climate will be made evident. Yet the fact remains that much more adjustment must be made, if indeed it is possible to develop an economy that can withstand the extreme weather variations of the Plains without outside help. The favorable prices and yields during the period dating from 1945 to 1950 were without precedent in the farming history of the Great Plains. Farmers improved their machinery and equipment, their homes, and their financial position. Yet it is doubtful whether many farming communities in the Plains states could successfully withstand another series of droughts as extensive and severe as those which occurred from 1933 to 1938 and again from 1951 to 1956 without outside help.

In North Dakota, the average cash income for a farm between 1924 and 1948, at 1947 constant prices, was $4,600. Yet in eight consecutive years out of these twenty-five, assuming constant prices, cash farm income dropped to less than one-half the average and in ten consecutive years out of the twenty-five, the cash farm income was less than two-thirds the average for the entire period. At the other extreme, for six consecutive years cash income at constant prices was more than 50 per cent above average.[9] It is the apparent tendency of favorable years to occur in sequence, followed by several consecutive years of low crop yields, that is most serious from the standpoint of farm finance. One or two unfavorable years may be met by drawing on reserves, savings, and by the use of credit.

---

[8] *The New York Times,* July 29, 1950, page 24.

[9] Rainer Schickele, "Farm Business Survival under Extreme Weather Risks." *Journal of Farm Economics,* Vol. 31 (1949), pages 931-936.

But all these are exhausted if a farm family, attempting to maintain living standards, suffers crop failures several years in a row.

Crop insurance, variable payments in farm purchase plans, feed and seed reserves, and family savings accounts are all helpful. They may prove adequate to meet any series of crop failures arising in the near future. The development and improvement of these types of flexibility, together with improvements in the technology of farming, are the more important activities designed to give farm families in the Great Plains increased stability and security in a basically unstable environment.

Continuing problems. In some ways, mistakes made in the use of land resources in the West are more serious than in other sections. If the range conservationists are correct in their expectations of continued decline in the productivity of the ranges under present use patterns and if the public does not become aware of this until the decline has taken place, it may be too late to reverse the trend. The same situation holds for dry-land crop farming. Although the issues in conserving the land and grazing resources in the West are similar to those in other sections of the United States, they take on a special importance in the arid and semi-arid climate. There is probably less understanding of the many problems involving our most economic use of land resources in the West than in any other major section of the country. This, in part, arises out of the relative youth of western agriculture, including grazing. Thus, we find that increased attention must be given to technical studies and educational activities concerned with resource conservation in this relatively new dry country.

Our experience in public management of land for private use is even more limited than our agricultural use of these lands. The Forest Service experience covers somewhat more than forty years, but only in the last thirty has scientific management been attempted. The management of grazing on the public domain is even newer. The central problem is one of perfecting means whereby the public's interest in the various uses of these lands can be made known to the administering agency. A corollary of this is the development of administration policies that give a maximum of security and stability to the livestock industry, yet permit necessary changes to be made in an evolving pattern of multiple land uses.

REFERENCES

Clawson, Marion, *The Western Range and Livestock Industry.* New York: McGraw-Hill Book Company, Inc., 1950.

Journal of Farm Economics, Vol. 31, No. 4, Part 2 and Vol. 32, No. 3, has a series of special articles on Western land use problems.

Renne, R. R., *Land Economics,* rev. ed. New York: Harper & Brothers, 1958.

Saunderson, Mont H., *Western Land and Water Use.* Norman, Oklahoma: University of Oklahoma Press, 1950.

The Future of the Great Plains. House of Representatives, Document 144, 75th Congress, 1st Session, 1937.

Webb, W. P., *The Great Plains.* New York: Ginn and Co., 1931.

POINTS FOR DISCUSSION

1. In what ways do the problems associated with land in the western states differ from those found in other sections of the United States?
2. Under what conditions does government ownership of land appear to be more desirable than private ownership?
3. What are the more important problems facing farmers in the Plains states?
4. How do you reconcile the construction of new irrigation facilities in the 1930's and 1950's when we had government restrictions on crop production?
5. What effect will more adequate conservation measures have on the economy of the western states?

PART SIX

Price-Income Policy
Problems

CHAPTER 25

The Growth of Government in Agriculture

EARLY BEGINNINGS

GOVERNMENT PRICE supports and production controls for crops undertaken in 1933 were not as new and novel as most of us believed. Governmental assistance in marketing staple crops began in early colonial days. Everett Edwards, relating the history of American agriculture in the first three hundred years, tells of the tobacco farmers' price difficulties and government help as early as 1619.

Tobacco became the chief exchange medium for Virginia in the early years. The Virginia Colonial Assembly in 1631 set a minimum price on tobacco of sixpence per pound; exchanges at prices lower than sixpence were punishable by imprisonment. By 1639, it became necessary to adopt a crop curtailment program to supplement the price-fixing measures. The Colonial government limited the crops of 1639 through 1641 to 1,200,000 pounds of good quality tobacco. Viewers (local Colonial officials) were authorized to destroy inferior tobacco and excess crops. The merchants cooperated in this program and agreed to pay not less than threepence per pound.[1]

Tobacco production became so popular in the early colonial years that the government found it necessary, or at least desirable, to require producers to plant minimum acreages to corn and other feed and food crops, rather than to plant tobacco alone. Here again, there is great similarity between the activity of the early colonial government and the Extension programs to increase the production of home feed and food crops on the cotton and tobacco farms.

---

[1] Everett E. Edwards, "American Agriculture—The First 300 Years," *Yearbook of Agriculture* (U.S.D.A., 1940), pages 184-185.

461

Agriculture depended less on export crops in the northern colonies than in the southern, hence, there was less emphasis on crop controls in the North. But the northern colonies had their problems, too. In New England, the agricultural problem took the forms of scarcity of labor and "oppressive" wage rates. Thus, continuous attempts were made through the courts and legislatures to regulate (place ceilings over) wage rates of "mechanics and day laborers." Taken as a whole, however, price fixing and governmental controls, which were important for some crops and in certain areas, were the exception, rather than the rule. Although tariffs and subsidies were employed from time to time, they usually were a part of the mercantilistic policies of the mother countries, instead of being regulations originating in the colonies.

Colonial times to 1862. Land ownership policies were a primary concern of our early national government. The colonists who came to this country were revolutionists. They believed in the right of every man to hold title to real property without restrictions. They also believed in an equal distribution of estates, in contrast to the traditional hereditary rights of the eldest son in the family, or similar semi-feudal customs. These two ideals dominated our land disposal and ownership policies from early Colonial days.

In the first years of our national government, another issue arose regarding land disposal. Should the public domain be held and disposed of in a manner that would bring in the greatest revenue possible to the national government, or should it be sold rapidly at nominal prices to settlers? Alexander Hamilton and the eastern businessmen favored getting the maximum revenue from these lands. But Thomas Jefferson and those who believed that widespread ownership of family farms was the "backbone of democracy" favored selling the lands at low prices on easy terms. As the nation became older, these latter views came more and more to prevail.

The legislation for disposing of land passed in 1796 provided for sales in units of 640 acres at $2.00 an acre. Four years later, the minimum size of unit was reduced to 320 acres, and in 1804 a family could buy 160 acres from the government at $2.00 an acre. Fifteen years later, the price was reduced to $1.25 an acre and the minimum size of unit was reduced to 80 acres. Again in 1841, the government took action to allow settlers to obtain property rights in land on still easier terms. The Pre-emption Act, passed in that year, gave squatters, who had tenanted public lands without purchasing them, legal rights to the land they had occupied.[2]

---

[2] This development is briefly summarized in Gaus and Wolcott, *Public Administration and the United States Department of Agriculture* (Chicago: Public Administration Service, 1940), pages 116-17.

This broad, public demand for the rapid disposal of public lands to settlers on easy terms reached its climax in 1862 after the southern states had seceded from the Union. The passage of the Homestead Act in that year represented the culmination of the efforts of the frontiersmen and the western politicians to give every family that wanted it enough free land to make a living. This act provided that any family could obtain title to 160 acres of public land by living on it and cultivating it five years. Unfortunately it came too late. Most of the public lands available for sale or settlement after 1862 were semiarid and arid lands located in what we now know as the Great Plains. Hundreds of thousands of families took up homesteads in these areas only to be forced to return to the more humid areas, after several seasons of toil and heartbreaking crop failures because of drought.[3]

Disposal of public lands was not the only activity of the early national government relating to agriculture. Mr. Chew reports that Thomas Jefferson, while he was the first Secretary of State, took a great interest in the introduction of new plants and animals.[4] The Patent Office, located in the Department of State, received and distributed foreign seeds and plant cuttings. As agricultural societies sprang up, they requested government help in promoting their activities of farm improvement. Thus, we find the Berkshire (Massachusetts) Association for the Promotion of Agriculture and Manufacturing petitioning Congress in 1817 to set up a national board to help agriculture and manufacturing.[5]

By 1839, demands of this sort resulted in the first specific appropriation for agriculture. In that year, Congress appropriated $1,000 to be spent by the Patent Office for the collection and distribution of seeds, carrying on agricultural investigations, and collecting agricultural statistics. This was the formal beginning of two governmental functions for agriculture, research and service, which have been of incalculable value to farmers and to the public, generally, over the last century.

Studies of tea and silk were undertaken. Peas and clover were recommended for worn-out lands. Collection and dissemination of statistics on crop production and marketing, forerunning our present outstanding government Crop and Livestock Reporting Service, were recognized as proper service functions of the government. This initial appropriation of $1,000 in 1839 was gradually increased and

---

[3] B. H. Hibbard, *A History of the Public Land Policies* (New York: Peter Smith, 1939).

[4] Arthur P. Chew, *The Response of Government to Agriculture* (U.S.D.A., 1937), pages 7-8.

[5] *Ibid.,* page 10.

the range of investigations widened, until, in 1854, Congress appropriated $35,000 for seed collection, investigations (research), and the collection of statistics. The growing importance of these services to agriculture was recognized by the members of Congress and, in 1862, they created a "Department" of Agriculture under direction of a Commissioner. The work and influence of the United States Agricultural Society, the forerunner of our present national farm organizations, is given credit for obtaining this legislation for agriculture.[6] The Commissioner of Agriculture and the newly created "Department" continued as a part of the Patent Office for twenty-five years, but this legislation of 1862 is generally recognized as the "organic act" of the present Department of Agriculture.

RESEARCH, EDUCATION, SERVICE, AND REGULATION, 1862-1916

The period from 1862 to 1916 was characterized by a great expansion in the scientific work of the Department of Agriculture. Adult educational activities were begun, governmental services were increased, and the first regulations needed to prevent the spread of insects and diseases were adopted. The first marketing regulations also were adopted during this period.

The year 1862 is a memorable one for agriculture. The passage of the Homestead Act and the legislation creating the Department of Agriculture have already been noted. The Morrill Act, also passed in 1862, provided for public land grants to the several states to assist in the establishment of state colleges and universities that included the teaching of agriculture and mechanic arts: the land-grant colleges and universities. Of the three laws, the Morrill Act was probably of greatest significance for it started a program of state and Federal support for an institution of higher learning in each state, devoted to the education of young people regarding the "practical problems" of agriculture and the mechanic arts.

This Federal assistance to state educational institutions was followed in 1887 with legislation authorizing continuing Federal assistance to state agricultural experiment stations, usually located at the state colleges, for carrying on research in the sciences relating to agriculture. It was twenty-seven years later, or 1914, before Congress authorized Federal aid to the states in carrying on adult educational work, the present Federal-State Extension Service. The

---

[6] Gaus and Wolcott, *Public Administration and the United States Department of Agriculture* (Chicago: Public Administration Service, 1940), page 5.

research and educational activities relating to agriculture were firmly established during this period.

Early regulatory work. In 1884, Congress was suddenly confronted with a problem that threatened the economic welfare of the nation's livestock producers. Arthur Chew relates the circumstances as follows:

> Another infection [of pleuropneumonia] broke out in 1859 in Massachusetts; it had been brought there by four cows from the Netherlands. Port inspectors saw that the animals were sick, but the infection escaped, and within four years it had appeared in 20 towns in Massachusetts. Soon it developed in Connecticut, Delaware, Pennsylvania, Virginia and the District of Columbia. Alarmed cattlemen demanded joint action by the states, but the states could not get together. It was necessary to invoke federal action. Congress had to pass laws to provide funds and to create an administrative organization, for it was a new type of emergency.[7]

This disease outbreak resulted in the creation of the Bureau of Animal Industry. Similar crop diseases and pest infestations led to Federal legislation covering the interstate movement of insect pests and disease-infected plants and seeds. Federal regulations forbidding the interstate movement of diseased plants and animals have been supplemented by similar legislation in many states designed to prevent or slow down the spread of diseases and pests within their borders.

Early conservation activities. Dwindling forest resources, as early as 1876, caused enough concern to result in a special study of encouraging timber growing and forest protection. A few years after this study was completed, a forestry research and educational unit was formed in the Department of Agriculture. These early studies awakened political leaders and Congress to the need for conservation of our natural forest resources. In 1891, Congress responded by authorizing the President to set aside forest reserves from the public domain to be held by the national government. These reserves were the beginning of our present national forests.

Land policies, 1862-1916. The Homestead Act of 1862 was far from the last legislation dealing with the disposal of public lands. When the 160-acre homestead proved to be too small a unit in the dry-land areas, Congress passed other legislation granting title to larger units when the settlers met certain requirements. Some of these requirements included the development of small irrigation works. In 1894, an act was passed granting lands to the western states on

---

[7] Arthur P. Chew, *The Response of Government to Agriculture* (U.S.D.A., 1937), page 31.

condition that they develop irrigation on them.[8] Then in 1902, as related earlier, the Federal government itself undertook the building of irrigation projects. The cost of these projects was to be liquidated over a ten-year period by the farmers' payments for the land and irrigation water. We have already pointed out that all too often the farmers were unable to pay the irrigation costs in the time period set.

THE PERIOD OF ECONOMIC ASSISTANCE 1916 TO DATE

Farm credit for agriculture. Great mechanical improvements were made in farming tools in the late 1800's and early 1900's. In spite of financial panics at irregular intervals, farmers came to depend more and more on markets and market prices in selling farm products and buying supplies. Industrial developments were moving ahead at an unprecedented pace. Farm leaders believed that urban and industrial progress was outstripping improvements in farming and farm life.

President Theodore Roosevelt, in 1908, was persuaded to appoint a "Country Life Commission." The commission's report covered a wide range of topics in the area of improving rural living. In the field of business, the commission reached the conclusion that farmers did not have credit facilities that served them as adequately as industry was served by the city banks. They believed that more adequate credit would help farmers attain their farm ownership goal more rapidly.

Following the report of the commission, a group was sent to Europe to study the cooperative land mortgage credit banks, especially those in Germany. The group was favorably impressed and recommended that the government sponsor a national farm-credit cooperative to make land mortgage loans to farmers. It was 1916 before these recommendations were embodied in legislation setting up 12 regional land banks with government capital. Seven years later, in 1923, a system of 12 Federal intermediate credit banks was established.

Funds were obtained from the sale of mortgage-secured bonds in the private bond market, and loans were made at uniformly low interest rates in all sections of the country. The first effect of this new act was to lower real estate mortgage credit interest rates in

[8] R. R. Renne, *Land Economics* (New York: Harper & Brothers, 1958), page 498.

the high interest rate areas of the West and elsewhere. It was not until the Great Depression of the 1930's, however, that the government-sponsored farm-credit system proved of greatest value to farmers.

At that time commercial banks, insurance companies, and other commercial lending agencies, finding many of their borrowers delinquent, started thousands of foreclosure proceedings. Special legislation was rushed through Congress in 1933 to supplement the Farm Loan Act and to permit the land banks to refinance delinquent notes held by commercial agencies. At the same time, the farm-credit system was expanded to include production (short-term) credit facilities and credit for cooperatives. Thus, we find that, when the need developed, the original farm-credit legislation was amended and broadened to deal with the new situation. This legislation in 1916 marked the beginning of the Federal government's direct assistance in the business aspects of farming and opened a new chapter in the relations of the farmers to their government.

The growth of cooperatives. Farmers and farm leaders were dismayed by the sharp fall in prices after World War I. Many proposals were put forward for dealing with the situation. Farm leaders had had little experience with direct price controls since Colonial times and found it difficult to agree on a plan for governmental help. Local cooperatives had been rendering effective service in the marketing of several farm products, however, and there was general agreement that more cooperative marketing should be encouraged.

The legal position of large cooperatives was not clear. As late as 1921, courts held that cooperative associations were in violation of existing antitrust legislation. Congressional leaders decided to strengthen the cooperative movement and give cooperatives a clear charter to expand their activities. The result was the Capper-Volstead Act of 1922 defining a cooperative association and exempting their usual business activities from antitrust legislation. This legislation gave impetus to a great expansion in cooperative activity. Certain cooperative leaders got the idea that, if a cooperative could sign up all the producers of a crop, they could control the supply of it and, hence, dictate prices. But they found it difficult to sign up all producers; some always wanted to remain outside the cooperative. Further, they discovered that controlling the crop after it is produced is one thing, and controlling production is another. They could control the former, but not the latter. Thus, their dreams of monopoly control and price dictation failed to materialize, and cooperatives failed to obtain satisfactory prices for farm products in the 1920's.

The need for governmental controls. Farm leaders, aware of the sharp drop in farm prices after World War I, as compared with the modest drop in nonfarm prices, believed that legislation should be adopted that would "make the tariff effective" for farmers. The central ideas of the leaders, who drafted a number of bills sponsored by Senator McNary in the Senate and Congressman Haugen in the House of Representatives, were: "(1) that the centralizing power of the Federal Government should be used to assist farmers to dispose of the surplus abroad and raise prices to the desired level in the domestic market, and (2) that the loss on the segregated exports was to be paid by the farmers themselves by means of an equalization fee."[9]

Bills embodying these principles passed both houses of Congress twice in the late 1920's, only to be vetoed both times by President Coolidge. John D. Black, writing on this topic in 1928, said the significance of the so-called McNary-Haugen movement was far more political than economic.[10]

The issue involved is more fundamental than McNary-Haugenism itself. It is agriculture's stand against the domination of its affairs and the affairs of the country by the commercial and industrial interests. Labor has never contested this supremacy successfully in the political field; and in its present condition of relative prosperity, it is even less inclined than before to contest. The agricultural interests of the country for a long time have felt the need of protecting themselves politically against the business interests. The formation of the "agricultural bloc" [in Congress] in May, 1921, was a visible expression of that feeling. But the bloc needed some vigorous measure around which to rally the forces of agriculture. The McNary-Haugen plan proved to be that measure.

Although the agricultural forces were unable to pass these McNary-Haugen bills over the President's veto, they did force both political parties to include measures "to give equality to agriculture" in their 1928 political platforms in the presidential election. Hoover and his associates in the Republican party proposed to set up a Federal Farm Board which would: (1) assist in organizing the producers of each commodity into large national cooperatives and (2) stabilize market prices through loans or direct purchases out of a $500 million revolving fund. President Hoover persuaded Congress to pass such a bill soon after he was elected; it was known as the Agricultural Marketing Act of 1929. The passage of this legislation marked a new departure in government, relative to agriculture.

---

[9] Chester C. Davis, "The Development of Agricultural Policy Since the End of the World War," *Yearbook of Agriculture* (U.S.D.A., 1940), page 307.

[10] John D. Black, "The McNary-Haugen Movement," *American Economic Review,* Vol. 18, No. 3, page 405.

Although farm leaders obtained popular support for their program on the basis of making the tariff effective for agriculture, the real difficulty was the continued disparity between farm and non-farm prices in the 1920's as compared with those between 1910 and 1914. This, in turn, was a reflection of the relatively inelastic supply and demand for farm products as a whole, which was discussed in Chapter 17. Farmers, faced with relatively low and certainly unsatisfactory prices, did not shift in sufficient numbers into nonfarm occupations to reduce total supplies and strengthen farm prices. Many left the farms during this period, but many did not because they could not. Financial distress in the 1920's, coupled with unemployment in the cities, held enough workers on farms to keep total output increasing. Continued technological advance in agriculture and the sustained output of farm families, trying to meet their interest, taxes, and family living obligations, increased total farm output in the face of relatively low prices.

The 1929 Agricultural Marketing Act committed the government to help farmers obtain better prices for their products. Financed by government stabilization loans, national cooperatives were to purchase and hold supplies from the market when individual commodities' prices were "temporarily" depressed. The experience of the Federal Farm Board, set up to administer this legislation, was most disappointing. The Great Depression of the 1930's caused the board's $500 million revolving fund to disappear like a snowball on a kitchen stove. Many loans advanced to the large cooperatives to purchase and hold distressed stocks were never repaid, because market prices kept right on falling.

Agricultural adjustment legislation. Farm Board members became convinced that farmers must reduce their production as a part of any government price stabilization measure. Largely as a result of the failure of the Farm Board, new legislation was enacted in 1933 permitting the government to enter into acreage adjustment (reduction) contracts with farmers. Processing taxes were levied on each commodity for which an adjustment program was undertaken, in order to raise funds to pay farmers for reducing their crop acreages and their hog production.

This began as a voluntary program, with payments set high enough to induce most farmers to cooperate. Both cotton and tobacco farmers, however, wanted compulsory production controls and Congress passed supplementary legislation levying high taxes on cotton or tobacco marketed in excess of that grown on the farm's allotment.

In 1936, the Supreme Court ruled that the Federal government's contracts with individual producers were an invasion of the powers reserved to the states; hence, the Agricultural Adjustment Act of 1933 was declared unconstitutional. After a few months of uncertainty, a new adjustment program was developed involving governmental grants to farmers who shifted specified percentages of their major feed grain and cash crops to soil-conserving forage crops. Funds for such payments, often amounting to $500 million a year, were appropriated from the general tax receipts of the treasury.

Farmers' benefits from this program were several fold: (1) the government check was an addition to their farm income; (2) the smaller supply of the products produced had some effect in increasing prices; (3) the farm land was improved by growing the soil-conserving forage crops; (4) farmers who complied with the adjustment program were eligible to receive nonrecourse government loans on their crops, often at above market price levels at harvest time. These nonrecourse loans were made as direct price stabilization loans, with the government's accepting delivery of the crop in settlement of the loan, if the market price failed to reach the loan level. Government officials believed that, with a production adjustment program and general business recovery, any accumulations of stocks in the hands of the government would be temporary.

In 1938, legislation was passed utilizing the authority of Congress to regulate interstate commerce, which re-enacted most of the production controls held to be unconstitutional in 1936. Under this legislation, whenever the reserve supplies of the important crops reached certain levels, producers, by a two-thirds majority vote, could impose marketing quota restrictions on themselves. When marketing quotas are in effect, each producer can sell only the product from his allotted acreage. A relatively high tax is imposed on all excess production. Growers of tobacco, cotton, wheat, rice, and peanuts have all made use of the compulsory marketing quota regulations.

Marketing agreements. Authority to undertake marketing agreements was included in the 1933 Agricultural Adjustment Act. When two-thirds of the growers of a commodity agree on a marketing program, they may petition the Secretary of Agriculture to issue an order that becomes binding on all shippers in the market. Thereafter, all shippers must operate in accordance with the order or their operating license would be revoked.

Marketing orders have been used in marketing dairy products in city fluid-milk markets, for such specialty crops as fruits, tree nuts, and vegetables, and, more recently, for potatoes. Excessive competitive price cutting in the fluid-milk markets was prevented by the marketing orders during the period of low prices in the pre-World

War II years. Marketing agreements, when used for fruits, often took the form of diverting inferior quality fruit from the fresh to the processed market, thereby strengthening fresh fruit prices and increasing total returns to growers. Potato-marketing orders have been used to prevent producers from shipping small-size and low-quality potatoes.

Court decisions have authorized Federal marketing controls over products processed and consumed within the state in which they are grown, if they come into competition with similar products moving in interstate commerce. Marketing agreements have obtained widespread support and will probably be used to an increasing extent in the years ahead.

Farm price supports during World War II. We noted that the Federal Farm Board attempted to stabilize prices with government loans and purchases, but failed. Then nonrecourse loans were undertaken as a supplementary part of the acreage adjustment program with a somewhat more satisfactory experience. A combination of factors—the rising general price level from the bottom of the depression, two serious droughts in 1934 and 1936 causing temporary shortages, the acreage adjustment programs, and finally and most important, the demands of World War II—combined to give the government a substantial profit on its lending operations through 1945. The nonrecourse loans were the most popular feature of the farm program. They made minimum prices (or price floors) effective to producers in a way that all could see and understand.

In view of this favorable experience, it was only natural that the government should turn to a wider use of government-announced price supports in its wartime food-expansion programs from 1941 to 1945. Congress, wishing to give farmers equal protection with industrial plants during the war and the postwar reconversion period, enacted legislation requiring the Secretary of Agriculture to support prices at 90 per cent of parity[11] for the basic farm crops (corn, cotton, wheat, rice, tobacco, and peanuts) and for those products for which the secretary requested an increase in production. This mandatory price-support legislation was to be effective for the duration of the war and two years beyond the first of January after the war ended. Twenty commodities met the requirements and received mandatory price supports during this period. In addition, the secretary, in the interests of stimulating increased production, announced price supports on a large number of other commodities during the war period. In 1945, government price supports were announced on 166 different commodities.

[11] The concept of parity is defined and explained in Chapter 27.

Again the experience was satisfactory; a strong demand, in addition to lend-lease and military requirements, made it relatively easy to carry out any price-support operations required. Government guarantees of minimum prices became increasingly popular with farmers and opposition to the government's assuming this role declined.

Other wartime food and agricultural programs. When the United States was drawn into World War II the Agricultural Adjustment Administration and other peacetime agricultural agencies were continued but, in many cases, their duties and responsibilities were changed greatly. The Chairmen of the County Agricultural Adjustment Committees were made chairmen of county war boards which included the local county agricultural agent and the county representatives of the Soil Conservation Service, the Farmers Home Administration, and any other local officers of agricultural agencies with offices in the county. These boards reported on labor and materials shortages and adopted and carried out national programs in the counties.

In the early months of the war it was recognized that the wartime requirements for materials and labor were so great and so different from those prevailing in the civilian peacetime economy that the market price system could not be relied upon to bring about shifts in resource use needed. Under the president's wartime authority a War Production Board was created which had control over all supplies of materials for both industry and agriculture. An Office of Price Administration was created which had primary control over prices, including prices of most foods and farm products. Control over labor was vested in a newly created War Manpower Commission.

In the early stages a Foods Requirements Committee was created within the War Production Board. This Committee was soon replaced, however, by a War Food Administration within the Department of Agriculture. Control of materials, such as metals used in farm machinery and food processing, remained in the War Production Board throughout the war period. The Office of Price Administration took over control of food distribution including direct consumer rationing of many foods as well as exercising price controls. The Office of Price Administration also rationed fuel and tires for both farm and nonfarm uses.

At the farm level relative prices were allowed to continue as the chief motivating incentives directing production but relatively inflexible price ceilings at the wholesale and retail levels made it necessary to substitute governmental orders and ration stamps for prices in guiding food distribution during the war years.

Government "setaside orders" were utilized to require cheese makers, fruit and vegetable canners, meat packers, dairy plants, and other food processors to set aside for government purchase a sufficient percentage of their product to meet military needs. An Office of Food Requirements and Allocations was established to plan and recommend quarterly allocations of limited food supplies among civilians, the military services and our allies. Special committees reviewed and questioned all aspects of the supply and requirement situation before an allocation was recommended.

Throughout the war and relief-feeding period after the war, lack of uniform civilian food distribution throughout the country required larger allocations for civilians than otherwise might have been necessary. People in the large cities farthest from the source of supply all too often found it difficult to get meats, butter, and other fats.

Wartime changes in Department of Agriculture. By far the greatest change in the Department of Agriculture in the war years was the increasing attention given food distribution and nutrition problems. The field staff of the Agricultural Adjustment Administration took over general field staff functions for the Department's wartime activities. Little change occurred in the functions of either the Soil Conservation Service or the Extension Service. The activities of the Farmers Home Administration were curtailed during the war years as economic conditions improved. In general Congress increased its direct controls over Department activities both by formal restrictions included in the appropriation acts and by informal conferences between administrators and members of Congress.

Processor influences on Department of Agriculture activities increased greatly during the war years. A special "branch" was set up in the War Food Administration to organize and supervise industry advisory committees. Toward the close of the war 115 national and 14 regional industry advisory committees were in existence. Business representatives paid all their expenses while attending advisory committee meetings and the War Food Administration took account of the "business point of view" presented in these committee meetings.

Reorganizations of the Department of Agriculture during the war and immediate post-war years realigned its activities relating to production and marketing primarily along commodity lines. Congress, in 1946, gave further impetus to the marketing activities of the Department of Agriculture by passing new legislation and authorizing additional funds for greatly expanding the research, education and service work in the field of marketing, both in the Department of Agriculture and at the Land Grant Colleges.

Government programs 1946-52. With the successful conclusion of military activities in 1945, a number of wartime controls were discontinued and within the next two years most governmental controls over prices and the uses of materials and labor were discontinued. Although many people had been concerned about the possibility of burdensome stockpiles of food existing at the end of the war, an opposite situation developed almost immediately. In 1946, within twelve months of the ending of the war, there occurred the most serious world-wide food shortage and the greatest famine in the civilized world's history.[12] These food shortages, which continued through 1947, were caused in part by the devastation and dislocations of the war and in part by unfavorable weather for crop production in Europe, Asia, and to a lesser extent, in the western hemisphere. Governmental activities in 1946 and 1947 were directed toward obtaining as large a supply of food as possible for world-wide relief and rehabilitation needs. By 1948, the more urgent post-war relief feeding needs had been met and favorable yields in the United States resulted in a harvest which exceeded commercial marketing needs. Prices of several major crops dropped to the government support levels for the first time since the pre-war years. In both 1948 and 1949, government price-support operations exceeded $2 billion, or 15 per cent of the farmers' marketings, and the pre-war regulations, authorizing acreage allotments when supplies exceeded normal market requirements, became operative again.

Mandatory price supports on the 20 commodities at 90 per cent of parity, as set forth in wartime legislation, expired at the end of 1948. In anticipation of this, new legislation was passed that set peacetime loan levels for the basic crops at 60 to 90 per cent of parity, depending on the amount of supplies on hand. A sliding scale of price support was incorporated in the 1948 legislation, indicating the extent to which price supports could be lowered as supplies (or surplus) accumulated. But in 1949 and again in 1950, the sliding-scale provisions were set aside, and basic commodities, as well as some others, were supported at 90 per cent of parity.

The debate during and following the enactment of this postwar legislation was concerned only with the level of the loans and the extent to which compulsory controls would be used to back them up. *The question of whether price guarantees to farmers was an appropriate governmental function had ceased to be an issue.* Thus, we entered the postwar period with government price supports as the central part of the farm program, whereas in the prewar years the emphasis had been centered on acreage adjustments, price-supporting loans playing a distinctly supporting role.

---

[12] Walter W. Wilcox, *The Farmer in the Second World War* (Ames, Iowa: Iowa State College Press, 1947), page 283.

All peacetime postwar trends were interrupted with the invasion of the Republic of Korea by the communist forces of North Korea in 1950. Within the next twelve months, many of the World War II controls over prices and the uses of materials and manpower were reinstituted. Stocks of food held by the Commodity Credit Corporation, as a result of its price support operations, were drawn down sharply as wartime demands for food again became dominant. Acreage allotments were discontinued and the emphasis again was on maximum agricultural production.

One of the activities of the government during this period which has had a far-reaching influence on agriculture was its policy of granting special tax benefits for industrial expansion needed to support increased military activities. If military activities were increased sharply, much of the nitrogen that was then going into agricultural fertilizers would have been required for munitions. In view of this, priorities for materials and special tax concessions were granted to industrial firms for a large expansion in commercial nitrogen production, thus setting the stage for a great expansion in nitrogen fertilizer supplies a few years later when military requirements dropped.

Postwar aversion to government controls. Americans are a great freedom-loving people. Government controls, unless required by compelling circumstances, are especially onerous to them. Because of this, the defense or wartime price and supply controls during the Korean War aroused widespread criticism and evasion where possible. A number of controls were discontinued while the settlement negotiations were still in progress and most of the controls which had been reinstituted in late 1950 and 1951 were discontinued in 1953.

In the years immediately following the Korean war, most organized groups in agriculture desired a reduction in governmental controls— less governmental participation in the economic affairs of agriculture. This was especially true of the largest general farm organization, the American Farm Bureau Federation.

Despite moderate and continued declines in farm prices and farm income beginning in 1953, a substantial number of farmers and farm leaders, for a period of years, continued to urge further reductions in government programs relating to agriculture.

When the Secretary of Agriculture in the mid-1950's attempted to require "cross compliance," that is, planting within all acreage allotments assigned to the farm in order to be eligible for the benefits under any single program, political opposition was so strong that the Secretary rescinded his order. Amid much advocacy of giving farmers more freedom on the part of government leaders, price-support levels were lowered moderately and production controls were eased.

Toward the end of the 1950's, however, it became evident that under the conditions of rapid technological advance, free competition in agriculture was incompatible with the maintenance of reasonably stable and satisfactory prices and income.

Although farm people continued to talk about the desirability of minimizing government controls in peacetime, as agricultural output continued to increase faster than available market outlets expanded, more and more producers and farm leaders became reconciled to the development of peacetime government programs which would help producers balance supplies with available market outlets at stable prices.

REFERENCES

Benedict, Murray R., *Farm Policies of the United States, 1790-1950.* New York: Twentieth Century Fund, 1953.

"Farmers in a Changing World," *Yearbook of Agriculture,* U.S.D.A. (1940), pages 177-276, 297-326.

Gold, Bela, *Wartime Economic Planning in Agriculture,* Chapters 1, 3, 6, 10, 11, and 12. New York: Columbia University Press, 1949.

Shepherd, Geoffrey, *Agricultural Price Policy,* Chapters 3 and 4. Ames, Iowa: Iowa State College Press, 1947.

POINTS FOR DISCUSSION

1. What is a good classification of governmental activities relative to farmers?
2. Do any of these activities put farmers in a special "favored" class?
3. Trace the historical development and expansion of governmental activities in the field of agriculture.
4. Do you believe that wartime experiences with widespread controls was an important factor in farmers' desire to "get the government out of agriculture" in the early post-war years?
5. Is there any basis for believing that governmental activities relative to agriculture will decline in the years ahead?

CHAPTER 26

Policies to Reduce Risk
and Uncertainty

AMERICAN AGRICULTURE is profoundly affected by the risks and uncertainties inherent in the commitment of resources over time in producing foods and fibers in an exchange economy. Entrepreneurship involves assuming these risks and uncertainties. The farmer, as an entrepreneur, makes decisions regarding the borrowing of funds, the amounts of different crops and livestock to produce, and the amount to invest in capital improvements. These risks and uncertainties fall under two general headings, those inherent in the technological production processes, since agricultural production is influenced by variable climatic conditions and periodic pest and disease outbreaks, and those inherent in a highly dynamic exchange economy where resources are committed in production processes months or years before the final product reaches the market.

Meeting immediate technological uncertainty. Two major sources of uncertainty in carrying out short-term farming plans are technological rather than economic in nature. They are variations in the weather and possibilities of disease or pest infestations. Uncertainty also exists in many biological processes. Thus, farmers save extra females for their breeding herds in order to compensate for any nonbreeders.

Farmers take account of weather uncertainty in their farming practices, their rotation of crops, and their harvesting methods. We have already noted that the possibility of an unusually dry year keeps farmers from applying as much fertilizer as normally would be profitable. Farmers follow conservation practices adapted to checking erosion in the event of a hard rain. In the Great Plains states,

where wind erosion is a problem, farmers follow cultivating practices designed to minimize the hazards of wind erosion. Examples of
management practices in crop production that do not increase output under normal weather conditions, but minimize reductions in
yield under adverse conditions, could be made indefinitely. The successful farm manager is skilled in deciding how much to invest in
these practices which help assure satisfactory yields under less than
optimum conditions.

Uncertainty regarding possible disease and pest outbreaks gives
rise to two sets of management practices. The first and most important is often called a preventive, or sanitation, program. Livestock
disease outbreaks are minimized by isolating new animals for a
reasonable period and keeping the livestock quarters clean. In the
case of hogs, poultry, and sheep, disease infestations are reduced by
rotating their pasture lands. Vaccination with preventive serums is
rapidly developing as a disease control measure. For years, it has
been possible to prevent outbreaks of hog cholera by vaccinating
the animals when they are young. Successful vaccines have been developed for other diseases in swine and for several diseases of cattle
and of chickens. Farmers decide whether or not to incur the expense
of vaccination for a disease largely on the basis of the probability
of an infestation occurring in the absence of vaccination. The risk of
the financial loss, resulting from an outbreak of the disease, is another
deciding factor (as it should be). The farmer with 25 hens seldom
vaccinates his poultry, although the large flock owner does, nor does
the farmer with 10 to 15 pigs vaccinate for hog cholera or follow
the system of putting his pigs in a new pasture each season. The
farmer with 100 to 1,000 pigs cannot afford the financial uncertainty
of disease infestations that can be prevented by vaccination and sanitation programs and, therefore, he does adopt these measures.

As a general principle, we can say that an important function of
management is making decisions regarding technical practices that
do not increase physical output under optimum conditions, but which,
under less than optimum conditions, may keep output from falling
sharply. All too often, however, the farm manager fails to undertake
the necessary technical practices to assure himself of a good output
under less than optimum conditions. This is especially true, even
though the cost is very small, if it is a relatively new practice.

All-risk crop insurance. The farmer cannot protect himself against
the majority of the many risks and uncertainties he encounters in
farming. He can, however, insure himself against fire or windstorm
damage to his buildings, equipment, and supplies; theft of his automobile and equipment; and personal injury or property damage to

other parties which might be caused by his automobile, equipment or livestock. Farmers in some areas may be able to insure certain of their crops against damage by hailstorms, but, in the past, other weather risks have been of such a nature as to prevent their successful transference to insurance companies.

In the 1930's farm leaders believed that with government research and experience it would be possible to develop an all-risk crop insurance which would result in a substantial reduction in the risk and uncertainties inherent in crop production. Accordingly, legislation was passed authorizing the creation of a wholly government-owned crop insurance corporation. It offered agricultural producers crop insurance providing protection from losses caused by such natural hazards, as insects and wildlife, plant diseases, fire, drought, flood, wind, and other weather conditions.

After experiencing heavy losses in its early years, the Federal Crop Insurance program was reorganized in 1947 and authorized to continue on a limited experimental basis. As a result, from 1948 to 1958, premiums collected equalled losses incurred. Much progress also has been made in developing a standard policy to cover all important crops grown on farms which raise several crops. Under this standard policy the production of all crops on the farm is used to determine whether or not a loss has occurred. Unless a general loss occurs, no insurance payment is made.

Premiums charged for Federal Crop Insurance are determined in large part by the history of losses in each individual county in which the Federal Crop Insurance program operates. In this way the premium rates for insurance are much higher in the western parts of such states as Nebraska and the Dakotas, where the crop production hazards are greater, than in the eastern parts of these states.

In 1958 Federal Crop Insurance was available in more than 800 counties with insurance coverage available on wheat, cotton, flax, corn, tobacco, beans, citrus, multiple crops, soybeans, barley, peaches, oranges, and grain sorghum. Although this insurance was available in more than one-fourth of the counties in the United States and the total value of crops produced in these counties probably exceeded $4 billion, insurance coverage in 1958 amounted only to $310 million. This suggests that only a minority of the farmers have found Federal Crop Insurance attractive.

Experience to date with this all-risk crop insurance indicates that in the high-risk areas, premium rates are so high that producers are unwilling to pay them. This type of crop insurance appears to be most attractive to producers in the moderate-risk areas where losses are less frequent and less severe and the premium rates are lower.

Even in these areas, however, crop insurance may become less popular when premiums are increased to the level necessary to cover administrative costs as well as crop losses.

As late as 1958 the government was paying the administrative costs involved in operating the crop insurance program although definite plans had been made gradually to increase premium rates and shift all administrative costs to the users of crop insurance. Many people fear that if and when premiums are raised to the level required to pay all costs, farmers will not voluntarily purchase such insurance in sufficient volume to permit it to play an important role in reducing the hazards and uncertainties of farming.

Diversification and outlook information. The time-honored method of adjusting farming operations to minimize the adverse effects of both unfavorable weather and price changes is to produce a variety of products for the market. Diversified farming not only reduces technological and price uncertainties, but, as was pointed out in earlier chapters, it also may make possible more complete utilization of the land, labor, and machinery on the farm. Diversification is most successful, however, in reducing variability of both output and income when weather conditions are not far from normal and when demand conditions are normal. All crops fail in years of extreme droughts and all prices fall when demand slackens because of unemployment.

When the sharp fall in prices occurred after World War I and agricultural economists were searching for ways and means of helping farmers improve their incomes, the government and the land-grant colleges (in an effort to help them improve their economic situation) launched a new "Agricultural Outlook Service" for farmers. In 1923 a National Agricultural Outlook Conference was called to study and evaluate farmers' economic problems. The economists attending this conference not only analyzed the economic situation for the major agricultural products but forecast the probable economic conditions for the coming year.

Similar annual conferences have been held each year since 1923, with economists from the land-grant colleges and those of the United States Department of Agriculture in attendance. By analyzing, interpreting, and relating the mass of information on supplies, consumer demand and prices for the various agricultural products, these professional economists provide farmers with a valuable economic service. Diversified farmers who have the opportunity to shift resources among several alternative enterprises find this service especially helpful.

Despite the fact that all statements about the future are only estimates, for the most part, the outlook reports have correctly forecast coming economic changes. Farmers can anticipate future economic changes and thereby make appropriate adjustments in their farming operations by following these reports.

The United States Department of Agriculture issues outlook, or, what are more appropriately called "situation" reports one to twelve times a year on 20 to 25 different subjects of interest to farmers. Situation reports are issued from four to six times a year for such commodities as cotton, dairy products, livestock and meat, poultry and eggs, and wheat. A demand and price situation report is issued monthly while the farm cost situation and the fertilizer situation reports are issued annually. Many land-grant colleges also issue outlook reports on a monthly or periodic basis throughout the year. These outlook analyses by professional agricultural economists, when properly applied, reduce somewhat the economic uncertainty farmers face when planning their breeding, seeding, and marketing operations.

Technological advance in agriculture in recent years, requiring high capital investments in specialized equipment, has resulted in greater specialization, less diversification, and less opportunity to make short term adjustments in farming plans based on outlook information. Larger amounts of credit also are required to finance the increased investment in specialized equipment and to permit operators to achieve the scale of operations necessary for the realization of minimum production costs. The increased vulnerability of specialized producers to fluctuations in prices and a more complete realization of the costs of these fluctuations in recent years, has led to the development of several proposals for further reducing the risk and uncertainty associated with fluctuating market prices.

Forward prices. One of the original proposals called for the establishment of a forward-pricing system, to announce a series of assured government prices or their equivalent in advance of the planting or breeding season.[1] The basic aspects of a forward-pricing system as outlined by Johnson and others who advocated its adoption were as follows:

1. The prices should be announced sufficiently far in advance to enable farmers to adjust their production programs to the prices.
2. The announced and guaranteed prices should cover a sufficient period of time to permit farmers to complete their production and marketing plans with considerable certainty.
3. The price announcements should be sufficiently clear and precise so that each farmer could readily interpret their implications for him.
4. The prices adopted should be those that would keep farm production in line with demand commodity by commodity.

---

[1] For a comprehensive and analytical treatment of this proposal, see D. Gale Johnson, *Forward Prices for Agriculture* (Chicago: University of Chicago Press, 1947).

The production period for crops would be considered the time that is required for planning, planting or seeding, growing, harvesting, and marketing the crop in any one year. Farmers need about sixteen months to plan for, raise, and sell hogs and lambs. They need about the same amount of time to plan and carry out a year's egg production. A forward price covering a period of sixteen to eighteen months has been suggested for milk production. Greater difficulties are encountered in establishing the period which should be covered by forward prices for beef cattle although about eighteen months would cover the longest time span required for planning and carrying through the usual grain-fattening operations for feeder cattle.

The announcement of forward prices for competing products, and of the factors used in their production, would have to be coordinated to be most useful to producers. Two basic rules have been suggested as appropriate guides in the determination of the length of period covered and the timing of the announcement of a system of forward prices: (1) Producers should be given sufficient time to compare alternative production opportunities under the announced forward prices, and (2) the prices should extend sufficiently far into the future to permit completion of marketings.

A system of forward prices as outlined above would not be a system of stable prices. Rather, it would be a system of prices approximating free market prices except that the prices would be determined and announced before the planting and breeding seasons rather than at the time the products were marketed. Prices for individual products would vary as necessary from one production period to the next to encourage increased production of some products and decreased production of others. The important advantage of a system of forward prices for producers is that the element of price uncertainty largely would be removed. Farmers could undertake their production plans using credit as needed with the assurance that when the product was ready for market the expected prices would be realized. The proponents of a system of forward prices suggest that if market prices should fall below the announced levels, rather than attempt government action to maintain market prices, government payments could be used to make up the difference between what the producers received at marketing time and what they would have received at the announced minimum forward price levels.

The removal of future price uncertainty by a system of forward prices made effective through compensatory government payments in cases where market prices fell below announced levels, would result in increased efficiency in the use of resources in food and fiber production. Credit could be used more widely in making investments needed for technological advance and to increase the size of business as needed to lower production costs. Present misdirection in the uses of farm land, capital and labor as a result of fluctuating market prices would be avoided. The additional price certainty gained by a system of forward prices would permit relative farm prices to function far more effectively in their primary role—that of guiding production—than is possible at the present time when the price level at the time the product is ready for market can only be guessed at when the seed is put in the ground or the breeding operations are undertaken.

Modified forward prices. Gray, Sorenson, and Cochrane,[2] reviewing the price and production responses in potato production, have suggested a modified forward price system for potatoes regardless of whether or not forward prices are adopted for other commodities. They found that both prices and the production of potatoes vary greatly from year to year with a tendency for producers to over-adjust to price changes. (See Figure 26-1.)

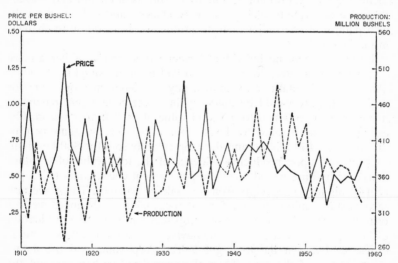

Fig. 26-1. Deflated seasonal average price and production of potatoes in the United States, 1910-58. (Price deflated by the index of prices received for all farm products.)

Their suggestion for reducing these annual fluctuations involves announcing an assured price for a supply of potatoes equal to but no greater than estimated requirements. At the same time the gov-

---

[2] Roger W. Gray, Vernon L. Sorenson, and Willard W. Cochrane, "An Economic Analysis of the Impact of Government Programs on the Potato Industry of the United States," *Technical Bulletin 211* (Minnesota Agricultural Experiment Station), pages 178-184.

ernment would announce lower guaranteed total crop values for quantities in excess of estimated requirements. The total crop values for supplies in excess of estimated requirements would be determined with reference to the demand curve for potatoes with an elasticity of demand of perhaps −0.5. Although a schedule of prices and total crop values assuming a demand elasticity of −0.5 would discourage excessive production it would be less inelastic than the demand in the market. Hence the assured crop values would decline less for large crops than in a free market and the annual incomes of potato producers would be more stable than in a completely free market.

The authors make the point that potatoes are one of the commodities for which the demand is extremely inelastic and for which price and production changes following the cobweb pattern explained in Chapter 15 are typical. The government by announcing a series of prices and total crop values which decline after estimated requirements are met, yet do not decline as sharply as in the market, reduces the price uncertainty facing potato producers, and reduces the cobweb pattern of over-adjustment in production in response to changes in market prices.

Under this plan no individual farmer would receive either a price or a value guarantee. After the crop had been marketed, so that the quantities and values were known, any deficiency in crop value for a given quantity would be made up in direct government payments to farmers, apportioned to the total value of each farmer's crop. For example, if the assured total value for a crop of the quantity produced were $460 million and the crop actually sold for $400 million, each farmer, upon producing evidence of the total value of potatoes marketed by him, would receive a government check equal to 15 per cent of his market receipts from the sale of potatoes. This price and income stabilization proposal for potatoes maintains the incentives for orderly marketing throughout the crop season and for the production of high quality potatoes, since the payment is based on the percentage difference between the total guaranteed crop value and the actual market value of the crop. Thus, the guaranteed cash receipts of the producer is increased by a flat percentage applied to his market receipts. This plan also avoids the many problems which are associated with direct price supports such as administrative determination of relative prices for different locations, different grades and qualities, and for different periods in the marketing season.

An expanded system of future markets. Some economists have suggested that an expanded futures market rather than a system of forward prices might be developed for farm products as a means of reducing the uncertainties which arise out of month-to-month and year-to-year price variations. Commodities such as corn, wheat and cotton, which can be stored and which can be bought and sold on the basis of federal grade specifications, for many years have been bought and sold for delivery some months in the future. In these futures markets buyers and sellers enter into contracts to deliver and to accept delivery within specified future time periods. Trading rules require that the product tendered for settlement of the contract must meet cerain minimum grade specifications.

At the present time few producers sell their products in the futures market at planting time. Rather, futures markets are used largely by the marketing agencies and processors as a means of protecting themselves against unexpected price changes while conducting their commercial processing operations.

If futures markets were developed to the point that producers at planting or breeding time could sell their products for delivery at harvest time or when they were ready for market much of the uncertainty associated with future price variations would be eliminated. This is not an entirely new idea. For many years vegetable-canning companies, in advance of planting time, have entered into firm contracts with growers with respect to prices to be paid for the canning crops at harvest. A few other processors and handlers of special products such as pure strains of seeds enter into contracts with producers before planting time, agreeing upon prices to be paid for the product when it is ready for sale.

Usually products are produced on the basis of contract prices when the product is so specialized that there are only one or two possible purchasers. The local canning or sugar-beet company is the only sales outlet for producers of sugar beets or of crops for canning. Under these conditions the processing company enters into contracts before planting time in order to assure itself of a supply that can be processed profitably and producers do not plant the crop unless they are assured of a market outlet by entering into a contract with the processor.

No doubt there are many reasons why futures markets have not developed to the point where producers can sell crops at planting time for delivery after harvest. One of the most important reasons, however, is that price uncertainty is a risk which must be borne by someone or some group in the economic system and future prices that processors and speculators are willing to offer at planting time usually are so low as to be unattractive to producers. Most producers prefer to assume the risk of still lower prices at harvest time than those offered in the futures market at planting time in the hope that when the crop is harvested market prices will be higher. Although the price risks and uncertainties in farming are high, it appears that no other group in society is willing to assume them at a cost which farmers are willing to pay. As in the case of government all-risk crop insurance, most farmers prefer to carry the risk themselves rather than accept future prices which prevail at the breeding or planting time.

Compensatory payments. During World War II and in the years immediately following, agricultural economists investigated a number of alternative policies for stabilizing farm prices and income against business cycle fluctuations, especially against a decline in demand for food and fiber resulting from substantial unemployment such as occurred in the 1930's.

A number of these investigations resulted in recommendations that market prices be allowed to perform their function of guiding production, and in directing products into consumption. Further, a system of compensatory payments should be followed to reduce the instability of farm income caused by business cycle fluctuations.[3] Ideally such a system of compensatory payments would make the payments:

1. In a manner and at a time that would give a counter-cyclical effect,
2. In such a way as to minimize their effect on agricultural production and trade, and
3. In an amount and at such a time as to substantially stabilize farm income.

Certain indices or statistical series were to be used to determine when to start and stop compensatory payments. Rather than relying on the level of farm prices to determine when compensatory payments are needed and justified, it was suggested that a composite index which would measure the state of economic activity of the nonagricultural sectors of the economy be employed as an automatic indicator.

Two varieties of compensatory payments. Compensatory payments were first suggested as a substitute for individual commodity price supports; they would be used to make up the difference between the seasonal market average and, say, 85 per cent of the pre-depression prices of the more important farm products. A compensatory plan of this type might be illustrated as follows: If, during a depression, the seasonal market average prices of corn, wheat, and potatoes dropped below an announced support level by, say $.10 a bushel on corn, $.25 a bushel on wheat, and $.25 a bushel on pota-

---

[3] For a comprehensive analysis of several types of compensatory payment plans, see Geoffrey S. Shepherd, *Agricultural Price Policy,* Chapters 26-28 (Ames, Iowa: Iowa State College Press, 1947).

toes, a farmer who produced these crops would get a payment from the government equal to the amount of the seasonal price deficiency multiplied by the number of bushels of each crop sold during the season.

A compensatory payment program of this type stabilizes the effective price of individual commodities at some percentage of the pre-depression level, yet individual producers continue to receive premiums for quality. Producers also continue to have an incentive to follow orderly marketing procedures throughout the season since the payment is related to the difference between the seasonal market average and the announced support price level rather than between the actual price received by the producer and the support price level.

Several agricultural economists have proposed that the compensatory payments be based on total farm income rather than on the seasonal price disparities of individual products. The essential features of an income payment plan may be illustrated as follows: The government might agree to support all farm prices as an aggregate at, say, 85 per cent of their pre-depression level. It might do this by offering to increase each farmer's income from the sale of farm products by a percentage equal to the percentage increase required to bring the annual index of all farm prices up to the announced support level. If the government agreed to make up the difference between the annual average and an index level equal to 85 per cent of the pre-depression price level, the computations would be relatively simple. If market prices fell to 77 per cent of the pre-depression base, an increase of approximately 10 per cent would be required to bring them up to the 85 per cent level. Each farmer could then submit evidence of his total sales and the appropriate payment would be one equal to 10 per cent of his sales. In this way, farmers in the aggregate would receive income from crop and livestock sales plus payments equal to the income they would have received from crop and livestock sales if prices had averaged 85 per cent of the pre-depression base period. (Some adjustments would have to be made for inter-farm sales, however.)

In principle, either of these systems of compensatory payments is an improvement over the practice of allowing farm income to decline sharply when the demand for food falls off because of unemployment. These systems are an improvement over the practice of maintaining stable prices by reducing production and marketing in depression periods. During depression periods there are as many people in the country in need of food as in boom periods. No social gains are achieved by reducing the level of farm production during such periods merely because consumers do not have the incomes they had in the pre-depression years. Compensatory payments tend to stabilize farm income, yet permit production of farm products to be maintained at pre-depression levels and the price of food to decline as necessary to clear the market.

The compensatory income payment plan which merely increases farmers' total income by a percentage would allow more flexibility in the incentives to change production patterns than one which stabilized the returns for individual crops. Thus, even though the price of potatoes fell more than the price of corn in the depression period, under the compensatory payment plan based on individual prices, the returns to both potato and corn growers would be made up (by payments) to the same 85 per cent of the pre-depression prices. Under the income payment plan, however, potato growers' returns would be lower than corn growers' returns, as a result of the greater decline in potato prices. The proportionately lower farm income of the potato growers and the higher income of the corn growers would be increased by an equal percentage.

Weakness of forward prices and compensatory payments. In spite of the apparent advantages that the systems of forward prices and compensatory payments have in reducing the uncertainty resulting from short-term market price and longer-run business cycle fluctuations, these plans have never won widespread political support. Instead, as will be pointed out in the following chapter, relatively stable price supports on the more important crops, that can be stored, have been continued from year to year.

Soon after the advantages of a system of forward prices were outlined, a modified version of this idea was incorporated in existing farm price-support legislation. The government was required to announce price-support levels in advance of the planting season, rather than at the beginning of the harvest as had often been done in earlier years. But farm people have been unwilling to accept the level of prices implicit in a system of forward prices as outlined. They have insisted on the maintenance of relatively stable support price levels regardless of the prices needed "to keep production in line with demand commodity by commodity."

The political problems involved in administering a system of forward prices in line with the requirements outlined earlier in this chapter appear to be almost insuperable. Price levels largely determine farm family income levels over short periods of time. For this reason, since both the demand for and supply of farm products are highly inelastic, it seems unlikely that any legislative body would delegate sufficient authority to an administrative agency to permit it to publish prices which would keep production in line with demand.

This is especially true under conditions of rapid technological advance where supplies increase more rapidly than market outlets.

Farm leaders, and farm people generally, also lack confidence in government payments as a dependable source of income. In the past, although Congress has been generous in its actions as related to farmers, it often has been erratic. Few farm leaders would feel that they had reduced their uncertainty with respect to future farm income if a substantial part of it was to come from government payments rather than from marketings of farm products at stable prices.

Although a system of compensatory payments may become more acceptable if a serious and extended depression occurs some time in the future, it seems unlikely that it will ever be accepted by farm leaders as other than an uncertain and inferior substitute for direct supply and price stabilization plans.

Farm income insurance. From time to time proposals have been advanced for self-financing farm income stabilization measures. One of the simplest of these was proposed by Professor Shepherd in 1947.[4] It would collect special income or processing taxes in boom periods when farm income rose above a certain point and make income stabilization payments to farmers when their income fell below that point by a certain amount. Shepherd's proposal is similar to the compensatory income payment plans in that the payments to individual farmers in the depression period would be proportional to gross income. He does suggest, however, that a part of the total fund for payments might be ear-marked for standard-of-living payments. Then, if net income plus payments fell below a minimum standard-of-living level for some families, additional payments would be available to them, based in part on the number of children in the family.

Another proposal in this field would provide income insurance for farm operators through a program similar to unemployment insurance for non-farm workers.[5] Farm operators might pay a small premium into an income insurance fund, based on both their farm and non-farm income. The Federal government also might make matching payments.

The insured income for each farm operator in a given year could be fixed at, say, 75 per cent of his base income. In any year in which his net earnings from self-employment on the farm and from non-farm activities fell below the insured income level, cash benefits would be paid out of the insurance fund. The payments would equal the

[4] Geoffrey S. Shepherd, *Agriculture Price Policy,* Chapter 28 (Ames, Iowa: Iowa State College Press, 1947).

[5] Boris C. Swerling, "Income Protection for Farmers: A Possible Approach," *The Journal of Political Economy* (April 1959), pages 173-186.

difference between the operator's earnings for the year and the insured income level, say 75 per cent of his earnings for the previous three years. An upper limit on net earnings might be set at the Old Age, Survivors and Disability Insurance maximum of $4,800 for purposes of computing both premiums and benefits in order to limit the insurance to something approaching a minimum income level.

An insurance plan of this type, would remove much of the uncertainty operators of moderate-sized farms have concerning year-to-year income. Income losses due to weather, disease, or any other physical factor, as well as those due to a fall in prices, would be insured against by such a plan. It seems probable, however, that unless the government contributes a substantial part of the premium payments, as in the case of all-risk crop insurance, farmers may prefer to assume the risks themselves rather than pay the premiums required for income insurance.

REFERENCES

Halcrow, Harold G., *Agricultural Policy of the United States*, Chapters 10 and 13. Englewood Cliffs, N.J.: Prentice-Hall, Inc., 1953.

Johnson, D. Gale, *Forward Prices for Agriculture,* Chapters 4 and 8. Chicago: The University of Chicago Press, 1947.

Schultz, T. W., *Agriculture in an Unstable Economy*, Chapter 10. New York: McGraw-Hill Book Company, Inc., 1945.

Shepherd, Geoffrey S., *Agricultural Price Policy*, Chapters 26-28. Ames, Iowa: The Iowa State College Press, 1947.

POINTS FOR DISCUSSION

1. What practices are followed in your farming area to reduce technological uncertainty over short periods of time?
2. What practices are followed to reduce price uncertainty over short periods of time?
3. What practices are followed to reduce price uncertainty over longer periods of time?
4. To what extent is the principle of forward prices utilized in existing price support programs?
5. To what extent are production contracts used in your farming area to reduce price uncertainty at time of marketing?
6. What are the major advantages of compensatory payments over other possible programs for stabilizing farm income against business cycle fluctuations? What are their limitations?

CHAPTER 27

Recent Price and Income Programs in Agriculture

THE FARM PRICE-SUPPORT PROGRAMS in operation at the present time are a direct outgrowth of earlier programs dating as far back as the 1920's. Changes in farm programs throughout the past thirty years have been evolutionary rather than revolutionary in character. When farm prices fell sharply following World War I and failed to recover their prewar relationship with the prices of nonfarm products, Congress authorized special intermediate-term agricultural credits for farmers and ranchers. This credit legislation was followed within a few years by the Capper-Volstead Act giving agricultural cooperatives a special status within the framework of antitrust legislation.

McNary-Haugen and Farm Board objectives. When, in spite of additional credit and the best efforts of farmer cooperatives, agriculture continued to lag behind the nonfarm sectors of the economy in the mid-1920's, leaders proposed legislation designed "to make the tariff effective" for such major agricultural export crops as wheat, cotton, and tobacco. These proposals became the McNary-Haugen bills authorizing exports at lower than domestic prices. The bills passed both Houses of Congress in 1927 and again in 1928, but were vetoed both times by President Coolidge.

The Agricultural Marketing Act of 1929, creating a Federal farm board with a stabilization fund of $500,000,000 was a direct outgrowth of the unsuccessful attempts to get the McNary-Haugen proposals enacted into law. This act was endorsed by President Hoover as a substitute for the proposal to increase the domestic price level for the major export crops relative to the world level. The Federal Farm Board had two major responsibilities: that of strengthening farmer cooperatives, and that of engaging in direct price stabilization

491

operations utilizing the $500,000,000 revolving funds made available to it. Mr. Alexander Legge, former president of the International Harvester Company, was recruited by President Hoover as the first chairman of the Board. In the first year of the Board's operation he was invited to appear before the critical United States Chamber of Commerce. In addressing the members of this body on April 30, 1930, he had the following to say about the background and general purposes of the Federal Farm Board:

. . . Nearly ten years of discussion, controversy and compromise led Congress, in its wisdom, to declare that permanent solution of the agricultural problem lies in collective action on the part of the farmers. It created the Farm Board to help producers organize for such action, both as to production and marketing of their crops, the purpose being to enable them to put their industry on economic parity with other industries. In that legislation Congress definitely committed this country to the principle of cooperative marketing of farm products.

. . . When it became apparent that a means had been provided that really would help the farmer to get organized cooperatively so that he, like other producers, would have some voice in determining the sale price of his commodity, the effort was branded as government price-fixing, putting the Government in business, and so forth. . . .

I do not recall in years gone by of hearing you business men making any such complaint against this Government aid that was extended to the manufacturing industry, to transportation and to finance. And these all played their part in adding to the disadvantages of the farmer as did also the preferential treatment to labor through immigration restriction and other measures.

We are not complaining about what the Government has done for others but it does seem to us that these beneficiaries ought to be willing that the farmer also be given a helping hand from the same source so that he, too, will be in position to take care of himself in the economic system that has been built up in this country so largely by special favors.

Protection of industry started over a hundred years ago in a tariff act that levied a twenty per cent ad valorem duty. During all these years the farmers have continued producing the staple commodities, looking forward to the time when they should get some relief from their country —and they are still waiting. Is it not about time that the farmer should be given some of this aid?

Is there any reason why those who have prospered and grown apace through governmental aid and assistance to various industries should object to the farmer getting his? . . .

. . . You fellows, better organized, got yours while the farmer, unorganized, failed to get anything. . . .

The farmers have little or nothing to say about what their product brings. Costs of production can be passed along to the buyer by nearly everyone but the farmer. Unorganized, he has to take for his produce what the other fellow is willing to give him.[1]

Early beginnings of production controls. Unfortunately, the depression of the 1930's began about the same time that the Federal Farm Board started its operations. Economic conditions deteriorated rapidly and the Farm Board soon found all its stabilization funds committed, yet farm prices continued to fall. Alexander Legge, drawing on his experience as former president of the International Harvester Company, soon became convinced that farmers should restrict the production of wheat and other major crops in view of the sharp decline in farm prices.

Mr. Legge addressed farm audiences in many parts of the United States, advising them that the Federal Farm Board could not improve farm prices and incomes unless there was a reduction in supplies offered for sale in the markets.[2] He was not alone in his belief in the necessity of production controls if farmers were to realize better prices. Most farm leaders, acquainted with the inability of the Federal Farm Board to improve economic conditions for farmers, were of the opinion that an adjustment (restriction) in the production of the major farm crops was needed at that time. When the Democrats took office as a result of the elections in 1932 they promptly sponsored passage of an Agricultural Adjustment Act. This act authorized production adjustment programs; a direct outgrowth of the experience of the Federal Farm Board. The Agricultural Adjustment Act of 1933 also authorized the use of marketing agreements and marketing orders which had been used successfully on a small scale by California producers to promote orderly marketing of perishable fruits and vegetables.

The first acreage adjustment programs for cotton, tobacco, wheat, corn, and hogs were financed by special funds made available by new taxes levied on the sale of these products to processors. These new taxes often were referred to as processing taxes. Generally speaking, each processing tax was set at a level which would create the funds needed to make attractive rental-benefit payments to producers for

---

[1] *The Agricultural Marketing Act,* addresses and general discussion (Washington, D.C.: Chamber of Commerce, 1930), pages 13-14.

[2] Forrest Crissey, *Legge, Alexander, 1866-1933* (Privately Printed, 1936), page 201. In his letter of resignation to President Hoover he said, "While there are still a few of the agricultural leaders who lower their voices when they speak of production control yet practically all of them have accepted the principle as essential." (page 206).

limiting their production to two-thirds or three-quarters of their recent level of ouput.

Production adjustment or control in the first Agricultural Adjustment Program was conceived of as entirely voluntary. It was planned to make the rental-benefit payments so attractive for holding the production of the selected crops and hogs at levels about one-third lower than in the previous three years that almost all producers would gladly enter into production adjustment agreements with the government. The crop acreage history was assembled for every farm in the United States where the products, listed above, were produced on a commercial basis. Each producer was offered a rental-benefit payment for limiting his acreage or limiting his marketings, in the case of hogs, to about two-thirds that of recent years.

It was believed that an adjustment in the market supplies of these more important farm products brought about in this voluntary manner would result in substantial improvement in the prices of these products. Farm leaders believed that an adjustment program for the major products, by reducing aggregate farm output, would indirectly result in an improvement in the prices of the less important farm products. Within the first year of its operation, however, the Agricultural Adjustment Program departed from its voluntary character with respect to tobacco and cotton. In order to achieve the desired results more promptly, the administration also shifted from complete reliance on production restrictions to achieve price and income improvement to the use of price supporting loans in conjunction with the adjustment program.

In the case of tobacco and cotton, producers showed such unanimity in desiring production adjustments to improve market prices that they secured the passage of additional legislation assessing high taxes on any tobacco or cotton produced on acreages not included in the acreage allotments announced under the voluntary adjustment programs for those crops. Also, in the fall of 1933 market prices of corn and cotton at harvest time had not yet responded to the adjustment program to the extent that could be expected if a similar program were continued for another year or two. In order to assure farmers' prices for their 1933 crops in line with prices which might be expected if the adjustment program were continued, the Secretary of Agriculture made available loans on cotton and corn at levels in excess of current market prices. These loans made available by the Secretary of Agriculture in the fall of 1933 mark the beginning of our current government price-support loan operations. The government loans were made to producers on the basis that if the market price did not rise to the level of the loan rate before the date for repayment, the producer might deliver his crop to the government in full repayment of the loan. Since these loans could be repaid in full by delivery of the crop regardless of its current market price, they were called "non-recourse" loans—no other property of the producer was obligated for repayment of the loans.

Objectives of agricultural programs in the 1930's. Throughout the 1930's, the Agricultural Adjustment Program attempted to adjust annual supplies of the major crops and marketings of the perishable crops in line with available market outlets at satisfactory prices. Marketing agreements and orders, which were authorized in the 1933 Act and strengthened by additional legislation in 1937, were utilized effectively by the producers of perishable fruits and vegetables and producers of milk for fluid use in city milksheds.

Marketing agreements and orders required a two-thirds majority vote on the part of producers before the Secretary of Agriculture could issue a marketing order which was binding on all producers and all handlers of the product. The more common provisions of marketing orders for fruits and vegetables have been regulations with respect to the minimum grade and size of the product which may be sold in commercial markets. Such marketing regulations tend to reduce quantities moving to market when production is greater than can be sold at satisfactory prices. Such regulations usually have been accompanied by a diversion program for the unacceptable grades and sizes of the product. Often the diversion program has been financed by government purchases utilizing funds from custom receipts which were earmarked for surplus removal activities for perishable products by Congress in 1935.

Marketing agreements and orders for fluid milk differed somewhat from the typical market orders for perishable fruits and vegetables. They had as their main objective the establishment of uniform producer prices and uniform market prices of the milk sold to the distributors, on the basis of its use. Sugar producers always have been in a special category. Since the United States imports much of its sugar, special legislation was passed in the 1930's allocating the domestic market between domestic producers, and Cuban and other offshore producers, and providing for supplementary payments to domestic producers from a special tax on all sugar.

A Supreme Court decision in 1936 declared that the collection of processing taxes to finance government production adjustment contracts with individual producers was in violation of the Federal Constitution, with the individual states having the right to legislate in this area. The entire production adjustment program was discontinued temporarily and the special tobacco and cotton production control programs were repealed. Before the 1936 crop was planted, however, production adjustment was made an integral part of the popular, relatively new nationwide soil conservation program.

Where the earlier program had been made possible by the collection of processing taxes and use of the funds to pay farmers for reducing their acreages of specific crops, the substitute program adopted after the Court decision was financed from general treasury receipts. Farmers were promised payments after harvest if they increased the acreage of close-growing soil-conserving crops and reduced the acreage of soil-depleting, intertilled and small-grain crops. Performance and payments were based on the amount of shift in acreages found on the farm at harvest time as compared with previous cropping practices.

Two years of experience with this type of program convinced farm leaders that a more effective program was needed to stabilize supplies and prices of the major crops. After much discussion new legislation was passed in 1938 authorizing comprehensive supply adjustment programs for each of the major crops. This new legislation was based on the interstate commerce clause of the Constitution and has never been successfully challenged in the courts. The Secretary of Agriculture was directed to make non-recourse loans available to producers of the major storable crops within a range of 52 to 75 per cent of parity. The support level for several of the crops was specified by a formula which related the loan level to the size of the supply in relation to normal marketings.

This new legislation also authorized the Secretary of Agriculture to invoke marketing quotas upon the approval of two-thirds of the producers if supplies reached certain levels in relation to normal marketings. When marketing quotas were invoked by the Secretary of Agriculture, penalty taxes were imposed on any products grown on acreages in excess of those allotted by the Agricultural Adjustment Administration.

It will be noted that it was 1938 before revisions in the basic agricultural adjustment legislation made it mandatory for the Secretary of Agriculture to offer price-supporting loans on the major storable crops. By that time, however, government price-supporting loans had become one of the most popular features of the "farm program." During the 1930's it is fair to say that the general philosophy of the farm program was that of assisting producers to adjust their production and marketings to improve and stabilize farm prices and income in a period of continued unemployment. Officially, the over-all ob- jective was the attainment of farm prices which gave farmers a "parity" in purchasing power with non-farm groups—a purchasing power equivalent to that enjoyed by farm products in the period between 1910 and 1914.

1933 definition of parity. The parity idea, which is essentially an equity concept, was developed by farm leaders in the 1920's. Price indexes compiled by government agencies indicated that farm prices had fallen much more than non-farm prices following World War I. As public discussions of "farm relief" measures continued in the late 1920's, more and more attention was centered on the disparity be- tween the levels of the farm and non-farm price indexes.

In view of the widespread acceptance of the idea that the postwar disparity in these indexes should be corrected by appropriate govern- ment action, it is not surprising that the achievement of a parity in farmers' purchasing power was made the goal of the Agricultural Ad- justment Act of 1933. The parity goal is stated in the opening para- graph of the Agricultural Adjustment Act of 1933 as follows:

It is hereby declared to be the policy of Congress—(1) To establish and maintain such balance between the production and consumption of agricultural commodities, and such marketing conditions therefore, as will re-establish prices to farmers at a level that will give agricultural commodities a purchasing power with respect to articles farmers buy, equivalent to purchasing power of agricultural commodities in the base period. The base period in the case of all agricultural commodities except tobacco shall be the pre-war period, August 1909-July 1914. In the case of tobacco, the base period shall be the post-war period, August 1919- July 1929.

The computation of parity under this act of 1933 was simple. Let us take, as an example, the computation of the parity price for wheat in June 1933. The average price of wheat on farms in the United States from August 1909 to July 1914 was $.884 per bushel. Prices paid by farmers were 3 per cent higher in June 1933 than in the base period; thus, the index of prices paid stood at 103. The parity price for wheat in June 1933 was $.884 times 1.03, or $.91 per bushel. The actual United States farm price in that month was $.59 per bushel, or 64 per cent of parity.

Wartime modified farm program objectives. Wartime demands for food and fiber and for manpower in World War II furnished a temporary solution for two of agriculture's basic problems. One of these problems is the fundamental tendency for agricultural production to expand more rapidly than domestic and foreign markets can absorb the supplies at prevailing prices. The other is the long-run excess of manpower in farming.[3]

When general price-control legislation was adopted soon after the United States was drawn into World War II, in view of the continued low farm prices at that time, the Secretary of Agriculture was given the veto power over price ceilings on farm products. The most important single farm price action taken during the war period, however, was the so-called Steagall Amendment requiring government support of many farm prices for two years following the close of the war (Public Law 792, October 2, 1942). In a sense, the precedent for the Steagall Amendment grew out of the commodity loans started in the fall of 1933 and made available to farmers each year since that time. In another sense it was considered an equitable method of compensating farmers for submitting to price ceilings during World War II after experiencing many prewar years of low prices.

President Roosevelt in his message to Congress, September 2, 1942, said "As a part of our general program on farm prices, I recommend that Congress in due time give consideration to the advisability of legislation which would place a floor under prices of farm products, in order to maintain stability in the farm market for a reasonable future time. In other words, we should find a practicable method which will not only enable us to place a reasonable ceiling or maximum price upon farm products but which will enable us to guarantee to the farmer that he would receive a fair minimum price for his products for one year, or even two years—or whatever period is necessary after the end of the war."[4]

Early postwar objectives. The wartime price supports adopted under the Steagall Amendment expired at the close of 1948. Congress, anticipating their expiration, in the Agricultural Act of 1948, extended price supports to 1950 on a substantial list of farm products at 90 per cent of parity and provided a range of price supports from 60 to 90 per cent of parity after that. The 1938 legislation providing for the invocation of marketing quotas on the basic crops—cotton, corn, wheat, rice, tobacco, and peanuts—when supplies became excessive, came back into use.

During the war and early postwar years a shift in policy emphasis had occurred. In the prewar years the central purpose of the government farm program was adjustment in supplies. Price supporting loans were a supplement to the adjustment programs. In the 1948 and

---

[3] Walter W. Wilcox, *The Farmer in the Second World War* (Ames, Iowa: Iowa State College Press, 1947), page 6.

[4] House Report Number IV (Misc.), 77th Congress, 2nd session, page 2472.

subsequent postwar legislation, major interest centered on the man-datory price-support levels. Little thought was given to the problem of keeping production in line with available market outlets at the support price levels. Acreage allotments and marketing quotas as provided for in the 1938 legislation were believed to be adequate.

Shift to modernized parity formula. During the war years there was increasing criticism of the 1933 parity formula which had been modified only in the case of a few commodities by giving them more favorable base periods than the common 1910 to 1914 base period. As a result of this criticism statisticians developed an alternative method of computing parity prices which was incorporated in the Agricultural Act of 1948, generally known as the formula for "modernized" parity. This formula makes the pattern of parity prices dependent upon the market price relationships of the most recent ten-year period. At the same time, the average level of prices is determined by the level of the prices-paid index, computed on a 1910-1914 basis. In respect to the prices-paid index, the wages of farm labor were included in the index for the first time. The formula that accomplishes all this involves the following steps:

a. Compute the average United States farm price of the product in the ten most recent calendar or crop years.

b. Compute the average of the index of prices received by farmers on a January 1910 to December 1914 base during the same ten-year period.

c. Compute an "adjusted base price" for the product by dividing (a) by (b) and multiplying by 100.

d. Compute the parity price by multiplying the adjusted base price by the current index of prices paid by farmers (the parity index), on the 1910 to 1914 base, and dividing by 100.

Let us take, as an example, the computation of the parity price for corn for January 1959. The one-hundred-twenty-month (Jan-uary 1949 to December 1958) average price of corn was $1.41. The one-hundred-twenty-month average of the index of prices re-ceived by farmers was 256. Dividing $1.41 by 256 and multiplying by 100 gives $.55, the adjusted base price. Multiplying this adjusted base price by 298, the parity index for January 1959, gives a parity price for corn, using the modernized formula, of $1.64 per bushel. The average of prices received by farmers for corn in January 1959 was $1.02 per bushel or 62 per cent of parity.

For several years use was made of both the old and the new for-mula. Support prices for basic commodities (corn, cotton, wheat, tobacco, rice, and peanuts) through 1954 were based on the parity calculation (old or modernized) that resulted in the higher price. When the shift to the modernized parity was made, parity prices, as calculated by the new formula were not permitted to drop more than 5 per cent a year below what they would have been under the old formula. Prices arrived at in this manner were called transitional parity prices.

The use of the modernized parity formula results in each farm product having a parity price which bears the same relation to the parity prices of other farm products as their market price relationships bore to each other in the most recent ten-year period. At the same time, the period from 1910 to 1914 is maintained as the base period for the index of all farm parity prices. Thus, there is no change in the base period with respect to all farm prices under the modernized parity formula and a farm price parity ratio of 80 indicates that farm products as a group have 80 per cent as much purchasing power as they did from 1910 to 1914 in terms of supplies and services purchased by farm families for use in production and for family living.

Adoption of flexible price supports. At the close of World War II, the sharp controversy which developed with respect to the appropriate level of price supports for the major storable crops overshadowed all other developments. Dissatisfaction with the low levels of support provided in the 1948 Act led to an upward revision in the minimum levels for normal crops in 1949. Increased domestic and foreign demands for farm products as a result of the hostilities in Korea temporarily reversed the build-up in Commodity Credit Corporation stocks which took place in 1948 and 1949, and led to a renewal of legislation making price supports on basic commodities through 1954 mandatory at a minimum level of 90 per cent of parity.

1954 stands out in the postwar period as the year when the new Republican administration made its first fully-considered recommendations to Congress with respect to desirable changes in the farm program. In that year the temporary legislation requiring price supports for basic commodities at 90 per cent of parity expired. Whether or not to allow the earlier permanent legislation of 1949 to become operative, providing flexible supports within the range of 75 to 90 per cent of parity for the basic crops was a sharply debated issue. The administration and the largest farm organization took the position that flexible price supports in the long run would be most effective in stabilizing farm prices and incomes in a favorable relation to other sectors of the economy. They believed that price supports at 90 per cent of parity were pricing the products, cotton and corn especially, so high that they were stimulating increased production and utilization of competitive products. Supporters of flexible price supports also advanced the argument that with the lower price supports in effect, fewer government controls would be necessary.

Opponents of flexible price supports insisted that within the range of flexibility proposed, 75 to 90 per cent of parity, any reduction in price supports would have little effect on either production or sales. They urged the continuation of price supports on the basic crops at 90 per cent of parity on the grounds that lowering price supports would merely lower producers' incomes without either reducing production and the need for government controls or having any important stimulating effect on commercial marketings. The Agricultural Act of 1954, as it was finally approved, provided for a range of price supports from 82.5 to 90 per cent of parity for the 1955 crops of basic commodities and for price supports within the range of 75 to 90 per cent after 1955.

Objectives of related legislation. Congress, in the same session, where more flexible price supports were approved, passed an Agricultural Trade Development and Assistance Act which permits sales of surplus stocks of farm products in foreign countries for local currencies and donations of surplus stocks to needy people, both at home and abroad. This Act and related legislative actions authorizing special foreign and domestic distribution programs were put forward as temporary measures. Many of those sponsoring the legislation believed that temporary foreign and domestic supplemental distribution programs were needed only to liquidate the surplus accumulated in the last years of stable price supports.

Bountiful harvests and sagging livestock prices in the fall of 1955, however, caused farmer leaders to propose additional emergency action aimed at bringing supplies into balance with available market outlets at reasonably stable prices. The emergency action agreed upon in 1956 took the form of a Soil Bank program made up of two parts. One part was an acreage reserve program for the three years 1956, 1957, and 1958. Under the acreage reserve program, farmers were paid for renting a part of their allotted acreage of the basic price supported crops to the government. Under this program any producer who had an allotment to produce corn (in the commercial corn-producing area), cotton, wheat, peanuts, rice, or most types of tobacco, if in compliance with all other acreage allotments, might elect to put up to one-half or more of his allotted acreage in the Soil Bank. Acreages placed in the Soil Bank could be devoted to soil-conserving uses, but no crop could be harvested or pastured (except in drought areas).

Producers were compensated for putting their corn land in the

Soil Bank under the acreage reserve program by the payment of $.90 a bushel (national average rate) multiplied by the normal yield on their allotted acreage. Except where unfavorable weather prevailed, normal yields tended to be lower than current expected yields if corn were grown on the land. For this reason farmers' compensation for not growing corn under the Soil Bank program usually was less than $.90 a bushel.

The national average rates of payment to allotment holders of the other basic crops for putting up to one-half or more of their allotted acreage in the Soil Bank was as follows:

Wheat	$1.20 per bushel
Rice	2.25 per hundredweight
Cotton	.15 per pound
Peanuts	.03 per pound
Tobacco	.08 to .19 per pound

Many farmers had completed their spring plantings in 1956 before the Soil Bank regulations were announced in the counties. However, a total of 12.2 million acres were placed in the acreage reserve in 1956, 21.4 million acres in 1957, and 17.2 million acres in 1958. Payments for compliance under this program exceeded $600 million a year in 1957 and 1958 without the program achieving a noticeable reduction in production. Crop production equaled the previous all-time high in 1957 and exceeded all previous records by some 11 per cent in 1958. In view of its ineffectiveness and high cost, the acreage reserve feature of the Soil Bank program was discontinued after 1958.

The conservation reserve part of the Soil Bank was designed to assist producers to reduce production of crops through shifting acreages of cropland to long-range conservation uses, by sharing the cost of the establishment of conservation practices and by making an annual payment for keeping such acreages in the conservation reserve. Producers wishing to place any or all of their cropland in the conservation reserve were required to sign a contract retiring the land from crop production for a minimum of three years and it might be placed in the Soil Bank for a maximum of fifteen years if the land were planted with trees. The national average annual rate of payment for placing cropland in the conservation reserve through 1958 was $10 per acre. In 1959 the national average rate of payment was increased to about $13 per acre. In 1956 only 1.4 million acres were placed in the conservation reserve of the Soil Bank. By 1960, however, 28 million acres of below-average productivity cropland had been removed from crop production on a long-term basis.

After 1957 the conservation reserve program featured the rental and retirement of entire farms in the belief that in those instances in which whole farms were rented, the operator and his buildings and equipment also would be retired from agricultural production. Local tradesmen in the less-productive areas soon became alarmed about the adverse effects which would result for their community if a substantial number of farm operators placed their entire farms in the Soil Bank for a period of years. Objections of this type, and lack of evidence that production was appreciably reduced by this program costing in excess of $300 million a year, led farm leaders to look for other more effective supply control measures.

Temporary measures and lower support levels ineffective. Beginning in 1955 price supports were lowered, intensive efforts were made to expand commercial markets both at home and abroad, to develop extensive domestic and foreign surplus disposal programs, and to establish a Soil Bank program to hold 15 to 30 million acres of cropland out of production in 1956, 1957, and 1958. Yet these efforts to bring supplies into balance with market outlets available at stable prices were not notably successful. In the four and one-half years of surplus disposal operations ending December 31, 1958, the government bartered, sold for local currencies, and gave away at home and abroad $8 billion of farm products. In the same period total loans and inventories of farm products held by the Commodity Credit Corporation increased from $6.0 to $8.7 billion, making a total of $10.7 billion of farm products removed from commercial markets by government programs. In spite of all the temporary or emergency measures which had been employed, surplus stocks reached new record levels in 1959 and 1960.

The basic problem facing agriculture in the late 1950's grew out of the fact that the populations of the Western World already were well fed, and in spite of a record migration of workers out of agriculture, technological progress continued to expand farm output faster than it was possible to expand markets. Some people mistakenly attributed the increases in agricultural output occurring in those years to the continuation of price supports at what they described as excessively high levels. However, acreage allotments (and the acreage reserve program) were more effective in holding down the production of the price-supported crops than was generally supposed (Table 27-1).

The great expansion in agriculture occurred in the nonprice supported products where no production controls were attempted. In the five years from 1952 to 1957, total population in the United States increased 9 per cent, yet the output of nonbasic farm products in-

creased 18 per cent. The unusually large harvests in 1958 brought
the output of basic crops 3 per cent above, and the output of all
nonbasics 23 per cent above, 1952 levels in contrast to an increase
in United States population of only 11 per cent during this six-year
period.

TABLE 27-1

Total Farm Output, Output of Basic Commodities, and Output of Basic Commodities
Plus Other Price-Supported Products, 1951-1958

[1952 = 100]

Year	Total Farm Output Other Than Basic Commodities	Output of Basic Price-Supported Commodities	Output of Basic Commodities, Feed Grains (Other Than Corn), and Milk*
1951	100	90	95
1952	100	100	100
1953	103	98	101
1954	109	90	99
1955	113	93	102
1956	113	94	101
1957	118	86	103
1958†	123	103	115

* A part of the land diverted from basic commodities went into other feed grain production and
milk used for manufacturing was the subject of mandatory supports.
† Preliminary.
Source: Agricultural Marketing Service and Agricultural Research Service.

Wide disagreement among farm leaders. The high levels of crop
production in the late 1950's, in spite of acreage restrictions and the
Soil Bank program, and the record level of farm program costs and
the record level of surplus stocks—in spite of widespread emergency
surplus disposal operations—subjected the farm program to continued criticism from the nonfarm public, the nonfarm representatives in
Congress, and from many farm people and their friends in Congress.
Many nonfarm leaders urged the dismantling of all production
controls and recommended that price supports be dropped to a percentage of recent market price levels or be discontinued entirely.
The Secretary of Agriculture and the officers of the largest farm
organization took the position that the increasing costs of the program and the continued buildup of surplus stocks were caused by the
failure of Congress to give the Secretary the authority he had requested to lower price supports for the basic commodities below 75
per cent of parity and to increase acreage allotments looking toward
their eventual removal.

Congressmen from farm states, especially those in the Democratic
party, and many farm organization leaders held that the results

noted above were to be expected from the policies followed by the Secretary of Agriculture and represented an attempt on his part to discredit government sponsored supply adjustment and price-support programs. They believed that if the Secretary were allowed to carry out his desire to lower price supports still further and remove acreage allotments, farmers would suffer a further decline in farm income while the rest of the economy was enjoying unprecedented prosperity.

This wide disagreement among the leaders of farm organizations and between the leaders of the two major political parties regarding desirable changes in existing legislation, became evident soon after the end of World War II, and continued through the 1950's. Leadership in agriculture became so divided in the late 1950's that no effective action could be taken to deal with the excess productive capacity in agriculture—to deal with the accentuated pressure of food and fiber supplying our domestic population. The many conflicting interests and the divided leadership simply paralyzed the policy formulation process in agriculture in the late 1950's. We could not take action—any action; policywise, we were at dead center.

REFERENCES

Benedict, Murray R., *Can We Solve the Farm Problem?* Chapters 7 and 11. New York: The Twentieth Century Fund, 1955.

Nourse, E. G., J. S. Davis, and J. D. Black, *Three Years of the Agricultural Adjustment Administration.* Chapters 1 and 15. Washington, D. C.: The Brookings Institution, 1937.

Soth, Lauren, *Farm Trouble*, Chapters 5 and 10. Princeton, New Jersey: Princeton University Press, 1957.

Wilcox, Walter W., *The Farmer in the Second World War*, Chapters 1-3, and 23. Ames, Iowa: Iowa State College Press, 1947.

POINTS FOR DISCUSSION

1. What were the basic economic factors in the 1920's which led to agitation for selling farm products abroad at prices lower than domestic market prices?

2. How was the experience of the Federal Farm Board utilized in creating the Agricultural Adjustment Administration in 1933?

3. Outline the major changes which have taken place in government price-support programs for farm products, 1933 to date.

4. Explain how marketing agreements and orders may be utilized to

increase the returns to the producers of a perishable fruit or vegetable. What, if any, farm products from your community are marketed under federal market orders?

5. What were the reasons for high government costs and the accumulation of large carry-over stocks of storable farm products after 1951?

6. Evaluate the relative importance of various institutional and political factors in the failure of government to exercise more effective fiscal and inventory controls over farm price support programs in the 1950's.

CHAPTER 28

Unsolved
Policy Issues

In this final chapter we will attempt to relate to each other the more important social and economic problems facing farmers and indicate the policy issues involved in dealing with them. These problems were analyzed individually in earlier chapters, especially in Chapters 15, 17, 19, and 27. The authors now wish to carry the analyses to the point of showing how the problems interact with each other and provide the setting for basic social and economic disparities between agriculture and other sectors of the economy.

Inadequate demand for underemployed rural workers. In Chapter 19 we analyzed this problem in considerable detail. For at least the past thirty years it has generally been assumed that, except in recessions, the demand for labor at the higher non-farm wage levels in non-farm activities was practically unlimited. It has been assumed that hundreds of thousands of additional workers would be employed if they were available. Low labor earnings in commercial agriculture relative to non-farm activities and especially in the low-income rural areas, in large part was attributed to lack of education and training for non-farm jobs, a lack of knowledge of non-farm job opportunities, the high cost of transferring to new places of work, or to other barriers to migration.

With the underemployment problem formulated in this manner the policy issues were relatively simple. How much should the government increase the educational facilities in the poorer rural areas? How much expansion in job placement services in rural areas is warranted? How much public funds should be devoted to special credits or grants to help farm families defray the cost of moving to new communities to find employment?

Society has made little progress in dealing constructively with these issues. Rural leaders holding political power often are employers, and rarely represent the underemployed and impoverished in agriculture. Leaders elected to public offices from rural areas seldom look with favor on government policies which tend to raise the wages they must pay for hired labor.

State aid to schools in the poorer rural districts has shown some improvement in recent years, but the improvement is far less than that needed to equalize the primary and secondary educational opportunities for farm children. Here again, many good reasons can be found by people in the higher income areas for not increasing their contribution to the educational facilities in the low-income areas. And the citizens in the low-income areas lack the political power to enforce a wider sharing of educational costs on the basis of ability to pay.

In addition to this lack of progress in taking corrective action to facilitate migration from the low-income areas, Hendrix in his recent studies finds the low-income problem itself far more complex than was previously assumed.[1] His studies indicate that although the number of low-income farm people has declined in the last decade, on a relative basis, incomes for those remaining in agriculture are lower than ten years ago. The income disparity between farm and non-farm families has increased.

Hendrix finds that monopoly elements in the market structure for nonfarm products and for hiring nonfarm labor results in satisfying the demand for labor at prevailing wages without providing employment for all who would like to work at the prevailing wage levels. Only in brief periods of rapid economic growth are sufficient farm people taken into nonfarm jobs to make an improvement in the chronic underemployment problem in agriculture.

Although we claim no more than an informed opinion on the subject, it appears unlikely that the rate of population increase and the rate of economic growth in the decade ahead will exceed that of the past ten or fifteen years. On the other hand, it is probable that the recent rates of technological advance and of substitution of capital for labor in agriculture will continue. The authors also see no reason to expect that existing rigidities or "stickiness" in prices and wage rates in the nonfarm sectors of our economy, which limit the demand for marginal workers relative to freely competitive markets, will be reduced or lessened under these conditions. It seems probable, for these reasons, that the pressure for farm labor to transfer out of

[1] W. E. Hendrix, "Income Improvement Prospects in Low-income Areas," *Journal of Farm Economics, Proceedings Issue* (December 1959).

agriculture will be intensified, and opportunities for nonfarm employment may decline relatively.

These considerations, together with such factors as the value of farming as a way of life and the high cost of mobility, suggest the possibility that underemployment and low returns in agriculture relative to other economic activities may be intensified in the years ahead. If this is to be avoided, national policies must be followed which will create an even more rapid rate of growth than was realized in the past fifteen years. In this sense the solution to the problem of underemployment and low incomes in the rural areas depends upon an improvement in the nonfarm product and labor markets and upon new growth records in the total economy.

The problem of over-rapid technical advance. As was pointed out in earlier chapters, farm technological advances are cost-reducing and irreversible in the aggregate. Typically, the marginal cost of added output achieved by using the new technology is lower than the average cost. Under these conditions, where unrestrained competition prevails, the level of total farm output is dependent primarily on the increased use of nonfarm inputs and on adoption of associated new technologies.

And the increased use of nonfarm inputs including the adoption of new technologies is dependent primarily upon the learning processes of farm people, the availability of new cost-reducing technologies for more general adoption, the educational, advertising and promotional programs devoted to obtaining their adoption, the asset position of the producers, and the extent to which the new technology breaks with custom and tradition. Capital investments and credit furnished by the mixed feed, marketing, and processing industries— often under contractual arrangements—also has become an important means of speeding up technical advance in agriculture.

With atomistic competition (competition of large numbers of small producers and sellers) prevailing in agriculture, individual farms find it profitable to adopt new technologies even though farm prices continue to decline. Competitive forces lead to the general adoption of new techniques even though the increased aggregate output results in a sharp decrease in aggregate income. Given the large backlog of output-increasing, cost-reducing technology not yet adopted on most farms in the early 1960's, aggregate output, in the absence of policies for balancing supplies with market outlets, may be expected to expand at such a rate that prices will fall faster than costs can be reduced on both the large and the small farms. This too-rapid rate of output expansion, made possible by the rapid and widespread dissemination and adoption of improved practices and techniques may well continue even though the number of farm operator families in agriculture drops by one-half or more.

The inability of the usual supply and demand forces to achieve an equilibrium in supplies and prices in agriculture under conditions of rapid technological advance derives: (1) out of the low elasticities of demand for food products which result in sweeping and drastic price level changes, and (2) the inability of committed resources in agriculture production to adjust rapidly enough in the aggregate to check production increases thus moderating and dampening down the drastic price level movements. Tractors, improvements in land, specialized machinery, and many of the middle-aged and older farm operators cannot shift to alternative employment. Hence these previously committed resources, in addition to the new cost-reducing investments, continue to be employed in agriculture throughout their productive life in spite of low returns which are gained from their use.

Briefly, new cost-reducing breeding stock, machinery, equipment, and supplies, when brought into agriculture via atomistic competition at rapid rates, expand and push aggregate output ahead of demand, which in turn precipitates and drives down farm prices and incomes for extended periods, where there are not offsetting movements of productive resources out of agriculture. And, typically, there have not been offsetting adjustments; this is the explanation for the inelastic aggregate farm output function described in Chapters 6 and 15.

Within this general framework, as should be clear, policies and programs that help bring supplies into balance with demand at reasonable or good prices on a commodity-by-commodity, and on an aggregate, basis would improve farmers' relative income positions even though widespread under-employment in agriculture continues.

Importance of cultural beliefs and values. At this point, it is desirable to observe that economic analysis is only a part of the total stream of influences at work in shaping group decisions and actions.[2] Cultural beliefs and values transmitted from earlier, less-industrialized societies and widely-held considerations of justice and equity, the desire that each one deserves what he gets and gets what he deserves —have largely shaped the rules which govern our economic life today. Economic life today is far different, however, from economic life at the time these beliefs, values, and governing rules were formulated. This is especially true in rural America. The technological revolution

---

[2] The following statements on the role of beliefs and values draw heavily on the recent writings of John M. Brewster, especially, "The Impact of Technical Advance and Migration on Agricultural Society and Policy," *Journal of Farm Economics, Proceedings Issue* (December 1959).

sweeping rural America is uprooting widely-held personal beliefs and values just as ruthlessly as it is uprooting long-established production and marketing practices.

Some of the more important beliefs and values which we have inherited from our cultural forefathers living in a less interdependent society may be listed as follows:

(1) The work ethic which gives high personal esteem to excellence in useful employment and low esteem to the "easy ways," and which expresses the judgment that society owes to each (a) the equivalent of his contribution, and (b) an equal opportunity to the means necessary for developing his creative potential to the fullest extent possible.

In its American environment the work ethic reserves for highest esteem those who achieved success "the hard way" and includes the optimistic judgment that men (and nations) in their workmanlike capacities possess ample means for closing the gap between present circumstance and aspiration.

(2) The democratic creed, with its two central value judgments that (a) all men are of equal worth and dignity, and (b) none, however wise or good, is wise enough to have dictatorial power over any other.

(3) The enterprise creed, with its three judgments that (a) proprietors or their legal representatives, deserve the exclusive right (power) to prescribe the working rules for their production units; (b) the individual (or family) is and ought to be wholly responsible for his (or its) own economic well-being throughout life; (c) therefore, government's prime functions are to prevent anyone, including government itself, from invading the unfettered freedom of proprietors or their legal agents, of running their business as they wish and to prevent the improvident from pressuring either government or business into assuming responsibility for their well-being.

While all three creeds are deeply rooted in American character, there is no connection between them. A people may feel deeply committed to the work ethic and yet totally reject the enterprise creed. Again, men possess no specific meritorious capacity in equal degree; hence there is a sharp clash between the democratic imperative that we accord all men a status of equal dignity and worth and the work-ethic imperative that we accord them differential status in line with the results of their productive effort.

In American life, however, these disconnected creeds became interlocked in one of the most unified belief systems in history. This came about through a three-hundred-year development and use of what is often called the Lockean model of social organization. This model takes its name from John Locke who, in his seventeenth-century *Treatise on Civil Government,* first held that the good world lies in a sharp division of society into a big economic sphere and a tiny political sphere of popularly controlled government. The government's role would be limited to that of protecting the "natural" rights of proprietors and the "State of Nature" later interpreted as the free market.

Farm people and rural communities today are experiencing many of the social conflicts which were common in the urban communities in the early years of the industrial revolution. Widely held personal value judgments and beliefs play a greater role in slowing economic change in the rural community than in the urban community, however, for in the urban community the management of technological change is largely in the control of the boards of directors of the corporations. In the rural communities, if there is to be any organized management of technological change, it must be placed in the hands of democratic government, subject as it is to the prevailing structure of political power.

Illustrative of the beliefs and values which are brought into conflict by efforts to change the rules which govern rural economic life is the conflict between the desire for equity or justice which points to collective action to achieve orderly marketing (and production) and the deep-seated belief that it is wrong to deny proprietors the freedom to run their business as they wish. Technical advance poses a dilemma for the conscience of farm people by placing in opposition their desire for equity or economic justice and their love of proprietary freedom. This is of utmost significance. In part, it explains the difficulties encountered by farm people in developing socially acceptable programs of collective action for retaining a part of the benefits of technical advance now going almost entirely to consumers.

As farm surpluses and government costs of farm programs continued to mount in the late 1950's, and farm income threatened to decline still further, a measure of public support developed for several distinctly different types of programs. Five of the more important of these program proposals are briefly outlined and evaluated in the subsequent paragraphs.

Less-restrained production and marketing as a policy. Throughout most of the 1950's, a large number of agricultural economists and farm leaders, including the Secretary of Agriculture and his policy-making staff in the years between 1952 and 1960 mistakenly believed that a policy of less-restrained production and marketing would improve the income and welfare position of farm people. It is probable that their own beliefs and values colored their economic evaluations. They held that the price and income stabilization programs developed in earlier years maintained the prices of a number of farm products at too high a level, thus "pricing them out of the market."

The maintenance of a stable price level on butter while consumers shifted to the lower-priced oleomargarine, was generalized far beyond its applicability as an explanation of what was wrong with existing agricultural price policies. The failure to sell cotton in foreign markets at competitive world prices in 1953 and 1954 and several other aspects of the cotton price policies during these years gave further substance to the belief that over the longer-run the income position of farmers would be improved by a general policy of lowering all price supports to some reasonable percentage of the past market average and by the removal of most or all acreage allotments.

Even though farm income continued to be depressed in spite of temporary surplus disposal programs and the accumulation of $9 billion in loans and inventories of farm products by the Commodity Credit Corporation, the Secretary of Agriculture and some other influential leaders in agriculture continued to advise farmers that the most appropriate policy for improving their incomes was progressively to remove planting restrictions and lower price-support levels on the price-supported crops. Evidently these leaders were either unacquainted with or unconvinced by the analyses presented in earlier chapters of this book.

Government assistance in shifting to nonfarm jobs. As mentioned earlier, a large number of agricultural economists and other students of the economic problems of agriculture in the mid- and late 1950's observed that continued new investments in cost-reducing technology were causing too many resources to be utilized in agricultural production. Since the land and the earlier capital investments could not be transferred to other activities, interest centered on accelerating the shift of farm workers to other lines of activity as a means of offsetting the over-rapid rate of technical advance.

Proposals for programs to achieve this objective were similar to the proposals outlined for improving the widespread underemployment and low-income problem in agriculture (Chapter 19).

Those who advocated these lines of activity as a means of improving the income and equity position of farm people usually did not propose them as the only programs to be utilized in achieving a balance between aggregate output expansion and aggregate demand expansion. They would place major reliance, however, on programs for accelerating the shift of farm workers to nonfarm jobs. Again, personal value judgments—in part acquired with their professional training—may have influenced their recommendations. The authors find much merit in these proposals. But to propose seriously these activities as the major program for achieving an important improvement in the income position of commercial farmers appears to the authors to involve a mistaken appraisal of the economics of technological advance. We believe it also involves a substantial overestimate of the effectiveness of such programs in view of the fact that nearly 25 per cent of the farm laboring force moved out of agriculture in the decade 1950 to 1959, and yet the excess productive capacity of American agriculture was greater in 1959 than in 1950. This excess productive capacity increased in spite of a rapid increase in population.

Retirement of land from agriculture as a policy. The retirement of large acreages of land from agriculture as a major program for improving farm income was advocated by a number of farm leaders and agricultural economists in the late 1950's. The advocates of land retirement as a major program for achieving a balance between agricultural output and available markets usually proposed that emphasis be placed on securing the retirement of whole farms.

Most often the proposals were made that the land be rented. In the late 1950's a conservation reserve program was in operation (Chapter 27) under which the government rented land from farm owners for periods of five to fifteen years and allowed it to be devoted to conservation uses. Some 28 million acres of cropland were rented to the government under this conservation reserve program in 1960. The rental rates offered under this program by the government were high enough in most cases to equal the value of the land in a ten-year period. With this in mind, a small minority of farm leaders proposed that the desired acreages be retired from farm production by government purchase on an offer basis rather than by the relatively expensive rental agreements.

There is little doubt that a large-scale rental or purchase program retiring 50 to 70 million acres of land from crop production would temporarily bring aggregate farm output into balance with available markets. As an example, the total of all crops including hay and rotation pasture approximates 470 million acres. The output of farm products in the late 1950's was 6 to 10 per cent greater than could be moved into commercial channels at reasonably stable prices. Assuming that the less-productive cropland and the less-productive farm workers and equipment would be removed from farm production by a conservation reserve program which emphasized the rental of whole farms, a total of 50 to 70 million acres would probably have to be retired to effect an 8 to 10 per cent reduction in crop output and a 6 to 10 per cent reduction in aggregate farm output.

Those who advocate this method of bringing total farm output into balance with available market outlets believe that a well-designed rental or purchase program which removed the less-productive lands and the farms operated by the older and otherwise less-productive farm operators would be the most efficient means of adjusting aggregate output downward to a level that would move through commercial markets at reasonably stable prices. Such a program would require a minimum of governmental activity. With this much land and a large number of farm operators taken out of agriculture on a completely voluntary basis, they believe that the remaining land and the remaining operators could be freed from production and marketing restrictions returning relative prices and costs to their appropriate role of directing the use of resources within agriculture. Such a program would leave the remaining operators free from production restrictions while shrinking the total land base to a point where aggregate output would not be excessive in relation to market outlets. The strongest advocates of this approach would retire additional land each year as necessary to offset potential aggregate output expansion in excess of aggregate demand expansion resulting from continued technical advance.

The weakness of land retirement appears to be its differential effect on rural communities and established trade centers. Small town tradesmen, especially those in the rural areas of the Southeast and those in other less-productive rural areas vigorously and effectively opposed further expansion of government land rental or purchase programs after their first years of operation. The most widespread support for this approach came from the more productive farming areas of the Midwest. People in these areas thought largely in terms of removal of small acreages including the less-productive farms in their home communities and the removal of large acreages of less-productive land "elsewhere."

The land retirement or conservation reserve approach as the major program for bringing aggregate output expansion into balance with aggregate demand expansion, also, is undesirable in that it proposes to affect total output by reducing the supply of only one of the input factors without measures for preventing the substitution of other factors for land. Recent technical studies indicate that land contributes about 15 per cent of the total annual inputs in agricultural production. Labor contributes about 30 per cent and capital contributes about 55 per cent of the total annual inputs. Technical advance is resulting in continued increase in the importance of capital as an input while the relative importance of inputs from labor and land in agricultural production are decreasing. Increased use of fertilizers and supplemental irrigation on the remaining farm land would offset much of the land retirement. From this point of view it appears unreasonable to expect that aggregate output can be kept in balance with available market outlets by a moderate reduction in cropland utilized, although placing a part of the cropland in a conservation reserve may be an important supplement when used in conjunction with other measures.

The public utility approach as a policy. W. W. Cochrane, in professional papers and in a book entitled *Farm Prices—Myth and Reality,*[3] has outlined a "public utility" approach for dealing with the problems as outlined in the opening paragraphs of this chapter. This approach would have Congress assume the responsibility for determining the fair price for each commodity coming under control, after which a national sales quota would be established, taking into consideration market and special demands. Sales quotas would be the estimated amount of the commodity which would move through the market at the defined fair price, hence, they would be determined by the Congress with the interests of both consumers and producers in mind. This is where the name "public utility" comes from.

Each farmer would receive a pro-rata share of the national sales quota for each commodity, based largely on his historical record of production or sales. Under this plan it would be illegal for a farmer to market any commodity having a national quota except insofar as he had a marketing quota covering the quantities marketed. One of the important features of this proposal is that the marketing quotas of individual farmers might be bought and sold under a minimum of restrictions—quotas would become negotiable. The total farm-marketing quota might be represented by marketing certificates having a face value equal to a part of the total marketing quota. A farmer could then sell any part or all of these marketing quota certificates if he so desired. In this way the individual farm operator would be free to expand production, or contract it, in the light of his production and marketing costs, including the cost of additional marketing certificates if he wished to expand output beyond the marketing quota allotted to him.

Control programs making use of quotas, where those quotas are tied to the land or to a farm, have long been criticized on the grounds that the short-term gains of the control program are capitalized into the land and in the long run, average unit costs rise to meet price

---

[3] W. W. Cochrane, *Farm Prices—Myth and Reality,* Chapter 8 (Minneapolis: University of Minnesota Press, 1958).

per unit. In this way the short-term gains of the program are imputed into costs, and nothing remains in the long run except the nuisance of the controls. And this "public utility" approach is criticized on similar grounds; namely, in the long run the short-term gains arising out of supply control would become capitalized into the negotiable certificates.

This constitutes a valid criticism. The capital value of the fixed factor, or factors, in farming is based on the residual share of the cash receipts from the sale of products which can be attributed to them after paying market prices for the variable factors used in the production process. All increases in net returns from farming tend to become capitalized into the fixed factors, whether this increase originates out of population growth or out of successful sales promotion, a change in tastes, output restriction, or war. This criticism of all programs designed to increase farm income by restricting marketings to quantities which can be sold at stable, reasonable or good prices applies equally to programs for expanding the utilization and demand for farm products.

Where wage rates and the returns to labor are below average for the various reasons outlined in Chapter 19, the asset value of fixed factors such as land or marketing quotas are greater in relation to product prices than they would be if wage rates were competitive with those in nonfarm activities. The extent to which increased income resulting from supply controls is capitalized into the value of the marketing quotas will depend to great extent on alternative employment opportunities for the rural people.

Tobacco marketing quotas have attained substantial capitalized values in many communities even though the returns to labor in tobacco production were low relative to industrial wage rates in other communities. In a few communities, however, tobacco allotments have been unused and had no value because alternative employment opportunities offered higher returns. Land prices in the irrigated valleys of California are influenced to a substantial extent by the availability of low-cost imported labor in part made possible by special labor import legislation.

Regardless of the other employment opportunities of rural labor, however, supply controls would have certain economic advantages for farmers. These advantages are: (1) they make possible short-term gains in income to farm operators who have not shared in the national prosperity of the 1950's, (2) they provide protection against major farm price level declines in the future that might destroy asset positions, and (3) they assure increased certainty in resource planning and use.

A storage program designed to stabilize year-to-year market supplies and diversion programs for perishable commodities in years of above-average yields would be needed to complement annual sales quotas. Where commodities such as wheat have both a food use and a feed use, the marketing quota might be limited to the product marketed for use as food. All products moving through commercial market channels would have to be accompanied by marketing certificates indicating that they were being marketed within the legal marketing quotas of the originating producers.

A plan of this kind, if properly administered, would be reasonably successful in coordinating aggregate output expansion with aggregate demand expansion. Such a plan, however, would be subject to the same technical and political difficulties in determining fair price levels as those involved in setting forward prices at levels which would keep supply and demand in equilibrium (Chapter 26). Also, the administrative problems involved in treating agriculture, with its 2,000,000 commercial producers and its hundreds of thousands of processing and marketing agencies, as a public utility are believed by many to make such an approach extremely difficult to administer.

The commodity self-help and domestic parity approach. In the late 1950's the National Grange and a substantial number of farm leaders in commodity organizations turned to what was loosely called a "commodity-by-commodity" approach for an alternative to the then-outmoded and excessively costly existing price support programs. In a leaflet published in 1959, the National Grange used the term "domestic parity concept" to refer to a whole array of programs—on a commodity-by-commodity basis—to raise farm income and put an end to Government's progressive destruction of private trade in farm products and Government's increasing control of production patterns in farming. Each program would call for the use of that combination of economic devices, marketing certificates, import duties, processing taxes, marketing orders, and direct assessments against products sold which would be best suited to the particular commodity involved.

Those who advocate this approach to the solution of the problems of over-rapid output expansion recognize that technological advance contributes to increased specialization and increased integration and that these trends are likely to continue at an accelerated rate for the foreseeable future. Increased specialization, in turn, is accompanied by the organization of new commodity groups and by increased staffing and expanded activities on the part of the older commodity organizations.

Given a highly inelastic demand for the aggregate output of foods and fibers and a relatively inelastic demand for most groups of foods such as dairy products, meats, turkeys, broilers, eggs, cereals, and potatoes, commodity groups can increase the income of their members by appropriate orderly marketing programs. Advocates of this approach note that marketing orders issued by the Secretary of Agriculture have facilitated orderly marketing of perishable fruits and vegetables and of fluid milk in urban markets. The marketing order approach, they believe, might be utilized by other commodity groups and it might be expanded to include the allotment of marketing "goals" or quotas among producers, as well as the collection of marketing fees by a check-off system.

Marketings by individual producers in line with allotted "goals" or quotas would be encouraged by returning the check-off fees to those who marketed products within their goals, but fees would not be returned to producers who marketed products in excess of their goals. Commodity proposals of this type have been loosely called "commodity self-help programs." In proposals of this type the government would perform the role of making sure that the legislation and the individual group actions taken under it would not result in serious inequities to other producer groups, or to consumers and that they were not in conflict with existing international trade policies.

The commodity self-help approach appears to be better for livestock products and for the crops which are domestically produced and consumed. Some form of differential pricing appears to be more appropriate for the major export crops—cotton, wheat, and tobacco. Feed grains present an especially difficult problem and there is less agreement on what are the most appropriate methods for stabilizing supplies and prices of feed grains than for other commodities.

The commodity-by-commodity approach has the merit of being very flexible. It allows producers a maximum of producer freedom in organizing productive resources. The marketing goals could be made negotiable as in the public utility approach, thus permitting regional specialization in production in line with relative costs. One of the outstanding difficulties in this approach is the conflicts of interests between producers within even a single producer group. Although the group as a whole may benefit from some specific proposal, a substantial part of the group may be inadequately informed regarding the group benefits and a minority may be adversely affected. These factions may block effective action on any group proposal. Also, there is a general tendency for commodity groups to overestimate the inelasticity of demand for their particular product and to underestimate its elasticity of supply with the result that the membership may become committed to a self-defeating program.

In view of the strong tendency of marketing to expand under advancing technology it appears probable that the success of self-help programs will depend largely on the effectiveness of their production and marketing controls.

Level of farm prices may become a chronic problem. In Chapter 15 we separated agriculture's price problems into two groups—those associated with the price variability of the individual commodities and those associated with the level of all farm product prices relative to nonfarm product prices. In the pre-World War II and early postwar years, most agricultural economists and farm leaders believed that in periods of great business activity, competitive market forces would keep the farm prices at a satisfactory level relative to nonfarm prices. Problems associated with the level of farm prices were thought of as problems arising in business recessions when the demand for food slackens because of unemployment.

We now believe that regardless of the level of business activity, the problem of maintaining a satisfactory level of farm prices relative to prices in other sectors of the economy will dominate farm policy considerations in the foreseeable future, because of the impact of over-rapid technical advance, the low elasticities of demand in food products, the limited extent of price competition in the nonfarm product and labor markets, the lack of mobility of previously committed resources in agricultural production, and the barriers to labor mobility.

The authors believe that society faced with this situation will take action to limit the adverse economic effects of over-rapid technical advance on the level of farm prices. If it should decide to place main reliance on voluntary retirement of land from agriculture, which seems unlikely on both technical and political grounds, problems associated with the price variability of individual commodities would continue as outlined in Chapter 15. If, however, the action takes some form of a public utility or a modified commodity-by-commodity supply control approach in dealing with the problem of excessive supplies in relation to market outlets, it will also reduce the price variability of individual commodities. For this reason we believe that for the most part those policies which will deal effectively with the general farm price level in the period of the 1960's and 1970's will also deal effectively with the individual commodity price variability problems.

Credit in agriculture with price stability. In recent years farm leaders have become concerned about the large volume of credit needed by individual farm operators to achieve the scale of operations they need to minimize production costs. Existing credit institutions and customary credit practices are not completely meeting the needs that have been created by technical advances in agriculture.

However, to a great extent it has been the great risks and uncertainties inherent in using credit in agriculture which have caused farm credit institutions and practices to develop as they have. If farmers succeed in developing programs for stabilizing market supplies, prices and incomes, they will have created immeasurably better conditions for the extension of credit to farm operators. Under more stabilized income conditions farm operators can safely use more credit than in the past and lending practices undoubtedly will change as justified by the reduction in risk. New credit institutions may be needed in some areas where an especially large volume of credit is required for efficient production methods. Problems associated with the creation of such new credit institutions will be minimized, however, if risk and uncertainty in agriculture are reduced by commodity supply adjustment programs. Somewhat parenthetically, it may be noted that family farming continues to flourish because there are such great risks and uncertainties in agriculture. The competitive position of larger farming units could be improved by reducing uncertainty and increasing the availability of credit.

Over-valuation of farm land. Another of the problems recurring for farm operators is the over-valuation of farm land for agricultural production purposes, which is most serious in heavily populated communities within commuting distance of nonfarm employment and in the more distant heavily populated low-income areas.

There are pervasive social and economic forces which cause most farm land to be over-valued in relation to its economic productivity in agriculture.

These forces result from the desire for land ownership for prestige purposes, as a hedge against inflation, and as an outlet for tax-deductible funds by individuals in the high income-tax brackets. Probably the most important single factor, however, is the inability of many farm people to find satisfactory nonfarm jobs during the period in their lives when they could most readily shift to nonfarm work. In many of the less-productive areas of the United States families earn an inadequate income on their small farms but value them so highly as a place to live and to eke out an existence, that commercial farmers cannot afford to buy them for consolidation into commercial producing units. This pressure of people firmly established on the land is being intensified by the rapid technical advance in agriculture. In most communities there is intense competition among the established farmers for additional land for farm enlargement purposes. Although established farmers can afford to pay more per acre for small acreages to enlarge less than optimum sized farms than for the entire farm, this type of competition may create artificially high community land values.

One of the serious problems farm families encounter is arriving at a fair and equitable basis of settlement where one of the children takes over the home farm and the others are paid in cash for their pro-rata share of the inheritance. It may not be fair and equitable for the son or son-in-law who takes over the home farm to pay off the other heirs on the basis of community-wide farm values. Although the forces which lead to over-valuation of land for commercial agricultural production purposes may change from time to time, the authors expect the current trends to continue indefinitely.

Equity problems encountered in supply management programs. As pointed out earlier, because there is an inelastic demand for food and fiber, a normal supply in relation to market demand yields farmers a larger aggregate income than would a supply larger than normal. This is the economic basis for supply control programs. The socially acceptable way of operating supply stabilization programs, as developed in the 1930's, involves government allocation of production rights (acreage allotments) on the basis of past production records. A small and sharply limited acreage allotment is usually retained by the government for later allocation to relieve special hardship cases and for new growers.

In some programs, such as the cotton and tobacco programs, the numerous small growers with low incomes, but whose representatives had considerable political power, were given special considerations. Allotments for the small farmers often did not involve as much of a reduction as the allotments on the larger farms. In some of the tobacco programs in the early years, allotments could not be cut below a certain minimum—a fraction of an acre per farm. Where payments were involved, payments for small farms sometimes were increased by a specified percentage. Also for many years the government set a maximum on the size of the agricultural conservation payment per farm and in the 1960 Agricultural Appropriation Act for the first time, a limit was placed on the size of the price-support loan to an individual or corporate producer.

Equity problems involved in sharing these rights to produce and market have been troublesome since the first Acreage Adjustment Programs were set up in 1933. In the Midwest it centered on the alleged discrimination of the use of the historical base approach against the more progressive farmers of the community. It was pointed out that such "good" farmers had been following rotations with only a small percentage of their farms in intertilled crops and a high percentage of their farms in soil-conserving legumes and grasses. It was "unfair" to require them to reduce their intertilled crops by the same percentage as for the farmers who historically had "run down" their farms by overcropping with cultivated crops. Great Plains farmers who had been following a summer fallow system also believed they were discriminated against by the early allotment setting procedures.

In the tobacco growing areas of the Southeast, alternative opportunities for employment have been so limited that more and more rural families have availed themselves of the opportunity to grow a minimum acreage of price-supported tobacco under the new-grower provisions of the program. This trend has continued to the point that the acreage allotments of the larger growers have been reduced sharply while thousands of new fractional-acre growers have been added.

Here it is of interest to note the difference in beliefs and values relative to property in land vs. property rights created by collective action programs limiting production and marketings. A landowner is never forced to allow an underemployed neighbor the free use of his land for tobacco production. Yet the new-grower provisions of the tobacco program allow an underemployed farmer to obtain a right to market a small amount of tobacco even though this reduces the marketing rights of established producers by an equal amount. Production and marketing property rights under the marketing quota programs are sharply limited. In 1941 established wheat growers were forced to take account of equity considerations of small potential growers by Congressional action granting any producer the right to harvest and market up to 15 acres of wheat without regard to marketing quota restrictions.

In recent years there has been considerable discussion of the desirability of making acreage allotment or marketing rights freely negotiable as has long been the practice with respect to property rights in chattels, real estate, and corporate stocks and bonds. Such a provision would avoid freezing existing production and marketing patterns and permit the continuation of trends toward regional specialization in production in line with relative production costs. Inherent in such provisions is the danger, however, that those in the strongest economic position would buy up the rights as they were offered for sale, thus increasing the disparity of incomes within agriculture. If the negotiability feature of marketing quotas is not adopted, however, then in the long run the equity problems involved in allocating these "rights" to a market supplied by different geographic areas and large- and small-scale producers will certainly plague farmers and politicians in the future far more than they have in the past.

The manner in which the individual production and marketing rights inherent in supply control programs are shared between geographic areas and between large and small established producers and other under-employed rural people will depend both on the organization of political power and on the prevailing beliefs regarding the nature of these rights as compared with other property rights. Such programs almost surely would be subject to more or less continuous modification on the basis of equity considerations as among the holders and potential holders of production and marketing rights.

REFERENCES

Cochrane, Willard W., *Farm Prices—Myth and Reality,* Chapters 6-8. Minneapolis: University of Minnesota Press, 1958.

"Policy for Commercial Agriculture, its Relation to Economic Growth and Stability," papers submitted by panelists, Joint Economic Committee Print, 85th Congress, 1st session (November 22, 1957).

"Prize Winning Papers in the Price Policy Contest Sponsored by the American Farm Economics Association." *Journal of Farm Economics,* Vol. XXVII, No. 4, (November 1945).

Schickele, Rainer, *Agricultural Policy,* Chapters 1-5. New York: McGraw-Hill Book Company, Inc., 1954.

POINTS FOR DISCUSSION

1. Why cannot a price and income policy in food and agriculture be laid down with scientific objectivity?
2. Make an outline of the principal schools of thought regarding a desirable price and income policy for agriculture. Set forth the main conceptual points of each of these schools.
3. What basic similarities and differences emerge from your outline?
4. With which school of thought do you find yourself most in agreement? Or do you prefer some combination of ideas not presented in this survey? If so, set forth your suggested price and income policy for agriculture.

Index

Acreage adjustment contracts, 469-470
Acreage Adjustment Programs, 522
Acreage allotments, 499, 503, 522-523
Aggregate demand curve, 276-279
Aggregate output curve, 271-276
Aggregate output problem in agriculture, 271-276
Aggregate supply relation, 71-86
  for the agricultural industry, 77
  of the farm firm, 71-72
  output of and inputs in agriculture, 82
  shifting, 83-86
  short- and long-run considerations, 77-78
  sources of increased productive efficiency, 82-83
  supply behavior of commercial farms, 73-77
  supply behavior of low-production family farms, 72-73
Agricultural Act of 1954, 501
Agricultural Adjustment Act of 1933, 138, 469-470, 493-495, 497
Agricultural Adjustment Administration, 472, 473
Agricultural adjustment program, 444, 469-470
  farmers' benefits, 470
  legislation, 469-470
  marketing agreements, 470-471
  in the 1930's, 495-497
  Supreme Court decision, 495-496
Agricultural industry, business fluctuations and, 298-301
Agricultural Marketing Act of 1929, 468-469
Agricultural Marketing Service, 164
Agricultural Research Service, 10-11, 180
Agricultural Trade Development and Assistance Act, 501
Agriculture:
  Brewster historical analysis, 321
  in the economy of the U. S., 314-337
Alfalfa, cost of production, 65
Allin, Bushrod W., 335
American Farm Bureau Federation, 475-476

Analysis, 45, 46
Areas:
  low-income (see Low-income areas)
  specialization in production, 29-38
  type-of-farming, 29-38
Asset position of farmers, adoption of technological advances and, 329-330
Auctions, 99, 123

Bankhead-Jones Farm Tenant Act of 1937, 377
Banks:
  federal land, 393-394, 466-467
  loans from, 393-395
Barley, marketing, 119
Bellerby, J. R., 333
Black, John D., 468
Bonnen, James T., 323
Breimyer, Harold F., 119n
Bressler, R. G., Jr., 319
Brewster, John M., 321, 331, 510n
Brewster historical analysis, 321
Browning, James W., 113n
Budgets and budgeting, 46
Buildings, investments in, 66
Bureau of Animal Industry, 465
Bureau of Census, 362
Bureau of Indian Affairs, 442
Bureau of Land Management, 441, 448, 451
Bureau of Reclamation, 442, 451
Burmeister, Charles A., 119n
Business fluctuation, 287-313
  agricultural industry and, 298-301
  effects of, 310-312
  farm credit and, 395-396
  generalized view of, 291
  income-expenditure approach, 295-298
  indicators of prosperity and depression (1948-59), 292-294
  investment in agriculture, 301-304
  population in agriculture, 304-308
  role of consumption, 295-298
Butter, 135, 214

California, 219
Calories, 176
Camps, farm labor, 415

525

Capital investment in agriculture:
  farm technology and, 53-55, 520-521
  requirements, 69
  technology as a form of, 51-52
Capper-Volstead Act of 1922, 467
Cattle (*see also* Livestock)
  fattening, 409
  prices, 214
Chain stores, 101, 144-145
Cheese, 136-137
Chew, Arthur P., 463, 465
Chicken (*see also* Poultry)
  consumer demand curves for, 192
Clawson, Marion, 451*n*
Climate:
  effect on farming in the Great Plains
    states, 447
  farm production affected by, 16-17
  risks and uncertainties of, 477-478
Clough, Malcolm, 113*n*
Cobweb analysis, resource allocation
  problem, 264-268
Cochrane, Willard W., 77*n*, 143*n*,
  268*n*, 314*n*, 355*n*, 483*n*, 516
Colleges:
  agricultural, 328
  agricultural experiment stations, 464
  land-grant, 464
Collins, Norman R., 143*n*, 144*n*, 148
Combination of enterprises, 22-25, 46-
  47
Commercial farms (*see also* Large-
  scale farming)
  management services, 383
  supply behavior, 73-77
Commercial trade policies, 349-352
Commodities:
  indices of prices received by farm-
    ers (1939-57), 201
  price movements, 205-206
  prices, 263
  retail markets for, 101
Commodity Credit Corporation, 347,
  475, 500, 503, 513
Commodity exchanges, 108
Commodity self-help program, 518-
  520
Commodity-supply relations, 71
Comparative advantage:
  changing nature of, 20
  of enterprise combinations, 25
  principle of, 17-20
Compensatory payments program, 486-
  489
Competition:
  imperfect, 237-240
  in marketing, 162
  perfectly competitive market, 229-
  230
Conservation:
  definition, 420-421
  divergence between practice and
    economic optimum, 427-428

Great Plains states, 455
  in low rainfall areas, 422
  public programs supplement the
    price system, 426-427
  soil (*see* Soil conservation)
  in the South, 422-423
Conservation reserve program, 502-
  503
  retirement of land from agriculture,
    514-516
Consumers:
  demands, 189-193
  central problem of choice, 185-189
  expenditures for current consump-
    tion, 187
  food costs and incomes, 206-208
  market demand, 193-194
  marketing process and, 174-175
  need, 175-183
  price spreads between farmers and,
    164-167
  role in economy, 174
  selling new foods to, 161-162
  wants and desires, 183-185
Consumption curve, 189-193
Consumption expenditures, 295-298
Contract farming, 155-156
Contracts, 388-389
Controls, government, 467-469, 471-
  476
Cooper, Maurice R., 128*n*
Cooperatives, 99, 151-154, 467
Corn (*see also* Feed grains)
  cost of production, 64-65
  fertilized for higher yields, 40-42
  futures market, 485
  hog-corn ratio, 211-212
  marginal cost of producing addi-
    tional, 44
  marketing, 118-119
  prices, 214
  price supports, 498
  Soil Bank program, 501
Corn Belt, 31-32
  farm tenancy, 381-382
  soil conservation, 422, 423
  types of farming, 31-32
Costs:
  as affected by size of farm, 65-68
  average production costs versus op-
    portunity costs, 63-65
  cash income and expenses on high-
    and low-income farms, 62
  dairying, 59
  economic basis of family farms,
    68-70
  fixed and variable, 57-59
  investment in typical farms, 10-11
  labor, 66, 170
  long-run analysis of cost-price re-
    lationships, 251-256
  marketing, 158-173
  transportation, 170-171

Costs (*Cont.*)
unique character of farmers' variable costs, 62-63
variable cash expenditures versus unit production costs, 59-62
Cotton:
areas specializing in, 32
consumption of, 128, 133
cottonseed, 132
division of consumer's cotton dollar, 131
futures market, 485
government controls, 469
industrial products, 131
lint, 92, 129
linters, 132
marketing, 128-133
prices, 205-206
price supports, 498
production controls, 494
situation reports, 481
textiles, 128-130
weaving, 129
Cottonseed, 131
Credit, 391-396
commercial and government farm real estate mortgage credit agencies, 393-394
criteria for use of production credit, 393
economic instability, 395-396
for farm improvement, 368
function of credit in farming, 391
government programs, 390, 466-467
large amount needed to minimize production, 520-521
non-real estate mortgage agencies, 394-395
production vs. consumption, 391-392
technological advances and, 396, 520-521
Crissey, Forrest, 493n
Crop and Livestock Reporting Service, 463
Crop insurance, 457, 479-480
Cropland:
acres harvested by different types of farmers, 5
harvested crops area stabilized, 36-37
index of, 80
irrigated land area increasing, 37
trends in total, 36
Crops:
production period for, 482
technology and production, 50-51
Curves:
consumption, 189-193
demand, 191-192, 222-226
derived demand and supply, 230-232
economies-of-scale, 67-68
supply, 226-229

Customs, price changes and production influenced by, 259-260

Dairy farming:
areas specializing in, 17, 32-33
cost of production, 67
seasonal workers, 409
costs, 58-59
Dairy products, 133-141
marketing agreements, 470
Federal marketing orders, for milk, 138-140
prices received by farmers (1910-58), 205-206
situation reports, 481
Davis, Chester C., 143n, 468n
DeLoach, D. B., 170n
Demand:
aggregate demand for food, 276-279
based on consumer decisions, 232
causes for shifts in, 315-318
consumer, 189-193
curves, 191-192, 222-226, 235
definition, 222
derived, 230-232
elasticity of, 225-226
farm prices determined by, 222-226
market, 193-194
race between aggregate supply and aggregate demand, 314
shifters, 315-318
Department of Agriculture, 108, 463-466, 473, 481
Depression:
business fluctuations, 287-313
foreclosure proceedings, 467
indicators of prosperity and (1948-59), 292-294
principal short-run effects on agriculture, 324
prosperity and (1920-60), 287-290
Dewhurst, J. Frederick, 171n
Diamond Walnut Growers, 154
Disease prevention programs, 478
Distribution costs, 171-172
Diversified farming, 480-481
specialization versus, 25-26
Dividing and packaging products, 106
Drought conditions, 453-454
Ducoff, Louis J., 406n

Economic analysis:
how farm prices are determined, 222-241
long-run cost-price relationships, 251-256
role of prices, 242-261
Economic conditions, forecasts, 480-481
Economic problems, of hired workers' families, 412-413
Economy of the United States, agriculture and, 314-337

Educational facilities, in low-income
    areas, 362, 367, 369-370
Education of farmers, 6
  low-income areas, 362
Edwards, Everett E., 461
Efficiency, source of increased produc-
    tive, 82-83
Eggs (*see also* Poultry and eggs)
  marketing, 145-146
  seasonal production and prices,
    213-214
Elasticity concept:
  of demand, 225-226
  supply curve, 228-229
Elevators, 99, 115
Employment in agriculture, 321
  changes in farm employment (1870-
    1950), 322
  low-income areas, 369-370
  number of persons employed on
    farms, 411
  statistics, 404*n*
  underemployment, 373-376
Enterprises:
  achieving the most profitable com-
    bination of, 46-47
  comparative advantage of enter-
    prise combinations, 25
  complementary relations among,
    24-25
  marginal cost supply curve, 48-49
  principles of combination, 22
  supplementary relations among en-
    terprises, 23-24
Equalization process, marketing farm
    products, 97-98
Erosion losses, 420-422, 478
Expansion in agriculture, 503-504
Expenses (*see also* Costs)
  cash income and expenses on high-
    and low-income farms, 62
  variable cash expenditures versus
    unit production costs, 59-62
Exports (*see also* Foreign trade)
  dumping, 341-342
  following World War II, 346
  government program, 347-348, 352-
    353
  peacetime stagnation of, 349-352
  U.S. agricultural exports (1925-
    58), 347, 348
Extension Services, 320, 326
Ezekiel, Mordecai, 264

Families, annual per capita consump-
    tion of food, 188
Family farms:
  capital requirements, 69
  commercial, supply behavior, 73-76
  continuing farm ownership prob-
    lems, 389-391
  economic basis of, 68-70
  extent of family assistance, 400

handicapped families in low-income
    areas, 368
  hired labor on, 407-409
  low production, supply behavior of,
    72-73
  ownership of, 377, 389-391
  transfers of, 386-391, 522
  two-man farms, 408
Farm Credit Administration, 394-395
Farmers Home Administration, 368,
    394, 395, 415, 472, 473
Farmers Union Program, 390
Farm firms, 308-310
  aggregate supply relation of, 71-72
  marketing, 110-112
  supply behavior of commercial
    family farms, 73-76
Farming regions, 29-38
Farm people, 1-15
  hired workers, 3-4
  migration in and out of agricul-
    ture, 272
  number of farms and cropland har-
    vested by tenure of operator, 5
  owners, 3
  price spreads between consumers
    and, 164-167
  tenants, 3
  three groups of, 3-5
  versus urban people, 5-6
Farm Prices — Myth and Reality
    (Cochrane), 516
Farm Security Administration, 395,
    415
Farms, 6-7
  classes of, 7-10
  geographic distribution of, 10, 13
  investment in typical, 10-11
  number of, 5
  tenancy, 377-386 (*see also* Ten-
    ancy, farm)
  tenure of operators by economic
    class of farms, 1954, 14-15
  transfers, 386-391 (*see also* Trans-
    fers, farm)
  U. S. farms by tenure, 379
  utilization of land in farms in U. S.
    (1910-1954), 36
Farm technological advance (*see*
    Technological advances)
Federal Crop Insurance, 479-480
Federal Farm Board, 468-469
  objectives, 491-493
Federal Farm Loan Act of 1916, 377,
    393-394
Federal Land Banks, 393-394, 466-467
Federal ownership of land, 397, 441-
    443, 449
  problems of, 448-449
"Federal Range Code," 451
Federal-state extension service, 320
Feed grains and livestock region
    (Corn Belt), 31-32

Feed grains:
acreage in, 114
areas specializing in, 31-32
government price-support program, 118
imports and exports, 118-119
irrigated land, 452
marketing, 113-119
normal flow of, 114-115
prices received by farmers (1910-58), 205-206
production, 114
Fertilizer:
input-output data, 40-42
investment in, 50
production function, 40
soil conservation and use of, 421
use of lime and, 50-51
Fish and Wildlife Service, 442
Fisher, Lloyd H., 416n
Fluctuations, business (see Business fluctuations)
Food:
aggregate demand for food, 276-279
annual per capital consumption, 188
changes in eating habits, 160-161
concentration, dispersion, and equalization process for products, 96-97
consumer demand, 189-193
convenience foods, 160-161
division of consumer's food dollar, 163-164
expenditures for current consumption, 187
frozen, 109, 161
future needs, 319
Government wartime programs, 471-475
index of aggregate food production for sale, 274
index of per capita food consumption, 188, 277
marketing system, 143-157
flow of foods in the U. S. (1935-39), 95
packaging, 160, 161
processing, 162-163
technological advances and supply of, 331
world consumption, 177-179
Forecasts:
outlook information, 480-481
prices, 258
Foreclosure proceedings during the 1930's, 467
Foreign surplus disposal programs, 352-357
Foreign trade, 141, 338-358
advantages for the farmer, 340-341
balance of trade, 339
policy of the U.S., 349-352
dollar exchange, 350

economic development of underdeveloped countries, 355-357
exports:
dumping, 341-342
peacetime stagnation of commercial exports, 349-352
U. S. agricultural exports (1925-58), 347, 348
value of post World War II, 346
feed grains, 118-119
government control, 349-352
government export programs, 347-348, 352-353
International Wheat Agreement, 352, 353
limitations, 341-342
post World War II trade developments, 346-349
principle of comparative advantage, 340
quantitative controls, 351n
Reciprocal Trade Agreements Program, 349
surplus disposal, 341-357
tariffs, 349-352
unilateral, 342n
Forest lands:
federal and state ownership, 441-443
grazing on national, 441, 448-451
number of acres, 36
recreational and wildlife use of, 448
special taxation of, 438-439
Forest Service, 441, 448, 450-451
Forward-pricing system, 481-484, 488-489
Frozen foods, 109, 161
Fruits, 17, 34
irrigated land, 452
marketing agreements, 470-471, 495
migrant workers, 413
prices, 214
substitution of resources, 271
Futures contracts, selling, 108
Futures market, 108, 485-486

Gaus, John M., 462n, 464n
General farming regions, 34
Geographic distribution of farms, 10, 13
Government:
agricultural adjustment legislation, 469-470
assistance in shifting to non-farm jobs, 513-514
assistance to agriculture, 461-476
early conservation activities, 465
early regulatory work, 465
controls:
after World War I, 467-469
1946-1952, 473-475
postwar aversion to, 475-476
crop insurance programs, 457, 479-480

Government (*Cont.*)
farm credit for agriculture, 466-467
farm real estate mortgage credit
agencies, 393-394
labor camps, 415
land policies, 465-466
marketing agreements, 470-471
ownership of land, 397, 441-443
problems of, 448-449
price-support programs (*see* Price
support programs)
Grades and grading, 104, 495
feed grains, 118
livestock and meat, 122
Grain Standards Act, 118
Grassland and pasture, number of
acres, 36
Gray, Roger W., 483*n*
Grazing:
conservation of range lands, 457
government fees for, 449-451
on public lands, 441, 448-451
Great Plains states, 120
conservation in, 422
drought conditions, 453-454
further adjustments needed in the
economy of, 456-457
land management, 453-456
principle of comparative advantage,
18
problems of, 453-456
real estate taxes delinquent, 436-437
Great Plains Conservation Program,
456
Griliches, Zvi, 77*n*
Griswold, A. Whitney, 377*n*
Gross national product (1929-58),
289, 290

Hamilton, Alexander, 462
Handicapped families, in low-income
areas, 367
Hathaway, Dale, 299-301, 303-304,
308, 310
Health facilities, need for, 367, 369
Hedging operations, 108
Hendrix, William E., 367*n*, 372-376,
508
Hibbard, B. H., 463
Hinds, Max K., 133*n*
Hired labor, 3-4, 401-417
on family farm, 407-409
labor organizations, 413
large-scale farms, 405, 408
living conditions, 409, 412
mechanization and, 410-412
migratory workers, 401, 405-407
importation of foreign labor, 414
social problems of, 412-414
trends in the use of, 403-404
wages of, 404-407
Hoffman, A. C., 147

Hogs:
diseases, 478
forward-pricing system, 482
hog-corn ratio, 211
prices, 210, 214, 269
production controls, 494
seasonal production, 121
Homestead Act of 1862, 377, 378,
463, 464, 465
Hoover, Herbert, 468, 491, 492

Imports (*see* Foreign trade)
Income, 62
demand for food fluctuates with,
315-316
farm, 214-219, 361
insurance, 489-490
per capita of agricultural workers,
218
relation of total net income to
national income, U. S. (1940-
58), 217-218
improvement prospects in low-
income areas, 372-376
incentive, 333-334
major low-income areas, 362-366
price-income structure of agriculture, 199-221
Independent grocer, 102-103, 144-145
Indexes:
cropland, 80
of total farm inputs (1939-1958),
81
Index numbers, 199-202
computation of, 200
indices of prices received by farmers for selected commodities
(1939-57), 201
weighted, 200-201
India, economic aid for, 356-357
Industrial workers, 218-219, 406-407
Input-output data, 40-42
Inputs in agriculture:
commercial farms, 73-77
data, 40-42
historical record, 78-82
labor, 74
land, 74
Insurance:
all-risk crop, 478-480
farm income, 489-490
Federal Crop Insurance program,
479-480
International trade (*see* Foreign trade)
International Wheat Agreement, 347,
352, 353
Investments:
in agriculture, 301-304
in land and buildings, 66
in machinery, equipment, livestock,
crops, and supplies, 391, 396
Irrigated land, 37
economic value of, 452

Irrigated land (*Cont.*)
property rights in water, 452-453
reclamation projects, 451-452
in Western states, 447, 451-452

Jamison, John A., 144n, 148
Jefferson, Thomas, 462, 463
Johnson, D. Gale, 481n
Joint products, 22-23

Korean War:
agricultural exports, 346
flexible price supports, 500
government controls, 475
Kriesel, Herbert C., 133n

Labor:
changes in farm employment, production, output per worker, and total population (1870-1950), 322
costs, 66, 169-171
decline in labor force, 332-333
distribution of the labor force (1910-57), 159
employment in production and distribution, 158-159
government assistance in shifting to non-farm jobs, 513-514
hired, 401-417
input, 80
labor-transfer problem, 374, 513
legislation affecting, 414-416
migration in and out of agriculture, 272, 374, 513-514
underemployment in agriculture, 373-376, 507-509
unions, 170, 413
Lambs:
forward-pricing system, 482
prices, 214
Land, farm:
federal and state ownership, 441-443
policy of retirement of land from agriculture, 514-516
utilization of farm land, 36
overvaluation of, 521-522
Landlords:
absentee, 381
management by, 382-383
Landowners, 3-4
Land use:
continuing problems of control of, 445
economic incentives to control, 444-445
educational programs for, 445
federal and state ownership, 441-443
Great Plains states, 453-456
influence of property tax on, 436-438

practices, 419
regulations, 444
reseeding less productive land, 455-456
rural zoning, 443-444
social control of, 440-445
Western land-use problems, 447-458
Large-scale farming, 68-69, 390
migrant labor, 405-407, 408
supply behavior, 76-77
Leases, 4, 383-385
Legge, Alexander, 492-493
Legislation:
affecting farm labor, 414-416
agricultural adjustment, 469-470
Limestone, use of, 50-51
Livestock (*see also* Feed grains and livestock)
areas specializing in, 31-32
cattle fattening, 409
feeder cattle, 120
feeds, 120
grazing and pasture area, 120
on public lands, 449-451
marketing, 119-123
per capita consumption of meat, 119-120
prices, 210-212, 214
received by farmers (1910-58), 205-206, 269
production:
per acre and per animal, 53
in the South, 26-27, 121
technology and, 52-53
range, 33-34
ratio between price of corn and production of, 122
sanitation program, 478
seasonal workers, 409
situation reports, 481
Living conditions, 409, 413-414
Loans (*see also* Credit)
nonrecourse, 470, 471, 494-496
Locke, John, 512
Low-income areas, 362-366
income improvement prospects, 372-376
educational facilities are inadequate, 507-509
employment, 368-370
poverty problem, 361-370
Lowenstein, Frank, 128n

McElveen, J. V., 72n
Machinery:
hiring owner of, on a custom basis, 410
investments in, 66, 301-304
labor-saving, 410-411
McNary-Haugen bills, 468, 491-493
Management:
analyses, 46

Management (*Cont.*)
commercial farm management services, 383
grazing land, 449-451, 457
hiring managers on a fee basis, 383
landlord, 382-383
public, 457
vaccination and sanitation programs, 478
Managers, farm, 3
Margarine, 135-136
Marginal analysis, 45
Marginal cost:
curves, 44, 55
data, 43
elasticity of, 47
soil conservation, 423-424
supply curve of the enterprise, 48-49
Marginal returns, definition, 23n
Market basket data, 164-167
Market day, price and demand in relation to, 247-248
Market demand, 193-194
Marketing, 89-141
agencies, 123
agreements and orders, 138-140, 470-471, 495
assembling products, 103-104
"atlas of marketing," 113-141
buying and selling, 102-103
chain stores, 101, 144-145
changing structure of farm markets, 143-157
channels, 93-95
complexity of the marketing system, 91-93
concentration and dispersion process, 96-97
consumers and, 174-195
contract farming and, 155-156
cooperatives, 151-154
corporate profits of food-processors, 171
costs, 158-173
cotton, 128-133
creating new products and services, 161-162
dairy products, 133-141
Federal marketing orders, 138-140
dividing and packaging, 106
equalization process, 97-98
farm surplus problem, 155
Federal marketing orders, 138-140
feed grains, 113-119
financing the operation, 106-107
firms, 110-112
flow of foods in the U. S. (1935-39), 95
flow of products from producers to consumers, 93-95
functions, 101-112
grocery stores, 144-145

historical development, 89-90
information, 108
livestock, 119-123
mass merchandising, 143-157
middlemen, function of, 107
needs of commercial agriculture, 90-91
policy of less-restrained production and, 512-513
price spread between farmers and consumers, 164-167
processing, 108-110
quotas, 499
rights, negotiability of, 523
risk-bearing, 107-108
services and costs, 158-173
standardizing and grading, 105
storing products, 104-105
sugar, 123-128
transportation, 105-106
wholesale markets, 100
Marketing-bill data, 167-171
Markets, 98-101
foreign, 338-358 (*see also* Foreign trade)
jobbing, 100
perfectly competitive, 229-230
Marshall Plan, 353
Meat (*see also* Livestock)
determining the price of pork, 222-241
grading, 122
per capita consumption, 119-120
Mechanization of farming, 66, 301-304
hired labor and, 411-412
Mehren, George L., 101, 143n, 144, 144n
Middlemen, function of, 90
Migrant farm labor, 405-407
labor contractor or crew leader, 414
living conditions, 413, 415-416
social problems, 413-414
Migration in and out of agriculture, 272
government assistance proposed for, 513-514
Milk (*see also* Dairy products)
consumption, 134-135
costs of producing, 58-59
Federal marketing orders, 138-140
forward-pricing system, 482
marketing, 133-141, 470, 495
nonfat dry milk solids, 136
prices and pricing, 137-138, 214
production, 133
storing and transporting, 140
substitution of vegetable fats for milk fats in food, 140-141
Miller, Marshall E., 123n
Mississippi, 219
Mitchell, James P., 414, 415

Morrill Act, 464
Mortgage credit agencies, 393-394
Mueller, 143*n*, 153-154

National Grange, 518
National Park Service, 442
National Research Council, Food and
   Nutrition Board, 175-177, 179
Natural resources, conservation, 429
New England, farm tenancy in, 378
Non-farming areas, 36
North Carolina Agricultural Experi-
   ment Station, 40
North Dakota, cash income, 456
Nutrition:
   annual per capita consumption of
      food, 188
   central problem of choice, 185-189
   diet plans, 180-183
   expenditures for current consump-
      tion, urban families, 187
   recommended daily dietary allow-
      ances by age groups, 176
   trends in eating habits, 184
   world needs, 177-179

Oats (*see also* Feed grains)
   cost of production, 65
   uses, 119
Occupations, of individual farm owners, 398
Office of Price Administration, 472
Oil-bearing crops, prices, 205-206
Oklahoma, 219
Operators of farms:
   gross and net income (1910-58),
      215-216
   tenure of, (1954), 14-15
Oranges, price movements, 208
Outlook information, 480-481
Output, farm, 318
   aggregate output problem in agri-
      culture, 271-276
   historical record, 78-82
   marginal, 43
   total farm output, output of basic
      commodities, 504
Owners of farms, 3-4
   experience of, 399
   occupation of individual farm own-
      ers, 398-399
   percentage of, living on farms, 399
Ownership of farm, 70
   absentee landlords, 381
   age at time of becoming owners,
      400
   age of owners at retirement, 387
   corporate, 398
   experience of farm owners, 399
   of family farms, 377, 400
   by Federal government, 397, 441-
      443
   extent of family assistance, 400

privately and publicly owned farm
   land, 398
size of holdings, 399-400
study of, 397-400

Packaging and dividing products, 106,
   160, 161
Parents maintenance contracts, 389
Parity:
   computation of, 497
   definition, 497
   domestic parity approach, 518-520
   ratio, 203-204
   shift to modernized parity formula,
      499-500
Patent Office, 463
Payments (*see also* Price support pro-
      grams)
   compensatory payment program,
      486-489
   soil conservation, 426-427
Peanuts:
   price supports, 498
   Soil Bank program, 501-502
People, farm, 3-15
   versus urban, 5-6
Pest infestations, controlling, 50, 478
Policy issues, unsolved, 507-524
   commodity self-help and domestic
      parity approach, 518-520
   credit in agriculture with price sta-
      bility, 520-521
   equity problems encountered in sup-
      ply management programs, 522-
      524
   government assistance in shifting to
      non-farm jobs, 513-514
   importance of cultural beliefs and
      values, 510-512
   inadequate demand for underem-
      ployed rural workers, 507-509
   less restrained production and mar-
      keting, 512-513
   level of farm prices, 520
   over-valuation of farm land, 521
   problem of over-rapid technical ad-
      vance, 509-510
   public utility approach as a policy,
      516-518
   retirement of land from agriculture,
      514-516
Population:
   in agriculture, 304-308
   effect on demand for food, 317
   marketing and the distribution and
      concentration of, 91
Pork, determining the price of, 222-
   241
Potatoes:
   fertilizing, 45
   forward-pricing system, 483-484
   irrigated land, 452

Potatoes (*Cont.*)
  marketing agreements, 470-471
  price and production of (1910-58), 483
  price movements, 208
  seasonal workers, 409
Poultry, diseases, 478
Poultry and eggs:
  forward-pricing system, 482
  situation reports, 481
Poverty problem, 361-370
  income improvement prospects in low-income areas, 372-376
  long-range programs for, 366-367
  low income in the South, 364-365
  many handicapped families in low-income areas, 367
  national economic policies required, 368-369
  problem for farm leaders, 369
Pre-emption Act, 462
Prices and pricing:
  automatically operating pricing system, 243, 245
  changes in prices, 235-237
    production responses to, 259-260
  commodity, 263
  cyclical price movements, 210-212
  determination of farm, 222-241
  effect of war on, 202, 204
  equilibrium price, 235, 240, 244
  extreme movements, 279-281
  factors influencing, 206-210
  farm income, 214-218
  forecasts, 258
  forward-pricing system, 481-484
  future, 256-257
  government intervention influences, 245-246
  index numbers, 199-202
  inflation, 202
  level of farm prices, 199, 520
  long-run analysis of cost-price relationship, 251-256
  long-run price trends, 202-206
  market, 240
  "Market basket" concept, 164-166
  market day analysis of cost-price relationship, 247-248
  marketing-bill data, 167-169
  price-income problem, 263-264, 268-270, 279-282
  price-income structure of agriculture, 199-221
  problems of, 219-220
  production responses to price changes, 259-260
  public utility approach as a policy, 516-518
  relative, 246-247
  resource-allocation problem, 263
    aggregate output problem in agriculture, 271-276

  cobweb analysis, 264-268
  role of farm prices, 242-261
  seasonal price movements, 212-224
  short-run analysis of cost-price relationship, 248-251
  spreads between farmers and consumers, 164-167
  structure of farm prices, 199-221
  theoretical explanation of farm-price behavior, 262-283
  two-farm price problems, 262-283
    aggregate demand for food, 276-279
    aggregate output problem in agriculture, 271-276
    analysis of the general price-income problem, 268-270
    analysis of the resource-allocation problem, 264-268
    general price-income problem, 279-282
    industry analysis, agriculture, 270-271
  wholesale prices, 202-203
Price-support programs, 491-506
  adoption of flexible price supports, 500-501
  announcement of supports, 488
  business fluctuations and, 311
  commodity self-help and domestic parity approach, 518-520
  during World War II, 471-472
  early beginnings of production controls, 493-495
  early postwar objectives, 498-499
  effects on prices, 240
  farmers demand, 245
  feed grains, 118
  historical development, 491-497
  limitations on size of loan, 522
  milk and butter-fat, 140
  McNary-Haugen bills, 491-493
  objectives of agricultural programs in the 1930's, 495-497
  objectives of related legislation, 501-503
  parity, 497, 499-500
  public utility approach, 516-518
  regional specialization and, 27
  sliding scales, 474
  temporary measures and lower support levels ineffective, 503-504
  wartime modified farm program objectives, 497-498
  wide disagreement among farm leaders, 504-505
Processing foods, 162-163
  costs, 169-171
  frozen foods, 109
  growth of industry, 162-163
  importance of, 109
  as a marketing function, 109
  sugar, 124

Processing foods (*Cont.*)
struggle between chains and processors, 148-150
Processors, futures market used to minimize risks, 485
Production:
area specialization in, 29-38
average costs versus opportunity costs, 63-65
basis of differentiation in, 16-17
budgeting changes in practices, 46
changes in price influence, 242-261
controls, 493-495
determining the most profitable level of production, 61
determining preferred plan for, 257-259
determining what to produce, 16-28
policy of less-restrained marketing and, 512-513
principle of comparative advantage, 17-20
responses to price changes, 259-260
soil conservation versus, 420-422
specialization in farming:
principle of comparative advantage, 17-20
trends in regional, 20-21
versus diversification, 25-26
transportation costs effect, 17
variations in soil and climate, 16-17
Production Credit Association, 394-395
Products:
complementary relations among enterprises, 24-25
determining what to produce, 16-28
joint, 22-23
principles of enterprise combination, 22
specialization vs. diversification, 25-26
supplementary relations among enterprises, 23-24
trends in regional specialization, 20-21
Profit:
determining the most profitable level of production, 61
most profitable combination of resources, 42-45
resources used to maximize returns, 39-56
Programs, farm:
price support programs (*see* Price support programs)
public utility approach as a policy, 516-518
recent price and income programs, 491-506
regional specialization and, 27
unsolved policy issues, 507-524

Property:
rights in water, 452-453
rights vs. property in land, 523
Public Health Service, 133
Public lands, 397, 441-443
grazing on, 448
Public utility approach as a policy, 516-518
Putnam, George E., 239

Rainfall, conservation in low-rainfall areas, 422
Range lands:
conservation of, 457
influence of property tax on land use, 436
Range livestock, areas specializing, 33-34
Ratchford, C. Brice, 72n
Ratios:
income-incentive, 333-334
input-output, 42-43
man-land, 11
Reclamation Act of 1902, 377
Reclamation projects, 451-452
Regions, farm, 31-36
trends in specialization, 20-21
trends in total cropland, 36
Renne, R. R., 377n, 466n
Rental of farm real estate, 380
Renters (*see* Tenants)
Reports, outlook and "situation," 480-481
Research in agriculture, 464-465
Resources (*see also* Technology):
allocation role of prices, 246-247
most profitable combination of, 42-46
production function, 40-42
used per unit of farm output, 80
used to maximize returns, 39-56
achieving the most profitable combination of enterprises, 46-47
budgeting changes in production practices, 46
marginal cost data, 43
most profitable combination of resources 42-45
production function, 40-42
supply curve of the enterprise, 48-49
Retail food trade:
battle between chains and packers, 148
concentration at the retail level, 143-146
procurement policies, 146-149
vertical integration, 148-149
Retirement of land (*see also* Conservation reserve program)
as a policy, 514-516
Returns (*see also* Profits)
resource use to maximize, 39-56

Rice:
  price supports, 498
  Soil Bank program, 501-502
Risks and uncertainties:
  all-risk crop insurance, 478-480
  disease or pest infestations, 477-478
  marketing process, 107-108
  policies to reduce, 477-490
  technological uncertainties, 477-478
  weather, 477-478
Roosevelt, Franklin D., 498
Roosevelt, Theodore, 466
Rotation, crop, 420
Rural areas:
  educational facilities inadequate, 507
  low-income areas, 361-365
  poverty problem, 361-370

Samuelson, Paul A., 244n
Saunderson, Mont H., 448n
Schickele, Rainer, 456n
Schultz, T. W., 314n
Scott, Forrest E., 162
Scoville, Orin J., 66n
Seasonal patterns:
  egg production, 213-214
  livestock prices, 214
  price movements, 212-214
Second World Food Survey, 177-178
Secretary of Agriculture, 494, 496, 498, 504-505, 513
Seeds, 50, 463
Selby, H. E., 447n
Sharecroppers, 4
  fair rental rates, 385-386
Sheep:
  diseases, 478
  production, 122
Shepherd, Geoffrey S., 486, 489n
Short-run situations, price and demand in relation to, 247-248
Size of farms, 387-400
  costs as affected by, 65-68
Small farming units, 68-70
Social action, adoption of technological advances and, 327-329
Social control of land use, 440-445
  basis of, 440-441
  federal and state ownership, 441-443
  land use regulations, 444
  rural zoning, 443-444
  use of economic incentives, 444-445
Social problems of farm labor, 412-414
Social Security program, 367
  hired workers covered by, 412
Soil, production affected by variations in, 16-17
Soil Bank program, 311, 501
Soil conservation, 420-421, 426
  divergence between practice and economic optimum, 427-428

economics of, 418-430
Great Plains states, 455
government programs, 419-420, 426-427
importance of, 418
influence of available new land, 419
influence of private ownership, 419-420
land use regulations, 444
local soil conservation districts, 444
in low-rainfall areas, 422
marginal costs, and marginal value, 423-424
payments for practices, 444
production versus, 420-422
public interest in, 424
publicly owned land, 419
society's value of conservation expressed in price system, 424-426
in the South, 422-423
terracing, 421
Soil Conservation Service, 472-473
Soil erosion, 420-422
Sorenson, Vernon L., 483n
Sorghum grains, marketing, 119
South:
  conservation in the, 422-423
  development of agriculture, 364-365
  growth of farm tenancy, 377-379
  livestock production, 26-27
  low-income farm families, 364-365
Soybeans, cost of production, 64-65
Special crops, and general farming regions, 35-36
Specialization in farming:
  diversification versus, 25-26
  farm programs and regional, 27
  major types of farming in the U. S., 30
  principle of comparative advantage, 17-20
  trends in regional, 20-21
Standardizing, grading products, 104
Starch, Elmer, 454-455
Steagall Amendment, 498
Stewart, Paul W., 171n
Stock ponds, 455
Storage facilities, 104-105
Storehouses, 100
Sugar, 124, 127
  annual consumption, 123
  industrial uses, 124
  marketing, 123-128
  marketing agreements, 495
  processing, 124
  Sugar Acts, 127, 415
  tariff on, 125
Sugar Acts, 127, 415
Sugar beets, 485
  irrigated land, 452
  mechanized farming, 411
  migrant workers, 407

Sunkist Growers, Inc., 152, 154
Sun Maid Raisin Growers, 154
Superette, definition, 144*n*
Supermarkets, definition, 144*n*
Supply:
  aggregate supply relation, 71-86 (*see also* Aggregate supply relation)
  based on producer decisions, 232
  behavior of farms, 72-76
  causes for shifts in, 318-321
  commodity-supply relations, 71
  control programs, equity problems encountered in, 522-524
  curve, 226-229, 274
    factors causing shift in, 235
  derived demand and, 230-232
  farm prices determined by, 226-229
  short- and long-run considerations, 77-78
Surplus disposal programs, 352-357, 501, 513
  for economic development of underdeveloped countries, 355-357
  marketing problems, 91, 155
  results of, 503
Sweden, foreign trade, 351
Swerling, Boris C., 489*n*
Swift and Co., 239

Tariffs, 349-352
  Smoot-Hawley Act, 349
Taxes and taxation, 431-440
  appraisal of farm property, 445
  continuing problems of, 445
  estimates of, paid by farmers, 431
  excise, 435
  exemption of homesteads, 438
  of forest lands, 438-439
  general property tax, 433-434
    appraisal of farm lands, 434
    characteristics of, 433-434
    general weaknesses of, 434
    incidence of, 439-440
    influence on land use, 436-438
    trend, on farm real estate, 434-436
  income, 432-433
  shifting and incidence to taxes in relation to agriculture, 431-433
  on special products or services, 432
  state and local revenue raised by selected states, 436
Taylor, H. C., 380*n*
Taylor Grazing Act, 441, 449
Technological advances, 273-275
  adoption of new processes:
    farmer asset positions and, 329-330
    market organization and, 325-327
    social action and, 327-329
  amount spent yearly on, 320
  Brewster historical analysis, 321
  causes changes in the supply, 318

consequences of, 330
definition, 53-55
farm credit and, 396
farmers' incentive incomes and, 333-334
food supply and, 331
lowers unit costs of production, 325
market organization and, 324-325
money spent for, 335
population growth and, 321
race between population growth and (1955-1975), 321-324
release of human resources, 331-333
research and development, 328
shifts the supply curve, 55
source of increased productive efficiency, 83
unsolved problems of, 509-510
Technology, 53-55
  as a form of capital, 51-52
  changing technology in agriculture and on the farm, 49-50
  crop production and, 50-51
  livestock production, 52-53
  shifts the supply curve, 55
Tenancy, farm, 377-386
  commercial farm management services, 383
  fair rental rates, 385-386
  functions of, 379-380
  growth of, 377-379
  improvements in leases needed, 383-385
  need for more landlord management, 382-383
  social status, 377
  undesirable aspects of, 380-382
Tenants, on farms, 3-4
  cash, 4
  share and sharecroppers, 4
Tenure of operators:
  by economic class of farm, 1954, 14-15
  number of farms and cropland harvested by, 5
Thailand, foreign trade, 351
Tobacco:
  acreage adjustment programs, 522
  and general farming region, 34-35
  government regulations, 461, 469
  price supports, 498
  production controls, 494
  Soil Bank program, 501-502
Tractors, 302-303, 318
  crop production affected by, 50
Transfer of family farm, 386-391
  continuing farm ownership problems, 389-391
  elements of the problem, 386-387
  parents maintenance contracts, 389
  written contracts for, 388-389

Transportation:
farm production affected by costs of, 17
marketing system and, 105-106
motor trucks, 105-106
refrigerator cars, 105
Treatise on Civil Government (Locke), 512
Truck crops, areas specializing in, 34
Twentieth Century Fund, 171
Two-man farms, 408
Type-of-farming areas, 29-38

Underdeveloped countries, surplus disposal, 352-357
Underemployment in agriculture, 373-376, 507-509
United Nations Food and Agricultural Organization, 177
Urban people, farm people versus, 5-6
Use Book, The, 451

Vaccination programs, 478
Valuation of land, problem of overvaluation, 521-522
Values, importance of cultural beliefs and, 510-512
Vegetables:
irrigated land, 452
marketing agreements, 495
migrant workers, 413
prices, 214

Wages, 404-407
minimum wage legislation, 415
War Food Administration, 473
War Manpower Commission, 472
War Production Board, 472
Water rights, 452-453
Watershed areas, 448
Webb, W. P., 453
Weighing and inspecting feed grains, 115, 118
West Virginia, 219
Western land use problems, 447-458
further adjustments needed in the Plains economy, 456-457
government charges fees for grazing, 449-451

growing out of public ownership, 448-449
irrigation in the western states, 451-452
issues in new reclamation projects, 452
major areas of Federally owned or administered land, 449
problems growing out of public ownership, 448-449
problems of the Plains states, 453-456
property rights in water, 452-453
Wheat and small-grain farming:
areas specializing, 33
futures market, 485
marketing channels and utilization of wheat products and, 94
price supports, 498
reseeding marginal wheat lands, 455-456
seasonal workers, 409
situation reports, 481
Soil Bank program, 501-502
Wholesale markets, price determination in, 232-235
Wholesale prices, 202-203
Wholesaling:
assembling products, 103-104
equalization provided by, 98
Wilcox, Walter W., 474, 498n
Winter cover crops, 422
Wisconsin:
rural zoning, 443
sour cherry production, 17
special taxation of forest lands, 438-439
Witt, Lawrence W., 349n
Wolcott, Leon O., 462n, 464n
World War I:
price movements, 208-209
World War II:
income incentive ratio after, 334
modified farm program objectives, 497-498
price movements, 208-209
price support program, 471-472

Zoning ordinances, 443-444
need for more studies, 445